# ANTIQUES
## SOURCE
## BOOK

THIS IS A CARLTON BOOK

Copyright © 2000 Martin Miller

This edition published 2001 for Index Books

First published 2000 by Carlton Books Limited
20 Mortimer Street
London
W1N 7RD

A CIP catalogue for this book is available from the British Library.

ISBN 1 84222 368 2

DESIGN: Bluefrog
PRODUCTION: Garry Lewis

# ANTIQUES
## SOURCE
## BOOK

The Definitive Annual Guide to Retail
Prices for Antiques and Collectables

## MARTIN MILLER

INDEX

# Contents

Acknowledgements . . . . . . . . . . . . . . . . . . . . . . . . . .6
How to Use This Book . . . . . . . . . . . . . . . . . . . . . .7
Introduction . . . . . . . . . . . . . . . . . . . . . . . . . . . . . .9

Antiquities . . . . . . . . . . . . . . . . . . . . . . . . . . . . . . .11
Architectural & Garden Furniture . . . . . . . . . . . . .19
Arms & Armour . . . . . . . . . . . . . . . . . . . . . . . . . .29
Automobilia . . . . . . . . . . . . . . . . . . . . . . . . . . . . . .40
Books, Maps & Atlases . . . . . . . . . . . . . . . . . . . . .44
Carpets & Rugs . . . . . . . . . . . . . . . . . . . . . . . . . . .59
Ceramics
          English . . . . . . . . . . . . . . . . . . . . . . . . . . . .64
          European . . . . . . . . . . . . . . . . . . . . . . . . . .93
          Islamic . . . . . . . . . . . . . . . . . . . . . . . . . . .105
          Oriental . . . . . . . . . . . . . . . . . . . . . . . . . .112
Clocks, Watches & Scientific Instruments
          Clocks . . . . . . . . . . . . . . . . . . . . . . . . . . .125
          Watches . . . . . . . . . . . . . . . . . . . . . . . . . .141
          Scientific Instruments . . . . . . . . . . . . . . . .151
Collector's Items
          Advertising & Packaging . . . . . . . . . . . . . . .160
          Aeronautica . . . . . . . . . . . . . . . . . . . . . . . .164
          Bicycles . . . . . . . . . . . . . . . . . . . . . . . . . .168
          Bottles . . . . . . . . . . . . . . . . . . . . . . . . . . .170
          Cameras . . . . . . . . . . . . . . . . . . . . . . . . . .174
          Chess Sets . . . . . . . . . . . . . . . . . . . . . . . .182
          Commemorative Ware . . . . . . . . . . . . . . . .187
          Ephemera . . . . . . . . . . . . . . . . . . . . . . . . .193
          Kitchenalia . . . . . . . . . . . . . . . . . . . . . . . .205
          Luggage . . . . . . . . . . . . . . . . . . . . . . . . . .215
          Mechanical Music . . . . . . . . . . . . . . . . . . .217
          Paperweights . . . . . . . . . . . . . . . . . . . . . . .223
          Photographs . . . . . . . . . . . . . . . . . . . . . . .225
          Posters . . . . . . . . . . . . . . . . . . . . . . . . . . .231
          Radio, TV & Sound Equipment . . . . . . . . .235
          Rock & Pop . . . . . . . . . . . . . . . . . . . . . . . .239
          Scripophilly & Paper Money . . . . . . . . . . . .247
          Sewing Items . . . . . . . . . . . . . . . . . . . . . .251
          Snuff Boxes & Smoking Equipment . . . . . .254
          Telephones . . . . . . . . . . . . . . . . . . . . . . . .256
          Walking Sticks . . . . . . . . . . . . . . . . . . . . .262
Coins & Medals . . . . . . . . . . . . . . . . . . . . . . . . . .264
Decorative Arts
          Figures & Busts . . . . . . . . . . . . . . . . . . . . .268
          Lighting . . . . . . . . . . . . . . . . . . . . . . . . . .270
          Metalware . . . . . . . . . . . . . . . . . . . . . . . . .276
Furniture
          Beds . . . . . . . . . . . . . . . . . . . . . . . . . . . . .284
          Bonheurs du Jour . . . . . . . . . . . . . . . . . . . .287
          Bookcases . . . . . . . . . . . . . . . . . . . . . . . . .289
          Boxes . . . . . . . . . . . . . . . . . . . . . . . . . . . .295
          Bureaux . . . . . . . . . . . . . . . . . . . . . . . . . . .299

Cabinets . . . . . . . . . . . . . . . . . . . . . . . . . . .304
Canterburies . . . . . . . . . . . . . . . . . . . . . . . .311
Chairs . . . . . . . . . . . . . . . . . . . . . . . . . . . . .313
Chaise Longues & Day Beds . . . . . . . . . . . .330
Chests of Drawers & Commodes . . . . . . . .332
Davenports . . . . . . . . . . . . . . . . . . . . . . . . .342
Desks . . . . . . . . . . . . . . . . . . . . . . . . . . . . .344
Dining Tables . . . . . . . . . . . . . . . . . . . . . . .350
Doors . . . . . . . . . . . . . . . . . . . . . . . . . . . . .352
Dressers . . . . . . . . . . . . . . . . . . . . . . . . . . .354
Dumb Waiters & Whatnots . . . . . . . . . . . .359
Lowboys . . . . . . . . . . . . . . . . . . . . . . . . . . .361
Mirrors . . . . . . . . . . . . . . . . . . . . . . . . . . . .362
Miscellaneous . . . . . . . . . . . . . . . . . . . . . .368
Screens . . . . . . . . . . . . . . . . . . . . . . . . . . . .375
Settees & Sofas . . . . . . . . . . . . . . . . . . . . . .377
Stools . . . . . . . . . . . . . . . . . . . . . . . . . . . . .381
Tables . . . . . . . . . . . . . . . . . . . . . . . . . . . . .385
Wardrobes . . . . . . . . . . . . . . . . . . . . . . . . . .395
Glass . . . . . . . . . . . . . . . . . . . . . . . . . . . . . . . . . .398
Jewellery . . . . . . . . . . . . . . . . . . . . . . . . . . . . . . .411
Marine Items . . . . . . . . . . . . . . . . . . . . . . . . . .421
Musical Instruments . . . . . . . . . . . . . . . . . . . . .429
Silver & Pewter . . . . . . . . . . . . . . . . . . . . . . . .435
Sporting Items
General . . . . . . . . . . . . . . . . . . . . . . . . . . . .457
Fishing . . . . . . . . . . . . . . . . . . . . . . . . . . . .468
Shooting . . . . . . . . . . . . . . . . . . . . . . . . . . .473
Taxidermy . . . . . . . . . . . . . . . . . . . . . . . . . . . . .476
Textiles & Fans . . . . . . . . . . . . . . . . . . . . . . . .480
Tools . . . . . . . . . . . . . . . . . . . . . . . . . . . . . . . . . .484
Toys, Games & Dolls . . . . . . . . . . . . . . . . . . . .490
Treen . . . . . . . . . . . . . . . . . . . . . . . . . . . . . . . . .505
Tribal Art . . . . . . . . . . . . . . . . . . . . . . . . . . . . .509
Twentieth-Century Design
Ceramics . . . . . . . . . . . . . . . . . . . . . . . . . . .515
Furniture . . . . . . . . . . . . . . . . . . . . . . . . . . .527
Glass . . . . . . . . . . . . . . . . . . . . . . . . . . . . . .537
Lighting . . . . . . . . . . . . . . . . . . . . . . . . . . .547
Metalware . . . . . . . . . . . . . . . . . . . . . . . . . .554
Wine-Related Items . . . . . . . . . . . . . . . . . . . . .559
Works of Art & Sculpture
Asian/Oriental . . . . . . . . . . . . . . . . . . . . . .565
European . . . . . . . . . . . . . . . . . . . . . . . . . .568
Middle Eastern . . . . . . . . . . . . . . . . . . . . . .572
Russian . . . . . . . . . . . . . . . . . . . . . . . . . . . .575
Writing Equipment . . . . . . . . . . . . . . . . . . . . .578

Period Reference . . . . . . . . . . . . . . . . . . . . . . .586
Glossary . . . . . . . . . . . . . . . . . . . . . . . . . . . . . . .590
Directory of Dealers . . . . . . . . . . . . . . . . . . . . .598
Directory of Antiques Markets . . . . . . . . . . . . .625
Index . . . . . . . . . . . . . . . . . . . . . . . . . . . . . . . . . .631

# ACKNOWLEDGEMENTS

GENERAL EDITOR
Martin Miller

EDITOR
Richard Bundy

DESIGN
Pauline Hoyle
Alexandra Huchet
Jessica Barr

PICTURE EDITOR
Simon Blake

EDITORIAL CO-ORDINATORS
Elizabeth Roebig
Kim Khahn

PHOTOGRAPHIC CO-ORDINATOR
Megan Smith

PRODUCTION CO-ORDINATOR
Warren Philbey

EDITORIAL ASSISTANTS
Jasper Graham
Cara Miller
Liz Cox
Lisa Bailey
Ozlem Gunay
Vicky Blake

PHOTOGRAPHERS
Chris Smailes
Lee Walsh
Ryan Green
Neil Fox
Carmen Klammer

# How To Use This Book

## by Martin Miller

This book is the first full-colour antiques retail price guide published in the United Kingdom, a distinction which possibly deserves a little explanation. I started publishing antiques price guides in 1969 – and they have always been very successful – but one criticism that I have heard is from people saying, rather wistfully, 'I loved the book, but what a pity that everything in it was already sold.' And it was perfectly true, the books were designed more as compilations of information from auction sales which had already taken place than as immediate guides; as reference books rather than handbooks.

The difference with this book is that here we have used retailers, rather than auction houses, as our sources of information. Everything in this book is actually for sale at the time of going to press and many items, certainly some of the more arcane, will remain so for the lifespan of the book. As the introduction explains, a reputable and experienced dealer's assessment of the price of an antique is at least as reliable – and usually a great deal more reasoned – than a price achieved at auction, and so even when the item you wish to purchase from the book turns out to have been sold, you have a reliable guide to the price you should pay when you happen upon another.

The book is designed for maximum visual interest and appeal. It can be treated as a 'through read' as well as a tool for dipping in and out of. The Contents and Index will tell you in which area to find anything which you are specifically seeking, but the collector, enthusiast or interior designer will profit most from reading through a section or several sections and gathering information and inspiration as they go.

Should you happen upon something that you wish to buy, simply note the dealer reference to the bottom right of the entry and look up the dealer's full name and details in the Directory of Dealers section towards the back of the book. You can telephone, fax and, in many cases, visit the dealer's website. All the dealers who have helped us with the book will be happy to assist you and, if the piece you wish to buy has already been sold, they will almost certainly be able to help you find another. Should you wish to sell an item, the relevant section and dealer reference will again be of help, but do not expect to be offered the same price at which the dealer is selling. We all have to make a living!

In each edition of this book, there will be areas of specialization which will carry more emphasis than others. In this issue, Cameras, Chess Sets, Guitars, Books, Maps & Atlases, Taxidermy and Telephones, among others, receive careful scrutiny, while Pewter, for instance, receives less attention, tucked in behind a large section of Silver. As the years go on, balance will be restored and, with low inflation and stabilizing prices, the in-depth information offered on these areas in previous editions will hold its currency, so start your collection.

Good luck and good hunting!

# Introduction

**A new approach to antiques publishing, tailored to suit the modern antiques marketplace.**

The way in which antiques are viewed and valued is constantly changing. The distinction, for instance, between 'antique', 'collectable' and 'second-hand' has become very fuzzy in recent years. Curiously, in this disposable age – or perhaps because so much is disposable – the artefacts of today are valued much more by modern collectors than their equivalents were by previous generations, who generally considered that anything owned by their parents was, *prima facie*, not worth having.

The definition of an antique as 'a work of art, piece of furniture or decorative item of more than a hundred years old' has become more flexible, as technology has speeded up and, consequently, the products of that technology have developed the invisible patina of age at a faster rate. And so in this book, which takes a completely new and modern look at antiques, we include such items as film posters, automobilia, kitchenalia, guitars, taxidermy, comic books and twentieth-century glass, ceramics, metalware, lighting and furniture alongside some treasures of the ancient world, classical pieces of porcelain and some of the most notable items of furniture on the market at the moment. There are, after all,

guitars out there that cost a few hundred pounds thirty years ago and are now retailing at over £50,000. You could hardly call them second-hand.

It is not just the monetary value that makes a modern antique, though. There are three other factors which we keep coming back to throughout the book: quality, rarity and personal preference. If you are looking at collecting and dealing in antiques from a purely commercial viewpoint – and this we heartily deplore – then good quality and rarity are your best hedges against failure. If you are collecting for the right reasons, for the love of the subject and the items involved, then obviously you will trust your own judgement and, if you finish up with something that may not be worth as much as you had hoped, at least its presence won't offend you.

Given the proliferation of antiques and collectables on the market, it is important to find the best way to buy and sell them. There are three traditional ways in which antiques change hands: at auction, in antiques fairs and markets and through retail dealers. In addition to these, there are direct sales through the placing of advertisements and, increasingly and amid an unquenchable blaze of publicity, buying and selling directly on the Internet.

If you are seeking to combine buying

and selling antiques with acquiring an adrenaline rush, then you can't beat the auction. From the big city salerooms to the smallest of provincial auction houses, there is always a buzz of excitement at the auction and, given the large throughput of lots, always the possibility, real or imagined, of uncovering a hitherto undiscovered masterpiece. The downside of the auction, from the point of view of both buyer and seller, is that it is quite expensive. Commission plus VAT will be added to the hammer price if you are buying, and commission and such overheads as insurance, if you are selling. If you do decide to sell by auction, try to get more than one valuer's opinion and make sure that you agree all charges in advance.

Antiques fairs and markets are great fun and a very painless way of buying antiques – although selling takes a little more time and effort. Fairs vary from the large, 'vetted' fairs, with serious dealers from across the country taking part and admission fees charged, to boot fairs and charity fairs, where only the seller pays. The former are very like buying from a dealer, but with the convenience of having a number of dealers under the same roof. In the latter, everything tends to be fairly inexpensive, but that doesn't necessarily indicate that it is a bargain – or that it is what it purports to be.

Permanent markets also have great amusement value, and give you a real chance of picking up something of worth and collectable interest that you may not find elsewhere. These markets are good places to discover dealers who specialise in unusual types of collectables which do not warrant the acquisition of a whole shop. These items will tend to be fairly priced, because they are priced by specialists.

It is the fairness of pricing which is the great advantage of doing your buying and selling in the shop of a reputable dealer. In this book, we list and illustrate antiques and collectables which are currently for sale in the shops of good dealers – all indentified and all members of at least one of the dealer's associations. The prices given in the book are real prices charged for real items, for sale in real shops – and they are prices set by the experts. Armed with this book, you may be lucky enough to find the exact item still for sale – the Directory of Dealers in the back of the book gives you the phone number to find out – but, if not, you will at least know what it is worth when you see it at auction or in another shop.

As to the Internet, visit our website on www.worldantiquesonline.com for a constantly updated treasure trove of antiques for gifts or for collecting, all at the right price!

# Antiquities

**The artefacts of long dead civilisations have, for centuries, made a fascinating field of study for both the collector and the forger.**

The sixteenth-century art historian, Vasari, apparently used to regale his audience with a story about the young and keen Michelangelo. According to Vasari, Michelangelo made a sculpture of a fawn in imitation of the antique, then broke a tooth to make it look more authentic. Whether the story is true or not, it highlights the point that many sculptors learned their trade by copying the earlier work of others.

A sculpture that has stood outside for several generations may look more worn and ancient than one which has been better protected, so that only a specialist who really knows his subject can tell whether a piece is Greek, Roman, Renaissance or merely an eighteenth- or nineteenth-century copy – and even then he may be wrong.

There are scientific tests which can be employed to date some antiquities – at a price. But, on the whole, be warned: this is one of the most rewarding of collecting areas, but it is also the one where some of the most expensive mistakes can be made.

## Master of Animals ▼
- *8th century BC*
A bronze icon showing the master of animals god. Persian, from Luristan in Western Iran.
- *height 12cm*
- £800 • Pars

## Pilgrim's Flask ▲
- *1st millennium BC*
An Egyptian, terracotta circular pilgrim's flask with spiral detail.
- *height 43cm*
- £250 • Pars

## Bronze of Selinus ▼
- *1st-3rd century AD*
Romano-Egyptian bronze casting of the dwarf god, Selinus, shown with wings which would have formed part of the base of, perhaps, a table.
- *height 10.5cm*
- £600 • Pars

## Foundation Cone ◄
- *circa 2100 BC*
Foundation cone from Gudea, Sumarian for Ningirso warrior of Enil, ruler of Lagash.
- *length 14cm*
- £300 • Pars

## Amethyst Necklace ▲
- **3rd-1st century BC**
Roman amethyst necklace with blue glass spacers.
- *length 52cm*
- **£2,500**                    • Pars

## Face Mask ▲
- **1st century AD**
A Romano-Egyptian face mask, with handle at back for holding in front of the face.
- *diameter 12cm*
- **£200**                       • Pars

### Expert Tips

*When spending significant amounts of money, always buy from a reputable dealer and make sure that the piece you are buying is well documented, with an export licence and museum certificate of authenticity.*

## Tablet ▼
- **circa 3000 BC**
A well preserved and well written fragment of a Mesopotamian pictographic tablet on clay.
- *length 10cm*
- **£1,200**                     • Pars

## Shabti ▼
- **5th century BC**
A large Egyptian Shabti in turquoise glaze with iridescence, with faded inscriptions.
- *height 19cm*
- **£800**                       • Pars

## Bactrian Idol ➤
- **3rd millennium BC**
A Bactrian idol from Central Asia, with granite base inscribed with geometric patterns.
- *height 8.5cm*
- **£1,900**                     • Shahdad

## Bull Oil Vessel ▲
- **circa 1000 BC**
Amlash Persian pottery bull oil vessel, on four legs with head upright and pronounced horns and hump.
- *height 22cm*
- **£3,000**                     • Shiraz

## Bust of Woman ▲
- **2nd century AD**
Terracotta bust of a Roman woman with good definition to hair, dress and face.
- *height 10cm*
- **£300**                       • Shahdad

## Babylonian Terracotta Statues ▲
- 1900-1750 BC
A group of statues all relating to fertility, modelled in the form of female figures with emphasis on the breast.
- *average height 8cm*
- £100 each                    • Shiraz

## Roman Deep Dish ▲
- 2nd century AD
Decorated with iridescent olive glaze. With a bevelled lip, standing on a raised base.
- *height 10cm*
- £500                          • Shiraz

## Spearhead ▲
- 8th century BC
Bronze, trowel-shaped spearhead, in fine condition. Persian from Luristan, Western Iran.
- *length 33cm*
- £150                          • Pars

## Animal Figure ▼
- 9th-8th century BC
Bronze model of a double-headed animal figure on four legs, with head at each end. From Luristan.
- *height 6cm*
- £400                          • Pars

## Pair of Roman Beakers ▼
- 3rd-1st century BC
Pair of Roman beakers with a green iridescence.
- *height 9.5cm*
- £800                          • Shahdad

## Isis and Osiris ▼
- 664-30 BC
Late to Ptolemaic period bronze statue of Isis and Osiris, the King of the Underworld and his wife/sister. Isis is shielding Osiris.
- *height 13cm*
- £5,500                        • Pars

## Earrings ▼
- circa 600 AD
Gold, pendulous earrings, probably Sassanian, from the Zoroastrian Persian Empire.
- *length 7cm*
- £1,000                        • Pars

## Oil Lamp ➤
- **100 BC-100 AD**
Fine Roman, bronze oil lamp with dolphin finials and stylized bird adornments and fantail scrolled handle.
- *length 15cm*
- **£2,800**                    • **Pars**

## Cup and Cover ▲
- **350-320 BC**
South Italian Lekanis cup and cover with female and leaf decorations. Black on terracotta.
- *height 11cm*
- **£500**                    • **Pars**

## Stele ▲
- **5th century AD**
Late Egyptian Coptic funerary stele with reclining lady in Greek dress and Greek pediment above. Inscription in Greek.
- *height 29cm*
- **£3,500**                    • **Pars**

## Egyptian Pot ▲
- **1st-3rd century AD**
Romano-Egyptian terracotta pot modelled in the shape of the face of Bes, the dwarf god.
- *height 6cm*
- *diameter 7cm*
- **£400**                    • **Pars**

## Expert Tips

*Antiquities do not need to be perfect in order to attract interest. The more interesting and rare the piece the less importance is put on the condition. Be suspicious of anything too pristine.*

## Samarian Clay Cylinder ▼
- **2300-2200 BC**
A clay cylinder bearing a royal inscription of Sin-Illinam, King of Larsa. Text refers to royal life.
- *height 15cm*
- **£4,000**                    • **Pars**

## Dagger ▼
- **circa 1000 BC**
A Persian, sand-cast bronze dagger from Luristan.
- *length 33cm*
- **£220**                    • **Pars**

## Bridle ◄
- **8th century BC**
A bit from a decorative bridle, fashioned in bronze in the shape of two horses.
- *length 10cm*
- **£1,500**                    • **Pars**

## Lion Paw  ⌄
- *8th-7th century BC*
An Assyrian lion's paw with royal inscriptions, with projection for slot in wall.
- *length 18cm*
- £2,500          • Pars

## Judaica Relief  ⌃
- *6th century AD*
A carved basalt relief showing a Jewish temple light with six branches and a master light to the centre. The image also shows a six-petalled flower on the right of the light, balanced by Judaic script on the left. The whole is set within a border.
- *60cm x 37cm*
- £25,000          • Pars

## Roman Flask  ⌄
- *7th century AD*
A Byzantine Roman five-sided glass flask with designs around body and ribbon handle.
- *height 18cm*
- £3,000          • Pars

## Bronze Zeus  ⌃
- *1 AD-200 AD*
A Roman statue of Zeus, cast in bronze. Mounted on a modern, wooden plinth.
- *Height 15cm*
- £2,200          • Pars

## Flask  ⌃
- *circa 1st century AD*
A mould-blown flask from Sidonia, of the Roman period, with floral designs.
- *height 13cm*
- £2,500          • Pars

## Roman Bottle  ⌃
- *1st–3rd century AD*
Roman, ribbed-body tear bottle with handle and splayed lip. With good iridescence.
- *height 12cm*
- £680          • Shahdad

## Earrings  ➤
- *7th century AD*
Late Roman, Sassanian earrings in the form of flat, semicircular bases with three garnets, the whole in solid gold.
- £1,500          • Pars

### Kantharos ➤
- *circa 320-300 BC*
A pair of South Italian, Greek
kantharos, urn-shaped with large,
elegant handles, hand-painted
with red figures.
- *height 25cm*
- £4,500 • Pars

### Lekanis ⋀
- *circa 350-320 BC*
Lekanis drinking vessel made in
Greek South Italy, hand-painted
with white floral decoration on a
black ground. With two large
handles all on a pedestal base.
- *height 11cm*
- £500 • Pars

### Camel Oil Burner ⋁
- *circa 2,000 BC*
Stylized two-headed camel oil
burner with raised pillar to its
back. Kerman, Southern Iran.
- *height 19cm*
- £400 • Shiraz

### Roman Jars/Vessels ⋀
- *2nd century AD*
Roman glass vessels with bulbous
bases and long conical necks.
One jar is made of aubergine
glass, decorated with irridescent
glaze, the other with an
interesting patina.
- *height 22cm, height 23cm*
- £1,500 each • Shiraz

### Tear Bottle ⋀
- *1st-3rd century AD*
Roman tear bottle with spiral
decoration running from base to
neck. Robert Maxwell Collection.
- *height 10cm*
- £1,200 • Shahdad

### Roman Mirror ⋁
- *1st-3rd century AD*
Bronze Roman mirror with two
handles from grotesque masks.
Circular and folding.
- *diameter 4.5cm*
- £2,200 • Pars

### Necklace ⋀
- *1st-3rd century AD*
Roman necklace with irridescent
beads of tubular, twisted form,
with ancient gold spacers.
- *length 39cm*
- £3,000 • Pars

## Glass Amphorae ➤

- *100BC - 300 AD*

Pair of Roman amphorae of amber-coloured glass, with applied blue ribbon handles and banding around neck.
- *height 12cm*
- £5,000     • Pars

## Marble Head ▲

- *1st-2nd century BC*

Marble head of a Syrian prince of the Palmyran period, with strong features showing wreath with gem at centre of forehead.
- *height 20cm*
- £3,000     • Shiraz

## Bronze Reliquary ➤

- *7th century AD*

Bronze cross with hinge showing Jesus and the Apostles.
- *height 25cm*
- £4,500     • Pars

## British Brooches ▼

- *2nd century AD*

Romano-British brooches. Lozenge-shaped with enamelled knob and 'piriform' type, with pin, the latter found in Wiltshire.
- £80/£130     • Pars

## Glass and Flask ▲

- *1st-2nd century AD*

Roman green glass cup with pad foot and pronounced banding around body. Bottle-shaped flask. Both with iridescence.
- £600     • Pars

## Ushabti ▲

- *1st millennium BC*

Egyptian blue-glazed ushabti with seven lines of hieroglyphic inscriptions, found in royal tomb.
- *height 17.5cm*
- £450     • Shiraz

Antiquities

## Cylinder Seal ➤
- **2300-2200 BC**
An Akkadian cylinder seal with impression, on a clay tablet, of a mythological subject.
- **£8,000**   • **Pars**

## Clay Cylinder ⌃
- *circa 2200 BC*
Royal cylinder bearing inscription of the King of Larsa.
- *length 33cm*
- **£220**   • **Pars**

## Marble Tablet ⌃
- *8th-7th century BC*
Large fragment of Assyrian royal inscription pictographic tablet in marble, with script.
- *length 30cm*
- **£3,000**   • **Pars**

## Amphoriskos ➤
- *9th-6th century BC*
An amphora fashioned on a cone, with band combed into a zigzag.
- *height 12cm*
- **£2,200**   • **Pars**

## Axe Head ⌃
- *circa 8th century BC*
An axe head from Luristan, Western Iran, showing good patination.
- *length 18cm*
- **£450**   • **Pars**

## Perfume Bottle ⌃
- *3rd-5th century AD*
Roman double phial balsamarium with iridescence.
- *length 11cm*
- **£600**   • **Pars**

### Expert Tips
*Beware of particularly vibrant iridescence on ancient glass. This may indicate a terrific piece – or that it has been applied rather recently.*

## Bronze Sword ⌃
- *circa 1200 BC*
Bronze Persian sword with engraved hilt and scrolled pommel. From Luristan.
- *length 98cm*
- **£2,500**   • **Pars**

# Architectural & Garden Furniture

**The television and the revival in all things Victorian have led to a boom in what used to be regarded as builders' scrap.**

Over the last twenty years, the architectural antique has gradually made its way from the junkyard to the saleroom. Architectural reclamation has become much more a branch of the antiques trade than the building business, and things that would once have been hidden in corners of builders' yards are now highly polished and taking pride of place in auction houses and showrooms. The rise in value of the architectural antique has been accelerated by numerous television programmes on interior design. Items such as Victorian lamp-posts, fireplaces, doors bricks, tiles, chimney pots, lavatory pans, rainwater hoppers and radiators, along with smaller pieces such as coat hooks, curtain rails and rings, door furniture, shelf brackets and bootscrapers are much in demand.

The situation is very similar with garden artefacts, furniture and statuary. Victorian and Regency cast- and wrought-iron furniture now fetch very good prices. The knock-on effect of these relatively ordinary items selling so well, is that the really good pieces – old and in marble – fetch astronomical prices. Make sure these items are included when you buy the house!

## Jardinières ▾
- *circa 1910*
An early 20th-century Art Nouveau period pair of galvanized steel hanging wall planters, with 'Theatre des Fleurs' engraving.
- *height 51cm*
- £380     • Myriad

## Garden Borders ▲
- *circa 1890*
Terracotta garden borders with relief decoration and glazing to the upper portion, unglazed and arched to the buried portion.
- *width 31cm*
- £12 each     • Curios

## Garden Chair ▾
- *19th century*
French garden chair with chain-mesh backrest and seat.
- *height 95cm*
- £650     • Riverbank

## Wall Fountain ◄
- *20th century*
A large, marble, 'Roman', carved lion wall fountain, with water aperture to the mouth.
- *height 57cm*
- £3,200     • Westland & Co

## Garden Chair ▼
• *late 19th century*
A French metal garden chair,
white-painted with pierced
decoration to back and seat and
scrolling to frame.
• *height 79cm*
• £210　　　　　　　• Myriad

## Pair of Urns ▼
• *circa 1720*
A fine pair of Istrian Rosso
d'Verona urns of semi-lobed
campano form, the beaded collar
above four carved panels.
• *height 89cm*
• £15,000　　• Westland & Co

## Chimney-Piece ➤
• *circa 1890*
Unique Catalonian Art Nouveau
modernista chimney-piece with
mosaic and burnished wrought-
iron work, by Luif Domenech I
Montener, an associate of Gaudi.
• *height 3.5cm*
• £215,000　• Westland & Co

## Terracotta Pot ▲
• *circa 1880*
A Victorian terracotta flower or
garden pot of the classic shape,
with drainage hole.
• *height 25cm*
• £15　　　　　　　• Curios

## Expert Tips

*Restoration of chimneypieces
and fireplaces is a difficult,
time-consuming and messy
business; it is well worth the
cost of a well restored piece in
comparison with a cheaper,
badly restored or unrestored
version, whose layers of paint
and grime may reveal
unsuspected flaws such as
cracked tiles and rust-pitted
decoration. Similarly, missing
members from a piece are hard
to track down.*

## Cistern ▼
• *circa 1660*
17th-century Italian marble
cistern, with lobed decoration.
• *height 62cm*
• £580　　　　• Riverbank

## Garden Bench ▼
• *circa 1850*
A finely carved, French marble
garden bench with elaborate
frieze to backrest and scrolled
armrests supporting statues.
• *width 2.26m*
• £24,000　• Westland & Co

## Pair of Stools ◄
- *20th century*

A pair of rustic, twig-style garden stools in fruitwood.
- *height 47cm*
- £220
- Myriad

## Heraldic Beasts ▼
- *circa 1820*

A magnificent pair of Regency statuary marble heraldic beasts, supporting the arms of the Dukes of Beaufort, in the form of a panther and a wyvern.
- *height 1.65m*
- £38,000
- Westland & Co

## Pair of Heraldic Beasts ▲
- *circa 1890*

A large Lion and Unicorn carved in Portland stone.
- *height 1.78m*
- £18,000
- Westland & Co

## Pair of Urns ▲
- *19th century*

A pair of statuary marble classical urns in the Campano shape.
- *height 93.5cm*
- £6,500
- Westland & Co

## Marble Fireplace ▼
- *circa 1750*

An Irish George III statuary marble Palladian chimneypiece, with large, scrolled jambs headed by Tuscan capitals.
- *height 2.21m*
- £200,000
- Westland & Co

### Expert Tips

*Make sure that your modern system is capable of producing sufficient hot water for you to enjoy your antique bath!*

## Drain Hopper ►
- *circa 1910*

Drain hopper with flower motif.
- *width 31cm*
- £35
- Curios

## Sandstone Plaque ▲
- *19th century*

A carved, sandstone plaque showing the arms of Lancaster.
- *height 91.5cm*
- £950
- Westland & Co

## Pair of Gates ▼
- *circa 1870*

A pair of fine-quality, 19th-century wrought-iron gates, each with a central oval panel and with profuse applied scrolling.
- *height 2.14m*
- £1,750 • Riverbank

## Shower Bath ▼
- *circa 1925*

A bath with all-round shower with numerous water-jets and large shower rose, in lime green.
- *height 2.25m*
- £7,900 • Drummonds

## Garden Recliner ▶
- *circa 1930*

A garden or conservatory recliner made from steamed and shaped bamboo with full-length cushion and original spoked wheels.
- *length 2.2m*
- £350 • S. Brunswick

## Vase and Cover ▲
- *circa 1880*

A late 19th-century baluster iron urn in the Roman manner, representing 'Tempus Fugit', with the winged hour-glass as a central feature and profuse acanthus-leaf decoration above a circular, pedestal base.
- *height 59cm*
- £750 • Westland & Co

## Garden Borders ▲
- *circa 1870*

Glazed terracotta garden borders with barley-twist top.
- *height 18cm*
- £6 • Curios

## Garden Bench ▼
- *circa 1880*

A 19th-century, green-painted wood and cast-iron garden bench with scrolled back-rest and seat.
- *length 1.8cm*
- £500 • Curios

## Deck Chair ▼
- *circa 1885*

A 19th-century rustic deck chair-style garden chair with slatted seat and backrest and scrolling to both.
- *height 88cm*
- £130 • Myriad

## Marble Chimneypiece ▲
- *circa 1880*
A very large, carved Carrara
marble fireplace, with frieze with
acanthus, arabesques and foliate
scrolling and armorial tablet.
- *height 2.54m*
- £123,000 • Westland & Co

## Classical Urn ▲
- *circa 1870*
An important 19th-century
classical urn, decorated with
swags and rosettes, mounted on a
pedestal with figurative relief.
- *height 1.67m*
- £13,800 • Ranby Hall

## Paraffin Heater ▼
- *circa 1930*
A decorative paraffin heater,
probably for use in a conservatory,
with floral piercing to the top and
base, a grilled door and coiled
metal handle.
- *height 60cm*
- £45 • Curios

## Pair of Urns ▼
- *19th century*
A pair of cast-iron urns, of fluted
melon shape, with egg and dart
decoration around the rim and
scrolled handles.
- *height 49cm*
- £620 • Myriad

## Chimneypiece ◄
- *circa 1920*
A rare, green ceramic
chimneypiece by Doulton of
Lambeth, in the Art Nouveau
style with fruit and floral motif.
- *height 54.7cm*
- £5,500 • Westland & Co

## Folding Table ▲
- *circa 1930*
An Eastern European green-
painted garden table in wood and
metal. The table and the legs fold
flat from the centre for storage
and removal purposes.
- *diameter 93cm*
- £150 • Curios

## Folding Chair ▲
- *circa 1930*
An Eastern European folding
garden chair with traces of paint
to wood, made to accompany
table above.
- *height 86cm*
- £40 • Curios

## Expert Tips

*Decorative fireplaces in cast
iron were mass-produced from
the 1840s onwards. When
buying, check that the fireplace
is complete, with original grate-
basket and hood.*

### Marble Chimneypiece ▲
- **20th century**
A fine Italian breccia marble rococo-style chimneypiece with serpentine mantle and central shell motif with scrolling to mantle and columns.
- height 1.07m
- £3,500 • Westland & Co

### Regency Chimneypiece ▲
- *circa 1820*
A fine English Regency chimneypiece of statuary marble with two architectural pilasters with recessed panels tapering to the top and moulded capitals.
- height 1.22m
- £3,750 • Westland & Co

### Expert Tips

*Decorative appeal and size are often more important than age when determining price.*

### Copper and Nickel Bath ➤
- *circa 1880*
A deep, late 19th-century nickel and copper bath of kidney shape, with a scrolled rim and central taps.
- length 1.78m
- £12,800 • Drummonds

### Stone Ball ▼
- *circa 1890*
A large, rough-hewn Yorkstone ball with good patina.
- diameter 29cm
- £200 • Curios

### French Plaques ▼
- *circa 1930*
A pair of French, Art Deco doors with armorial plaques.
- height 2.15m
- £1,850 • Westland & Co

### Chimney Piece ▲
- *circa 1750*
A chimney piece after the style of Robert Adam, the 18th-century designer who, together with architect Sir William Chambers, was most influential in introducing neoclassicism, reviving interest in the styles of ancient Greece and Rome. The fireplace is in statuary marble with verde-antico inserts.
- height 1.44m
- £24,000 • Old World

### French Chairs ▲
- *circa 1890*
A pair of metal chairs having curved seats with scrolled terminations and metal tassels and a heart-shaped back-splat.
- height 61cm
- £475 • Rosemary Conquest

### Garden Set  ▽
• *circa 1890*
A late 19th-century three-piece garden set in wrought iron and teak, the chair shown with oval back-splat.
• **£3,000**          • **North West 8**

### Roof Finial  ▽
• *circa 1870*
A Victorian fleur de lys finial terracotta rooftile with heavily moulded decoration.
• *height 1.1m*
• **£450**          • **Drummonds**

### Marble-Topped Table  ▶
• *19th century*
Serpentine, marble-topped table with ornate ironwork base.
• *height 72cm*
• **£1,050**          • **Drummonds**

### Steamer Chair  ▲
• *circa 1920*
A folding, reclining, steamer chair with caned seat and backrest, with teak frame.
• *height 87cm*
• **£390**          • **North West 8**

### Chimney Pot  ▲
• *circa 1900*
A glazed chimney pot.
• *height 71cm*
• **£65**          • **Curios**

### Swiss Deck Chair  ▽
• *circa 1920*
Swiss deck chair with original cloth, in beechwood, with pull-out footrest.
• *height 96cm*
• **£220**          • **S. Brunswick**

### Marble Columns  ▽
• *circa 1760*
A set of six Solomonaic Istrian marble columns.
• *height 2.82m*
• **£25,000**          • **Westland & Co**

## Oak Chimneypiece ▲
- *circa 1880*
Carved oak chimneypiece with architectural detail and masque decoration.
- *height 3.1m*
- £4,200            • Drummonds

## Stone Lions ▲
- *17th century*
A pair of English standard holders in the form of stone lions, with forefeet clasped as recepticles for standard staffs.
- *height 94cm*
- £5,700       • Andrew Berwick

## Watering Can ▼
- *circa 1940*
Galvanized watering can of classic design with large-bore spout and pivotal carrying handle.
- *height 45cm*
- £12              • Curios

## Deck Chairs ▼
- *circa 1955*
A pair of 1950s deck chairs with original painted cloth.
- *height 95cm*
- £75              • S. Brunswick

## Wall Fountain ▼
- *circa 1880*
Cast-iron wall fountain with trough and profuse decoration.
- *height 1.38m*
- £1,775            • Drummonds

## Spherical Urns ▼
- *circa 1910*
Set of four spherical, composite urns for use as planters.
- *height 37cm*
- £500 each         • David Ford

## French Urns ◄
- *18th century*
A pair of classical French cast-iron urns, with pedestal base on a square plinth.
- *height 40cm*
- £1,200            • Sieff

## Wall-Masque  ⌄

- **19th century**
Stone-carved wall-masque.
- *height 38cm*
- **£1,550**          • **Drummonds**

## Planters  ⌄

- *circa 1890*
A pair of late 19th-century cast
alloy planters with leaf motif.
- *length 1.10m*
- **£1,950**      • **French Country**

## Gothic Windows  ⌃

- *circa 1860*
A stone, Gothic, mullioned
double window with coining,
gothic tracery and quarter-lights.
- *height 1.98m*
- **£1,750**          • **Drummonds**

## Wall Fountain  ⌃

- *circa 1890*
A late 19th-century carved stone
water fountain in the shape of a
man's face with facial hair and
distended cheeks.
- *height 41cm*
- **£1,150**          • **Drummonds**

## Cupboard Doors  ⌄

- *circa 1860*
A mid 19th-century pair of glazed
and gesso cupboard doors with
fanlight.
- *height 1.9cm*
- **£875**            • **Drummonds**

## Pair of Garden Chairs  ⌄

- *circa 1900*
A pair of continental, painted
metal garden chairs with circular
faux-cane seat and balloon
backrest, the whole on double
legs with pad feet.
- *height 82cm*
- **£245**        • **Lacquer Chest**

## Chimneypiece  ⌃

- *circa 1880*
A Victorian black marble
chimneypiece with double marble
columns, including grate.
- *height 1.39m*
- **£8,700**          • **Drummonds**

### Garden Rocker ▼

- *circa 1920*

A cast-iron garden rocking chair with floral designs and new beechwood slats.
- *height 82cm*
- £560
- Fiona McDonald

### Sandstone Carving ▼

- *circa 1870*

A 19th-century sandstone carving of a naturalistic wolverine head.
- *height 30cm*
- £650
- Annette Puttnam

## Expert Tips

*Belfast sinks – the deep white ones – are relatively inexpensive because so many were made for labs, school kitchens etc. They are virtually indestructible.*

### Stone Frieze ▶

- *circa 1870*

A 19th-century carved stone frieze, with bulls and cherubs among heavily carved leaf designs.
- *length 2.49m*
- £5,200
- Drummonds

### Metal Arch ▲

- *circa 1870*

Decorative, wrought-iron, over-door arch of Gothic form with scrolled, foliate decoration inside and an outer arch with scrolled decoration within the border.
- *height 1.02m*
- £385
- Drummonds

### Corbel ▲

- *circa 1840*

A terracotta corbel, used in the support of a projecting ledge, with acanthus-leaf and scrolled decoration to surface and architectural mouldings to sides.
- *height 40cm*
- £80
- Drummonds

### Chairs ▼

- *circa 1880*

A pair of white-painted bentwood armchairs with curved, slatted seats.
- *height 78cm*
- £585
- Drummonds

### Garden Gate ▼

- *circa 1865*

A Victorian, iron, pedestrian garden gate with Gothic architectural forms.
- *height 1.05m*
- £625
- Drummonds

# Arms, Armour & Memorabilia

**From suits of English Civil War armour, through early firearms, edged weapons and World War II medals, the collection of militaria remains a fascination.**

There will always be a fascination with the engines of war, be they large and complicated or small, sharp and extremely basic, because of their historical interest, their high quality craftsmanship and because of man's atavistic interest in things which can destroy his fellow man.

The collectables which come under the broad heading of Arms and Armour – or Militaria – include such diverse items as armour, edged weapons, medals, badges, uniforms and firearms and even extend into the areas of prints and cigarette cards.

Edged weapons, which include swords, sabres, dirks, daggers and bayonets, come up for sale very often and are probably the least expensive way to start a collection. Firearms, from match- and flintlocks onwards, tend to require a greater outlay and more arcane knowledge. One thing they all have in common is that they must be useable and well-made, so practice in handling is important, as is the ability to spot a 'marriage' or a fake.

### Brass Powder Flask ◄
- *circa 1840*
A larger than most brass powder flask, with brass nozzle for fowling or hunting.
- *length 25cm*
- £60                    • C.F. Seidler

### Remington Pistol ▼
- *date 1862*
.44 Remington New Model Army. Percussion cap and ball. Original varnish and inspector's stamp in the grip. Hexagonal barrel. Military weapon.
- *length 36cm*
- £795                   • C.F. Seidler

### Two-Cornered Hat ▲
- *date Imperial German*
Two-cornered Reichsmarine hat for Korvetter Kapitan with Sperrverbande epaulettes in original condition. Very rare. With twisted and spun gold wire decoration.
- *height 23cm*
- £950                   • Gordons Medals

### Tibetan Helmet ▲
- *circa 1500*
Very rare Sino-Tibetan helmet with pierced derge work and gilded Tibetan characters.
- *height 28cm*
- £9,000                 • Robert Hales

## Expert Tips

*Rarity value aside, the most important quality to look for in a firearm is the "feel". Firearms must be well-balanced. Anything that feels top-heavy or unbalanced in the firing position loses value.*

## Patterned Plaid Brooch ▼
- *circa 1836-71*
Patterned plaid brooch of 93rd
Highlanders (Sutherland)
decorated with thistles and
inscribed in solid silver. Not
hallmarked; as worn by the thin
red line in the Crimea.
- *diameter 10cm*
- £550 • C.F. Seidler

## Japanese Facemask ▼
- *circa 18th century*
Late 18th-century Japanese
mempo facemask of iron and
lacquer. With neck guard,
original cord and badger hair
moustache. Fine quality.
- £950 • Don Mayney

## Beer Stein ▶
- *circa 1900-10*
Beer stein from the Cavalry
Division. Five-litre stein. Maker
is Mettlach. Nice piece. Lid of
the stein is decorated with a
model of an eagle.
- £950 • Gordon's Medals

## World War II Tunic ▼
- *date World War II*
An NCO Artillery dress tunic of
the 79th Artillery Regiment.
Complete with ribbons bar, breast
eagle, shoulder boards, two pips
and number 79. In very good
condition.
- £325 • Gordon's Medals

## Percussion Pistol ◀
- *date 1840*
An English .50 calibre cap and
ball Turnover pistol with turn off
barrels. Retail by Tipping Lorden,
made in Birmingham.
- *length 21.5cm*
- £350 • C.F. Seidler

## Cup Hilt Rapier ▲
- *date 1630*
A fine 17th-century cup hilt
rapier with signed blade. Pierced
cup guard with leaf designs. Wire
bound wood handle and twist
pattern quillions.
- *length 117cm*
- £3,900 • Michael German

## World War I Sniper's Helmet ▲
- *date 1916*
World War I sniper's helmet with
sniper's plate in the 1916 model.
Matching camouflage colours and
paint. Stamped with Krupp logo
showing three concentric circles.
Leather line slightly worn. No
chin strap.
- *height 20cm*
- £450 • C.F. Seidler

## Regimental Belt Clasp ▲

- *date 1881*
Derbyshire Regiment special
pattern officer's belt clasp; 95 per
cent original finish. Blue enamel
missing. Shown with Maltese
Cross and recumbant stag within
a wreath and oak leaf decoration.
- *length 10cm*
- **£175** • **C.F. Seidler**

## Persian Helmet ➤

- *circa mid 19th century*
Oversized Persian parade
helmet etched with figures
and silver decoration. Brass
and steel chain mail. Large
nose guard and two plume
holders. With helmet spike.
- **£2,800** • **Robert Hales**

## Amercian Trapdoor Trowel Bayonet ▲

- *date 1873*
American trapdoor Springfield
trowel bayonet as used by
plainsmen as a trenching tool
and also as a defensive weapon.
- *length 36cm*
- **£230** • **C.F. Seidler**

## Tap Action Pistol ▲

- *date 1790*
Flintlock tap action pistol, screw-
off barrels by Spencer of London.
London proofed 45 calibre with
walnut grip.
- *length 19cm*
- **£575** • **C.F. Seidler**

## French Cavalry Cuirass ▼

- *date 1833*
French heavy cavalry cuirass
comprising breastplate and
backplate with straps. Brass
fittings with interlaced linkages.
Signed with arsenal of
manufacture, 'Klingenthal' dated
and numbered.
- **£900** • **Michael German**

## Photograph of Field Marshal Montgomery ▲

- *circa 1972*
Photograph of Montgomery of
Alamein.
- **£395** • **Gordon's Medals**

## Colt Police 36 Calibre ◄

- *date 1862*
Colt police 36 calibre smooth
barrel. Matching numbers
throughout including barrel
wedge for civil use on military
back up.
- *length 27.5cm*
- **£675** • **C.F. Seidler**

## Colonial Cork Helmet ▲
• *date 1879*
Colonial foreign service cork Helmet of the Lancashire 4th of Foot King's Own regiment. Showing lion passant with spike and gilt chin chain.
• *height 32cm*
• £600          • C.F. Seidler

## Indo-Persian Dagger ▲
• *date 1800*
Indo-Persian dagger with curved watered steel blade. The iron hilt inlaid with gold floral designs and two semi precious stones with original wood and velvet scabbard.
• *length 37cm*
• £800          • Michael German

### Expert Tips

*Evidence of honest wear in swords may be a help in establishing authenticity. Blades should be wiped clean after handling, waxed after cleaning. Rust spots may be cleaned by rubbing with a copper coin.*

## Manhatten Percussion Pistol ▼
• *date 1860*
36 calibre Manhatten fine arms company. Hexagonal barrel. 5 shot percussion cap and ball. Matching numbers throughout. Original varnish and grip.
• *length 31cm*
• £895          • C.F. Seidler

## Indian Steel Shield ▶
• *date 1820*
A fine Indian circular shield. Steel inlaid overall with gold designs including four metal bosses. Complete with original padded velvet lining and handles.
• *diameter 39cm*
• £1,400          • Michael German

## World War II Kriegsmarine Sextant ▲
• *date 1940*
World War II Kriegsmarine sextant in original wooden box by C. Plath of Hamburg. Complete with brush and lens cover. Maker's plaque inside lid together with original proof certificate dated 3 May 1940. Nice quality in excellent condition.
• £1,175          • Gordon's Medals

## British Navy Cutlass ▲
• *date 1899*
British Navy Cutlass without scabbard. Checkered leather grip. 1899 pattern dated April 1902 with sheet steel guard. Originally with leather scabbard and iron mounts.
• *length 85cm*
• £130          • C.F. Seidler

## Kulah Khad Helmet ▼
• *date 1820*
Fine Indian kulah khad helmet. The shallow bowl inlaid overall with gold decoration and three plume holders with moving nosebar and chain mail camial.
• £1,600          • Michael German

## W & J Rigby Service Pistol ▼
- *date 1820*
Rigby service pistol used by Irish, Police, Customs and Inland Revenue. .16 bore of unusual weight. By W & J Rigby with typical Irish fishtail grip. Converted to percussion 1840.
- *length 37cm*
- £700 • C.F. Seidler

## Officer's Gorget ▼
- *circa 1830-1848*
Officer's gorget – Garde National de Paris. With original leather liner. Shield showing Bourbon cockerel over French flags with wreath chocker.
- *height 14cm*
- £280 • C.F. Seidler

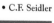

## Military Sabre ▶
- *date 1800*
British military cavalry sabre 1796 pattern complete with steel scabbard. Steel stirrup hilt with leather covered wooden grip.
- *length 99cm*
- £680 • Michael German

## Regimental Belt Clasp ▲
- *circa late 19th century*
Of the Cheshire regiment, shown with crown over regimental number 22. Of silver and gilt with 90 per cent of gilt absent. 1855 pattern.
- *length 9cm*
- £135 • C.F. Seidler

## Civil War Breast Plate ▲
- *date 1640*
17th-century English Civil War reinforced breast plate forged in one piece by local armourers with original black finish. English.
- *height 36cm*
- £950 • Michael German

## Pepper Box Revolver ◀
- *date 1845*
English Pepper box revolver signed with maker's name, 'Thornton'. Engraved German silver frame. Six barrels with top bar hammer.
- *length 20cm*
- £680 • Michael German

## Japanese Kabuto ▲
- *circa early 19th century*
Eight plate Japanese kabuto (helmet) with maidate. Lacquered and gilded, with a four lame shikoro lace neck guard.
- £2,700 • Don Bayney

## Venetian Rapier ▲
- *circa 1580-1622*
Venetian rapier with traditional swept hilt iron guard. Acorn shape pommel with chiselled ornament grip. Wooden bound with iron wire. Blade with two fullers.
- *length 112cm*
- £900 • C.F. Seidler

### Holster Pistol ➤

• *date 1630*
Rare 17th-century wheel-lock
holster pistol. Ebony stock,
external wheel and sliding pan
cover. With steel fittings. English
or Dutch.
• *length 60cm*
• £4,200    • Michael German

### Officer's Helmet Plate ◄

• *date 1900*
Officer's helmet plate of East
Surrey. Showing the coat of arms
of Guildford with the Queen's
crown device. 95 per cent
original gilt finish.
• *height 12.5cm*
• £200    • C.F. Seidler

### Churchill Photograph ➤

• *circa 1940*
Very fine framed photograph of
Winston Churchill, wearing his
medals, walking between two
ranks of soldiers with bayonets
fixed as he inspects them.
Churchill's signature in black ink
on the mount.
• £450    • Gordon's Medals

### Officer's Belt Clasp ▼

• *circa late 19th century*
The Royal Fusiliers Officer's belt
clasp with Tudor rose and crown
in silver and gilt. 95 per cent
original finish with conventional
floral designs. Post 1881 pattern.
• *length 9cm*
• £125    • C.F. Seidler

### Japanese Ko Bizan Blade ▲

• *date early 16th century*
Early 16th-century Ko Bizan
blade. A single-handed court
tachi nobleman's sword. With
nashiji lacquer and silver wash
mounts with gold brocade.
• *length 59cm*
• £4,500    • Don Bayney

### Scottish Dress Dirk ▲

• *date 1880*
Full Scottish dress dirk with silver
mounts embossed with thistle and
complete with companion knife
and fork. Carved bog oak hilt
inset with silver studs and three
faceted stones.
• *length 48cm*
• £1,450    • Michael German

### Indian Katar Dagger ◄

• *date 1780*
Large Indian katar dagger. The
thick blade has armour piercing
point. Partly inlaid with silver
floral decoration.
• *length 58cm*
• £1,200    • Michael German

### Brass Blunderbuss ◄
• *date 1870*
Brass barrelled blunderbuss for merchant navy ships' defence in the Eastern seas. 20 gauge percussion cap. Walnut stock and brass mounts.
• *length 85cm*
• £600          • C.F. Seidler

### German Officer's Ski Cap ➤
• *date 1942*
German officer's ski cap (mountain troops). Fine quality quilted lining and Edelweiss cockade. With ear flaps, in blue-green.
• *height 16cm*
• £300          • C.F. Seidler

### Lancer Chaple Plate ▲
• *circa 1900*
Lancer chaple plate with royal coat of arms and battle honours showing the Death Head of 17th Lancers.
• *height 12cm*
• £90          • C.F. Seidler

### French Cuirassier's Helmet ▼
• *date 1890*
French cuirassier's helmet with Medusa head and horsehair plume. Steel skull with ostrich feathers side plume and original scaled chin strap.
• £1,100          • Michael German

### S.A. Dagger ▲
• *date 1933*
NSKK type with black enamel finish to scabbard. S.A. dagger etched blade with 'Ulles fur Deutschland'. Wood handle with Nazi insignia.
• *length 37cm*
• £245          • C.F. Seidler

### RAD Dagger ▲
• *World World II*
RAD HAUER honour dirk. Has marker's mark. Is numbered. Reasonably scarce.
• £375          • Gordon's Medals

### Henry Noch Pistol ◄
• *date 1800*
A pocket flintlock English pistol. Made by Henry Noch of London. Silver butt cap and turn off barrel
• *length 24cm*
• £600          • Michael German

## German Crossbow ➤

- *circa 1620*

Fine early German hunting crossbow, stock inlaid with numerous engraved stag horn plaques, depicting a hunting lodge. The steel bow struck with armourer's mark. Original cord with set trigger.
- *length 71cm*
- £4,600 • Michael German

## British Cavalry Helmet ◄

- *date 1910*

British Cavalry Helmet 1st Dragoon Guards. Black plume representing a farrier. Nickel skull with eight metal mounts and linked chin strap leaf with leaf decoration.
- £1,200 • Michael German

## Bristol Tipstaff ▲

- *date 1819*

Bristol tipstaff dated and inscribed "Saint Ewins Ward No 4" with typical bull finial and ash or elm shaft.
- *length 36cm*
- £650 • C.F. Seidler

## Adams Percussion Pistol ▼

- *date 1848*

A fine double-barrelled percussion cap and ball travelling pistol. Made by Adams of London with back action locks and swivel ram rod.
- *length 24cm*
- £1,200 • Michael German

## Japanese Kabuto ▲

- *circa 1810*

An early 19th-century red lacquer kabuto with doe skin vizor. Three come-mons in gilt. Four lame shikiro wide-splayed neck guard.
- £2,000 • Don Bayney

## English Civil War Piece ▲

- *date 1640*

English Civil War piece found in a castle moat. A Linstock or Gunner's head. A touching off stick for lighting cannon.
- *length 42cm*
- £200 • C.F. Seidler

## Indian Dagger ➤

- *date 18th century*

Indian water blade with signature of the maker. Menooher intricate floral gilding. Bone handle and shark skin scabbard with stylised floral silver mounts.
- *length 36cm*
- £1,500 • Shadad

### Katena Sword ▼
• *circa 17th century*
17th-century katena sword. The blade is 17th century, unsigned, probably mino den. Lacquer and wood scabbard with manta-ray skin hilt.
• £2,500    • Don Bayney

### Japanese Kabuto ▼
• *circa 18th century*
Sixty-two plate 18th-century Japanese kabuto with mempi face mask, maidate crest of a demon and gilded lacquer neck bard.
• *height 51cm*
• £3,500    • Don Bayney

### Officer's Dispatch Pouch ▼
• *date 1842*
Officer's dress dispatch pouch. A cartridge box of 1st Dragoons with silver flap. Hallmarked, London 1842. Leather backed with detailing of an eagle taken from French Pensinsular War.
• *length 19cm*
• £575    • C.F. Seidler

### Marching Drum ▼
• *circa 1950*
1st Battalion Coldstream Guards marching drum. Good condition. Painted and enamelled.
• *height 40cm*
• £1,200    • The Armoury

### Expert Tips
*Complete sets of armour virtually never appear on sale these days, and helmets, breastplates and even good 19th-century reproductions are very collectable. Armour should be protected with wax after polishing.*

### Rootes Colt ◄
• *date 1855*
.28 calibre Rootes colt. Five shot cap and ball revolver. Hexagonal barrel with a sheath trigger.
• *length 21cm*
• £495    • C.F. Seidler

### SMF Solinger German Dirk ▲
• *date 1937*
German Luftwaffe flying personnel dirk. Bakelite handle, plain blade with hanging straps and epée portepée. Made by SMF Solinger.
• *length 42cm*
• £350    • C.F. Seidler

### Japanese Dagger ▲
• *date 1900*
Profusely carved elephant ivory aikuichi showing scholarly scenes with kodzukea and hrrimono dragon carved on the reverse.
• *length 23cm*
• £1,600    • Don Bayney

### Albanian Dagger ▲

- *circa 1850*
Albanian jambaya dagger with
walrus ivory hilt, silver wire and
chased work. Watersteel blade
with gold damascening of floral
and leaf design.
- *length 56cm*
- £1,400    • Robert Hales

### Left Handed Dagger ▼

- *date 1620*
A fine Main Gauche left handed
dagger with engraved steel guard.
Long twisted quillions. Thick
blade with chiselled decoration
thumb indentation. Italian or
German. Wood grip.
- *length 51cm*
- £2,300    • Michael German

### Bavarian Helmet ◄

- *date 1913*
Patent leather Bavarian helmet of
the Royal Bavarian airship flying
section. With original blue and
white woollen cockade, helmet
plate and chin strap.
- *height 23cm*
- £590    • C.F. Seidler

### Pair of Nicholsen Pocket Pistols ▼

- *date 1790*
Pair of 50 calibre flint box lock
pocket pistols by Nicholsen,
Cornhill, London. Brass barrels,
walnut grip with safety catch.
- *length 15cm*
- £750    •C.F. Seidler

### Flintlock Pistol ▲

- *circa 1770*
30 bore flintlock box lock
travelling pistol. Walnut slab
butt.
- £400    • Ian Spencer

### Japanese Facemask ▲

- *circa late 18th century*
Late 18th-century mempo face
mask. Mask is made from iron
and lacquer. Is in the form of a
grimace with neck guard and
badger hair moustache.
- £900    • Don Mayney

### Indonesian Dagger ►

- *circa 19th century*
Indonesian keris dagger from
Celebes with burr wood and
gold and black lacquer. Silver
mendak and nine lock pattern
welded blade.
- *length 43cm*
- £280    • Robert Hales

## Turkish Rifle ➤

• *circa 1800*
Turkish rifle with fine Damascus twist barrel. Inlaid with silver and brass roundels with ebony, ivory and green stained ivory stock with miquelet lock.
• *length 107cm*
• **£2,500**        • **Robert Hales**

## Navy Colt
## Percussion Pistol ▲

• *date 1862*
Navy Colt 36 calibre with round barrel. Percussion cap and ball. Revarnished matching numbers. Military weapon.
• *length 34.5cm*
•**£795**        • **C.F. Seidler**

## Percussion Pistol ▲

• *circa mid-19th century*
30 bore percussion pistol. 7.5 inches. Plain walnut full stock with plain flat lock.
• **£450**        • **Ian Spencer**

## Officer's Sword ▲

• *date 1850*
Victorian with Marmaluke hilt with ivory grips. Crossed battens inset into cross guard etched with maker's name, 'C Smith' London.
• *length 100cm*
• **£900**        • **Michael German**

## Turkish Killig ▲

• *date 1780*
Turkish killig with patterned welded steel blade, silver gilt mounts, ass skin scabbard and horn hilt. Silver quillons and hanging rings.
• *length 84.5cm*
• **£2,200**        • **Robert Hales**

## Imperial Russian
## Epaulettes ▼

• *date 1870*
Imperial Russian Field Marshal's epaulettes. Reputedly those of Emperor Wilhelm 1st of Prussia. Of twisted and spun gold wire.
• **£6,500**        • **The Armoury**

## Horn Powder Flask ▼

• *circa 1770*
Very simple 18th-century horn powder flask with screw top. Good condition.
• **£30**        • **Ian Spencer**

## Mail and Plate Shirt ◄

• *date 17th century*
A rare officer's mail and plate shirt with Islamic inscriptions. Previously preserved at the Bikaner Fortress and in recent times worn by the palace camel corp at the coronation durbars in Delhi of Edward VII.
• *height 83cm*
• **£1,600**        • **Robert Hales**

# Automobilia

**There is still a romance in the motor car – especially harking back to the time when there really was an open road.**

Since the motor car is usually the second most expensive purchase that most people ever make, there is obviously a great deal of ancillary material – be it commemorative, promotional or aspirational – surrounding it. Models, children's pedal cars, badges, helmets, goggles, clothing, posters, paintings, photographs, autographs, clocks, lights, hub caps, radiator caps, garage equipment, cigar lighters, cigarette boxes, match strikers, log books and much more. They all have their collectors and so they all have their price.

It is hard to believe that there is any romance left in motoring, when speed limits restrict what little freedom the weight of traffic lets through, but it seems that there is – and people are prepared to pay large sums to harness a little of it.

Rarity and condition are obviously important in the field of automobilia. Arcane knowledge is essential in establishing what is rare – some oil pouring cans were made in great numbers, some are unique.

Much of automobilia collecting is based around the cult of the personality. The helmet worn by Sir Malcolm Campbell when winning the land speed record, for instance, properly authenticated, is valuable. Today's heroes, on the other hand, have a different cap for every occasion – and many of them. Invest with care.

### Club Badge ▾
• *circa 1935*
Radiator badge for the Junior Car Club, of circular form with wheel design on reverse, standing on a marble base.
• *height 7cm*
• £150　　　• CARS

### Club Badge ▾
• *circa 1935*
A chrome and enamel member's badge for the Brighton and Hove Motor Club.
• £300　　　• CARS

### Morgan Badge ▲
• *circa 1990*
A 'Morgan in Coburg' pressed steel badge, with Art Deco polychrome design, with front of red Morgan in foreground.
• £30　　　• CARS

### Bentley DC Badge ➤
• *circa 1960*
Bentley Drivers' Club badge in pressed steel with alloy finish, in green and white design.
• £45　　　• CARS

## Jaguar Mascot ◄
- *circa 1936*
A Jaguar SS 100 leaping-cat mascot, mounted on a Panther J72 radiator cap.
- £300                    • CARS

## Club Badge ▼
- *circa 1985*
Brighton Morgan Sports Car Club. Perspex front on steel, chrome-plated badge.
- £35                    • CARS

## RAC Badge ▲
- *date 1977*
A Royal Automobile Club Queen's Silver Jubilee badge – a limited edition in chromium plated and enamelled brass.
- £200                    • CARS

## Club Badge ▲
- *circa 1958*
A radiator membership badge of the Brighton & Hove Motor Club, in navy blue and sea blue chrome and enamel.
- £30                    • CARS

## Autocourse ▼
- *date 1980-81*
A copy of *Autocourse* annual for 1980-81, published by Seymour Press Limited.
- £125                    • Motor

## Club Badge ▲
- *circa 1957*
A British Motor Racing Marshals' Club badge, in pressed steel and polychrome enamel.
- £150                    • CARS

## Spirit of Ecstasy ▲
- *circa 1915*
A nickel-plated Rolls Royce mascot, designed by Charles Sykes, on a trophy base. Would have adorned a Silver Ghost.
- £1,500                    • CARS

41

## Bentley Mascot ▲
• *circa 1955*
The Bentley 'Flying B' mascot, on the pressure cap of an "S" series Bentley.
• £250                    • CARS

## Measuring Cans ▲
• *circa 1930*
A two-gallon and a five-gallon metering vessel with copper bodies and heavy-duty brass banding. The cans show funnel tops and brass spouts, positioned to prevent over-filling. The five-gallon vessel with hinged carrying-handle.
• £195; £180              • Castlegate

### Expert Tips

*The most famous car mascot, The Spirit of Ecstasy, was created for Rolls Royce by Charles Sykes in 1910. The earliest company mascot – and the most prized – is the Vulcan Motor Company's, from 1903.*

## Formula I Book ➤
• *circa 1999*
A pop-up book entitled *The Formula I Pack*, by Van der Meer.
• *height 32cm*
• £30                     • Motor

## Badge / Trophy ▼
• *circa 1930*
A Brooklands Automobile Racing Club badge converted to a trophy, with enamelled decoration showing cars banking.
• £450                    • CARS

## Bugatti Book ▼
• *circa 1997*
*Memoirs of a Bugatti Hunter* by Antoine Raffaëlli.
• *height 42cm*
• £32.50                  • Motor

## Bentley Emblem ▲
• *circa 1935*
Bentley 'Flying B' designed by Joseph Fraey for the Derby open roadster. In nickel-plated bronze mounted on a marble base.
• *width 20cm*
• £500                    • CARS

## Carrera RS ▲
• *circa 1992*
Illustrated Porsche book entitled *Carrera RS*, by T. A. G. Verlag. Printed in Austria.
• *height 34cm*
• £139                    • Motor

## Jaguar Mascot ◄
- *circa 1935*

An early version of the Jaguar leaping-cat mascot, commissioned by Jaguar and designed by Gordon Crosby.
- £200     • CARS

## Club Badge ▼
- *circa 1935*

A Junior Car Club radiator badge in pressed steel with enamel in black, red and white with chromium-plated wings.
- £250     • CARS

## Motor Club Mascot ▼
- *circa 1915*

A Brighton & Hove Motor Club dolphin in nickel-plated bronze on a marble base. The oldest motor club in England.
- £150     • CARS

## Klemantaski Books ▼
- *circa 1998*

The memoirs of Louis Klemantaski with photographic portfolio. Edition limited to 300, signed by the author.
- £400     • Motor

## Kneeling Spirit ▲
- *cica 1920-1940*

A kneeling Sprit of Ecstasy, designed for the ergonomics of the bonnets of the Phantom III and the Silver Wraith.
- £450     • CARS

## Club Badge ▼
- *circa 1962*

A Brooklands Society badge in pressed steel and chrome with enamelling, showing an aerial view of the track against a black background. By Charles Sykes.
- £150     • CARS

## Radiator Grill ►
- *circa 1960*

A Mercedes radiator grill with mascot and enamelled badge.
- *height 90cm*
- £50     • CARS

# Books, Maps & Atlases

**Most books are more prized for their binding than for their contents. Where the contents were most prized, the print dealers have usually benefitted.**

The first real books were produced during the fifth century AD, after the fall of the Roman Empire. Much of the old writing in the form of scrolls and tablets had been destroyed, but many were saved by monks who hid them in their monasteries and continued with the writings on parchment, often adding drawings or paintings to decorate the sheets. As the sheets grew in numbers, they were sewn together in sections so that the sequence of writing was maintained. Later, several sections were gathered together and bound between wooden boards, the outer surfaces of which were often beautifully carved. In the unlikely event of your coming across one of these, it will make you very rich indeed.

The real production of books in any quantities started in the middle of the fifteenth century, but they were not available to the masses until much later – basically, when books became cheaper and the masses could read.

By the nature of the materials used in their manufacture, books have not lasted well. As with almost all antiques, it is unwise to pay heavily for books which have been considerably restored. On the other hand, books with good interiors, but broken bindings or torn boards, can be rebound by hand relatively cheaply, and this is a practice which can only enhance the book's value.

### Journal of a Residence ➤
- *date 1824*
Journal of residence in 19th-century Chile. In English, including 14 aquatint plates. Published by John Murray. Of fine quality.
- £1,200        • Paul Orssich

### Gulliver's Travels ▼
- *date 1909*
By Jonathan Swift. 'Journey Into Several Remote Nations of the World'. Illustrated by Arthur Rackham. Published by J.M. Dent & Co., London. A fine quality book.
- £150-180
- **Adrian Harrington**

### A Map of Portugal ▼
- *date 1635*
Map maker Willem and Johann Blaeu of Portugal. Copper line engraving on laid paper. Handcolouring. Based on the 16th-century map maker Fenazlo Averez Secco, 1560.
- £450        • Ash Books

### Asle Maps ▲
- *date 1579*
Titled Angliae, Scotlae, et Hiberniae. By Abraham Ortelius in the late 16th century. Copper line engraving on laid paper. Engraved 'Theatum Orbis Terraram' of Abraham Ortelius, Antwerp 1570. Latin text on reverse.
- £750        • Ash Books

## A Midsummer Night's Dream ▼
- *date 1914*
By William Shakespeare.
Illustrations by W. Heath
Robinson. Constable & Co Ltd.
- £200-£250
- Adrian Harrington

## The Surgeon's Mate ▼
- *date 1980*
By Patrick O'Brian. 'A New
Jack Aubrey Story'. Collins,
London. Naval fiction. A
fine copy in a like dustwrapper.
First edition, the rarest of
the Jack Aubrey novels.
- £800 • Adrian Harrington

## The Sporting Adventures of Mr Popple ➤
- *date 1907*
By G.H. Jalland. Bodley Head,
London. Landscape folio.
Illustrated title page. Ten full-
page captioned colour plates.
each with facing illustrated
textleaf in sepia. Original linen-
backed colour pictorial boards.
A very good copy.
- £250 • Bernard Shapero

## Bibliothéque des Predicateurs ▲
- *date 1716*
4 volumes. Full bound in 18th-
century calf.
- £375 • Mark Ransom

## Synopsis Plagae Septemtrion alis Duecia Daniae ▲
- *date 1740*
By Matthaeus Seutter. Copper
line engraving on paper with
original hand colour. Produced
by the Auysberg geographer
Matthaeus Seutter.
- *56x49cm*
- £450 • Ash Books

### Expert Tips
*If an author is
American, then the first US
printing is generally the most
valuable, even if it was
not the true first.*

## The House of the Temple ▼
- *date 1930*
By Frederick W. Ryan. Burns
Oates, London. A study of Malta
and its knights in the French
Revolution. First edition. 8vo.
Numerous illustrations, original
red cloth gilt. A very good copy.
- £95 • Bernard Shapero

## Washington Square ▼
- *date 1881*
By Henry James. Illustrated by
George du Maurier.
- £200-250
- Adrian Harrington

## Illmo D. D. Rogerio Duplesseis ▲
- *date 1729*
By Francois Perrier. Half calf over marbled boards. Written in Paris 1638 but not printed until 1729. Pictorial title, index of plates and 98 (of 100) plates on 49 sheets of classical statues.
- *43x30cm*
- £900    • Russell Rare Books

## Sharpe's Enemy ▲
- *date 1984*
By Bernard Cornwell. Collins. Near fine in like wrapper. First edition. Featuring the celebrated rifleman Richard Sharpe.
- £150-180    • Ash Books

## Madeira, Canary Islands, Azores, Western Morocco ▼
- *date 1939*
By Karl Baedeker. Karl Baedeker, Leipzig, 1939. First edition. Extremely rare. 23 maps and plans, original pictorial wrappers, slight wear to the covers; overall a very good copy.
- £1,000    • Bernard Shapero

## Dawiae Regni Typus ▼
- *date 17th century*
A copper line engraving on kid paper bearing the imprint of Eueraduj Cloppenbeigh, Dutch school. Early 17th century. The engraving work has been attributed to Joducas Hondius.
- *49x38cm*
- £650    • Ash Books

## Journeys London ▲
- *date 1870*
By James Greenwood (1832-1929). A book concerning a journalist and social explorer, investigating aspects of contemporary life and fleshing out the facts with domestic incident and anecdote.
- £125    • Ash Books

## Print of Conil ▲
- *date 1580*
A print of the views of Conil. J. Gerez De la Frontera. The author is the publisher, Braun Hogenburg. Showing allegorical views of costume and trades of the 16th century.
- £220    • Paul Orssich

## Expert Tips

*Books and old maps dedicated to holiday destinations are very marketable, not least because of the increasing wealth in the destinations themselves.*

## Captain Cook Voyages ◄
- *date 1773-1784*
A complete set of first editions of Cook's Southern Hemisphere, Pacific and Polar voyages. Eight volumes with Atlas. Bound in recent full antique panelled calf.
- £15,000  • Adrian Harrington

### Castle and Andolucia ◄
- *date 1853*
Lady Louisa Tennyson. With gate-folding frontispiece and 23 lithographs showing panorama of Alhambra.
- £650  • Paul Orssich

### Spain ▼
- *date 1881*
By Davellier. This book belonged to Isadora Duncan's lover. Attractive cloth binding with gilt. Illustrated by Gustave Dore.
- £320  • Paul Orssich

### Aart Van America ▲
- *date late 18th century*
Nieuwe K. Aart Van America. Published by D.M. Tangueld. Copper line engraving on paper with original hand colour. Dutch school.
- *22x18cm*
- £195  • Ash Books

### Book by Baron Taylor ▲
- *date 1853*
Book on the Alhambra showing one plan and 10 lithographs.
- *45x62cm*
- £2,500  • Paul Orssich

### Koran ▼
- *date 16th-17th century*
Persian Koran, illuminated double page. Many illuminations. Sura headings. Illuminated leather binding.
- *20x14cm*
- £800  • Oasis

### Atlas National Illustre... 1852 ▲
- *date 1852*
By V. Levasseur. 98 handcoloured maps of France. Attractive and very decorative atlas.
- *38x55cm*
- £600  • Russell Rare Books

### The Panorama. A Traveller's Instructive Guide ▲
- *date 1620*
17th-century book, 'A Traveller's Instructive Guide'. Published in London by J. Wallis & W.H. Reid. Original cover. 40 English county maps, 12 Welsh county maps. Clean and complete copy.
- *12x9cm*
- £250  • Russell Rare Books

## Map by J. Mettullus  ▼
- *date 1601*

Very rare. Includes the Canary Islands. Showing galleons with slight lines and inset of Madiera.
- £220
- Paul Orssich

## World Map  ▶
- *date 1662*

Double hemisphere world map. Published by Johannius Blaeu, Amsterdam. Hand coloured and copper engraved. At the top, outside the twin hemispheres are celestial figures seated amid clouds.
- £9,850
- The Map House

## Scrambles Amongst the Alps  ▲
- *date 1900*

'Scrambles Amongst the Alps in the Years 1860-69' by Edward Whymper. John Murray, London. Fifth edition. 8vo, numerous maps and illustrations throughout. Original blue cloth gilt, slight wear.
- £220
- Bernard Shapero

## Views in Palestine  ▲
- *date 1803*

By Luigi Mayer. Two works in one volume. First editions. Titles and text in English and French. Historical and descriptive account of the country. 48 handcoloured aquatint plates. Spine gilt in compartments.
- £3,500
- Bernard Shapero

## A History of the River Thames  ◀
- *date 1794-96*

Published by John and Josiah Boydell, London. Spine with single gilt rubs on raised bands. Printed by W. Bulmer & Co. for John and Sonia Boydell.
- *height 40x32cm*
- £3,200
- Russell Rare Books

## Le Relatiani Universali di Giovanni Botero Beines  ▼
- *date 1605*

By Giovanni Botero, Venice. Renaissance geographical and anthropological 'relatives' of Giovanni Butero. With maps and illustrations.
- *14.5x20cm*
- £1,450
- Ash Books

## La Terre Sainte  ◀
- *date 1843*

Original half green morocco, folio, Brussels. Tinted lithograph title, 30 half-page and 30 full-page plates. A little foxing and marginal damp staining but a good copy.
- *38x55cm*
- £2,900
- Russell Rare Books

## Moses and Geology ▲
• *date 1882*
'The Bible in Harmony with Science', by Samuel Kinns, London. Tinted frontispiece, with 110 illustrations. Near fine copy in superb presentation style. Binding of full polished calf.
• £200-£250
• **Adrian Harrington**

## Viala Paul V. Vermod ▲
• *date 1910*
Traité Gérard de Viticulture: Amplography. 6 volume folio, Paris: Marsonet Cie. 500 chromolithograph plates of grapes. Publisher's maroon cloth. Blind-stamped art nouveau.
• *35x26cm*
• £7,500  • **Russell Rare Books**

### Expert Tips

*Many beautifully bound volumes have never been read. This was because the purchaser will have read the contents in the bookshop before deciding on the purchase and binding.*

## Armorial Map ▼
• *date 1659*
By J. Willem Blaeu. A fine armorial map of the county of Wiltshire, decorated with an attractive scale bar, depicting a surveyor at work. Amsterdam. Blaeu produced the finest maps of the 17th century. Hand coloured.
• *49x41cm*
• £350  • **Ash Books**

## Lives of the Necromancers ▼
• *date 1834*
By William Godwin. Published by Frederick J. Maso, London. First edition. The final literary endeavours of the ageing Godwin (1756-1836), summoning all his powers to attack people's credulity. Original linen backed. Paper label. A little worn at the foot of the spine.
• *15x24cm*
• £750  • **Ash Books**

## Climbing in the Himalayas' ➤
• *date 1894*
By William Martin Conway. Fisher Unwin, London. First edition. Large 8vo. Map and 300 illustrations, original pictorial cloth, top edge gilt. A fine copy.
• £525  • **Bernard Shapero**

## Fairy Tales ▲
• *date 1924*
By Hans Anderson. Illustrated by Kay Nielsen. Hodder & Stoughton, London. First edition. 4to. Book has original green moiré cloth. Pictorial gilt with slightly faded spine. A very good copy.
• £650  • **Bernard Shapero**

## Travels in Turkey ▲
• *date 1803*
By William Wittman. Richard Phillips, London. First edition, 4to. Illustrated with 15 hand-coloured costume plates, five engraved plates (one folding)and two folding maps (one coloured). Speckled calf leather, skilfully rebacked to match.
• £1,500  • **Bernard Shapero**

## English Map ➤
- *date 1680*
By Robert Marden. Map showing the seasons in hemisphere. A prolific and inventive cartograph. Copper line engraving on paper. Handcoloured.
- *15.5x9.5cm*
- £300 • Ash Books

## The World is Not Enough ➤
- *date 1999*
By Raymond Benson. Hodder & Stoughton. As new. First edition. Signed. Very small print run.
- £80-£100
- Adrian Harrington

## The First Men in the Moon ▲
- *date 1901*
Early 19th-century novel by H.G. Wells. Illustrated with 12 monochrome plates. Publisher's blue cloth. A very good copy with bright boards. This is the first edition.
- £150-180
- Adrian Harrington

## Large Landscape Folio ◄
- *date 1839*
By Heinrich von Mayr. A very rare coloured copy. This is a collection of Mayr's engravings of Egypt, Syria and Palestine. Hand-coloured lithograph title and 60 hand-coloured plates. Contemporary morocco backed boards. A fine copy.
- £20,000 • Bernard Shapero

## Through the Looking Glass ➤
- *date 1872*
By Lewis Carroll. Macmillan, London. First edition, 8vo. Illustrations by Tenniel throughout. Modern full red morocco gilt, all edges gilt.
- £350 • Bernard Shapero

## Expert Tips

*Centrally heated rooms are good for preserving books, as long as the atmosphere is not too dry. Books should be kept away from direct sunlight and the fire.*

## Sallustius; Et L Annaeus Florus ▲
- *date 1773*
By C. Crispus. Birmingham, Baskerville. Latin text printed at the Baskerville Press. In full mottled calf, gilt floral decoration, morroco label, marbled endpapers, all edges gilt.
- £120-140
- Adrian Harrington

## Pyrus Malus ▼
• *date 1831*
By Hugh Ronalds on selected apples. Old green cloth recently rebacked with green morocco. London. 42 fine hand-coloured lithograph plates; drawn by author's daughter, Elizabeth Ronalds.
• *33x25cm*
• £2,400    • Russell Rare Books

## Spanish Sea Chart ▼
• *date 1799*
Published by the Spanish Hydrographic Office. Attributed to Vincent Tolfino of Cartagana. Fine copper engraving with minute detail and various depth readings. Good detail of the town.
• *52x37cm*
• £140    • Paul Orssich

## Persian Koran ▲
• *date 17th century*
Illuminated double page with divider of sura heading illumination, lacquer binding and stamped leather.
• *31x19cm*
• £700    • Oasis

## Master and Commander ➤
• *date 1969*
By Patrick O'Brian. J.B. Lippencott Co., New York and Philadelphia. First edition, precedes the later edition by Collins, 1970. Very good condition.
• *15x22.5cm*
• £650    • Ash Books

## Lithographs of Architecture ▼
• *date 1836-1837*
By Joseph Philibert Girault de Prangey. Hauser, Paris. Lithographs of Moorish architecture. Both volumes housed together in a slipcase.
• £ 8,500    • Bernard Shapero

## Stiff Upper Lip, Jeeves ◄
• *date 1963*
Stiff Upper Lip, Jeeves, by P.G. Wodehouse. New York, Simon & Schuster. First edition precedes the London edition by five months. Very good quality.
• *14x21cm*
• £100    • Ash Books

## Map of London ◄
• *date 1598*
One of the earliest maps of London. A 16th-century wood engraving published in Switzerland, based on the famous Braun & Hogenberg map of 1572. The map includes the arms of the city, the royal arms and figures.
• *39x23.5cm*
• £950    • Ash Books

## The Mill on the Floss ▼
- *date 1860*
By George Eliot. William
Blackwood & Sons,
Edinburgh and London. First
edition, in the more elaborate
gilt binding. Three volumes.
Original cloth gilt, expertly
recased and refurbished.
- *20x13cm*
- £750          • Ash Books

## Map by Ortelius ▼
- *date 1586*
Ortelius was the first person to
publish a map. Shows Iberian
peninsula in full contemporary
colour. The language text, page
number and pagination signature
are the key to dating the copper
engraving on paper.
- *38x50cm*
- £250          • Paul Orssich

## Six Volumes of Spain ▶
- *date 1725*
An 18th-century set of six
volumes by Mariana. Covers the
history of Spain. With
contemporary binders and four
engraved maps.
- £600          • Paul Orssich

## Terrestrial and Celestial Globes ▲
- *date 1783-85*
Accurate and complete terrestrial
and celestial globes with turned
mahogany stands. Made in
London, celestial date 1785.
- *diameter 23cm*
- *height 33cm*
- £19,500          • The Map House

## Book of Mexico ▲
- *date 1855*
A 19th-century copy by Carl
Christian Sartorius. Written
in Germanand entitled 'Land
Shafesbilden und Skizzer'.
Contains 18 plates. A good
quality copy.
- *23x15cm*
- £800          • Paul Orssich

## A Grammar of Japanese Ornament and Design ▼
- *date 1880*
Japanese. By Thomas Cutler, with
introductory text.
- *32x38cm*
- £450          • Bernard Shapero

## Map of Europe ➤

- *circa 1836*

Early 19th-century map of Europe by Thomas Bower. A new and accurate map, showing engravings on paper. Thomas Bower was the son of noted English map maker, Emmanuel Thomas. Colours remain vivid.
- £ 8,500     • Ash Books

## Mogg's London ⋀

- *date 1854*

Mogg's travel guide to London. The leading London guide of its day – very comprehensive with accurate, pull-out map.
- *18x13cm*
- £250     • Bernard Shapero

## Expert Tips

*The odd repair can be made to pages of books, provided a non-staining paste is used. Rebinding should be undertaken by an expert, but is not a very expensive job and should increase the value by more than the cost.*

## Four Landscape Annuals ⋀

- *date 1836-1838*

Four volumes by Jennings; landscape annuals of Spain, produced each year. 20 steel engravings in each volume.
- £850     • Paul Orssich

## Map by Van Santer ⋀

- *date 1640*

Hand-coloured map of Granada and Murcia, with superb high-lighting in gold, by Van Santer. The publisher is Johann Blaeu.
- *49.5x38cm*
- £600     • Paul Orssich

## Kufic Page ⋁

- *date 9th century*

Kufic page from the Koran on vellum, with illuminated sura heading. Middle East.
- £900     • Oasis

## Don Quixote ⋀

- *date 1742*

By Cervantes. This book contains 18th-century plates engraved by Vander Gucht, London. Of fine quality.
- *25x16cm*
- £800     • Paul Orssich

## Sea Chart of West Morocco ➤

• *circa 1700*
By Pierre Mortimer. Sea chart showing the west coast of Morocco. Published in Holland. 32- and 16- point compasses. Raised lines.
• £280          • Paul Orssich

## Magic ▲

• *date 1897*
By Albert A. Hopkins. Stage illusions and scientific diversions including trick photography. Publisher's cloth.
• £120-150
• Adrian Harrington

## Map of New York ▼

• *date 1720*
By Johann Baptist Homann. Striking map of New York, New Jersey and New England, up to Maine. J.B. Homann was the geographer to the Holy Roman Empire. Full original hand colour. Of good quality.
• *48.5x57cm*
• £995          • Ash Books

## Tales of Mystery and Imagination ▼

• *date 1919*
By Edgar Allan Poe. First edition. 4to. Original blindstamped limp suede. Rebacked preserving original covers.
• £150          • Berbard Shapero

## Monograph of Ramphastidae ▲

• *date 1854*
This 19th-century book by John Gould, London. Of fine quality.
• £55,000          • Bernard Shapero

## The Book of the Dead ▲

• *date 1913*
'The Papyrus of Ani' by Sir Ernest Alfred Wallis Budge. Phillip Lee Warner, London and G.P. Putnam Sons, New York. A reproduction in facsimile. Two volumes, 8vo. 37 folding colour plates and numerous illustrations in the text. Signature on endpapers, original gilt blindstamped red cloth, gilt lettering to spines.
A fine and scarce copy.
• £450          • Bernard Shapiro

## Map of Menorca ▲

• *date 1974*
By John Armstrong, the governor of Menorca. Published by Laurie and Whittle. Showing an inset of Mahon and two inset views of the harbour. This harbour was an important position for controlling the Mediterranean Sea.
• *55x45cm*
• £450          • Paul Orssich

## French Fashion    ▼
- *circa 1881*
'La Mode'. Contemporary half black cloth. Four volumes, 91 attractive hand-colour, engraved fashion plates. 'La Mode Illustrée' was one of the most important publications to appear in the mid-19th century.
- *38x27cm*
- **£1,000**  • **Russell Rare Books**

## English Books 1475-1900    ▼
- *date 1927*
By Charles J. Sawyer and F.B. Darton Harvey. A signpost for collectors. London. First edition. 2,000 copies. Two volumes.
- *15x23cm*
- **£200**  • **Ash Books**

## Map of Africa    ➤
- *date 1674*
By Herbert Jaillot showing the Mediterranean and part of South Africa.
- **£450**  • **Paul Orssich**

## Map of Vigo Harbour    ▲
- *date 1750*
18th-century map of the harbour of Vigo. Hills shown in profile and vegetation pictorially represented. Shows naval engagement in the Bay of Vigo, northwestern Spain.
- *47x35.5cm*
- **£120**  • **Paul Orssich**

## Map of Brazil    ▲
- *date 1649*
By J. Janssonius. Copper line engraving on paper with original handcolour. Originally produced for the Hondius-Janssonius. The present version is dated 1649. Amsterdam. Showing figures cannabalising one another.
- *49x58cm*
- **£595**  • **Ash Books**

## A Map of Portugal    ▼
- *circa 1660*
Published by Johann Janssonius. Latin text. Figures taking scientific readings depicted in the heralding.
- *49x38cm*
- **£240**  • **Paul Orssich**

## Australian Pictures    ▼
- *date 1886*
Hand drawn pen and pencil sketches, landscapes and portraits by Howard Willoughby.
- *34x25cm*
- **£125**  • **Bernard Shapero**

## The Rubaiyat of Omar Khayyam ➤
- *date 1884*
Signed first edition. The astronomer-poet of Persia. Rendered into English verse by Edward Fitzgerald. Drawings by Elihu Vedder. Japanese tinted paper. A superb first edition. Signed by the artist.
- *45x38cm*
- **£700-£900**
- **Adrian Harrington**

## The Ladies' Flower Garden ⌄
- *date 1843-44*
'The Ladies' Flower Garden of Ornamental Perennials'. Published by Smith,113 Fleet St, London.
- *23x30cm*
- **£3,500**  • **Russell Rare Books**

## Bertius of America ◄
- *date 1616*
Engraving on paper. Originally produced for the 1616 edition of the Bertius 'Tabularem Geographicarum Contracterum libi Septem'. Published by the younger Hadius at Amsterdam.
- *15x11cm*
- **£350**          • **Ash Books**

## Tschudi Helvetiae ▲
- *date 1579*
Tschudi (Aegedicus) Helvetiae. Copper line engraving on laid paper. Originally engraved for the 'Theatrum Orbis Terrarum' 1529. Maps utilised by both Munston and Orrelius.
- *45x34cm*
- **£750**          • **Ash Books**

## Crow ⌄
- *date 1970*
By Ted Hughes. From 'The Life and Songs of Crow'. Published by Faber & Faber, London. First edition.
- *22x15cm*
- **£125**          • **Ash Books**

## The Earth-Owl and Other Moon People ⌄
- *date 1963*
By Ted Hughes. Faber & Faber, London. First edition. Illustrated by R.A. Beard. Very good copy.
- *16x23cm*
- **£95**          • **Ash Books**

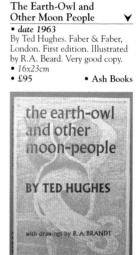

## Graeciae Universae ◄
- *date 1584*
By Glaomo Gastaldi. Copper line engraving. Latin text on verso dates from 1581. Based on the work of Gastaldi and originally engraved for the 'Theatrum Orbis Terrarum' of Abraham Ortelius in Antwerp.
- *51x38cm*
- **£500**          • **Ash Books**

## The British Colonies ➤
- *date 1870*

Late 19th-century book by R. Montgomery Martin. The London Printing and Publishing Company. 12 volumes with 40 double-page hand-coloured Tallis maps plus 33 engraved plates and portraits. Publisher's cloth with slight rubbing.
- £1500-£1800
- Adrian Harrington

## The Frequent Gun and a Little Fishing ▲
- *date 1950*

By Patrick R. Chalmers. Published by Phil Allan & Co., London
- *22.5x15cm*
- £80 • Holland & Holland

## Animal Portraiture ▲
- *date 1930*

By B.A. Ludekken. Contains fifty studies. Reproduced original paintings in full colour. Frederick Warne & Co., New York.
- *37x29cm*
- £350 • Holland and Holland

## Bouquets et Frondaisana ▼
- *date 1920*

By Segay Eugene. Original cloth backed portfolio. Paris. 20 sticky pochoir plates, comprising 60 designs based on flowers and foliage.
- *45x32cm*
- £250 • Russell Rare Books

## To Lhasa in Disguise ➤
- *date 1924*

By William Montgomery McGovern. The Century Co., New York & London. An Account of a Secret Expedition through Mysterious Tibet. First American edition. 8vo, profusely illustrated with attractive photographic plates throughout. Previous bookseller's label pasted on rear endpaper. Original blue decorated cloth. Gilt lettering to upper cover and spine. Original pictorial dustjacket. An excellent copy.
- £200 • Bernard Shapero

## The Congo ▲
- *date 1885*

'The Congo and the Founding of the Free State'. This is a late 19th-century publication by Henry M. Stanley. Published by Sampson Low, London.
- £650 • Bernard Shapero

## Chart of Mediterranean Sea ➤

- *date 1747*
'A Correct Chart of the Mediterranean Sea' by Richard William Sene. Copper line engraving on laid paper. Originally produced for an English edition of Paul Rapin de Thoyzes (1661-1721). Translated by Nicholas Tindal (1687-1774).
- *71x35cm*
- £400 • Ash Books

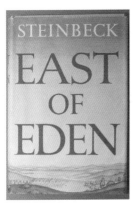

## East of Eden ▲

- *date 1952*
By John Steinbeck. The Viking Press, New York. Superb copy in dustjacket. First edition.
- £120-£150
- Adrian Harrington

## Holy Bible ▲

- *date 1872*
Holy Bible. Philadelphia. With illustrated maps and full-page steel engravings. Coloured map of Palestine. Bound in full black morocco, ornate gilt.
- £90-120
- Adrian Harrington

## A Morbid Taste for Bones ▼

- *date 1977*
By Ellis Peters. Macmillan, London. A mediaeval whodunnit. A fine copy.
- £800-£1000
- Adrian Harrington

## The Spy Who Loved Me ▼

- *date 1962*
By Ian Fleming. Near fine first edition of James Bond caper, in dustwrapper.
- £200-£250
- Adrian Harrington

## Harry Potter and the Philosopher's Stone ▲

- *date 1997*
By J.K. Rowling. London. Tiny print run intended for schools and libraries. Exceedingly rare. Signed. First edition of the first title in the phenomenally successful Harry Potter series.
- £8,000-£10,000
- Adrian Harrington

## Seutter (Matthaeus) ▲

- *late 18th century*
A line engraving on paper, with original hand colour. Published by Seuter at Auysbey. The cartouche by Ruog and engraved by Rhein. German school, second quarter of the 18th century.
- *57.5x49cm*
- £1,750 • Ash Books

# Carpets & Rugs

**Oriental carpets and rugs have been collected by Europeans for many centuries and need not be prohibitively expensive.**

The older the civilisation, the better the carpets and rugs. In the West, the Romans invented the dome, which allowed for vast spaces within rooms and, with light pouring in from all the windows, gave some point to decorative floor covering – it was nice to look at and it kept their feet warm. During the European Dark Ages, there was a flourishing carpet industry in the Near and Middle East, creating floor coverings, wall hangings and canopies. Oriental carpets have been collected in Europe for several centuries, but somewhat sporadically. Even in this century there was little interest up until the 1960s, when a new generation of travellers started to revere the wisdom of all things Eastern.

European needlework carpets of the nineteenth century have become a very interesting area for the collector over the past few years, and carpets from Aubusson, where the first workshop was set up under the auspices of Louis XIV, fetch serious prices.

Frequent handling, observation and buying according to your taste are the rules. Good antique carpets and rugs need not be prohibitively expensive.

## Indian Rug ➤
- *circa 1998*
A rug from Rajput with an old Mughal design, using all natural dyes and clay washing.
- *length 159cm, width 91cm*
- **£575**  • **Oriental Rug Gallery**

## Tibetan Cushion ▾
- *circa 1995*
A modern Tibetan cushion with a traditional design of stylized lotus flower in part silk.
- *40cm x 40cm*
- **£90**  • **Oriental Rug Gallery**

## Turkish Cushion ▾
- *circa 1960*
A Turkish (Anatolia) kilim cushion, the cover of which originally came from a rug.
- *40cm x 40cm*
- **£39**  • **Oriental Rug Gallery**

## Persian Rug ▲
- *circa 1940*
A Persian bidjar kilim, the blue ground woven with geometric patterns, with a strong border.
- *length 212cm, width 120cm*
- **£770**  • **Oriental Rug Gallery**

### Expert Tips

*Silk rugs are the most expensive, followed by silk/wool mix. But even wool rugs can command high prices. Look to the reverse of the rug to ascertain the tightness and fineness of the knots. This is not only an indication of the quality, but also of the longevity. More knots last longer.*

## Persian Kilim ▼

• *early 20th century*
A rare kilim from a dowry
treasure found in Luristan. Little-
used, with fine naive design in
natural dyes.
• *length 198cm, width 128cm*
• £1,200 • Gordon Reece

## Persian Rug ▲

• *circa 1950*
A Karaja Persian rug.
• *length 137cm, width 107cm*
• £550 • Oriental Rug Gallery

## Indian Rug ▼

• *circa 1996*
A vegetable-dyed Indian kilim
rug with squared, polychrome
pattern, with the red colouring
derived from the madder plant.
• *length 269cm, width 188cm*
• £950 • Oriental Rug Gallery

## Persian Rug ▼

• *circa 1998*
A fine vegetable-dyed Persian
jajim, originally used to cover the
bedding of nomadic people.
• *length 247cm, width 157cm*
• £1,100• Oriental Rug Gallery

## Persian Cushion ▲

• *circa 1960*
A Persian cushion with cover
woven by the Shasavan into
geometric, polychromatic designs
with a hexagonmal central panel.
• *40cm x 40cm*
• £69 • Oriental Rug Gallery

## Shahsavan Cushion ▼

• *circa 1940*
A Persian Shahsavan kilim
cushion. Woven by the nomadic
Shahsavan people.
• *40cm x 40cm*
• £69 • Oriental Rug Gallery

## Bag End Panel ➤

• *19th century*
End panel from a maprush bag.
From the Shirvan area of the
Caucusus. Slit-woven with
natural dyes.
• *length 55cm, width 32cm*
• £310 • Gordon Reece

## Nomadic Rug ◄
- *19th century*
Nomadic tent decoration. From Azari, Southern Caucusus with a Soumak weave.
- *length 110cm, width 65cm*
- £680 • Gordon Reece

## Turkish Stool ▼
- *circa 1970*
Old Turkish malatya kilim stool. Flat woven textile on a medium stool base.
- *length 91cm*
- £295 • Oriental Rug Gallery

## Nepalese Cushion ▲
- *circa 1995*
A Tibetan design cushion from Nepal in part silk, with a key-pattern border and floral central decoration.
- *40cm x 40cm*
- £90 • Oriental Rug Gallery

## Persian Rug ▲
- *circa 1940*
A Persian Baku rug, from the Caucasus, showing a typical quincunxial medallion arrangement with repetitive floral border on a white ground.
- *length 160cm, width 107cm*
- £550 • Oriental Rug Gallery

## Turkish Cushion ▼
- *circa 1960*
A cushion, from Antalya in Western Turkey.
- *40cm x 40cm*
- £39 • Oriental Rug Gallery

## Tekke Turkman ▲
- *circa 1940*
A carpet from the Tekke confederation of East Turkmenistan with a predominantly red pattern.
- *length 137m, width 94cm*
- £790 • Gordon Reece

## Expert Tips

*The presence of cochineal as a dying agent indicates that a rug dates from after 1850, when cochineal was first imported to the East.*

## Indian Rug ▲
- *circa 1999*
An Indian Agra rug. An interpretation of the 16th-century Indian Agra designs. Using vegetable dyes.
- *length 190cm, width 124cm*
- £750 • Oriental Rug Gallery

## Expert Tips

*Proper cleaning is essential to the well-being of the carpet. Vacuum cleaning should be avoided, as too much of the rug ends up in the machine, but beating is acceptable unless the rug is very frail. Dry cleaning should be avoided.*

### Chinese Cushion    ∨
- *circa 1999*
Based on the 16th- and 17th-century French Aubusson carpets. Hand-made.
- *40cm x 40cm*
- **£45**    • **Oriental Rug Gallery**

### Tabriz Carpet    ∨
- *circa 1890*
An antique rug from Tabriz, in East Azerbaijan, in Northern Iran. The rug shows scrolling, foliate designs in red, blue and brown.
- *length 198cm width 142cm*
- **£2,900**• **Oriental Rug Gallery**

### Indian Rug    ➤
- *circa 1996*
A dyed Indian kilim rug.
- *length 186cm, width 126cm*
- **£495**    • **Oriental Rug Gallery**

### Bazouch Nimruz Kilim    ∨
- *19th century*
Bazouch Nimruz kilim from Afghanistan. Weft faze patterning.
- *length 207cm, width 97cm*
- **£1,400**    • **Gordon Reece**

### Indian Rug    ∧
- *circa 1996*
An Indian Rajput rug, with pattern using vegetable dyes.
- *length 568cm, width 368cm*
- **£14,000**
- **Oriental Rug Gallery**

### Chinese Stool    ∨
- *circa 1995*
A Chinese Aubusson-style stool of medium/small size.
- *length 91cm*
- **£295**    • **Oriental Rug Gallery**

### Kilim Prayer Rug    ∧
- *19th century*
A most unusual kilim form with a multiple mirhab layout in two directions with striking colours.
- *length 256cm, width 135cm*
- **£1,700**    • **Gordon Reece**

### Kurdish Rug >

- *early 20th century*
A central field of interlocking
diamonds, wool on wool warp.
From Eastern Iran.
- *length 140cm, width 90cm*
- **£1,800** • **Gordon Reece**

## Expert Tips

*Camels, lions, monkeys and
peacocks are commonly used on
collectable Caucasian rugs.*

### Persian Rug ▲

- *circa 1955*
A Persian Tabriz rug.
- *length 215cm, width 139cm*
- **£6,500** • **Oriental Rug Gallery**

### Caucasus Knotted Rug ▲

- *19th century*
A long knotted rug from the
Kuzak area, with central diamond
pattern and wide border.
- *length 309cm, width 100cm*
- **£8,250** • **Gordon Reece**

### Chinese Cushion ▼

- *circa 1999*
Aubusson cushion based on a
16th- and 17th-century French
design.
- *40cm x 40cm*
- **£45** • **Oriental Rug Gallery**

### Plain Weave Kilim ▼

- *late 19th century*
An Azari or Shahsavan kilim
with natural dyes.
- *length 2.6m, width 1.8m*
- **£1,400** • **Gordon Reece**

### Shirvan Kilim Runner ▲

- *19th century*
Caucasus runner. Slit-woven
wool on a cotton warp, one
selvedge wiped, the other turned.
- *length 260cm, width 100cm*
- **£950** • **Gordon Reece**

### Early Antique Kilim ▲

- *early 19th century*
With stunning panels in vibrant
colours. By the Quashqui tribe
form the Zagros mountains.
Natural dyes throughout.
- *length 286cm, width 156cm*
- **£2,999** • **Gordon Reece**

# Ceramics

**Pottery and porcelain need to be perfect to command top prices. Conversely, great pleasure can be derived by the enthusiast in finding slightly flawed bargains.**

The term 'ceramics' is used to cover all artefacts which are fired in a kiln. Ceramics can be divided into two main groups, pottery and porcelain. The distinction between these can be easily identified by holding them up to the light; pottery is opaque, porcelain translucent. Porcelain has long been highly prized and tends to be more expensive than pottery. Unfortunately, particularly with European porcelain, makers' marks are no guarantee of authenticity, since many factories copied each other's marks. Value is usually a matter of size, age, rarity and, above all, condition.

Because fine pottery and porcelain have been produced in China for longer than anywhere else, it is a mistake to believe that all of it is wildly out of your price range. It is, in fact, not hard to find pieces which are both decorative and inexpensive.

The Dutch first imported Chinese porcelain into Europe in the seventeenth century and, because of the quality unattainable in Europe, there was a huge demand, leading to the manufacture in China of 'export wares', which were in more varied colour schemes than the traditional blue and white, with which all Chinese porcelain

## English Ceramics

### Jug ▼
• *circa 19th century*
A commemorative jug depicting the Duke of Wellington and General Hill in military fashion.
• *height 14cm*
• **£365**     • **Jonathan Horne**

### Derby Soup Tureen ▶
• *date 1885*
Late 19th-century large Crown Derby soup tureen, being part of a dinner service consisting of one hundred and six pieces. Heavily patterned on the body and lid of the tureen.
• **£7,500**     • **Judy Fox**

### English Coalport Plate ▲
•*date 1893*
English Coalport plate heavily gilded, with scene of Rothwell Castle. Signed by the Artist.
• *diameter 24cm*
• **£450**     • **David Brower**

### Musician with French Horn ▼
• *circa 1800*
Musician wih french horn, wearing theatrical dress.
• *height 24cm*
• **£895** • **Jacqueline Oosthuizen**

**Teapot** ▲
- *circa 1780*
A creamware teapot, probably Wedgwood, with a cabbage spout design. Decorations of a church and a house by a river, with decoration to the lid. Some restoration evident.
- *13.5cm*
- £995 • Garry Atkins

**Balm Pot** ▲
- *circa 1826*
Lead-glazed balm pot, possibly Halifax, with repetitive dot and wave pattern, inscribed 'JW'.
- *height 12cm*
- £350 • Garry Atkins

**Money Box** ▼
- *circa 1850*
A Sussex pottery money box. Lead glaze in inverted baluster form with wide slot.
- *height 17.5cm*
- £150 • Garry Atkins

**Worcester Vase** ▼
- *circa 1872*
Royal Worcester vase with spiralling terrapins.
- *height 9cm*
- £575 • David Brower

**Staffordshire Cottage** ◄
- *circa 1860*
Staffordshire cottage with flower encrustation and triple bower front.
- *height 18cm*
- £240
- Jacqueline Oosthuizen

**Cabaret Set** ▲
- *circa 1920*
Royal Worcester cabaret set by Harry Stinton, with spoons by Henry James Hulbert. Porcelain gilded and painted with fruit designs; spoons engraved with fruit designs.
- £3,850
- London Antique Gallery

**Drinking Cup** ▼
- *circa 17th century*
English double-handled, fluted and lead-glazed cup.
- *height 16cm*
- £1,150
- Jonathan Horne

## Copeland Cup and Saucer ◀
- *circa 1770-82*
Copeland cup and saucer produced for Thos. Goode and Co., gilded and jewelled on royal-blue base.
- *height 13.5cm*
- £1,950
- London Antique Gallery

## Creamware Teapot ▶
- *circa 1770-82*
A creamware teapot painted with overglaze in enamel colours, showing the subject 'Aurora'. With acanthus decoration to spout and the finial lid.
- *height 13.5cm*
- £1,950 • Garry Atkins

## Salt-Glaze Bottle ▼
- *circa 1750*
Restored, Staffordshire salt-glaze bottle with floral relief and crown and rose detailing.
- *height 25cm*
- £1,650 • Garry Atkins

## Tulip Vase ▲
- *circa 1800*
Rare Staffordshire fluted vase, finished in pink lustre with green dolphins. Interlaced flutes, after the Ralph Wood design.
- *height 20cm*
- £850 • Constance Stobo

## Urn and Covers ▲
- *circa 1790*
Very rare Wedgwood basalt urns and covers, decorated in gold and bronze. Typical Wedgwood ivy borders, with acanthus-leaf finials and floral swags from satyr masks.
- *length 19.5cm*
- £3,500 • R.A. Barnes

## Staffordshire Windmill ◀
- *circa 1870*
Brightly coloured windmill with adjoining house.
- *height 21cm*
- £170 • Jacqueline Oosthuizen

## Worcester Pot Pourri ▲
- *date 1904*
Worcester pot pourri and cover.
- *height 25cm*
- £800 • David Brower

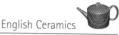

## Chamber Pot ▼

• *circa 17th century*
Early lead-glazed chamber pot
with handle.
• *height 13cm*
• £1,350    • Jonathan Horne

## Basalt Figure ▼

• *circa 1850*
Wedgwood solid basalt figure
showing father with infant
against a tree stump with vines
growing about it. On a rock base.
• *height 47cm*
• £1,800    • R.A. Barnes

## Staffordshire Figure ▶

• *circa 1800*
One of a pair of Staffordshire
groups depicting friendship and
tenderness. Minor repairs. Figures
shown embracing.
• *height 18cm*
• £1,350 pair • Jonathan Horne

## Sunderland Lustre Jug ▲

• *circa 1850*
Commemorative jug for the
Crimea. Sailor's return on the
reverse with an anecdote panel
under lip of jug. Pink lustre.
• *height 19cm*
• £450    • Constance Stobo

## Chamber Pot ▲

• *circa 17th century*
Early chamber pot with glazed
interior and unglazed exterior,
with handle.
• *height 19cm*
• £1,650    • Jonathan Horne

Friendship

## House with Bower ▼

• *circa 1850*
Flower-encrusted house with
bower and various doors and
windows.
• *height 13cm*
• £250
• Jacqueline Oosthuizen

## Expert Tips

*Factory marks can often be
found on the base of objects.
These changed periodically and
can help with dating. Do not
take them as sole indications of
authenticity, however, since
they were often faked.*

## Sunderland Mug ▼

• *circa 1850*
Fine-quality mug, with the
mariner's arms showing success
and commerce. With name and
anecdote on reverse. The whole
with pink lustre finish.
• *height 9cm*
• £315    • Constance Stobo

### Creamware Shoe Buckles ➤

- *circa 1770*
A pair of creamware shoe buckles with floral decoration. Item has been restored.
- *height 8cm*
- £600        • Garry Atkins

### Worcester Cup and Saucer Set ◄

- *circa 1782-92*
Worcester cup and saucer, French influenced, of the flight period. Marked with blue crescent moon and gilded with floral decoration.
- *height 8cm*
- £185
- **London Antique Gallery**

### Basket With Kittens ▼

- *circa 1880*
English Staffordshire basket with kittens, 'Charles Ford' model.
- *height 20cm*
- £850        • David Brower

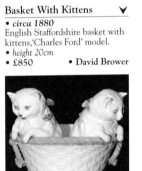

### Small Floral House ▼

- *circa 1870*
Late 19th-century Staffordshire house decorated with colourful flowers. Shows chimney and front door, with steps leading to it.
- *height 13cm*
- £250 • Jacqueline Oosthuizen

### Creamware Jug ▲

- *circa 1780-90*
A creamware jug by James Sculthorp with ribbing and floral decoration. Restored.
- *height 23cm*
- £1,850        • Garry Atkins

### Crown Derby Cup and Saucer Set ◄

- *circa 1931*
Early 20th-century Crown Derby cup and saucer set, decorated with an Imari pattern. Both pieces have gilding around the edges.
- *height 6cm*
- £95
- **London Antiques Gallery**

## A Soup Ladle  ∨
- *circa 1780*
A creamware soup ladle with a scallop design. The item is slightly cracked.
- *height 29cm*
- £195          • Garry Atkins

## Cup and Saucer  ∧
- *circa 1780*
A cup and saucer with matching floral decoration. The cup has a cross-over strap handle.
- *height 7cm*
- £225          • Garry Atkins

## Pastille-Burner Cottage  ∨
- *circa 1850*
Pastille-burner cottage with floral design. Working chimney.
- *height 12cm*
- £295
- Jacqueline Oosthuizen

## Terracotta Tile  ∧
- *circa 14th century*
English terracotta tile with grotesque design.
- *dimensions 11cm x 11cm*
- £435          • Jonathan Horne

## Worcester Plate  ∧
- *circa 18th century*
Worcester plate with mixed oriental influence, showing Kakieman and birds of paradise with oriental floral decoration.
- *diameter 16cm*
- £585
- London Antique Gallery

## Drinking Cup  ∨
- *circa 18th century*
An English lead-glazed drinking cup with handle.
- *height 10cm*
- £220          • Jonathan Horne

## Royal Worcester Cup & Saucer Set  ∧
- *circa 1877*
An English Royal Worcester 'Honeycomb' cup and saucer with jewelled detailing with an intermittant rosette motif and raised decoration to the outside of the cup. Gilded rim to cup and saucer.
- *height 6cm*
- £1,500          • David Brower

## Worcester Cup & Saucer  ‹
- *circa 1765*
Worcester cup and saucer of the first period. Open crescent marking with ribbed design to cup and saucer.
- *height 6.5cm*
- £265          • Jonathan Horne

## Creamware Plate ▲
- *circa 1780-90*
A creamware plate, in excellent condition, with pierced rim.
- *diameter 24cm*
- £165 • Garry Atkins

## Staffordshire Mug ▲
- *early 19th century*
Rare commemorative mug celebrating Vauxhall Gardens. Picture shows pipe-organ band stand, decorated with ivy. Probably Staffordshire.
- *height 15cm*
- £660 • Jonathan Horne

## Chelsea Sugar Bowl ▼
- *circa 1760-65*
A Chelsea sugar bowl of the Gold Anchor period. Decorated with floral sprays and a graduated cell pattern with border in purple and gilding. Gilding is also shown on the lip and base. The lid shows similar decoration and gilding, with a finial top.
- *height 8cm*
- £3,200 • E. & H. Manners

## Tapered Vase ▼
- *circa 19th century*
English Worcester square tapered vase with gilt decoration. Frog and branch design.
- *height 9cm*
- £475 • David Brower

## Metallic Glaze Jug ◄
- *circa 1815*
Jug from the early 19th century showing two rounded panels depicting parkland settings with a house and lake. Sheep and people painted in the foreground. Wide banding to the rim of the jug and ribbon handle.
- *height 14cm*
- £580 • Constance Stobo

## Staffordshire Model of 'The Lion Slayer' ▲
- *circa 1850*
Mid 19th-century Staffordshire figure depicting 'The Lion Slayer'.
- *height 40cm*
- £265
- Jacqueline Oosthuizen

## Watch Holder ▲
- *circa 1855*
Castle of floral decoration. Watch stored in the clock tower.
- *height 27cm*
- £265 • Jacqueline Oosthuizen

## A Sauceboat ▽
- *circa 1760*
An 18th-century creamware
sauceboat with underglazed
oxide, probably Wedgwood.
Slightly damaged.
- *height 7cm*
- £850 • Garry Atkins

### Expert Tips

*Staffordshire figures became
established in the 1840s with
strong colours. There was a
move towards more sparse
colouring post-1860. Look for
1854-56.*

## Liverpool Tile ▽
- *circa 1770*
Liverpool tile, printed and
overpainted in green enamel,
showing an urn.
- £175 • Garry Atkins

## Cottage with Dog ▲
- *circa 1860*
Staffordshire cottage with
flowering encrustation on
moulded base, with dog.
- *height 15cm*
- £220
- **Jacqueline Oosthuizen**

## Chamberlain Worcester Plate ▲
- *circa 1820*
An armorial plate with gilded and
floral decoration, on a green
background.
- *diameter 26cm*
- £350
- **London Antique Gallery**

## Staffordshire Jug ▽
- *circa 1830*
Metallic glaze with panels
showing flower arrangement,
with acanthus-leaf handle and
acanthus-leaf spout.
- £250
- **Constance Stobo**

## Olive Green Jug ▽
- *circa 14th-15th century*
A very early lead-glazed jug,
turned with rich olive-green
glaze, heavily restored. The item
was discovered at Watton Priory,
Humberside, in 1923.
- *height 27cm*
- £3,300 • **Jonathan Horne**

## Minton Trio ◀
- *circa 1856*
Minton trio with Empire gilded
design and pink bands. The trio
comprises tea cup, coffee cup and
saucer.
- *height 7cm*
- £95
- **London Antique Gallery**

## Staffordshire Dog Jugs ➤

• *circa 1870*
Mid to late 19th-century
Staffordshire. With scrolling
handles, painted faces with gilt
flecks. The spouts of the jugs are
hat-shaped.
• *height 20cm*
• **£495**     • Constance Stobo

## Chelsea Dish ▲

• *circa 1753-53*
A Chelsea famille rose dish,
painted in the famille rose style,
showing songbird and flower
heads on a lattice border.
• *height 16cm*
• **£4,000**   • E. & H. Manners

---

## Expert Tips

*Before the 18th century, all
European porcelain was soft-
paste. This can be identified
because the body will have a
granular appearance and the
glaze tends to sit on the surface.*

## Earthenware Jug ▲

• *circa 15th century*
15th-century earthenware glazed
jug, probably from North Wales,
runed with lip. Maker's mark on
neck; around the belly is a
distinct groove.
• **£4,400**    • Jonathan Horne

## Staffordshire Plate ▼

• *circa 1770*
An 18th-century creamware
underglazed oxide Staffordshire
plate.
• *diameter 23cm*
• **£375**        • Garry Atkins

## Royal Worcester Spaniel ▼

• *circa 1909*
Royal Worcester model of a
brown and white spaniel
recumbent on a tasselled gilt
cushion. Mark to the base.
• *height 4cm*
• **£355**
• London Antique Gallery

## Worcester Teapot ▲

• *circa 1723-92*
Of the first period. Blue and
white, with the Mansfield
pattern. Decorated similarly to
the lid.
• *height 13cm*
• **£455**
• London Antique Gallery

## Staffordshire Cottage ▲

• *circa 1850*
A flower-encrusted cottage with
clock. Peach glaze.
• *height 17cm*
• **£190** • Jacqueline Oosthuizen

## Terracotta Tile ▲
- *circa 19th century*
English terracotta tile, part of a set of four, depicting courtly scenes. Motif shown has a priest giving benediction.
- *height 15cm*
- £440    • Jonathan Horne

## Staffordshire Plate ▲
- *circa 1765*
Staffordshire salt-glazed plate, with polychrome floral decoration to central panel and raised basket design to lip.
- *diameter 19cm*
- £995    • Jonathan Horne

## Wedgwood Jasper Vase ▼
- *circa 1880*
Wedgwood jasperware vase. Yellow and black with white binding and relief acanthus on lip, with vine-leaf frieze. Acanthus and bell flower to base.
- *height 26cm*
- £1,500    • R. A. Barnes

## Expert Tips

*Inexpensive household and decorative 19th-century items from the Staffordshire area were produced in abundance. They are still widely available and an ideal way to start a collection of pottery wares.*

## Staffordshire House ▼
- *circa 1855*
Commemorative piece – scene of a murder committed by the owner of Pot Ash Farm against the owner of Stansfield Hall.
- *height 20cm*
- £495 • Jacqueline Oosthuizen

## A Sunderland Jug ▲
- *circa 1870*
A Sunderland lustre jug with scenes of the coal trade and a comical sailor farewell scene.
- *height 19cm*
- £850    • Garry Atkins

## Worcester Cup & Saucer ▲
- *circa 1785*
Worcester pagoda pattern cup and saucer with gilding.
- *height 8cm*
- £135
- **London Antique Gallery**

## Castle ▲
- *circa 1850*
A castle with grape and flower encrustation and clock.
- *height 16cm*
- £170 • Jacqueline Oosthuizen

## Worcester Cup and Saucer Set ➤
- *20th century*
Early 20th-century Worcester cup and saucer, decorated with gilded swirls to the rim and solid gilding to centre and handle of cup, the whole on a blue ground.
- *height 5.5cm*
- £45
- London Antique Gallery

## Wedgwood Trophy Plate ▲
- *circa 1960*
Wedgwood trophy plate dipped in black jasper with white cameos, decorated with musical instruments and trophies. Centre shows Pegasus surrounded by ribbons intertwined with grape vines and fruit.
- *diameter 22cm*
- £750 • R.A. Barnes

## Pastille Burner ▼
- *circa 1845*
Staffordshire pastille burner depicting Windsor lodge.
- *height 14cm*
- £185 • Jacqueline Oosthuizen

## Terracotta Tile ▲
- *1720-30*
English terracotta tile, with pattern showing musicians.
- *height 14cm*
- £95 • Jonathan Horne

## Staffordshire Flask ▲
- *circa 1780*
Rare flask depicting scenes from Shakespeare's Othello. Staffordshire, signed 'Voyez'.
- *height 18cm*
- £1,350 • Jonathan Horne

## Drinking Barrel ▼
- *mid 19th century*
A lead-glazed drinking vessel from Sussex.
- *height 15cm*
- £295 • Garry Atkins

## Pepperette ▲
- *circa 1780*
A creamware pepperette, slightly damaged.
- *height 11cm*
- £75 • Garry Atkins

## Elijah and the Widow ▲
- *circa 1800*
Showing Elijah on one plinth with the widow and child on the other, with bocage.
- *height 27cm*
- £1,200
- Jacqueline Oosthuizen

## Staffordshire Plate ▲
- *early 19th century*
Probably Staffordshire prattware, incorporating rural scene, with decorative rim.
- *diameter 16cm*
- £235 • Jonathan Horne

## A Tea Canister ▲
- *circa 1770-80*
A creamware tea canister with chinoiserie design. Probably made in Leeds.
- *height 8.5cm*
- £295 • Garry Atkins

## Pair of Vases ➤
- *circa 1890*
A pair of English baluster vases with floral gilding and gilding to inside and outside of lip. With polychrome panels of flowers all on a powder-blue ground.
- *height 15cm*
- £450 • Ian Spencer

## Staffordshire Figure ▲
- *circa 1900*
Staffordshire figure of Baden-Powell in Boer War, depicted with cannon.
- *height 41cm*
- £395 • Jacqueline Oosthuizen

## Expert Tips

*You should always try and buy the best piece you can afford, rather than two or three damaged or indifferent pieces, especially if you are thinking in terms of investment. It is, however, also sensible to buy what you like rather than what you think you should like. You make fewer mistakes that way.*

## Cupid and Bocage ▼
- *circa 1880*
Royal Crown Derby statuette of Cupid, having laid down quiver of arrows, reaching into tree to retrieve a bird.
- *height 17.5cm*
- £400 • Ian Spencer

## Staffordshire Patch Box ◄
- *circa 1780*
A Staffordshire patch box depicting the pinch of snuff.
- *height 6cm*
- £295 • Jonathan Horne

## Liverpool Bottle ➤
- *circa 1760*
An English Delftware Liverpool
bottle, with blue and white floral
decoration.
- *height 25cm*
- £650 • Garry Atkins

## Terracotta Tile ▲
- *circa 19th century*
Part of a set of four English
terracotta tiles, this decorated
with a coat of arms.
- *dimensions 15cm x 15cm*
- £440 • Jonathan Horne

## Expert Tips

*Identification can be difficult
with much sought-after, early
Victorian teawares, since few
pieces bear a factory mark.
Learning shapes and styles used
by individual factories – and
frequent handling – helps.*

## Staffordshire Dogs ▼
- *circa 1850*
A pair of Staffordshire pipe-
smoking dogs.
- £6,000
- Jacqueline Oosthuizen

## Prattware Jug ▼
- *circa 1810*
Showing a touching farewell
scene between a man and a
woman. Decorated with acanthus
leaf with blue bands around base
and lip.
- *height 13cm*
- £395 • Constance Stobo

## Prince of Wales ▼
- *circa 1862*
A slim, young Prince of Wales
with hound.
- *height 36cm*
- £475 • Jacqueline Oosthuizen

## Delftware Tile ▼
- *circa 1720-30*
Delftware tile depicting the
biblical scene of Judith with the
head of Holofernes.
- *height 14cm*
- £95 • Jonathan Horne

## Salt-glazed Sauceboat ▼
- *circa 1760*
A salt-glazed sauceboat with pear
design in relief.
- *height 8cm*
- £275 • Garry Atkins

## Delftware Plate ▼

- *circa 1740*
An English poylchromed
Delftware plate, Bristol. Shows
oriental scenes of flowers, birds
and butterflies.
- £275　　　• Garry Atkins

## Madonna and Child ▼

- *circa 1790*
Madonna and Child, she seated
on a naturalistic base.
- *diameter 34cm*
- £1,395
- Jacqueline Oosthuizen

## Coalport Cup & Saucer ▲

- *late 19th century*
Coalport demi-tasse octagonal
cup and saucer, gilded and
jewelled on red background.
- *height 5.5cm*
- £180
- London Antique Gallery

## Staffordshire Fox ▲

- *circa 1800*
Staffordshire English scene
depicting fox with prey upon base
of a grassy knoll.
- *height 14.5cm*
- £1,450　　　• Jonathan Horne

## Cased Coffee Set ▲

- *circa 1932*
A Royal Worcester cased coffee
set signed by Stinton. Each piece
is painted with Highland cattle in
a mountain landscape. Pace
factory mark.
- £2,785
- London Antique Gallery

## Wedgwood Jasper Vase ➤

- *circa 1860*
Wedgwood solid blue jasperware
vase, pilastered to head and foot
with floral design, interpieced
with panels. Ribbons and ivy
accentuating lip and base.
- *height 19cm*
- £575　　　• R.A. Barnes

## Jelly Mould ▲

- *circa 1760*
A salt-glazed jelly mould.
- *height 3.5cm*
- £325　　　• Garry Atkins

## English Jug ▼

- *circa 14th century*

An early English jug with green lead bib glaze. Of bulbous form with handle.
- *height 19.5cm*
- **£950** • **Garry Atkins**

## Barber's Bowl ▶

- *circa 1780*

A creamware matching barber's bowl and jug from Leeds pottery. The jug has a crossover strap handle with acanthus terminals.
- *height 33.5cm*
- **£1,850** • **Garry Atkins**

## Expert Tips

*Early blue and white porcelain, particularly from Lowestoft, Worcester and the early Liverpool factories, is always a good buy. Minor damage is often acceptable.*

## Bristol Tile ▲

- *circa 1740-60*

Bristol tile depicting a European scene of an 18th-century lady in a pretty landscape.
- *height 14cm*
- **£70** • **Garry Atkins**

## Musician ▶

- *circa 1800*

A musician in clothing of the period playing the hurdy gurdy.
- *height 24cm*
- **£895** • **Jacqueline Oosthuizen**

## Sauce boat ▼

- *circa 1755*

Agate creamware sauceboat with twin handles.
- *height 5cm*
- **£3,300** • **Jonathan Horne**

## Painted Teapot ◀

- *circa 1770*

A creamware painted teapot with crossover strap handle and acanthus spout. A finial lid with beading. There is also beading to the base of the pot. Painted in a Chinese design with floral sprays.
- *height 16cm*
- **£2,200** • **Garry Atkins**

## Staffordshire Zebras ▼

- *circa 1850*

Staffordshire zebras with bridles.
- *height 22cm*
- **£1,500 pair**
- **Jacqueline Oosthuizen**

## Staffordshire Figure ▼

- *circa 1810*
A rare Staffordshire female figure leaning in classical pose against an obelisk.
- *height 20cm*
- £780 • Jonathan Horne

## Staffordshire Lion ▼

- *circa 1820*
Staffordshire lion in red glaze on base, with silvered mane, eyes and nose and a protruding tongue. One paw is raised, resting on a singular rock. Small amount of restoration.
- *height 13cm*
- £1,780 • Jonathan Horne

## Dish & Cover ▶

- *circa 1750*
Staffordshire dish and cover with cow in relief on cover, and floral decoration throughout.
- *height 7cm*
- £1,750 • Jonathan Horne

## An English Tile ▲

- *circa 1760*
An English blue and white tile, made in Liverpool. The tile depicts a scene of a windmill amongst a diaper design.
- *height 14cm*
- £55 • Garry Atkins

## Siamese-Twin Circus Act ▲

- *circa 1860*
Chang and Eng, the famous Siamese-twin circus act, shown under bower.
- *height 28cm*
- £595 • Jacqueline Oosthuizen

## Staffordshire Scene ▼

- *circa 1820*
Made by Sharratt. Showing the scene 'Persuasion'. An eager male and a coy female on a garden seat with dog; spreading pineapple bocage behind.
- *height 20cm*
- £6,200 • Constance Stobo

## Toby Jug ▼

- *mid 19th century*
Showing a lady snuff taker in green coat with candy-striped underdress. Holding a snuff bag and taking a pinch to her nose.
- *height 19cm*
- £260 • Constance Stobo

## Stoneware Jug ➤

- *circa 1850*
A good English stoneware jug
with embossed rural scene
decoration, including windmills,
dogs and bucolic characters. The
tin-glazed jug has a pewter cover
with a highly unusual, open,
chair-back thumbpiece.
- *height 9.5cm*
- £150 • Jane Stewart

---

### Expert Tips

*Staffordshire 'flat back' figures
are not as in demand as those –
usually earlier – which were
modelled completely.
Staffordshire was very much at
the ordinary end of the spectrum
of Victorian ceramics and
represented a quality which was
accessible to the burgeoning
middle class. Figures could be
won at fairs and other
attractions – hence the
commemorative aspects of some
pieces. It was only in the latter
half of the 20th century that
they became collectable.*

## Pair of Plates ▼

- *circa 18th century*
One of a pair of plates, possibly
Staffordshire or Yorkshire,
showing oriental garden scenes.
- £125 pair • Jonathan Horne

## Wemyss Ware Piggy Bank ▼

- *circa 1930*
Early 20th-century Wemyss ware
piggy bank painted with pink
clover. Pink ears, nose, feet and
tail. With slot for pennies below
head.
- *height 28cm*
- £2,500 • Constance Stobo

## Creamware Jug ▲

- *circa 1765*
An early Wedgwood creamware
underglazed oxide jug with
crossover strap handle and
beading to the base. There is a
moulded band at the shoulders
and a pigeon-beak spout. The jug
is 'marbled', the brown, ochre,
white and pale blue clays wedged
and thrown to form well-defined
striations.
- *height 23cm*
- £950 • Garry Atkins

## Chamber Pot ▲

- *circa 1680*
Chamber pot. Found in
Devonshire among waste from
disused kiln.
- *height 16cm*
- £1,250 • Garry Atkins

## Staffordshire Soldier Returning ▲

- *circa 1855*
Staffordshire 'Soldier's Return'
depicting couple on a base
embracing after Crimean War.
- *height 21cm*
- £270 • Jacqueline Oosthuizen

## Bristol Tile ▲

- *circa 1740-60*
A tile made in Bristol, depicting
'Joseph Interpreting a Dream'.
- *height 14cm*
- £65 • Garry Atkins

## Slipware Dish ▾
- *circa 1780*
A Buckley or Staffordshire
slipware dish.
- *height 44cm*
- **£1,750**    • **Garry Atkins**

## Staffordshire Jug ▾
- *circa 1765*
Rare little blue Staffordshire
salt-glazed jug.
- *height 19cm*
- **£990**    • **Jonathan Horne**

## Tile ▾
- *circa 1760-80*
A polychrome tile from Bristol
with floral arrangement.
- *height 14cm*
- **£280**    • **Garry Atkins**

## A Salt-glaze Mug ▲
- *circa 1750-60*
A Staffordshire salt-glaze mug.
The mug has been restored and
contains a crack. It shows a
ribbon handle.
- *height 10cm*
- **£650**    • **Garry Atkins**

## Terracotta Teapot ▲
- *circa 1770*
Terracotta teapot decorated with
oriental designs in relief. Flower
finish on lid.
- *height 9cm*
- **£550**    • **Jonathan Horne**

## Figure of Ceres ▾
- *circa 1756*
Modelled by Joseph Williams, the
figure is shown in classical pose,
wearing a wreath and holding a
wheat sheaf and blue cornflowers.
She is strategically swathed in
purple. Wheat sheaves and
flowers also at her feet.
- *height 33cm*
- **£7,500**    • **E. & H. Manners**

## A Cow Creamer ▾
- *circa 1830*
A Staffordshire cow creamer with
milk maid.
- *height 13cm*
- **£600**
- **Jacqueline Oosthuizen**

## Staffordshire Figure
## of Diana ◄
- *circa 1800*
A Staffordshire figure of Diana
with hound and bocage.
- *height 28cm*
- **£1,295**
- **Jacqueline Oosthuizen**

## Quatral Cup and Saucer ◄
- *circa late 19th century*
Coalport demi-tasse quatral cup
and saucer. Polychrome, gilded
and jewelled.
- *height 5.5cm*
- £175
- **London Antique Gallery**

## Cow Creamer ▼
- *circa 1800*
Speckled brown naturalistic cow
on a green base.
- *height 15cm*
- £800 • **Jacqueline Oosthuizen**

## Polychrome Tile ▲
- *date 1750-75*
A polychrome tile from
Liverpool. The tile shows a floral
design and some restoration.
- *height 14cm*
- £135 • **Garry Atkins**

## Printed Tile ▲
- *circa 1770*
Late 18th-century tile, printed
and overprinted in enamel. The
painting shows an urn in green
with green enamel foliate designs
to the edge, the whole on a white
enamel ground.
- *height 14cm*
- £150 • **Garry Atkins**

## Royal Worcester
## Cup and Saucer ◄
- *date 20th century*
Royal Worcester cup and saucer
with fruit decoration. Gilded to
the inside of the cup, the centre
of the saucer and on the rims.
- *height 7cm*
- £450
- **London Antique Gallery**

## Expert Tips

*Craftsmen painters
seldom stayed with the same
employer for their whole
careers, so identifying a painter
is only an indication of the
provenance of a piece unless
you are familiar with his
career moves.*

## Delftware Bowl ➤
- *circa 1750*
A mint-condition Delftware
bowl, showing oriental designs of
landscapes. The designs are
inside, outside and around the lip
of the bowl.
- *diameter 30cm*
- £1,750 • **Garry Atkins**

## Staffordshire Meat Drainer ▽

- *circa 1830*
A transfer. Unusual colouring –
purple – showing riverside scene
with horse, bridge and cathedral
in distance.
- *height 36cm*
- £240      • Constance Stobo

## Slipware ▲

- *circa 1780*
Buckley or Staffordshire oval dish
with linear and circular design.
- *height 44cm*
- £1,750
- Garry Atkins

## Dog Vases ▲

- *circa 1860*
Pair of vases used for spills.
- *height 53cm*
- £295
- Jacqueline Oosthuizen

## Staffordshire Lion ▲

- *circa 1740*
Staffordshire lion, recumbent on
base with claw raised. Ex Rous
Lench collection.
- *height 17cm*
- £1,950      • Jonathan Horne

## A Bristol Tile ▲

- *circa 1750-70*
A European river scene of a man
fishing on central panel, with
floral decoration surround.
- *height 14cm*
- £60      • Garry Atkins

## Classical Figure ▽

- *circa 1800*
A rare classical figure of Mars,
possibly Yorkshire, in armour,
with hand resting on sword hilt.
- *height 19cm*
- £750      • Jonathan Horne

## Expert Tips

*Highly collectable Rockingham
porcelain was produced with a
soft paste including bone ash.
Genuine Rockingham can be
identified – all other signs being
present – by minute crazing.*

## Staffordshire Leopard on Base ▽

- *circa 1855*
Very rare stylised leopard.
- *height 18cm*
- £1,895
- Jacqueline Oosthuizen

## Flower Bricks ▲
- **date 1760**
A very unusual pair of English
Delftware flower bricks. The
bricks have oriental designs.
Probably from Liverpool.
- *height 8.5cm*
- **£1,650**      • Garry Atkins

## Pair of Spaniels ▲
- *circa 1860*
A pair of spaniels, in alert, seated
pose, with rounded shape.
- *height 16cm*
- **£400** • Jacqueline Oosthuizen

## Crested Bowl ▲
- *circa 1770-80*
An English Delftware flower-
drainer crest bowl. The diaper
shows oriental designs and
flowers. The bowl has a
perforated top.
- *diameter 22.5cm*
- **£600**      • Garry Atkins

## Staffordshire Lion ▲
- *circa 1860*
Staffordshire lion with bocage.
- *height 18cm*
- **£1,395**
- • Jacqueline Oosthuizen

## Expert Tips

*Chips in soft-paste porcelain
pieces, such as Chelsea figures,
look floury, like fine pastry,
easily distinguished from the
glassy appearance of hard-paste
porcelain chips.*

## Drinking Cup ▼
- *circa 1790*
English drinking cup in the style
of a fox's head, enthusiastically
painted to represent a fox.
- *height 12cm*
- **£850**      • Jonathan Horne

## Wedgwood Vase ▼
- *circa 1918-20*
Wedgwood fairyland lustre vase.
Pilaster-shaped, showing patterns
and decorations with fairies and
scenes from folklore. Made by
Daisy Makeig Jones.
- *height 31cm*
- **£4,500**      • R.A. Barnes

## Tea Canister ◄
- *circa 1800*
Tea canister showing rather
comical scene of two ladies. Two
gentlemen on reverse.
- *height 13cm*
- **£215**      • Jonathan Horne

## Staffordshire Figure ▲
- *circa 1820*
Figure of Elijah in an Arcadian setting. Small repair to bocage.
- *height 14cm*
- £880 • **Jonathan Horne**

## Staffordshire Vase ▲
- *circa 1765*
Staffordshire vase with oriental floral decorations in pink and green. Small chips to body.
- *height 17cm*
- £3,300 • **Jonathan Horne**

## An English Tile ▼
- *date 1760-80*
An English blue and white tile, with nautical scene. Made in Liverpool.
- *height 14cm*
- £45 • **Garry Atkins**

## Pink Lustre Mug ▼
- *circa 1820*
*The mug shows scenes of Remembrance of Home with domestic scenes by river setting. Reverse with children and The Verse of Love. Pink lustre rim.*
- *height 7.5cm*
- £195 • **Constance Stobo**

## Staffordshire Greyhounds ▼
- *circa 1845*
Pair of Staffordshire greyhounds reclining on blue base. Pen holders.
- *diameter 8cm*
- £545 • **Jacqueline Oosthuizen**

## Staffordshire Model ▲
- *circa 1820*
Staffordshire model depicting Romulus and Remus, with their adoptive mother, in wilderness.
- *height 20cm*
- £3,950
- **Jacqueline Oosthuizen**

## Expert Tips

*You will not necessarily pay more in a specialist dealer's shop. He will know the 'right' price. A general dealer is as likely to overcharge as he is to undercharge.*

## Uncle Tom's Cabin ▼
- *circa 1860*
Uncle Tom and Eva from the novel by Harriet Beecher-Stowe. Staffordshire.
- *height 24cm*
- £465 • **Jacqueline Oosthuizen**

## Series of Plates ▼

- *circa 1830*
One of a series of ten plates showing scenes from 'The Sacred History of Joseph and his Brothers'. Daisy pattern to rim with pink lustre dots.
- *diameter 20cm*
- **£600 the set**
- **Constance Stobo**

## Quatral Cup and Saucer ▲

- *late 19th century*
Demi-tasse quatral cup and saucer gilded and jewelled on a royal-blue base.
- *height 4.5cm*
- **£175**
- **London Antique Gallery**

## Delftware Tile ▲

- *circa 1720-60*
An English Delftware tile, London. The tile is slightly damaged. The design depicts an urn and floral arrangement.
- *height 14cm*
- **£30**         • **Garry Atkins**

## Royal Worcester Cup and Saucer Set ▼

- *circa 1800-10*
Royal Worcester cup and saucer. German influence. Scene of the Rhine and a view of Bedfordshire, on the reverse. Floral decoration and gilding.
- *height 7cm*
- **£895**
- **London Antique Gallery**

## Hip Flask ▲

- *circa 1800*
A hip flask decorated with floral design on front and reverse, Staffordshire or Yorkshire.
- *height 18cm*
- **£660**         • **Jonathan Horne**

---

### Expert Tips

*Chelsea and, perhaps, Bow are accepted as the first manufactory porcelains in England. Chelsea dates from 1743 and is noted for its clear, white glaze.*

## Prattware Cow ▲

- *circa 18th century*
Prattware, probably Staffordshire, showing mother and calf. There is some restoration to the horns.
- *height 5.5cm*
- **£660**         • **Jonathan Horne**

## Staffordshire Greyhounds ◄

- *circa 1860*
Pair of Staffordshire greyhounds with their catch.
- *height 28cm*
- **£995**  • **Jaqueline Oosthuizen**

### Davenport Trio ➤
- *circa 1870-86*
Davenport ceramic trio of cup,
saucer and plate, with Imari
pattern.
- *diameter 16cm*
- *height 6cm*
- **£75 each**
- London Antique Gallery

### Liverpool Tile ▲
- *circa 1750-70*
A Liverpool tile depicting a scene
of 'Jesus and the Leper'.
- *height 14cm*
- **£68**          • Garry Atkins

### Slipware Mug ➤
- *circa 1720-50*
An 18th-century slipware mug
with Midlands streaked-lead
glaze. Mug is of a bell-shaped
form with a ribbon handle.
- *height 11cm*
- **£950**          • Garry Atkins

### Salt-glaze Teapot ▲
- *circa 1760*
Staffordshire teapot, with
damaged neck and base which
has been reconstructed.
Interesting detailing, with
serpentine handle.
- *height 15cm*
- **£850**          • Garry Atkins

### Bear Figure ▲
- *circa 1800*
Staffordshire figure of chained
and muzzled bear in sitting
position on a green base.
- *height 9cm*
- **£780**          • Jonathan Horne

### Pair of
### Staffordshire Poodles ▼
- *circa 1835*
Pair of Staffordshire poodles with
basket and flowers, standing on a
cushion base.
- *height 12cm*
- **£695** • Jacqueline Oosthuizen

### Knife Handle Set ◀
- *circa 1755*
A set of Staffordshire knife
handles with leaf scroll design.
- *height 7cm*
- **£3,850**          • Jonathan Horne

## Princess Louise ▽
- *circa 1870*
Princess Louise and the Marquess of Lorne shown as a pair in Highland dress.
- *height 26cm*
- £395 • Jacqueline Oosthuizen

## Pastille Burner ▽
- *circa 1850*
Flower-encrusted pastille burner with pagoda roof.
- *height 14cm*
- £950 • Jacqueline Oosthuizen

## Portland Vases ▲
- *circa 1885-90*
Wedgwood Portland vases in various colours – bleeding green, dark blue and black – with Victorian draping.
- *height 10cm*
- £350 • R.A. Barnes

## Prattware Jug ▽
- *circa 1800*
Showing Toby Philpot holding a tankard and a man smoking a pipe on reverse. There is leaf design around base and neck.
- *height 12cm*
- £395 • Constance Stobo

## Deer with Bocage ▽
- *circa 1790*
Pair of prattware deer with bocage, reclining on grass base.
- *height 14cm*
- £2,500
- Jacqueline Oosthuizen

## A Bristol Tile ▲
- *circa 1740-60*
A slightly damaged tile showing 'The Shearing of Samson'. The tile was made in Bristol.
- *height 14cm*
- £95 • Garry Atkins

## Staffordshire Teapot ▲
- *circa 1765*
Staffordshire teapot with oriental floral decorations; panels showing oriental gentlemen in period dress. Looped finial top.
- *height 10cm*
- £2,450 • Jonathan Horne

## Staffordshire Spill Holders ◄

- *circa 1860*
A pair of Staffordshire leopard spill holders. Very rare.
- *height 16cm*
- £3,995
- Jacqueline Oosthuizen

## Bristol Plate ▲

- *circa 1760*
A restored English Delftware plate, from Bristol. Depicts a European scene of a gentleman and a lady in18th-century dress against landscape.
- £275    • Garry Atkins

## Stoneware Mug ◄

- *circa 1860*
Mid 19th-century stoneware mug in baluster shape. Tin-glazed with curved handle and lip.
- *height 5cm*
- £65    • Jane Stewart

## Delftware Tile ➤

- *circa 1740*
Delftware tile depicting a biblical interpretation of Jacob wrestling with the angel.
- *height 14cm*
- £98    • Jonathan Horne

## Staffordshire Cup ◄

- *circa 1765*
Very rare Staffordshire cup. With floral decorations throughout and inside rim, fluted with detailing and ribbon handle.
- *height 7.5cm*
- £3,650    • Jonathan Horne

## Staffordshire Teapot ▲

- *circa 1795*
Staffordshire teapot with fleur de lys design on lid and grotesque design on pot.
- *height 8cm*
- £1,990    • Jonathan Horne

## Wedgwood Plaque ➤

- *circa 1850*
Wedgwood cameo plaque, dipped black and white, showing 'six Dancing Hours'. Originally modelled by Floxam in the 18th century. Extremely popular mantel in black laquer frame with gilded mounting.
- *length 56cm*
- £1,250    • R.A. Barnes

## Staffordshire Elephant ▲

• *circa 1860*
Staffordshire elephant, with
bocage, on plinth.
• *height 18cm*
• **£1,195**
• **Jacqueline Oosthuizen**

## Loving Cup ▲

• *circa 1840*
A two-handled loving cup with
'God Speed the Plough' written
to lip on obverse, with 'The
Farmers' Arms' and 'In God We
Trust' surrounding a central
depiction of a sheaf of corn. On
the reverse is a verse decrying
wealth, with various other
homilies and illustrations.
• **£350**          • **Ian Spencer**

## Cow Creamer ▲

• *circa 1810*
A Staffordshire cow creamer with
yellow spots
• *height 13cm*
• **£630** • **Jacqueline Oosthuizen**

## Water Jug ▼

• *circa 1270-1350*
A lead-glazed water jug probably
Hill Green, Essex. Potter's marks
feature on handle.
• *height 22cm*
• **£4,450**     • **Jonathan Horne**

## Longcase Clock ▼

• *circa 1820*
Prattware model clock, showing
the time as 11:45. Yellow glaze
with white face and leaf design.
• *height 25cm*
• **£560**       • **Constance Stobo**

## Wedgwood Candle Holders ▲

• *circa 1800*
A pair of rare Wedgwood candle
holders mounted on gilt bronze.
Bases show classical cameos with
frieze motifs.
• *height 26cm*
• **£2,500**       • **R.A. Barnes**

## Expert Tips

*Spaniels have always been
popular subjects, because of
their royal connections, but look
out for modern copies. Modern
copies have blander expressions
and duller colours and display
fewer signs of attention to detail
than originals.*

## Dog-head Window Rests ▼

• *circa 1850*
Mid 19th-century Staffordshire
dog-head window rests. Yellow
ochre glaze showing spaniel dogs
with collars.
• *height 13cm*
• **£220**
• **Constance Stobo**

## Pair of Field Spaniels ◄

- *circa 1850*
Pair of eager field spaniels on an ornate base.
- *height 16cm*
- £800 pair
- Jacqueline Oosthuizen

### Wedgwood Planter ➤

- *circa 1870*
Wedgwood lilac planter decorated with frieze of roses and vines from lilac heads.
- *height 19cm*
- £575            • R.A. Barnes

### English Tile ▲

- *circa 14th century*
English tile with panther-head design made at Penn, Buckinghamshire.
- £250            • Garry Atkins

### Wemyss Pig ▼

- *circa 1890*
Early Wemyss Pig from the late 19th century, with pressed mark, 'Made in Scotland, RH&S'. Black, white and pink glaze with wrinkles to snout.
- *length 46cm*
- £3,300            • Constance Stobo

### Sunderland Plaque ▲

- *circa 1825*
Transfer with coloured wash. Pink lustre showing sailing ships and anecdote to peace and plenty. With copper lustre.
- *height 23cm*
- £295            • Constance Stobo

### Derby Vase ▲

- *circa 1800*
Derby vase, painted in a soft palette, with foliage, grass and scattered sprigs of leaves on a white ground. Pattern primarily depicting red-legged grouse. There is some inexpert restoration to the rim.
- *height 16cm*
- £480            • Ian Spencer

### Teapot ➤

- *circa late 18th century*
A Staffordshire third quarter 18th-century teapot. There are chips to the outer and inner rims of the lid. The tip of the spout has been restored. There is a pyramid in a woodland scene painted on the reverse.
- *height 13cm*
- £1,850            • Garry Atkins

## Pot Pourri Vases ▽

- *circa 1765*

A pair of Chelsea pot pourri vases with pierced lids. Gold Anchor period., with finial top and pierced lid, Mazarin blue gilding and notable gilt floral swags. The pots stand on three goat legs on a gilt base. Also feature three outward looking goat heads.
- *height 120cm*
- £ 5,500    • E. & H. Manners

## Tureen ▽

- *circa 1780*

A creamware tureen and cover, probably Staffordshire. Some restoration has been made to the body of the tureen.
- *height 25cm*
- £850    • Garry Atkins

## Sunderland Mug ▶

- *circa 1810*

Sunderland pink lustre mug, showing sailor's return and pastoral scenes of sailor with his family, ship in distance. Anecdote on reverse.
- *height 13cm*
- £295    • Constance Stobo

## Pair of Copeland Vases ▲

- *circa 1880*

With covers depicting courtly scenes in a woodland setting to the front and cherub panels to rear, decorated with gilded, interlaced knob on the cover and ribbon handles.
- *height 31cm*
- £2,250    • David Brower

## A Creamware Dish ▲

- *circa 1780-1800*

A creamware dish with a hyacinth design.
- *diameter 22cm*
- £275    • Garry Atkins

## Monkey Teapot ▽

- *circa 1875*

A Minton monkey teapot in majolica. Torquoise/green glaze.
- *height 16cm*
- £675
- **London Antique Gallery**

## Wedgwood Jam Pot ▽

- *circa 1880*

A Wedgwood jam pot shown with silver-plated handle. Lilac and sage green with floral swirls and goat-heads decoration with classical cameos.
- *height 18.5cm*
- £520    • R.A. Barnes

## Expert Tips

*Early bone china was suitable only for small-scale objects. Some of the best examples were by Minton, but do not usually carry a Minton mark. They can be identified by the impressed shape number.*

# European Ceramics

## Meissen Figure ▼
- *circa 1880*
A Meissen figure of cherub with broken heart. Part of a series of 26.
- *height 22cm*
- £1,750 • David Brower

## Terracotta Bull Terrier ▼
- *late 19th century*
Recumbent on a stylised fur rug. Black marble base. French.
- *height 17cm*
- £600 • Elizabeth Baldwin

## Vienna Tray ▲
- *circa 1850*
Heavily gilded. Scene of the 'Shepherds of Arcadia' after Nicholas Poussin.
- *height 31cm*
- £2,750 • David Brower

## Meissen Tureen ▲
- *date 1745*
Bombe form, decorated in deep purple with figures on horseback hunting boar and deer through wooded landscapes, alternating with flower sprays. The cover decorated with a boar's head as finial, with gilding.
- *height 25.5cm*
- £6,500 • Anita Gray

## Lead Glazed Jug ▼
- *17th century*
Low Countries jug with lead glaze and scroll design to body with pinched handle.
- *height 16.5cm*
- £575 • Garry Atkins

## Model of Red Squirrel ▼
- *date 1856*
A Vienna model of a red squirrel holding a walnut. The figure is perched on an acorn-encrusted tree stump base.
- *height 26cm*
- £720 • David Brower

## Alberello Vase ◄
- *circa 1500*
Montelup Alberello, decorated with stylised feathers.
- *height 20cm*
- £2,000-£3,000 • Bazaart

### Italian Albarello Faenza Jar ▾

- *16th century*

Painted in yellow, green, blue and white, with an oval medallion portrait of a woman in profile at the centre, against a blue and white ground of stylised flowerheads and foliate scrolls. All above a basal frieze in the form of a scroll of paper, with the inscription 'FILONIUM R.S.M.'
- *height 18cm*
- **£4,200**            • Anita Gray

### Sèvres Compotière ▾

- *date 1772*

From the Sefton service, part of a dessert service. With leafy garlands on '*oeil de pedrix*' base
- *width 23cm*
- **£6,800**            • E&H Manners

### Meissen Pugs ▶

- *circa 1860*

A pair of Meissen models of pug dogs with pup. Brown and black underglaze. Pugs of this type vary in size and age, both are important factors when assessing value.
- *height 18cm*
- **£3,300**            • David Brower

### Gallé Rooster ▲

- *circa 1870*

A Gallé model of rooster with unusual mark. Signed Gallé. Hand painted and glazed.
- *height 19cm*
- **£150**            • Cameo Gallery

### Berlin Plaque ▲

- *circa 1880*

Plaque depicting a Renaissance lady printed on porcelain in a heavily gilded frame.
- *24x16cm*
- **£4,200**            • David Brower

### Cabaret Set ▾

- *19th century*

French cabaret set in Sèvres style with original fitted case.
- *box 29x14cm*
- **£650**            • David Brower

### Gallé Water Jug ▾

- *circa 1870*

Showing a characterful musician, elegantly modelled and painted, with lute, seated on a drum.
- *height 40cm*
- **£4,800**            • Cameo Gallery

## Meissen Figures ▲
- *circa 1860*
Pair of Meissen gardening
figures, incorporating watering
can and spade details.
- *height 35cm*
- £6,500 • **David Brower**

## Wet Drug Jar ▲
- *1600-1620*
Montelupo, majolica vase
with sea horse handles.
- *height 36cm*
- £4,000-£6,000 • **Bazzart**

## Early Italian Tin Glazed Dish ▼
- *16th century*
Scene painted to the centre of
Roman soldiers dividing up the
spoils of war. The rim with a
narrow yellow band, the reverse
decorated with similar yellow
lines around the rim and base.
- *height 13.5cm*
- £4,500 • **Anita Gray**

## Alberello Vase ▼
- *circa 1670*
Probably Bassano. Of dumbbell
form with floral swags from mask
decoration.
- *height 27cm*
- £1,200-£1,500 • **Bazaart**

## Vienna Tea Caddy ◄
- *19th century*
A tea caddy with painted panels
depicting coastal scenes of
woman and child with ship in
background, on a burgundy
ground.
- *height 16cm*
- £1,100 • **David Brower**

## Cup and Saucer ▲
- *circa 1880*
Dresden cup and saucer with
cover, by Helena Watson.
- *height 12cm*
- £650 • **David Brower**

### Expert Tips
*Collectors tend to concentrate
on majolica by George Jones,
Minton and Wedgwood, but
look out for good French and
Portuguese examples – they will
prove rewarding.*

## Porcelain Dog ▼
- *date 1894*
French bisque porcelain
model showing an attentive
bitch. Original artist Charlotte
Bertrand from the factory of
Richard Eckert & Co.
- *height 18cm*
- £700 • **Elizabeth Baldwin**

## Gallé Cat ▲
• *circa 1890*
Highly decorated model of a
cat with painted gems and
scrolled design. Russian crest
on hindquarters. Glass eyes,
Gallé marked.
• *height 34cm*
• £4,000 • Constance Stobo

## Ceramic Wall Plate ▼
• *8th May 1896*
Dutch wall plate by Rozenburg of
den Haag. Painted by Theodorus
Verstraaten. Landscape with
chestnut border.
• *diameter 56cm*
• £6,500 • Pieter Oosthuizen

## Armorial Alborello ▼
• *circa 1580*
One of a pair of Armorial
alborelli. Naples or Sciacca
polychrome with castle motif.
• *height 3cm*
• £8,000-£12,000 • Bazaart

## Porcelain Vase ▲
• *circa 1870*
One of a pair of ormolu mounted
Sèvres porcelain vases, with hand
painted galant scenes.
• *height 62cm*
• £14,000 • Judy Fox

## Expert Tips
*Never lift any piece by its
handle. Remove the lid and grip
with the finger inside and the
thumb outside. The piece may
have been weakened by an
invisible crack or bad luting.*

## Meissen Candelabra ▲
• *date 1860*
Pair of Meissen candelabra,
flower encrusted with detachable
arms and cherub decoration.
Figures depicting the four seasons.
• *height 46cm*
• £4,250 • David Brower

## Vincennes Sucrier ◀
• *date 1754*
Early Vincennes sucrier
painted with birds on
cartouches on a blue lapis
ground. A chrysanthemum finial
gilt decoration. With interlaced
'L' and the date letter 'B'.
• *height 10cm*
•£5,000 • E&H Manners

## Vienna Dish ▼
• *mid 19th century*
A silver mounted Vienna dish
with painted panels of maidens
and swans at play by a river,
entitled 'Sommer Lust'.
• *diameter 36cm*
• £1,880 • David Brower

## Hollandaise Vases ◀

- *date 1860*
A pair of Sèvres style Hollandaise vases with under dishes, painted with 'jewelled' panels of maidens with instruments, music and flowers.
- *height 19cm*
- £3,250          • David Brower

## Pear-Shaped Bottle ▶

- *date 1730*
A Meissen bottle of square section. Shown with kakiemon panels of flowers and bamboo on a sea green/blue base.
- *height 32cm*
- £15,000          • David Brower

## Pipkins ▲

- *date 17th century*
Low Countries pipkins showing a turned, two-handled pot with tripod base, in lead glaze.
- *height 18cm*
- £150          • Garry Atkins

## Gallé Salt ▼

- *date 1875*
Showing two women in one dress. Signed 'Gallé'.
- *height 20cm*
- £1,200          • Cameo Gallery

## Stirrup Cup ▲

- *circa 1880*
A Meissen stirrup cup, modelled and painted as a fox's head.
- *height 13cm*
- £595          • David Brower

## Meissen Figure ▲

- *circa 1880*
Meissen figure of cherub in costume of 'St George', standing upon a dragon coiled about the base. One of a series of 26.
- *height 23cm*
- £1,750          • David Brower

## Carlsbad Cup and Saucer ◀

- *late 19th century*
Decorated with flower and leaf design with gilding to the interior of the cup.
- *height 6cm*
- £350          • David Brower

## Expert Tips

*A market which
has increasing prices
dependent on the condition
of the objects, is open to abuse
by the unscrupulous.
Improvement in restoration
techniques with the use of
modern chemicals
and compounds is ongoing
and becoming more difficult
to identify. Do not immediately
trust the bargain, and question
further the popularly used
phrase 'purchased as perfect'.
However good the
restoration, do not be
misled into thinking that a
damaged piece can be worth
anything like as much as
a perfect one.*

### Vase and Cover  ▽
- *circa 1860*
A Meissen flower encrusted vase
and cover with cherub
adornment, decorated with a
Watteau pastoral scene.
- *height 61cm*
- **£3,500**  • **David Brower**

### Gallé Coffee Pot  ▽
- *circa 1870*
Coffee pot with twisted and
fluted design. Leaf lid, vine
handle, swan neck spout. Lion
mask to lip.
- *height 26cm*
- **£1,800**  • **Cameo Gallery**

### Italian Majolica Vase  △
- *19th century*
Urn shape with snake handles
emerging from lion masks.
Painted with battle scenes, with
cherubs on reverse and a castle to
the base.
- *height 49cm*
- **£750**  • **Shadad**

### Slipware Dish  ▽
- *date 1738*
Low Countries pottery slipware
dish with date. Banded with
interlacing wavy pattern in lead
glaze.
- *diameter 35cm*
- **£850**  • **Garry Atkins**

### Fruit Plate  △
- *circa 1570*
Extremely rare Urbino
fruit plate. Majolica.
- *diameter 27cm*
- **£10,000-£15,000**  • **Bazaart**

### Model of Cat & Dog  ◁
- *circa 1770*
Brussels faience models of a cat
and dog naturally modelled with
pale blue green, black glaze. On a
green base.
- *height 20cm*
- **£8,500**  • **E.&H. Manners**

## Swan Centrepiece ➤
- *circa 1870*
With three bowls in the
form of swans with interlaced
necks. With gilding and
floral decoration.
- *height 18cm*
- £2,800 • Cameo Gallery

## Alborelli Vases ▲
- *circa 1700*
Pair of Alborelli vases from
Sciacca, Sicily. Predominantly
blue with cartouches showing
maritime scene framed with
leaf design.
- *height 22cm*
- £3,000-£4,000 • Bazaart

## Hispano Moresque Dish ▲
- *16th century*
An unusual and highly
collectable Spanish Hispano-
Moresque dish from Catalunia,
probably Valencia. In a lustre
glaze. The dish is of silver
form and it has a raised
central boss and is elaborately
decorated with oak leaves
and geometric patterns.
- *diameter 45cm*
- £2,500 • E.&H. Manners

## Majolica Vase ▼
- *circa 1880*
One of a pair of majolica vases by
W. Shiller & Son. With blue
shaped dolphin glazed handles,
rosette decoration.
- *height 37cm*
- £1,250 • David Brower

## Model of Harvester ▼
- *1785-90*
Model of harvester reclining on
a wheat sheaf. From the Gera
factory, Germany. The figure
rests on a base with Omega mark.
- *height 23cm*
- £1,250 • E&H Manners

## Orvieto Jug ▲
- *18th century*
Orvieto, lattice and panel,
strap handle.
- *height 11cm*
- £500-£700 • Bazaart

## Sicilian Wet Drug Bottle ▲
- *date 1599*
Workshop of Geronimo Lazzario
Palermo. Majolica with 'A
Tropei' decoration.
- *height 26cm*
- £4,000-£6,000 • Bazaart

## Cup and Saucer ◄
- *date 1766*
Cup and saucer Sèvres
textile based design, with
floral meanderings, gilt foliage
with '*oeil de perdrix*' decoration to
both cup and saucer.
Interlaced 'L' with date mark
'N'. Painter's mark 'Mereaud'.
- *height 8cm*
- £6,500     • E&H Manners

## Cantagalli Vase ▼
- *19th century*
In 15th-century fienza style,
baluster form vase.
- *height 35cm*
- £800-£1,200     • Bazaart

## Terracotta Dog ▲
- *late 19th century*
Austrian painted terracotta
model of a puggish dog, lying
in an alert position, with glass
eyes, collar and curling tail.
- *height 20cm*
- £1,450     • Elizabeth Baldwin

## Sicilian Drug Jar ▲
- *17th century*
Italian drug jar with scrolling
flowers on blue ground.
- *height 28cm*
- £2,500-£3,500     • Bazaart

## Delft Dish ▼
- *17th century*
Late 17th-century
Dutch Delft lobed dish.
- *diameter 33cm*
- £700     • Guest & Gray

## Drug Jar ▲
- *circa 17th century*
Rare Sicilian Caltagirone
ovoid drug jar with painted,
scrolling foliage, in green,
orange and manganese.
- *height 30cm*
- £2,200     • Guest & Gray

## Two-Handled Urn ▲
- *date 1893*
Rozenburg, the Hague. Urn
shaped vase with mask handles.
By W.P. Hartgring.
- *height 42cm*
- £1,755     • Pieter Oosthuizen

## Santareli Tea Set

- *19th century*
A 19th-century majolica tea set consisting of eight pieces, each cup with a different portrait, with profuse decoration and lustre finish.
- **£780** • Shadad

## Dollmaker Group

- *circa 1860*
An unusual Meissen group entitled 'The Dollmaker', incorporating a male and female looking on at the doll being crafted.
- *height 18cm*
- **£2,500** • David Brower

## Meissen Cup and Saucer

- *circa 1880*
A flower and insect encrusted cup and saucer, with flower detailing underneath saucer and insects inside cup.
- *height 8x13cm*
- **£650** • David Brower

## Tazzie Plates

- *circa 1820*
Pair of Etruscan style 'Tazzie' plates on pedestal foot. Classical figures, Giusiniani factory Naples.
- *diameter 22cm*
- **£1,500-£2,500** • Bazaart

## Trapani Alborelli Jar

- *16th century*
Apothecary jar, slightly cracked, with panel showing figure.
- *height 28cm*
- **£2,600** • Bazaart

## Berlin Campagna

- *circa 1880*
Urn shaped vase, heavily gilded, deep blue background decorated with a floral band. Featured on the 'Antiques Roadshow'.
- *height 32cm*
- **£5,500** • David Brower

## Charger

- *circa 1880*
Ginai factory majolica. Bacchanal scene in romantic setting with grotesques.
- *height 47cm*
- **£2,000-£3,000** • Bazaart

## Bisque Group ➤
- *late 19th century*
After a French bronze showing two dogs fighting over a duck in flight with lakeside setting.
- *height 20cm*
- £1,100    • Elizabeth Bradwin

## Meissen Figure ▲
- *circa 1880*
A cherub in a classical pose, piercing two hearts with an arow.
- *height 27cm*
- £2,850    • David Brower

## Water Jug ▼
- *circa 1870*
Gallé. Musician on a drum with scrolling leaf design and gilding and goat painted on the drum.
- *height 40cm*
- £4,800    • Cameo Gallery

## Porcelain Group ▲
- *circa 1772*
A Sèvres biscuit porcelain group, showing Cupid, with a broken bow, igniting a fire, with a female figure, holding a heart in the flames.
- *height 31cm*
- £3,800    • E&H Manners

## Sèvres Vase ▲
- *circa 1890*
Single Sèvres vase, ormolu mounts, courtley scenes.
- *height 73cm*
- £2,800    • Judy Fox

## Rinfrescatoio Bowl ▼
- *circa 1880*
Italian 'Rinfrescatoio'. Le nove majolica with flowers and birds.
- *height 25cm*
- £2500 3500    • Bazaart

## Ponte Negro Dish ▲
- *circa 1560*
Castel Durante Crespina. With Susanna and the Elders. Three crosses in foreground are a hallmark of his work.
- *diameter 24.5cm*
- £18,000    • Guest & Gray

## Cabinet Plate ▲

- *circa 1900*
A Vienna-style cabinet plate.
Hand painted, with a religious
scene of a martial angel aiding a
woman and children. Decorated
in gold with red scrolled panels
and green cartouches.
- *diameter 24cm*
- **£450** • **Ian Spencer**

## Flemish Tile ▲

- *18th century*
Flemish tile with geometric
patterns and stylised floral
designs with rearing lion.
- *height 15cm*
- **£75** • **Garry Atkins**

## Sèvres Box ▼

- *circa 1860*
Ormolu mounted Sèvres style
box, painted and jewelled with
painted pastoral scenes.
- *height 7cm*
- **£1,400** • **David Brower**

## Oil Lamp ▼

- *circa mid-17th century*
Dutch oil lamp with handle on
pedestal base. The piece shows
irregularities caused through the
firing process. This type of ware
would be for use by a modest
domestic family unit.
- *height 12cm*
- **£375** • **Garry Atkins**

## Gallé Pot ▲

- *circa 1870*
Reputedly from the house
of Gallé with full signature
'Emille Gallé'. Decorated
with geometric designs and
moths with partial gilding.
- *height 21cm*
- **£6,000** • **Cameo Gallery**

## Bell-Shaped Jug ▲

- *circa mid-17th century*
Dutch bell-shaped jug in a
green glaze, with a pinched
handle. Jug on a tripod base.
- *height 9cm*
- **£150** • **Garry Atkins**

## Expert Tips

*Before washing ceramic pieces,
examine each one very closely to
ensure that there are no repairs,
unfired decoration or delicate
gilding. Old repairs were often
made with water-soluble
adhesive.*

## Meissen Group ◄

- *circa 1870*
A romantic arrangement of
two figures and a dog upon a sofa
with musical instruments.
- *height 14cm*
- **£2,900** • **David Brower**

## German Dessert Plate ▼
- *date 1765*
Nymphenburg dessert plate with
trellis border with birds and
flower design at centre
(tulips/roses) and gilt border.
- *diameter 23cm*
- **£1,400** • **E. & H. Manners**

## Vase ▼
- *circa 1910*
Very large, Galileo Chini
lustre with decoration from
Manfactura Di Fontebuoni.
- *height 55cm*
- **£6,000-£8,000** • **Bazaart**

## Stoneware Jug ▲
- **13th century**
A German stoneware jug,
showing the effects of having
partially collapsed in kiln when
being fired, with throwing lines.
- *height 19cm*
- **£550** • **Garry Atkins**

## Slipware Dish ▲
- *date 1740-60*
A feathered slipware dish in lead
glaze from the northern Rhine
with distinctive wavy pattern.
- *diameter 18cm*
- **£135** • **Garry Atkins**

## German Jug ▼
- *circa 1480*
A German pottery jug. Rare
with incised face pattern and
banding with handle.
- *height 19cm*
- **£850** • **Garry Atkins**

## Fruit Basket ▼
- *circa 1870*
Signed Galle on the underside.
With cross twig handles, butterfly
and moth decoration and grass
and flower designs. With gilding.
- *height 18cm*
- **£2,800** • **Cameo Gallery**

## Sèvres Cup and Saucer ◄
- *circa 1880*
Sèvres-style 'jewelled' cup and
saucer. Cup painted with named
portraits on three panels. Saucer
with floral decoration to centre.
- *height 9cm*
- **£1,850** • **David Brower**

# Islamic Ceramics

## Chrome Bowl ▾
- *10th-11th century*
A hand-painted earthenware polychrome bowl with stylized palm-leaf design, from Nishapur, Northwestern Iran.
- *diameter 19cm*
- £4,000 • Yacobs

## Expert Tips

*Half-glazed pieces are not failures or rejects; that is how they are made.*

## Kushan Tile ▾
- *13th century*
Eight-pointed lustre star-tile in blue and black glaze, with phoenix and floral pattern. From Kushan, Afghanistan.
- *height 21cm*
- £700 • Samiramis

## Islamic Ceramics ▶
- *13th century*
Islamic mouse-head water jug and cockeral-head jug with vertical striped glaze. Both from Nishapur.
- *height 14-18cm*
- £1,000 & 2,200 • Shiraz

## Lustre Tile ▲
- *13th century*
A lustre tile from Kashan, Iran, with Islamic inscription and floral and animal designs.
- *width 30cm*
- £3,000 • Shiraz

## Bamiyan Bowl ▲
- *12th century*
Bright turquoise deep blue bowl with Kufic calligraphic inscriptions to the rim.
- *diameter 17cm*
- £1,000 • Pars

## Mamluk Bowl ▾
- *13th-14th century*
Ayyoubid mamluk measuring bowl. Syria or Egypt, with black, blue and white glaze, splayed lip with handle and iridescence.
- *height 11cm*
- £3,000 • Samiramis

## Kashan Water Jug ▾
- *12th-13th century*
Earthenware bulbous form with splayed neck and strap handle.
- *height 20cm*
- £1,000 • Pars

## Sandcore Ure ▽
- *2nd century BC*
Pinchel lip with a comb design
overglaze, in brown and cream.
- *height 12cm*
- £4,000       • Aaron

## Kashan Sprinkler ▽
- *11th-13th century*
Turquoise, monochrome glaze
sprinkler with bosses to neck.
- *height 11cm*
- £550       • Pars

## Expert Tips

*Many people were influenced by
early Islamic ceramics,
especially the French. Many of
these pieces, those by Emile
Gallé in particular, are worth
much more than the originals.*

## Persian Vases ➤
- *19th century*
A pair of baluster-form vases
decorated with flora, birds and
animals in a blue glaze.
- *height 27cm*
- £800       • Shahdad

## Nishapur Bowl ▲
- *13th century*
A Nishapur bowl with the Kufic
calligraphic inscription 'healthy
and long life'.
- *diameter 30cm*
- £2,000       • Shiraz

## Parthian Pitcher ▲
- *1st-3rd century*
Pre-Islam earthenware pitcher of
concial, teardrop form, with
green glaze and iridescence.
- *height 20cm*
- £800       • Pars

## Terracotta Pipe ▽
- *circa 1855*
Silver and gold gilded Tophane
pipe with gilded floral base.
- *height 5cm*
- £850       • Sinai

## Tiled Panel ▽
- *circa 1760*
A North African, hand-painted,
tiled panel showing urn with
floral and leaf meanderings.
- *height 88cm*
- £2,000       • Sinai

### Ceramic Ewer ▲
- *12-13th century*
A Persian Gorgon ewer with original glaze and inscriptions. With pronounced iridescence.
- *height 17cm*
- **£18,000** • Aaron

### Nishapur Bowl ▼
- *12th century*
Nishapur serving bowl with Kufic calligraphic inscriptions.
- *diameter 27cm*
- **£6,500** • Aaron

### Ink-Well Holder ▼
- *14th century*
Raqa Syria. Three circular holes for ink wells in black and blue.
- *diameter 23cm*
- **£3,600** • Dealer

### Early Ewer ◄
- *8th century*
Green glazed ewer with iridesence, tapered neck and strap handle, raised on a small foot.
- *height 20cm*
- **£700** • Pars

### Afghanistan Cup ▲
- *13th century*
Small Afghanistan cup with turquoise and black glaze.
- *height 11cm*
- **£7,000** • Samiramis

### Kufic Tile ▲
- *13th century*
A turquoise glazed tile with Kufic inscription.
- *height 25cm*
- **£1,750** • Pars

## Expert Tips

*The more common a piece is, the better condition it needs to be in. Collectors tend to stick to their subject and will pay good money for rare pieces, even when they are fragmented.*

### Persian Earthenware Jar ◄
- *13th century*
A moulded, green-glaze jar with stops halfway to base.
- *height 19cm*
- **£700** • Aaron

### Kashan Bowl ➤
- *12-13th century*
Islamic inscriptions on rim with
centred fish and floral design.
- *diameter 19cm*
- £7,000 • Yacobs

### Persian Jar ▲
- *13th century*
Small Kushan jar with bulbous
body and cobalt-blue glaze with
splayed footing and strap handle.
- *height 13cm*
- £800 • Pars

### Islamic Ceramic Jug ➤
- *12-13th century*
Jug of globular form, glazed in
turquoise and black with stops to
base and two handles to the lip.
- *height 18cm*
- £2,500 • Aaron

### Nestorian Bowl ▲
- *10th-11th century*
A bowl from Central Asia, with
green, brown and black glaze,
with image of cross and scrolling
decorations.
- *diameter 13.5cm*
- £2,250 • Axia

### Shallow Saljuq Dish ▲
- *12th century*
Splayed lip on four globular feet
with iridescence.
- *diameter 15cm*
- £100 • Pars

### Terracotta Pot ⌄
- *8-9th century*
Blue-glazed terracotta pot with
knob handles, on three feet.
- *height 12cm*
- £2,000 • Samiramis

### Afghanistan Stands ◄
- *12th century*
A pair of green glazed
Afghanistan stands with organic
designs depicting animals.
- *length 23cm*
- £1,500 • Samiramis

### Kashan Water Jug

- *11-12th century*
Cockerel-headed water jug with lajvar glaze and strap handle.
- *height 29cm*
- £5,500　　　　• Yacobs

### Tiled Panel

- *circa 1760*
A North African, hand-painted, tiled panel showing with floral and leaf meanderings.
- *height 88cm*
- £2,000　　　　• Sinai

## Expert Tips

*When buying pieces in the country of origin, be sure you are fully acquainted with the law and up-to-date on the paperwork required.*

### Clay Goddess　　▼

- *3000 BC*
Mother goddess statue from Tel-Halaf in Syria offering fruitfulness.
- *height 17cm*
- £3,000　　　　• Aaron

### Drug Jar　　▼

- *12th century*
Persian drug jar with floral design on black and blue glaze.
- *height 23cm*
- £3,200　　　• Samiramis

### Kushan Tile　　▶

- *13th century*
Eight-pointed star with phoenix and floral decoration.
- *height 21cm*
- £700　　　• Samiramis

### Nishapur Dish　　▲

- *11-13th century*
Nishapur polychrome dish with stylized deer.
- *diameter 18cm*
- £300　　　• Pars

### Kushan Bottle　　▲

- *13th century*
Balloon body with long neck and cup-shaped lip. Turquoise glaze with Kufic writing.
- *height 28cm*
- £3,405　　　• Samiramis

Water Jugs and Bowl ◄

### Water Jugs and Bowl ◄
- *10th-11th century*
Two water jugs and one bowl with Kufic insription 'Blessing to the owner', from Central Asia.
- £60,000 • Yacobs

### Syrian Drug Jar ▼
- *12th century*
Syrian drug jar with black and blue glaze and geometric designs to body, with inscriptions around base and neck.
- *height 28cm*
- £2,300 • Samiramis

### Terracotta Pipe ▲
- *circa 1850*
A terracotta Tophane pipe with gold and silver floral gilt design. From Morocco.
- *height 5cm*
- £550 • Sinai

### Mumluk Bowl ▲
- *16th century*
A Mumluk bowl from Egypt/ Syria, with central panel with Islamic inscriptions and blue and black glaze.
- *diameter 20cm*
- £1,000 • Samiramis

### Ceramic Bowl ▼
- *circa 9th century*
A blue and white, tin-glazed ceramic bowl of the Abbasid period, the rim with blue swags.
- *diameter 21cm*
- £15,000 • Axia

### Vase ▲
- *circa 1860*
A copy of an Isnik ceramic vase, of baluster form, with calligraphic inscriptions and floral design.
- *height 35cm*
- £2,600 • Sinai

### Tiled Panel ▲
- *circa 1765*
An 18th-century polychrome tiled panel with a mixture of Turkish and Islamic representations, showing mosque with floral decoration. Of North African origin.
- *height 88cm*
- £2,000 • Sinai

## Kushan Tile ▲

- *13th century*
Eight-pointed tile depicting
phoenix and deer, with floral
meanderings, finished in lustre.
- *length 21cm*
- £700        • Samiramis

## Nishapur Bowl ▼

- *10th-11th century*
A Nishapur bowl with slip-
painted decoration. The bowl is
in earthenware, with boldly
painted lozenge designs. From
Northwestern Iran.
- *diameter 19cm*
- £250        • Pars

## Painted Wishapur Bowl ➤

- *10-11th century*
Wishapur earthenware bowl with
polychrome lozenge decoration.
- *diameter 19cm*
- £250        • Pars

## Turkish Icutahya Tiles ▼

- *18th century*
A pair of blue and white tiles
with stylized leaf mottif.
- *length 7.5cm*
- £700        • Shahdad

## Ewer ◄

- *13th century*
Ewer of bulbous form with rooster
neck, strap handle, and turquoise
glaze, with iridescence.
- *height 33cm*
- £4,000        • Samiramis

## Vase ▼

- *11th-13th century*
A green, monochrome vase from
pre-Ottoman Empire Syria, of
baluster form, with a wide lip and
two handles to the shoulders.
There is extensive, open-work
decoration to the body of the
vase and stops to the base. The
whole is raised on a circular foot-
ring and shows lustre.
- *height 11cm*
- £450        • Pars

## Nishapur Dish ◄

- *11th-13th century*
Iranian Nishapur dish with
stylized bird and signature.
- *diameter 23cm*
- £800        • Pars

# Oriental Ceramics

## Chinese Celadon Dish ▼
- *date*1276-1368

Barbed rim incised decoration with repeated leaf decoration. Yang dynasty with floral central panel.
- *diameter 35cm*
- **£1,950** • J.A.N. Fine Art

## 17th Century Swatow Dish ▲
- *date early 17th century*

Painted to the centre with a circular panel of two Kylins playing with a brocaded ball surrounded by symbolic objects and scroll work.
- *diameter 37cm*
- **£1,600** • Anita Gray

## Cantonese Vases ▼
- *date 1870*

Pair of Cantonese vases. Decorated with rose medallions.
- *height 37cm*
- **£1,600** • Judy Fox

## Famille Rose Dinner Plate ▼
- *date 1730*

A dinner plate enamelled with design of two goat herds and their flock with river and mountains in background. Border painted with floral vignettes within a pink and blue diaper ground.
- *diameter 22cm*
- **£950** • Cohen & Cohen

## Mandarin Punch Pot ▲
- *1735-1796*

A Qianlong punch pot with cover, decorated in bright famille rose enamels with two mirror-shaped cartouches.
- *height 15.2cm*
- **£3,200** • Anita Gray

## Tea Cup and Saucer ▼
- *date 1730*

Yung Chêng (Yongzheng) tea cup and saucer. Eggshell porcelain with scroll border. Blue 'Y'- shaped diaper.
- *height 5cm*
- **£600** • Cohen & Cohen

## Blue and White Tankard ➤
- *Transitional period*

Tankard of cylindrical form painted with an unusual scene of a man and horse. The beast is standing facing his master in front of a well beneath the sun, as an insect hovers above.
- *height 20cm*
- **£3,800** • Anita Gray

## Anamese Dish ▼

- *15th century*

Anamese dish, from South China, with underglaze blue and leaf and floral decoration to the central panel.

- *diameter 37cm*
- £2,900    • J.A.N. Fine Art

## Rare Junyao Tripod Censer ▼

- *date 960 - 1280*

Junyao tripod censer, Song Dynasty, of compressed globular form.

- *diameter 8.75cm*
- £4,800    • Guest & Grey

## Blue Glazed Vase ▼

- *19th century*

A 19th-century vase with cylindrical ears on a Mazarin blue ground, with a flared lip.

- *height 32cm*
- £240    • Namdar

## Ornamental Duck ▼

- *19th century*

A nicely modelled famille verte model of a duck in recumbent pose. The duck is naturalistically styled with excellent detail.

- *length 30cm*
- £500    • Guest & Grey

## Japanese Arita ▼

- *circa 1700*

Pair of chicken water droppers used for calligraphy, with red painted faces. Some restoration.

- *height 14cm*
- £2,600    • J.A.N. Fine Art

## Pair of Canton Vases ◄

- *Qianlong Period  1736-95*

Of flattened pear-shaped form with applied 'C'-scroll handles, each decorated with two large moulded oval panels on the bodies.

- *height 23cm*
- £750    • Anita Grey

## Hirado Incense Burner ▲

- *circa 19th century*

Hirado incense burner with pierced lid and body. Two animal heads showing on the body. Blue flower decorations.

- £480    • J.A.N. Fine Art

## Chinese Caddy ▲

- *circa 1662 - 1722*

Famille verte caddy with alternating panels of ladies in fenced garden and flowers growing from rock work. Kangxi period. Of hexagonal form.

- *height 18.5cm*
- £1,250    • Guest & Grey

## Sake Bottle ▲

• *circa late 19th century*
Hirado Japanese porcelain sake
bottle with polychrome painted
dragon chasing its tail, and gilding.
• *height 20 cm*
• £850        • J.A. N. Fine Art

## Famille Rose Oval Dish ▲

• *circa 1740*
Unique and spectacularly
decorated famille rose oval
dish depicting a 'Wysng' killing
the Yeti.
• *length 44cm*
• £12,000    • Cohen & Cohen

## Famille Verte Vase ▼

• *date 1662-1672*
Fine famille verte vase of
octagonal ballister form,
decorated with panels of flowers,
landscapes and precious objects.
Floral border showing flowers
reserved on fish roe ground.
• *height 92cm*
• £5,500     • Cohen & Cohen

## Bojoab Pattern Bowl ▼

• *date 1750*
Milk style bowl. Found in the
1990s. Shows the Bojoab pattern.
Landscape scenes are shown on
the body in blue glaze.
• *height 10cm*
• £850        • Cohen & Cohen

## Chinese Nankin Vase
and Cover ◄

• *date 1736-1795*
Vase and cover of the Qianlong
period. Of baluster form, painted
in underglaze blue with a
continuous scene of two
pavillions beside a lake. With a
domed cover and flaring rim.
• *height 39cm*
• £1,600             • Anita Gray

## Imari Jar & Cover ▲

• *date early 18th century*
Of octagonal section, painted in
underglaze blue, iron-red, green
and gilding with two main lobed
cartouches on either side, one
depicting a kylin leaping over
stylised rockwork, also with
peonies, cranes and chicks.
• *height 13cm*
•£3,200              • Anita Gray

## Expert Tips

*There are copies, forgeries, and
fakes – and there are marks of
respect. Dynasty reign marks
alone cannot be used for dating,
as many were retrospective out
of respect for earlier wares.*

## Kraak Dish ▼

• *circa 1580*
Large dish of Ming Dynasty,
Wantii period. Deep cobalt
underglaze with scenes of
scholars, fans and scrolls.
• *diameter 50cm*
• £5,500     • Cohen & Cohen

## Teacup and Saucer ➤
- *date 1720*
Chinese teacup and saucer.
Decorated with strong famille
rose enamels showing an East
Indiaman under full sail.
Yongzheng period.
- *height 4cm*
- £800 • Cohen & Cohen

## Chinese Coffee Pot ▼
- *date 1750*
Unusual and rare Chinese export
coffee pot. Meissen with closed
cover and dragonhead spout. Blue
underglaze decorated with
peonies. Qianlong period.
- *height 28cm*
- £4,500 • Cohen & Cohen

## Chinese Imari Vase ◄
- *Kangxi Period 1662-1722*
Moulded ribbed body and flanged
neck. Underglaze blue and
overglaze iron red. Four floral
sprays of peony.
- *height 26.5cm*
- £2,200 • Anita Gray

## Famille Verte Fluted Bowl ▲
- *Kangxi Period 1662-1722*
Decorated in underglaze blue and
famille verte enamels with four
different pairs of designs in
alternating panels. The interior is
in famille verte enamels.
- *diameter 15cm*
- £750 • J.A.N. Fine Art

## Earthenware Bowl ▲
- *date 19th century*
Satsumaware. Made in Japan.
19th-century earthenware.
Painted with goldfish interior.
- *height 9cm*
- £1,700 • J.A.N. Fine Art

## Chinese Famille Rose Tankard ▼
- *date Qianlong period 1736-95*
Tankard of barrel form. Decorated
in bright enamels in the
Mandarin palette; the front of the
body with a large cartouche.
- *height 12.2cm*
- £700 • Anita Gray

## Okimono Porcelain Puppy ▼
- *date 19th century*
Aritaware Okimono of a
porcelain puppy scratching his
ears. With painted polychrome
ruff painted eyes
- *height 12.5cm*
- £2,000 • Greg Baker

## Armorial Plates ▼
- *date 1745*
Pair of Chinese porcelain plates
decorated in bright enamels with
the arms of 'Minchin of
Monnegall'.
- *diameter 22.5cm*
- £3,500 • Anita Gray

### Famille Verte Bowl ▼
• *Kangxi period 1662-22*
A Chinese export bowl decorated on the exterior with overglaze enamels in the famille verte palette with birds flying amid prunus plants, issuing from stylised rockwork.
• *diameter 22cm*
• £980 • Anita Gray

### Chinese Famille Rose Urn and Cover ▼
• *Qianlong period 1736-95*
After a Lowestoft original, of two-handled form, raised on a domed foot, with domed cover surmounted by a fruit finial, brilliantly decorated in famille rose enamels.
• *height 27cm*
• £2,200 • Anita Gray

### Ginger Jar ▲
• *Kangxi period 1662-22*
Chinese export ginger jar in underglaze blue. Boldly painted with narrative scenes of domestic life. Shown with wooden, 19th-century cover.
• *height 24cm*
• £2,200 • Cohen & Cohen

### Pair of Blue and White Vases ▲
• *Kangxi period 1662-1722*
Of baluster form, bodies painted in bright underglaze blue with a repeated pattern of meandering floral scrolls.
• *diameter 31cm*
• £1,800 • Anita Gray

### Koryo Ewer ▼
• *date 13th century*
Korean Celadon Koryo ewer, with twisted rope handle, slip decoration in black and white and Floral panels to front and reverse.
• *height 31cm*
• £8,500 • J.A.N. Fine Art

### Chinese Transitional Blue and White Jar ▼
• *Transitional period 1650-60*
Of ovoid form. Decorated in underglaze blue with a scene of three figures dressed in flowing robes. The rim with a series of single-pointed lappets.
• *height 27.9cm*
• £2600 • Anita Gray

### Pair of Dishes ◄
• *mid 17th century*
A pair of Chinese export sweetmeat dishes, with Chenghua marks of the Chongzhen period, of chrysanthemum flowerhead form, painted with bands of waves. Rim dressed in brown.
• *diameter 15cm*
• £2,600 • Cohen & Cohen

## Fluted Bowl ▲
- *Kangxi period 1662-1722*
Famille verte bowl with
underglaze blue. Four different
pairs of designs in alternating
panels, with interior of seated
maiden with hummingbird.
- *diameter 15cm*
- £750          • Anita Gray

## Kangxi Teapot ▼
- *date 1700*
Kangxi period blue and white
teapot and cover decorated with
peony branches below a Ruyihead border with floral sprays.
- *height 12cm*
- £1,000          • Cohen & Cohen

## Pair of Armorial Dinner
## Plates ▼
- *date 1760*
Qianlong plates, probably for the
French market, with unknown
coat of arms with floral swags
Motto 'Niagra sum sed …'
- *diameter 23cm*
- £1,250          • Cohen & Cohen

## Double Gourd ◀
- *circa 19th century*
Japanese Kutani double gourd
bottle vase, with original cover,
decorated with a frieze of lions,
peonies and foliage. The upper
sections have panels showing
pagodas, birds and flowers. The
whole profusely gilded.
- *height 46cm*
- £560          • Namdar

## Famille Rose Cream Jug ▲
- *Qianlong period 1736- 95*
Qianlong jug, with painted scene
from The Judgement of Paris.
Shows Paris seated wearing puce
robes, with a hunting dog beside
him. He is offering a golden apple
to Aphrodite, who is flanked by
Hera and Athena with Cupid
looking on.
- *height 9.5cm*
- £680          • Anita Gray

## Punch Bowl ▲
- *Qianlong period 1736-95*
Richly decorated in famille rose
enamels in the Mandarin style,
the exterior with two large panels
containing figures in a terraced
garden and two smaller
cartouches containing birds
perched on flowering branches.
- *height 8cm*
- £275          • Anita Gray

## Blue and White Jar ▲
- *Kangxi period 1662-1722*
Chinese jar, decorated in brilliant
underglaze blue with peacocks
upon blossoming branches and
stylised rockwork. Narrow,
triangle-work border at the
shoulder and double-line at the
foot. Later pierced wood cover.
- *height 20cm*
- £1,400          • Anita Gray

## Expert Tips

*Ming dynasty patterns were
often repeated over later
periods. Genuine Ming pieces
have a tendency to reddish
oxydisation and a thick, bluish
glaze suffused with bubbles.*

## Armorial Jug ▲
• *date 1745*
Armorial mask jug of Qianlong period. Shows 'Hankey quartering Barnard and Impaling Wyvern' coat of arms. With moulded spout and acanthus leaf handle.
• *height 73cm*
• £2,200    • Cohen & Cohen

## Chinese Famille Rose Libation Cup ▲
• *Qianlong period 1736-95*
Of deep bowl form, moulded as an open flower with foliate rim. The exterior with applied decoration of flowering branches, the stalk forming the handle of the cup and base finished with a large leaf in green.
• *diameter 9cm*
• £650    • Anita Gray

## Famille Plate ▼
• *circa 1690*
Octagonal famille verte plate with pie crust border of the Kangxi period. Finely painted with two birds, probably phoenixes, within an elaborate border.
• *diameter 31cm*
• £4,000    • Cohen & Cohen

## Chinese En Grisaille Coffee Pot ▼
• *Qianlong period 1736-1795*
Squat, moulded ribbed body on flaring foot ring. Decorated with turquoise enamel and gilt. Each side decorated with flowers and leaves beneath a border of diaper cartouches. Rim of spout and handle edged in gold. Gilded knob.
• *height 27.9cm*
• £2600    • Anita Gray

## Kraakware Saucer Dish ◄
• *early 17th century*
Painted to the centre with an eight-pointed star-shaped panel. The sides decorated with eight oval panels charged with symbolic objects. The moulded, serrated exterior rim of the dish has stylised radiating panels.
• *diameter 14.5cm*
• £350    • Anita Gray

## Teabowl and Saucer ▲
• *circa 18th century*
European figures fishing for spider, painted on bowl and saucer. Qianlong period.
• *height 5cm*
• £600    • Cohen & Cohen

## Large Chinese Figure ▲
• *Kangxi period 1662-1722*
Guanyin, the Goddess of Mercy, standing upon a moulded base, draped in layered robes beneath elaborate headdress.
• *height 64cm*
• £2,800    • Anita Gray

## Fine Japanese Satsuma Box and Cover ▲

- *date 19th century*
Box is of squat barrel form with moulded mock loop handles and rivet-like border to rim and foot. Finely painted with graduating scene of procession. Base with a gold seal mark.
- *diameter 8cm*
- £1,500          • Anita Gray

## Yyan Dynasty Vase ▲

- *date 1279 - 1368*
Yyan dynasty vase, with damage sustained in kiln, in underglazed copper red with scrolling floral decoration and banding.
- *height 24cm*
- £7,500          • J.A.N. Fine Art

## Kang-Xai Vase ▼

- *circa 1700*
Vase with three panels depicting insects and river scene on a blue background.
- *length 24cm*
- £1,200          • J.A.N. Fine Art

## Soup Plate ▼

- *date 1795*
Polychrome soup plate decorated with tree-shrews and pheasants. Tobacco leaf pattern with blue underglaze.
- *diameter 23cm*
- £2,200          • Cohen & Cohen

## Libation Cup ◄

- *date 18th century*
Qianlong dynasty libation cup of deep bowl form, moulded as open flower with foliate rim, stalk as handle. The applied work painted in famille rose enamels.
- *diameter 8cm*
- £650          • Anita Gray

## Tea Caddy ▲

- *circa 1745*
Qianlong, baluster shaped tea caddy and cover with famille rose pattern. For Swedish market, with arms of Gyllenhok, decorated with moulded base.
- *height 13cm*
- £2,000          • Cohen & Cohen

## Expert Tips

*Japanese 'Arita' blue and white pieces can be distinguished from the Chinese because of the more granular porcelain and the very dark or very soft underglaze blue. There will be spur marks on the underside.*

## Swatow Dish ▼

- *early 17th century*
Decorated at centre with circular panel of two Kylins playing with a brocaded ball. Sides decorated with flowering plants. Has serrated edges.
- *diameter 37cm*
- £1,600          • Anita Gray

## Armorial Dinner Service ◄
- *circa 1785*
Qianlong dinner service,
exported for Swedish market,
showing pair of wine coolers,
salts, an oval meat dish and
charger. Total 62 pieces, each
with arms of Colonel Tranefelt.
- **£66,000** • Cohen & Cohen

## Blue and White Nankin Tureen ▲
- *Qianlong period 1736-95*
Elongated, octagonal form.
Decorated with tiny figures
among pagodas and bridges over
waterways. Well-modelled fruit as
knob and handles.
- *length 35cm*
- **£1,200** • Anita Gray

## Kraakware Saucer Dish ▼
- *early 17th century*
Centre painted with an eight-
pointed star-shaped panel. With
moulded serrated rim.
- *diameter 14.5cm*
- **£380** • Anita Gray

## Nankin Butter Tub Cover and Stand ▲
- *Qianlong period 1736-95*
Of oval form, the cover and stand
decorated with ogival petal
panels radiating from a central
oval panel of pomegranates.
Surmounted by fruit finial.
- *length 15cm*
- **£950** • Anita Gray

## Chinese Plates ▼
- *circa 1740*
Set of 14 Qianlong, famille rose
enamelled plates, showing two
mandarin ducks in dead-leaf
brown, within elaborate border.
- *height 22cm*
- **£5,800** • Cohen & Cohen

## Snuff Box ▲
- *date 1760*
Snuff box unusually handpainted.
Famille rose and floral spray
decorations.
- *height 4cm*
- **£1,760** • Cohen & Cohen

## Chinese Blue and White Tankard ▲
- *Kangxi Period 1662-1722*
Of pear-shaped form, the spiral
moulded body painted in the
underglaze blue with sprays of
flowers and fruiting branches.
- *height 14cm*
- **£550** • Anita Gray

## Expert Tips

*The colours of 'famille rose' were
used on Chinese export wares
after 1720. The name derives
from the use of a distinctive rose
pink colour originating in the
reign of Qianlong.*

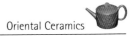

### Famille Rose Soup Plate ▼
- *date 1735*

A pair of soup plates of famille rose style painted with arms of Rose of Kilvarock within a border of flowers and inner rim diaper of trelis en grisaille.
- *diameter 23cm*
- **£2,600**　• **Cohen & Cohen**

### Blue and White Kangxi Dish ▼
- *circa 1690*

Fine deep dish decorated with panels of mounted warriors in underglaze blue with six-character reign mark on the reverse and ruyi-heads on rim underside.
- *diameter 24cm*
- **£1,650**　• **Cohen & Cohen**

### Expert Tips

*Copies made by Böttger at Meissen, in c.1710, of the first Chinese porcelain to reach Europe, are few in number and have a very much higher historical and financial value than the originals which he copied.*

### Famille Rose Style Dish ▲
- *date 1740*

A Qianlong famille rose style dish enamelled with peonies inside an unfolded scroll on a diaper ground strewn with floral sprays.
- *diameter 35cm*
- **£1,900**　• **Cohen & Cohen**

### Armorial Milk Jug ▲
- *circa 1740*

Export armorial milk jug with the Dutch arms of van Zandijk of Zeeland, a rouge de fer and gilt spearhead border to rim.
- *height 10cm*
- **£1,400**　• **Cohen & Cohen**

### Small Pair of Fine Chinese Mandarin Vases ▼
- *Qianlong period 1736-95*

Qianlong vases of flattened baluster form, moulded with fluted, flaring neck and two side handles. Decorated in the mandarin palette.
- *height 15.4cm*
- **£1,100**　• **Anita Gray**

### Blue and White Stemcup ▼
- *Kangxi period 1662-1722*

Standing on a domed base, the stem with raised middle section, decorated around the body with flowers and foliage, with bands of stiff leaves at the stem.
- *height 15cm*
- **£850**　• **Anita Gray**

### Famille Verte Bowl ◄
- *Kangxi period 1662-1722*

Decorated with four cartouches of kylins and deer with a border of four bird cartouches. The inside rim has a border of four floral cartouches reserved on a diaper ground.
- *height 8cm*
- **£650**　• **Anita Gray**

## Okimono of a Tiger ◄

- *circa 19th century*
Porcelain okimono of a tiger with
unusual expression. Tail is raised.
- *height 13cm*
- £850　　　　　• Gregg Baker

## Japanese Group ▼

- *circa 19th century*
Figure of a lohan, in shell boat,
talking to a caricatured octopus
the whole on a carved and
painted wooden base representing
the sea.
- *length 36cm*
- £850　　　　　• Gregg Baker

## Tureen ▲

- *Qianlong period 1736-1795*
Of canted rectangular section,
with boar's head handles.
Decorated in underglaze blue
with floral sprays.
- *height 10cm, length 18.5cm*
- £1,400　　　　• Anita Gray

## Kraakware Saucer Dish ▲

- *early 17th century*
Painted to the centre with an
eight-pointed star-shaped panel.
The sides decorated with eight
oval panels. The exterior rim
with stylised radiating panels.
- *diameter 14.5cm*
- £280　　　　　• Anita Gray

## Kraakware Saucer Dish ▲

- *early 17th century*
Kraakware saucer dish, painted to
the centre with eight-pointed
star-shaped panel, with artemisia
leaf. The sides decorated with
eight oval panels, charged with
symbolic objects, alternating with
scrollwork.
- *diameter 14.5cm*
- £350　　　　　• Anita Gray

## Kangxi Bowl ▼

- *Kangxi period 1662-1722*
Bowl in underglaze blue with
inverted rim with trellis diaper,
showing scenes of boys at play.
The exterior with scenes from
Chinese life. Six character
reign mark.
- *diameter 20cm*
- £2,300　　　• Cohen & Cohen

## Celadon Vase ▲

- *circa 12th century*
Chinese Sung Long Quan
celadon vase. Perfect mallet
shape with double handles and
incised banding.
- *height 14cm*
- £4,500　　　• J.A.N. Fine Art

## Kutani Jar and Cover ▼

- *circa 19th century*
Kutani jar and cover, two panels with river setting. Dragon decoration on base and finial.
- *height 20cm*
- £490        • J.A.N. Fine Art

### Blue and White Mustard Pot ▲

- *Kangxi period 1662-1722*
The moulded body decorated with alternating panels of maidens and baskets of flowers, between borders of stylised flowerheads. The base with an artemisia leaf.
- *height 10cm*
- £850        • Anita Gray

## Fluted Bowls ▼

- *circa 1700*
Pair of Kangxi fluted bowls, decorated with panels of flowers and mythological beasts.
- *diameter 18.5cm*
- £2,500        • Guest & Grey

## Kangxi Famille Verte Dish ▼

- *circa 1700*
Polychrome lobed dish with scholarly items and flowers with gilding. Central panel shows woman in domestic setting with butterflies.
- *height 22cm*
- £850        • J.A.N. Fine Art

## Kangxi Famille Verte Dish ▼

- *circa 1700*
Decorated with a basket of flowers at the centre. Radiating panels of flowers and rock work. Rim border with cartouches of peaches.
- *diameter 35cm*
- £2,500        • Guest & Grey

## Qianlong Vase ◄

- *Qianlong period 1736-96*
Quinlong Chinese coral monochrome glaze vase. Globular body with narrow flared neck, splayed foot
- *height 19cm*
- £1,250        • Guest & Grey

## Joss-Stick Holders ►

- *circa 1662-1722*
A pair of Chinese egg and spinach biscuit joss-stick holders, modelled in the shape of Dogs of Fo Buddhist lions
- *height 8.5cm*
- £2,300        • Guest & Grey

## Satsuma Koro ▼
- *circa 19th century*
Japanese satsuma koro with silver cover decorated with gilt.
- *height 13cm*
- £3,600 • Gregg Baker

## Cantonese Bowl ▼
- *circa 1860*
Enamelled with figures, flowers and butterflies, with profuse gilding.
- *diameter 31cm*
- £400 • Namdar

### Expert Tips

*Eighteenth- and nineteenth-century copies of Japanese Imari porcelain can be very valuable in their own right. Beware of modern copies from Korea.*

## Two Hares ▲
- *circa 20th century*
Figure of two hares, one with red eyes. A fine piece.
- *height 22cm*
- £1,850 • David Brower

## Jar and Cover ▲
- *circa 618-906*
Tang dynasty jar and cover in baluster form. The jar is in a white glaze which falls short of the base, a sign of hand-dipping and thus authenticity.
- *height 30cm*
- £1,800 • David Baker

## Chinese Tankard ▼
- *circa 18th century*
Chinese blue and white tankard. Peonies and bamboo trees shown with lattice fence decoration. Heart decoration around lip and handle.
- *height 15cm*
- £680 • J.A.N. Fine Art

## Dynasty Vase ▼
- *circa 1800*
Korean blue and white 'chosen' dynasty case. Decorated with a dragon chasing a flaming pearl.
- *length 29cm*
- £1,200 • David Baker

## Katani Bijin Entertainers ◄
- *circa late 19th century*
Three Katani Bijin entertainers wearing kimono and obi. Made in Japan. One is holding a drum and the other a fan.
- £3,200 • J.A.N. Fine Art

# Clocks, Watches & Scientific Instruments

**This category includes all forms of clock from carriage to longcase, fine watches to the antiques of the future and all scientific artefacts.**

Scientific – and, particularly, timekeeping instruments – have never been more popular. Perhaps the change of millennium and the chaos it was supposed to cause among those reliant on high technology has re-engendered a love of those accurate instruments which sailed through the millennium barrier without missing a beat. In any case, man will always be fascinated by the ingenuity of his forebears.

At the top end of the market, prices are high, largely because there have been very few really good English clocks coming onto the market. Rare English longcase specimens by good makers are fetching very much higher prices than they were two or three years ago. Lower down the market, mahogany longcases with painted dials have almost caught up in value with earlier, brass-dialled specimens.

This is largely because the clock market is now no longer dominated by serious collectors, but is catering for those who desire them as beautiful objects to adorn the home.

## Clocks

### Bell Strike Clock ∨
- *circa 1830*
Patinated bronze, ormolu and marble clock by Causard Horologer Du Roy. Bronze designed by Druz of Austria.
- *height 55cm*
- £6,250      • Gavin Douglas

### French Carriage Timepiece ∨
- *date 1900*
A French carriage timepiece combined with barometer, thermometer and compass with gilt brass, glass panels and carrying handle.
- *height 16cm*
- £1,750      • A. Brocklehurst

### French Art Deco ◄
- *date 1939*
Clock by JAZ. Typical of French Art Deco style. Maroon and black case with chromium embellishments. Embossed with stylised face.
- *height 18cm*
- £300      • Decadence

### Swinging Cherub Clock ∧
- *date 1880*
Made in Paris by Farcot with scroll-shaped alabaster case.
- *height 22cm*
- £450
- Old Father Time Clock Centre

### Porcelain Mantel Clock ▼
• *circa 1860*
Gilt bronze and blue jewelled French mantel clock. Finely chiselled case with original mercury gilding with three blue porcelain urns. Eight-day French movement.
• *height 41cm*
• £2,700    • Gütlin Clocks

### French Mantel Clock ▼
• *circa 1830*
Gilt bronze, mounted with soldier and poet. Eight-day silk suspension movement with hour and half-hour strike on bell. With a white enamel dial and black roman numerals. Made by Gaulin.
• *height 41cm*
• £3,500    • Gütlin Clocks

### Perpetual Calendar Clock ❯
• *circa 1880*
A large French black slate and malachite mantel clock. Two-week movement with visible escapement and mercury pendulum. Chimes hours and half-hours on bell.
• *height 56cm*
• £5,500    • Gütlin Clocks

### Cupid Watering a Rose ▲
• *circa 1810*
Patinated bronze and ormolu clock showing Cupid with rose of love. Attributed to Thonire.
• *height 45cm*
• £8,500    • Gavin Douglas

### Flame Mahogany Clock ▲
• *date 1823*
Charles X flame mahogany and ormolu tombstone-shaped clock. Acanthus moulding with turned bun feet.
• *height 43cm*
• £3,750    • Gavin Douglas

### Walnut Mantel Clock ▼
• *date 1830*
An early 19th-century walnut mantel clock. With anchor escapement movement, pendulum and separately mounted numerals on the dial plate.
• *height 54cm*
• £3,500    • A. Brocklehurst

### Scottish Longcase Clock ▼
• *circa 1830*
Flame mahogany trunk with eight-day breakarch dial. By Christie and Barrie of Arbroath.
• *height 2.06m*
• £6,500    • Gütlin Clocks

## French Mantel Clock ▲
• *circa 1820*
French patinated bronze and
original ormolu mantel clock
showing a child seated by an
oil lamp.
• *height 93cm*
• £3,250     • Gavin Douglas

## French Pendule d'Officer ▲
• *circa 1880*
Gilt bronze clock with French
eight-day movement and English
lever escapement. Engine-turned
silvered dial with black arabic
numerals. Showing wreath, floral
decoration and a carrying handle
with snake eating its tail.
• *height 18cm*
• £1900     • Gütlin Clocks

## Expert Tips

*When buying a clock at
auction, request a "condition
report", which will give a run-
down on the three essential
elements: the movement, the
case and the dial.*

## Oak Longcase Clock ▼
• *date 1790*
Late 18th-century four-pillar
movement with calendar dial
and pendulum. Made by Taylor
of Manchester. The hood is
decorated in two columns
with Corinthian capitals.
• *height 2.25m*
• £7,000     • A. Brocklehurst

## Egyptian Revival Clock ▼
• *circa 1815*
Patinated bronze and ormolu
temple-shaped clock. Movement
by Hemon of Paris with sacred
bull in alcove below dial. Panel
showing Egyptian figure with
floral decoration.
• *height 38cm*
• £3,750     • Gavin Douglas

## Vitascope Clock ▶
• *date 1944*
'Vitascope' electric automation,
240v mains-powered. From Isle
of Man, with bakelite case.
• *height 32cm*
• £450
• Old Father Time Clock
  Centre

## Striking Mantel Clock ▲
• *circa 1810*
English marble with silver-plated
dial and double fusée movement.
Signed Huntley & Edwards,
London. On bun feet.
• *height 41cm*
• £5,750     • Raffety & Walwyn

## Swiss Timepiece ▲
• *circa 1960*
Swiss Jaeger-le Caultre atmos
timepiece. White chapter ring
with gilt arabic numerals.
Stamped 'Swiss made'.
Never needs winding.
• *height 23cm*
• £1,200     • Gütlin Clocks

## German Brass Clock ▼

- *circa 1900*
Elephant mystery clock with
spelter figure and swinging
brass clock by Junghans.
- *height 22cm*
- £700
- **Old Father Time Clock
Centre**

## English Bracket Clock ▼

- *circa 1715*
Striking bracket clock in ebony.
Veneered case with rise and fall
regulation and eight-day fusée.
Five-pillar movement. Signed.
- *height 54cm*
- £16,000  • **Clock Workshop**

## Greek Figurative Clock ▲

- *circa 1720*
Gilt and bronze clock by Robert
Molyneux, London. With Greek
figures of Sappho and Cupid.
- *height 60cm*
- £3,500  • **Clock Workshop**

## Lighthouse Mantel Clock ▲

- *1890-1900*
Oak four-sided cased French
eight-day timepiece. Unusual
French movement with original
English lever escapement within
the base. Signed Hry.
- *height 41cm*
- £1,500  • **Gütlin Clocks**

## Art Nouveau Timepiece ▼

- *circa 1900*
French, polished brass. Cream
white dial, faint pale blue arabic
numerals and gilt hour markers.
Eight-day French movement.
- *height 15.5cm*
- £450  • **Gütlin Clocks**

## English Mantel Clock ▼

- *circa 1805*
Marble and ormolu mantel clock,
neoclassical style, showing Cupid
and Venus. Fusée movement by
Graite, London. Bronze panels.
- *height 45cm*
- £6,250  • **Gavin Douglas**

## Horse and Jockey Mantel
## Clock ◄

- *circa 1860*
Victorian black slate and rouge
marble French mantel clock, with
bronze model. Eight-day French
movement, chiming the hours
and half hours on bell.
- *height 46cm*
- £1,700  • **Gütlin Clocks**

## Armorial Clock ▼

- *circa 1770*
George III, giltwood, by James
Scofield, London. Showing arms
of Hewitt impaling Stanhope.
- *height 1.17m*
- **£32-42,000** • **Norman Adams**

## German Brass Clock ▼

- *date 1900*
Diane mystery clock with spelter
figure and swinging clock face
by Junghans.
- *height 28cm*
- **£650**
- **Old Father Time Clock
Centre**

## French Carriage Clock ▲

- *circa 1900*
Gilt bronze, champleve
serpentine cased miniature clock.
Eight-day French movement,
silvered English lever platform
escapement. White enamel dial.
- *height 18cm*
- **£950** • **Gütlin Clocks**

## Smiths Mystery Clock ▲

- *date 1930*
English, 240v mains-powered, in
chrome, bakelite and glass. Hands
move without apparent reason.
- *height 22cm*
- **£275**
- **Old Father Time Clock
Centre**

## Basket Top Bracket Clock ▼

- *late 17th century*
Ebony basket top bracket clock
with eight-day, hour striking
movement and strike silent.
- *height 37cm*
- **£16,500**
- **Raffety & Walwyn**

## English Gravity Clock ▼

- *date 1910*
Made by Eleison, London. With
mahogany pillared case and clock
in serpentine marble case. The
weight of the clock powers
the movement.
- *height 30cm*
- **£1,200**
- **Old Father Time Clock
Centre**

## French Desk Compendium ◄

- *circa 1902*
Gilt bronze, green enamel with
original leather travelling case.
Eight-day French movement.
- *height 16cm*
- **£2,300** • **Gütlin Clocks**

## French Striking Clock ▼

- *circa 1860*

Clock with anchor and pendulum escapement. White marble and ormolu mounted with pillars and floral swags on six bun feet.
- *diameter 18cm*
- £750          • A. Brocklehurst

## George III Bracket Clock ▼

- *circa 1760*

Fine brass moulded and ebonised bracket clock. Eight-day hour striking movement, strike silent.
- *height 48.5cm*
- £9,850          • Raffety Clocks

## French Chiming Regulator ➤

- *circa 1880-1890*

Kingwood and parquetry. By Bing of Paris. 25-piece dial. Central second sweep hand of three-week duration.
- *height 2.26m*
- £17,500          • Gütlin Clocks

## Drop Dial Wall Clock ▼

- *circa 1835*

Regency mahogany. Brass inlaid with convex dial.
- *height 58cm*
- £2,300
- **Pendulum of Mayfair**

## Maiden on a Horse Clock ◄

- *circa 1890*

Large French clock. A romantic figure on winged horse. Eight-day movement. Striking hours and half hours on a bell.
- *height 79cm*
- £1,900          • Gütlin Clocks

## French Mantel Clock ▲

- *date 1795*

A fine French 18th-century skeletonised ormolu and white marble mantel clock. Original gilding and beautiful case. Eight-day escapement and bells strike.
- *height 47cm*
- £5,750          • Gavin Douglas

## Marine Chronometer ▲

- *date 1900*

English, by Victor Kulber, in rare coromandel, brass-strung case. 56 hours duration.
- *height 20cm (closed)*
- £3,500
- **Old Father Time Clock Centre**

## Longcase Clock ◀

- *date 1715*

A walnut longcase clock by
Daniel Quarne. High quality with
eight-day, five-pillar movement
and calendar dial in the arch.
Walnut-veneered oak case.
- *height 2.24m*
- **£24,000**   • A. Brocklehurst

## Ebonised Bracket Clock ▼

- *circa 1730*

Fine quarter-chiming clock, brass
dial, eight-day movement, hour
strike and three subsidiary dials.
- *height 47cm*
- **£18,500**
- Raffety & Walwyn

## Charles X Mantel Clock ▲

- *circa 1830*

French patinated bronze and
ormolu clock showing Puck
descending from the trees, with
relief showing Titania Queen
of the Fairies, a scene from 'A
Midsummer Night's Dream'.
- *height 44cm*
- **£3,150**   • Gavin Douglas

## English Electric Clock ▼

- *date 1910*

By Frank Holden, powered by
1.5 volt battery.
- *height 26cm*
- **£1,250**
- Old Father Time Clock
  Centre

## English Longcase Clock ▼

- *circa 1710*

Lacquered clock by Peter Wise,
London. Chinoiserie sryle with
gilt mouldings and finials.
Silver chapter ring, date aperture,
engraved and matted centre with
crown and cherub spandels. The
trunk has a bullseye window and
pendulum movement.
- *height 2.45m*
- **£12,000**   • A. Brocklehurst

## Rosewood Mantel Clock ▼

- *circa 1840*

Very good four-glass rosewood
mantel clock with eight-day
movement and hour strike.
- *height 22cm*
- **£7,800**   • Raffety & Walwyn

## French Carriage Clock ▲

- *date 1922*

Brass corniche-cased repeating
carriage clock retailed by Barraud
& Lunds Ltd, London. French
eight-day movement.
- *height 18cm*
- **£1,450**   • Gütlin Clocks

### Small Travelling Clock ◄
• **date 1903**
English silver-cased clock with hallmark and French eight-day movement. Original English lever platform escapement. Signed on the movement.
• *height 10cm*
• £1,100          • Gütlin Clocks

### Wooden Mantel Clock ▼
• **late 18th century**
First Empire, French, birds-eye maple and ebony strung with silk suspension movement.
• *height 36cm*
• £2,500          • Gütlin Clocks

### Regulator Longcase Clock ▲
• *circa 1810*
Cuban mahogany, glass door and Richie's patented bi-metallic pendulum.
• *height 1.88m*
• £30-35,000
• **Pendulum of Mayfair**

### French Electric Clock ▲
• **date 1920**
'Bulle', powered by 1.5 volt battery with heavy cut-glass crystal cover.
• *height 34cm*
• £900
• **Old Father Time Clock Centre**

### French Directoire Clock ▼
• **date 1800**
Patinated bronze and ormolu clock. Gôut d' Egypt by Thonissen of Paris.
• *height 45cm*
• £6,750          • Gavin Douglas

### 'Eureka' Clock ▲
• **date 1908-14**
Made in London, powered by 1.5 volt battery, serpentine brass case.
• *height 32cm*
• £2,000
• **Old Father Time Clock Centre**

### Striking Bracket Clock ▲
• *circa 1790*
Mahogany bell top. Eight-days duration, silvered dial signed Andrews, Dover.
• *height 51cm*
• £9,200          • Clock Workshop

## German Novelty Clock ▼

- *date 1900*
By Junghans. In papier maché, original glass dome. The head and tail move as clock ticks.
- *height 30cm*
- £1,250
- **Old Father Time Clock Centre**

## Bracket Clock ▼

- *circa 1780*
By Alex Wilson, London. A bell-top mahogany bracket clock with eight-day striking movement.
- *height 54cm*
- £10,950  • **Raffety & Walwyn**

## English Mantel Clock ▼

- *circa 1890*
Flame mahogany and boxwood strung, lancet shape and sitting on brass ogee feet. Eight-day French movement.
- *height 29cm*
- £1,300    • **Gütlin Clocks**

## French Carriage Clock ▼

- *date 1880*
Porcelain enamelled sonnerie carriage clock by Drocourt, Paris. On original stand. Repeats at five-minute intervals, with an alarm.
- *height 22cm*
- £11,975
- **Pendulum of Mayfair**

## Expert Tips

*English bracket clocks were made mainly in London and a few other major cities. Clocks which appear to carry the name of provincial makers are, in fact, carrying the name of the retailer.*

## Mahogany Wall Clock ◄

- *date 1840*
Mahogany, eight-day duration wall clock. The six-pillar movement is jewelled on the first three pillars. A mercury-compensated pendulum is attached to the back board and has a hexagonal weight pully system. Silver dial enclosed in a dome-shaped case.
- *height 1.85m*
- £30,000
- **Pendulum of Mayfair**

## French Lyre Clock ▲

- *circa 1860*
Gilt bronze with bronze figural side pieces. Painted porcelain panels depicting lovers in the park. Eight-day French movement chiming hours and half hours on a bell.
- *height 51cm*
- £3,800    • **Gütlin Clocks**

## 'Reason' Electric Clock ▲

- *date 1910*
English, powered by 1.5 volt battery. Invented by Murday.
- *height 32cm*
- £3,800
- **Old Father Time Clock Centre**

### Muse of Learning Clock  ▼
• *circa 1805*
French patinated bronze, ormolu and green marble mantel clock showing a muse of learning.
• *height 53cm*
• **£7,750**    • **Gavin Douglas**

### George II Longcase Clock ▼
• *circa 1760*
English lacquer, with pagoda hood. Painted scenes to front door and base of stories from the Bible. Five-pillar London-made eight-day movement.
• *height 2.36m*
• **£9,500**    • **Gütlin Clocks**

### Musical Longcase Clock  ➤
• *circa 1850*
Cuban mahogany, eight-bell quarter striking, by Herbert Blockley. Brass dial and subsidiary dials for chime/silent. Whittington and Cambridge tune changer with subsidiary silvered second ring.
• *height 2.39m*
• **£12,500**    • **Gütlin Clocks**

### Marine Chronometer    ▼
• *circa 1840*
By Owen Owens, Liverpool. Two-day marine chronometer in brass-bound mahogany case.
• *height 19cm*
• **£5,500**  • **Raffety & Walwyn**

### Striking Carriage Clock  ◄
• *circa 1800*
Rococo gilt ormolu with ornate design. Highly decorative gilt case with caryatid figures to sides and a well-cast cherub carrying handle. Two train French movement, chiming hours and half hours.
• *height 20.5cm*
• **£2,900**    • **Gütlin Clocks**

### French Mystery Clock    ▲
• *date 1870*
French mystery clock with crystal pendulum, black marble and bronze case with spelter figure.
• *height 57cm*
• **£2,750**
• **Old Father Time Clock Centre**

### French Mantel Clock    ▲
• *circa 1830*
Gilt ormolu, First Empire. By Lugrunge à Paris. Finely chiselled gilt bronze case with a maiden and Cupid. Convex enamel dial.
• *height 42cm*
• **£2,300**    • **Gütlin Clocks**

## French Mantel Clock ▼
- *date 1806*

French patinated bronze and ormolu, respresenting astronomy and learning with two busts in double base, on acorn feet.
- *height 53cm*
- **£6,150**     • **Gavin Douglas**

## Skeleton Clock ▼
- *circa 1845*

Double fusée movement. By French Royal Exchange, London. Hour strike on bell. Lancet shape, brass pendulum. Baluster pillars.
- *height 37cm*
- **£7,000**
- **Pendulum of Mayfair**

## Gilt Bronze French Clock ➤
- *circa 1870*

Chiselled case with maidens to sides surmounted by an urn with draping ormolu swags. Eight-day French movement, hour and half-hour strike. Back engraved 'Antony Bailly à LYON'.
- *height 62cm*
- **£4,500**     • **Gütlin Clocks**

## French Mantel Clock ▼
- *circa 1830*

Ormolu and bronze Cupid and Psyche clock by Gaulin à Paris. Eight-day silk suspension movement with engine-turned watersilk gilt dial. Hour and half-hour striking on a bell.
- *height 59cm*
- **£5,900**     • **Gütlin Clocks**

## Grandfather Clock ◄
- *circa 1820*

Biedermeier grandfather clock. Swedish, birchwood. Signed 'Beurling, Stockholm'.
- *height 2.19m*
- **£6,900**     • **Rupert Cavendish**

## French Mantel Clock ▲
- *circa 1840*

A fine gilt ormolu and bronze clock with a bronze figure of Napolean resting his arm on a rock. The bottom section is engraved with his victories. Eight-day movement with hour and half-hour strike on a bell.
- *height 55cm*
- **£3,500**     • **Gütlin Clocks**

## Mahogany Balloon Clock ▲
- *circa 1790*

Late 18th-century mahogany balloon clock by Davis, London. With ormolu handles and white enamel dial.
- *height 61.5cm*
- **£16,000**     • **Norman Adams**

## French Clock ▼

- **date 1880**

A windmill automaton clock and barometer/thermometer in brass with revolving windmill sails.
- *height 45cm*
- £2,750
- Old Father Time Clock Centre

## 'Moving Eye' Clock ◀

- **date 1930**

Novelty dogs by Oswold, Germany. One eye is on the hour, the other on the minute.
- *height 14cm*
- £350
- Old Father Time Clock Centre

## French Mantel Clock ▼

- **date 1893**

Gilt ormolu and bronze. Retailed by Goldsmith's Co., London. Paris made.
- *height 31cm*
- £1,900    • Gütlin Clocks

## Brass Carriage Clock ▲

- **circa 1900**

Small sized pediment-topped polished brass carriage clock timepiece. Eight-day movement with platform escapement.
- *height 18cm*
- £1,900    • Gütlin Clocks

## Boullé Clock ▲

- **circa 1880**

Ormolu mounted tortoiseshell, in Renaissance style. Eight-day French square plate movement.
- *height 59cm*
- £750    • Gütlin Clocks

## Charles X Clock ▶

- **date 1820**

A Charles X patinated bronze and ormolu mantel clock depicting Caeser burning a scroll. Fine military trophies and floral swags.
- *height 52cm*
- £3,750    • Gavin Douglas

## 'Scott' Electric Clock ▲

- **date 1910**

English, powered by 1.5 volt battery. By Herbert Scott in oak, nickel plated and glass case.
- *height 40cm*
- £2,000
- Old Father Time Clock Centre

## Longcase Clock ▲

- *circa 1810*
Mahogany longcase clock with
moonroller sweep. Second hand
and centre date with quarter
strike on two bells. By W. Reece.
- *height 2.5m*
- **£8,500**
- **Ronald G. Chambers**

## Miniature Longcase Clock ▲

- *circa 1890-1900*
Jacobean-style oak, weight
driven. Eight-day duration with
brass dial. Chimes hours and
half hours on a gong.
- *height 153cm*
- **£3,800**  • Gütlin Clocks

## William IV Mantel Clock ▼

- *circa 1830*
Fine quality William IV mantel
timepiece in mahogany.
- *height 32cm*
- **£4,400**  • Raffety & Walwyn

## French Empire Mantel Clock ▼

- *circa 1830*
Gilt ormolu and bronze, by
Douillon. Case with two cherubs
supporting the face with gilt swag
mounting to the centre.
- *height 46cm*
- **£2,400**  • Gütlin Clocks

## Hobnail Mantel Clock ◀

- *circa 1840*
French First Empire cut-glass.
clock. Eight-day movement,
knife-edge suspension.
- *height 51cm*
- **£4,500**  • Gütlin Clocks

## Charles X Clock ▲

- *date 1820-25*
A very fine French Charles X
clock in patinated bronze ormolu
and marble vert. Showing 'Diana
the Huntress'. Signed by Ravrio
Bronzien. Eight-day escapement.
Bell strike, with silk suspension.
- *height 64cm*
- **£5,750**  • Gavin Douglas

## Bracket Clock ▲

- *date 1770*
Mahogany inverted bell, double
fusée. Brass dial, calendar, with
recessed name plate by Thomas
Grinnard. Ormolu mountings.
- *height 53 cm*
- **£ 14,000**
- **Pendulum of Mayfair**

### French Clock Set ➤
- *circa 1860*
French ormolu and white marble
clock set. Two nymphs holding
aloft time. Repeated floral
wreath.
- *height 56cm*
- £8,750    • Gavin Douglas

### Boudoir Balloon Clock ⌄
- *circa 1903*
Silver and enamel, French and
English hallmarked, Birmingham.
Signed L. Leroy & Cie of Paris.
- *height 16cm*
- £1,600    • Gütlin Clocks

### Steamhammer Clock ⌃
- *date 1870*
French 'steamhammer' industrial
automation, bronze and ormolu.
- *height 45cm*
- £2,750
- Old Father Time Clock
  Centre

### Drumhead Timepiece ⌃
- *circa 1830*
Regency clock on ormolu and
porphyry marble. By Tupman.
- *height 19.5cm*
- £4,850    • Raffety & Walwyn

### Propeller Blade Clock ⌄
- *circa 1900*
Industrial timepiece with ships,
capstan with a compass, gilded
lifebelt, apothec, anchor and
eight-day cylinder escapement.
- *height 35cm*
- £1,600    • Gütlin Clocks

### Gilt Table Clock ⌃
- *17th century*
Rare continental gilt metal
tabernacle clock with engraved
side panels.
- *height 22cm*
- £4,500    • Raffety & Walwyn

### French Mantel Clock ⌃
- *date 1890*
Four-glass clock with bronze and
ormolu case and mercury
compensating pendulum.
- *height 31cm*
- £1,500
- Old Father Time Clock
  Centre

## French Comptoise Clock ▲
- *late 19th century*
Wall clock with eight-day
movement, anchor escapement,
stamped sheet brass and
enamelled face. By B. Cadillan
of Bazas.
- *height 47cm*
- £2,000     • A. Brocklehurst

## English Longcase Clock ▲
- *circa 1790*
George III, black lacquer pagoda
hooded eight-day longcase clock.
Chinoiserie decorated case with
original hood housing a brass dial
and four-pillar movement.
- *height 2.39m*
- £8,500     • Gütlin Clocks

## Regency Timepiece ◄
- *circa 1830*
Gilt and bronze mantel timepiece
with single fusée movement.
- *height 19.5cm*
- £2,950   • Raffety & Walwyn

## Reims Cathedral Clock ▼
- *circa 1830*
Mercury gilded mantel clock,
eight-day movement, hour and
half-hour strike on gong, in
rosewood and boxwood strung case.
- *height 59cm*
- £6,500     • Gütlin Clocks

## Portico Mystery Clock ▼
- *date 1830*
With the clock as the pendulum
bob. White marble frame with
ormolu case.
- *height 54cm*
- £7,500
- Old Father Time Clock
  Centre

## French Empire Clock ▲
- *circa 1805*
Gôut d' Egypt. Superb casting,
female figures supporting gallery
and movement on an oval base.
- *height 44cm*
- £4,250     • Gavin Douglas

## French Swinging Clock ▲
- *date 1880*
Mystery swinging clock with
spelter figure and brass case.
- *height 46cm*
- £1,250
- Old Father Time Clock
  Centre

### Expert Tips

*Signatures were sometimes
added to clocks at a later date.
Test the engraving by touch –
the newer the engraving the
sharper it feels.*

### English Bracket Clock ▲
• *late 18th century*
Mahogany case with gilt brass
feet, side frets and gilt finials.
Made by Rivers & Son.
Cornhill, London
• *height 45cm*
• £10,000    • A. Brocklehurst

### French Mantel Clock ▲
• *circa 1810*
Patinated bronze and ormolu
clock showing an allegory of
horticulture. Made by Lesieur
of Paris. The whole on
machined bun feet.
• *height 35cm*
• £3,750    • Gavin Douglas

### Musical Carriage Clock ▼
• *date 1870*
Striking and repeating carriage
clock with musical alarm. Leroy
and fils no:5324. Musical
movement with two airs.
• *height 18.5cm*
• £4,500
• Pendulum of Mayfair

### French Pendulum ▼
• *date 1930*
Designed by ATO. First battery-
operated French pendulum clock.
Spider's web design to dial. Aztec
Gothic numerals.
• *height 17cm*
• £350    • Decadence

### Paris Bisque Timepiece ➤
• *circa 1890*
White mantel clock with small
French eight-day movement.
White convex enamel dial
with roman numerals and
counterpoised moon hands.
With white bisque case showing
a figure of a maiden.
• *height 26cm*
• £750    • Gütlin Clocks

### Bronze Mantel Clock ▲
• *circa 1870*
French gilt ormolu and bronze
in the form of an oil lamp with
a figure of an angel in offering.
Eight-day movement and
enamel dial.
• *height 35cm*
• £2,800    • Gütlin Clocks

### Musical Clock ▲
• *circa 1880*
Carved walnut Swiss chalet clock
with eight-day French movement,
hour and half-hour strike on bell
and musical box in base of clock.
Opening door reveals figures.
• *height 48cm*
• £3,500    • Gütlin Clocks

# Watches

## Masonic Watch ➤
- *circa 1950*
A gold-plated watch with
masonic symbols as numerals.
- £150    • A.M. P.M.

## Repeating Watch ➤
- *circa 1891*
Keyless half-hunter in 18ct. gold,
with lever minute repeating
movement.
- *diameter 53mm*
- £6,750    • C. Frodsham

## Cartier Cocktail ▲
- *circa 1930*
Cartier lady's cocktail watch, in
platinum with diamonds.
- £1,000    • Sugar

## Waterproof Watch ▼
- *circa 1930*
Omega rare, double-case
waterproof wristwatch.
- £3,250    • Anthony Green

## Omega Dynamic ▲
- *circa 1968*
Omega Dynamic automatic day
and date watch.
- £350    • A.M. P.M.

## Pocket Watch ▲
- *circa 1910*
A 14ct. gold-filled pocket watch,
with top-wind button set, by
Thomas Russell.
- £800    • Sugar

### Expert Tips

*There is a difference between
watches that appreciate and
ones that simply depreciate more
slowly than expected.*

## Gold Watch ◄
- *circa 1960*
Jaeger LeCoultre 18ct. gold
movement watch, designed by
Kutchinsky, with nine diamonds
and seven graded rubies on either
side of the band.
- £3,250    • Emmy Abé

### Rolex Watch ▼
• *circa 1923*
A medium-sized Rolex
gentleman's watch in Sterling
silver, with 'Sunray' dial, hinged
lugs and subsidiary seconds.
• £1,800    • Anthony Green

### Openface Karrusel Watch ▼
• *circa 1930*
An 18ct. gold, keyless lever
chronograph watch with register
and vari-coloured tracking for the
tachometer. Swiss, unsigned.
• *diameter 50mm*
• £850    • C. Frodsham

### Art Deco Lady's Rolex ▼
• *circa 1945*
With hooded lugs. The case, dial
and movement signed by Rolex.
• £1,550    • Anthony Green

### Cartier Wristwatch ▲
• *circa 1998*
Wristwatch with 18ct. gold body
and bracelet. Roman numeral dial
with date.
• £4,500    • A.M. P.M.

### Lady's Cartier ▲
• *circa 1925*
Cocktail watch of 18ct. gold,
platinum and diamonds set with
matching deployant buckle.
• £16,000    • Somlo

### Expert Tips

*The popularity of
well-made, recent wristwatches
began in the 1980s, as a
reaction to quartz movements.
Some manufacturers
started reproducing their
popular models.*

### French LIP Watch ▼
• *circa 1950*
Military-style wristwatch with
stainless-steel case and subsidiary
seconds. Clear digits on face.
• £140    • Sugar

### Gent's Triple Date Watch ▼
• *circa 1940*
Gentleman's triple date calendar
wristwatch with moonphase, in
10ct. gold. By Jaeger LeCoultre.
• £4,850    • Anthony Green

## Rolex Oyster Perpetual

- *circa 1952*
18ct. gold Rolex Perpetual
wristwatch with moonphase
calendar.
- **£35,000**          • Somlo

## Cartier Pocketwatch   ▼

- *circa 1930*
18ct. gold and onyx. With
European Watch and Clock Co
movement.
- **£9,200**          • Somlo

## Open Face Pocketwatch   ▲

- *circa 1884*
A late 19th-century, 18ct. gold,
minute repeating pocket watch
by Dent of London, with white-
enamel face with Arabic
numerals and subsidiary seconds.
- **£5,900**          • Somlo

## Pierre Cardin   ▲

- *circa 1960*
Pierre Cardin-designed watch
with original white-leather strap
and Jaegar manual-movement.
- **£220**   • **Themes & Variations**

## Verge Watch   ▼

- *circa 1710*
Silver pair-cased verge watch
with silver champlevé dial. By
John Ogden, Bowbridge.
- **£3,450**          • C. Frodsham

## Aviator's 'Antimagnetic'   ▲

- *circa 1953*
Rare, Swiss-made watch with
military specification fixed-strap
bars and screw-on waterproof
back. Made of high-grade
stainless steel.
- **£1,750**          • Anthony Green

## Small Silver Fob Watch   ▲

- *circa 1890*
Silver hunter with enamelled dial
with red numerals. Incised floral
decoration to the cover.
- **£125**          • Sugar

## 'Eiffel Tower' ◀
- *circa 1953*
An 18ct. gold, rectangular dialled Patek Philippe wristwatch with enamel and gold face and subsidiary seconds.
- £29,000 • Somlo

## Gentleman's Rolex ▼
- *circa 1959*
9 ct. gold precision wristwatch. With black dial and sweep second hand. Coin edge to case.
- £1,100 • Sugar

## Victorian Gentleman's Pocketwatch ▲
- *circa 1866*
Chester hallmarked, gold open-faced watch with white-enamel dial and subsidiary seconds. By Thos Russell and Son.
- £1,650 • Anthony Green

## Dress Pocketwatch ▲
- *circa 1915*
An 18ct. gold, Swiss pocketwatch with gold-washed dial and subsidiary seconds.
- £395 • Sugar

## Gold Cartier Watch ▼
- *circa 1920*
An 18ct. gold and platinum Cartier tank watch with square face and enamelled dial with black, Arabic figures.
- £22,000 • Anthony Green

## Chronometer ▲
- *circa 1945*
A gentleman's Chronometer wristwatch. The centre seconds dial signed Rolex Chronometer. Swiss made.
- £3,650 • Anthony Green

## Lady's Rolex ▲
- *circa 1924*
A 9ct. gold, lady's Rolex watch, with expanding bracelet holding 15 rubies.
- £1,000 • Cartier

### Expert Tips

*. . . are simply good, second-hand purchases, being less expensive than the new.*

## Fob Watch ▲
• *circa 1890*
A small, silver, Swiss fob watch with enamel dial and red numerals and gold floral pattern to centre, with incised floral decoration to covers.
• £125 • Sugar

### Expert Tips

*Check that the case of a pocket watch labelled 'gold' really is gold, particularly with American watches. Rolled gold – plating with gold fused to other metals – cases of excellent quality were produced in quantity and are not always easy to spot.*

## Open Face Pocketwatch ▲
• *circa 1830*
A fine quality open-face pocket watch, the cylindrical case with turned sides. The engine-turned dial with Roman chapter-ring and signed 'Simmons Finsbury London'; the English lever movement with fusée signed and numbered 778. The balance has a diamond endstone.
• £1,500 • Anthony Green

## First World War Officer's Watch ▼
• *circa 1913*
Original, enamelled dial with Roman numerals and traditional red twelve. Subsidiary second dial and minute recording. Fabulous example of one of the very earliest wristwatch chronographs. Good condition and extremely attractive.
• £2,650 • Anthony Green

## Double-Dialled Watch ▼
• *circa 1910*
A silver, keyless, lever double-dialled calendar watch with moon phases, time and subsidiaries on an enamel dial with Roman numerals on the obverse, and world time indications for seven cities on the reverse dial. The watch, which is unsigned, was made in Switzerland.
• £2,750 • Anthony Green

## Pocket Chronometer ▲
• *circa 1895*
An 18ct. gold openface keyless fusée, free sprung pocket chronometer.
• *diameter 58mm*
• £9,500 • C. Frodsham

## Gold and Enamel Watch ▲
• *date 1801*
A rare 18ct. gold and polychrome enamel watch, Peto-cross-detent escapement with scene of children feeding chickens. By Ilbery, London.
• *diameter 6cm*
• £42,500 • C. Frodsham

## Art-Deco Wristwatch ▲
• *circa 1935*
Gentleman's high quality wristwatch of Art-Deco design. Case with hooded lugs and thick raised UB glass. The jewelled lever movement with original gilt dust cover.
• £775 • Anthony Green

## Gentleman's Rolex ▼

- *circa 1915*
9ct. gold precision watch, by
Rolex, with subsidiary seconds
and a white-metal dial.
- **£950** • **Sugar**

## Longines 'Lindbergh' ▲

- *circa 1940*
Steel and silver cased Longines
'Lindbergh' aviator's wristwatch.
This design first used by the pilot,
Charles Lindbergh, during his
famous transatlantic crossing.
- **£9,000** • **Somlo**

## Gentleman's 'Prince' Chronometer ▼

- *circa 1950*
A rare wristwatch with case
signed by Rolex and movement
signed 'Rolex Chronometer'.
- **£11,750** • **Anthony Green**

## First World War Wristwatch ▼

- *circa 1916*
A very rare officer's First World
War 'Hunting' cased wristwatch,
with waterproof screw-back. The
movement is signed by Rolex and
the case is marked 'Rolex' with
'W&D', standing for Wilsdorf and
Davis, the original founders of
the Rolex company. The case is
numbered 773185 and the
enamel face shows luminous
numerals and subsidiary seconds.
- **£3,450** • **Anthony Green**

## Deck Watch ▲

- *date 1883*
Shows hours left to run in the
main spring and chronograph
stop mechanism to synchronize
the watch to the main ship's
chronometer. Shows little wear.
Signed 'Thos. Russell
Chronometer Makers to The
Queen'.
- **£2,300** • **Anthony Green**

## Asprey Rectangular ▼

- *circa 1916*
Silver Asprey rectangular curved
watch with white-metal dial and
Roman numerals.
- **£260** • **Sugar**

## Verge Watch ◄

- *circa 1800*
An 18ct. gold and enamel verge
watch, by Vauchez of Geneva,
showing a pastoral scene, with
jewelling.
- **£6,500** • **Somlo**

---

## Expert Tips

*Watches should be in working
order. Repairs can be expensive.*

## Lady's Rolex ◄

- *date 1914*

Lady's silver Rolex watch, of circular form, with original expanding bracelet and early example metal dial with Roman numerals in black, 'XII' in red.
- £675     • Sugar

## 'Naviquartz' Timepiece ▼

- *circa 1975*

Brass-bound mahogany timepiece with certificate, by Patek Philippe of Geneva.
- *length 16cm*
- £3,500     • C. Frodsham

## Art Deco Rolex ▲

- *circa 1937*

A gentleman's Art Deco period Rolex wristwatch in 9ct. gold, with stepped sides and high-grade movement timed to two positions. British import marks for the year 1937.
- £3,650     • Anthony Green

## Pilot's Wristwatch ▲

- *circa 1951*

An RAF-issue, pilot's wristwatch with centre 'hacking' seconds hand and screw-back case with anti-magnetic inner case. Made by the International Watch Company with case, dial and movement signed and showing the Ministry of Defence arrow insignia. With factory guarantee.
- £2,850     • Anthony Green

## Ladies Cartier ▼

- *circa 1950*

An 18ct. gold and sapphire set bracelet watch with backwind movement.
- £9,500     • Somlo

## Expert Tips

*The more complex the watch, the more expensive the repair, so the larger the discount you will be looking for.*

## Chronograph ▲

- *circa 1945*

Chronograph by Eberhard & Co, showing hour/minute registers.
- £3,500     • Anthony Green

## Omega Chronograph ►

- *circa 1932*

Rare, steel-cased Omega single button chronograph wristwatch with enamel dial in red and black and sweep second hand.
- £7,000     • Somlo

## German Air Force Issue Chronograph ▲

• *circa 1970*

A rare German Air Force issue aviator's 'fly-back' chronograph wristwatch, with the chronograph operated by two pushers on the case band. Made by Heuer, the chronograph has the benefit of a 'fly-back' facility, allowing the centre second hand to zero and immediately resume timing. The black dial has subsidiary seconds and minute recording dial and the steel-case body has a non-reflective, anti-glare finish and a rotating, dull matt-finish black bezel with minute increments.

• £1,950    • Anthony Green

## Hermetique Waterproof ▲

• *circa 1923*

Rare, hermatically sealed 'Waterproof' wristwatch, in double case with hinged lugs. Swiss make, by Hermetique, in 9ct. gold.

• £2,750    • Anthony Green

## Half Hunting Pocket Watch ▼

• *date 1880*

A high quality, English, 18ct. gold half-hunter pocketwatch, with enamelled dial and enamel chapter-ring to the outer case. The movement is signed 'W. Lockwood 3 Devonshire Buildings Victoria Lane Huddersfield'.

• £1,950    • Anthony Green

## Rolex 'Prince' ▼

• *circa 1929*

Rare 'Prince' Chronometer gent's watch. Dial with original, enamelled numerals and tracks.

• £6,650    • Anthony Green

## Openface Keyless Fusée ▼

• *circa 1895*

An 18ct. gold, open-face keyless fusée, free sprung pocket chronometer with spring detent escapement, enamel dial with up and down indicator, and thief proof swivel bow. By Charles Frodsham, London.

• *diameter 58mm*

• £9,500    • C. Frodsham

## Keyless Lever Watch ▲

• *circa 1900*

18ct. gold, openface, keyless lever watch with enamel dial and original, leather presentation box. By Charles Frodsham, London.

• *diameter 49mm*

• £1,500    • C. Frodsham

## Gent's Rolex ▲

• *circa 1956*

A gentleman's high grade 9ct. gold wristwatch with subsidiary seconds and dial signed 'Rolex Precision', with British import marks for the year 1956. The dial has been sympathetically restored to the highest standard.

• £3,350    • Anthony Green

## Chronograph Watch ▼
- *circa 1905*
An 18ct. gold hunter, keyless lever, minute-repeating chronograph watch with register, enamel dial and thief-proof swivel bow, by Dent, London.
- *height 53mm*
- £11,500    • C. Frodsham

## Cylinder Watch ▼
- *circa 1800*
An 18ct. gold, open-face, keyless lever, minute-repeating, split seconds chronograph watch with original box and certificate, by Patek Philippe of Geneva; retailed by Spaulding & Co of Chicago.
- *diameter 45mm*
- £14,750    • C. Frodsham

## Oyster Submarine Diving Watch ▲
- *circa 1964*
Oyster Perpetual Submariner automatic diver's wristwatch, on Rolex steel 'flip-lock' bracelet.
- £2,950    • Anthony Green

## Pocketwatch ▲
- *circa 1940*
Silver/steel. By Movado. With triple date and moon phase. Case with winding mechanism operating when opening and closing. Covered in crocodile skin.
- £1,850    • Anthony Green

## Enamelled Watch ▲
- *circa 1801*
Very rare 18ct. gold and polychrome enamel watch with scallop-form case. By Ilbery.
- *diameter 63mm*
- £42,500    • C. Frodsham

## Rolex Oyster Waterproof ▼
- *circa 1937*
Fine example of an early Oyster waterproof gentleman's 'Chronometer' wristwatch, the case with the original, screw-down 'Oyster' button.
- £2,650    • Anthony Green

## Cylinder Watch ▼
- *circa 1800*
A Swiss-made, gold and enamel double-dialled watch with visible diamond-set escapement and calendar.
- *diameter 43mm*
- £8,000    • C. Frodsham

## Expert Tips

*It is principally the efficacy of the wristwatch as a time-keeping instrument that determines its value. The Rolex Oyster first appeared in 1927 and was the first model to be waterproofed and able to withstand climatic changes. Technically years in advance, it is its sheer reliability that has kept it collectable.*

### British Military Issue ▼
- *circa 1940*
A British military issue
wristwatch, with black dial and
subsidiary seconds dial and MOD
arrow. By the International
Watch Company.
- £2,250 • Anthony Green

### Silver Pocket Watch ▲
- *circa 1878*
English, large sized silver
chronograph, with key wind and
key set. White-enamel face with
black numerals and gold hands.
- £195 • Sugar

### Keyless Lever Watch ▼
- *circa 1908*
An 18ct. gold open-face watch
with split seconds chronograph
and register. By Dent of London.
- *diameter 54mm*
- £4,750 • C. Frodsham

### Spaceman Watch ▼
- *circa 1970*
Swiss-made watch with stainless
steel body and bracelet. Manual
and water resistant.
- £220 • Themes & Variations

### Gold Watch ▼
- *circa 1915*
A 9ct. gold, English watch with a
porcelain dial and manual
movement, by J.W. Benson.
- £380 • A.M. P.M.

### Rolex Oyster ▲
- *circa 1970*
Date precision with silver face,
stainless body. Bracelet style
band.
- £725 • A.M. P.M.

### Golf Ball Watch ◄
- *circa 1920*
Swiss watch with silver case
modelled as a golf ball. With
subsidiary seconds.
- £550 • Sugar

# Scientific Instruments

## Microscope With Case ▲
- *circa 1820*
Fully portable with original
wooden box that doubles as a
stand, with all original fittings.
- *height 16cm*
- £640 • Howard & Hamilton

### Zeiss Microscope ▼
- *circa 1910*
A brass and steel Zeiss monocular
microscope with lenses of three
different magnifications on a steel
rotating nosepiece.
- *height 28cm*
- £250 • Finchley

## Microscope ▲
- *circa 1910*
Monocular brass microscope,
with lenses of two magnifications
by W. Watson and Sons, 313
High Holborn, London.
- *height 34cm*
- £650 • Howard & Hamilton

## Prismatic Compass ▲
- *circa 1900*
Major Hutchinson's Improved
Surveyors' Prismatic Compass,
with original leather case, by
Troghton & Simms of London.
- £169 • Ocean Leisure

### Travelling Microscope ▼
- *circa 1890*
A predominantly brass monocular
microscope, with original case by
Henry Grouch of London.
- *height 35cm*
- £750 • Finchley

## Theodolite ▲
- *circa 1860*
Theodolite by Elliott. All brass
with compass and levels.
- *height 36cm*
- £950 • Howard & Hamilton

## Brass Level ➤
- *date 1880*
An all-brass level with vertical
and horizontal measurements.
- *height 46cm*
- £350 • Howard & Hamilton

## Octagonal Telescope ▼
- *late 18th century*
Mahogany and brass single-draw octagonal telescope, with slide lens cover.
- *length 64cm*
- £1,700 • Howard & Hamilton

## Signalling Telescope ◄
- *circa 1860*
All-brass, leather-bonded single-draw telescope with flag chart.
- *length 75cm*
- £680 • Howard & Hamilton

## Expert Tips

*Patination is often more to the taste of the true collector than polish, which may detract from the appearance of brass.*

## Theodolite ▼
- *circa 1890*
All brass theodolite by Stanley. Fitted with compass and levels.
- *length 36cm*
- £1,000 • Howard & Hamilton

## Deviatometer ▲
- *circa 1880*
Ship's deviatometer by Mugnes, London. Fully gimballed and weighted in mahogany box.
- £650 • Howard & Hamilton

## Microscope ▲
- *circa 1920*
A brass monocular microscope by C. Baker of London.
- *length 34cm*
- £130 • Howard & Hamilton

## Equinoctical Instrument ▼
- *circa 1830*
Newman & Co Calcutta compass and Roman numeral dial.
- *diameter 14cm*
- £1,605 • Howard & Hamilton

## Transit ►
- *late 18th century*
Very rare transit by Troughton, mounted on a stay base with level and dial.
- *length 64cm*
- £1,700 • Howard & Hamilton

### Brass & Wood Telescope ➤
- *circa 1840*
A wood and brass, three-draw
telescope with slide lens cover.
- *length 30cm*
- £440 • Howard & Hamilton

### Telescope ▲
- *18th century*
Single-draw two-inch diameter
telescope, signed by Spencer
Browning & Reist of London. A
large telescope for use in the field,
probably for ordinance purposes,
it has a substantial tripod of a
later date.
- *height 1.75m*
- £879 • Ocean Leisure

### Specimen Cabinet ▲
- *circa 1830*
A William IV specimen cabinet,
in mahogany, with gadrooned
decoration, the whole on claw
feet. Has two locking doors to
front and one on each side,
protecting six slide drawers to the
front and concealing test-tube
holders at the sides.
- *height 41cm*
- £1,250 • Mathias

### Polyhedral Dial ▲
- *late 18th century*
A 25-sided polyhedral dial which
combines the horizontal and
vertical in several orientations.
- £4,000 • T. Phillips

### Pocket Barometer ▲
- *circa 1900*
A brass pocket aneroid barometer
with silvered dial. The barometer
is contained in its original hinged
leather case. Compensated.
- *diameter 6.5cm*
- £160 • Howard & Hamilton

### Barometer ▼
- *circa 1880*
Unusual oak cased 'Royal
Polytechnic Barometer', in
carved case with scalloped
sunmount shell.
- *height 1.07m*
- £1,490 • A. Walker

### Brass Rule ◄
- *19th century*
Brass rule stamped 'Arian', with
multiple scales.
- *length 15cm*
- £65 • Howard & Hamilton

## Stick Barometer ▲

- *circa 1830*
Mahogany bow-fronted stick
barometer with swan neck
pediment and silver-brass register.
Operated by rack and pinion
vernier with tortoiseshell knob.
- *length 1.02m*
- £6,350 • A. Walker

## Astronomical Telescope ▲

- *circa 1848*
Equatorial three-inch
astronomical telescope by
Troughton & Simms, with
mahogany turned handles.
- *length 1.39m*
- £12,000 • Talbot

## Ship's Compass ▼

- *circa 1830*
All-brass ship's compass, on
gimbals, with black and white
dial, in a mahogany box.
- *length 12cm*
- £150 • Howard & Hamilton

## Brass Pantograph ▼

- *circa 1950*
A brass pantograph instrument,
consisting of pivoted levers for
copying drawings etc, to scale.
Complete with case.
- *length 87cm*
- £985 • Hatchwell

## Aquatic Microscope ▼

- *circa 1780*
An Ellis design, botanist's aquatic
microscope. In brass, with
original sharkskin fitted box.
- *height 16.5cm*
- £750 • Talbot

## Reflecting Telescope ▲

- *19th century*
A 12cm reflecting telescope by
John Gail, on a pillar and claw
stand with brass and ivory keys
for moving from the azimuth to
altazimuth plane.
- *length 12cm*
- £4,000 • T. Phillips

## Diptych Sun Dial ▲

- *date 1595*
Hand-held diptych dial signed
and dated with Daucher's mark.
Vertical dial with zodiac scale.
- *length 32cm*
- £5,500 • T. Phillips

## Expert Tips

*Fakes of early instruments do
exist, but more frequently found
are copies, which were honestly
made for instructional purposes
to demonstrate the principles.*

## Aneroid Barometer ▼

• *circa 1840*
English aneroid barometer with exposed movement, silver dial and curved thermometer.
• *diameter 30cm*
• £420    • A. Walker

## Screw-Barrel Microscope ▲

• *late 18th century*
Travelling screw-barrel microscope housed in a compartmentalised shagreen case. Complete with two objectives, talc box and specimen slide.
• *width 24cm*
• £1,000    • T. Phillips

## Reflecting Telescope ▲

• *late 19th century*
Reflecting telescope with an equatorial mount. Clockwork drive and mahogany tripod stand.
• *height 1.75m*
• £6,000    • T. Phillips

## Explorer's Sextant ▲

• *circa 1800*
Gimballed explorer's sextant on stand, by Cary of London.
• *height 49cm*
• £4,000    • Talbot

## Portable Equinoctial ▼

• *circa 1800*
A portable equinoctial by Francis West, with signed chapter ring, housed in original travelling case.
• *diameter 8cm*
• £2,000    • T. Phillips

## Stick Barometer ▼

• *circa 1740*
A George II mahogany stick barometer with three brass finials and carved termination. By Joseph Hurt, London.
• *height 1m*
• £16,000    • Norman Adams

---

### Expert Tips

*Surveying instruments such as compasses, circumferentors and graphometers, must be carefully maintained and serviced and handled with great care. Instruments polished up for decorative purposes will be rendered useless.*

## Hour Glass ▼

• *mid 19th century*
Turned mahogany framed hour glass of hand-blown glass.
• *height 18cm*
• £750    • Talbot

## Expert Tips

*Any doubts as to a microscope's originality can be resolved by a museum, such as the Science Museum in London, the Oxford Museum of the History of Science or the Whipple Museum in Cambridge.*

### Drawing Instruments ▼
• *circa 1820*
Architect's brass drawing instruments in a shagreen and silver-mounted case.
• *12.5cm*
• £1,000          • T. Phillips

### Wheel Barometer ▼
• *circa 1830*
Mahogany wheel barometer, with swan neck, in flame mahogany by John Messar, Gravesend.
• *height 1.03m*
• £1,050          • A. Walker

### Drawing Instruments ▲
• *circa 1780*
French drawing instruments for the German retailer, Ring. Ten instruments together in a calf-skin étuis box.
• £3,500          • Talbot

### Terrestrial Telescope ▲
• *circa 1790*
Reflecting terrestrial telescope. Interchangeable eye pieces on tripod base and fitted mahogany box. By Dudley Adams.
• *length 71cm*
• £6,000          • Talbot

### Nautical Protractor ▲
• *circa 1860*
Nautical protractor of 360°, with original velvet-lined mahogany box. By John Casarelli.
• *diameter 30cm*
• £150          • Talbot

### Stick Barometer ▼
• *circa 1790*
A George III mahogany stick barometer, by William Watkins, St James's Street, London.
• *height 1.08m*
• £6,000          • Norman Adams

### Pocket Monocular ▼
• *circa 1790*
Pocket monocular made from wood, ivory and brass with original shagreen case. Made by Adams of London.
• £600          • T. Phillips

### Miniature Microscope ▲
- **late 18th century**
Cuff-type miniature monocular
microscope housed in its original
mahogany box which doubles as
the stand.
- *width 24cm*
- **£5,000**          • **T. Phillips**

### Aneroid Barometer ▼
- *circa 1920*
Aneroid barometer with painted
dial, bearing the legend for the
southern latitudes.
- *diameter 20cm*
- **£559**          • **Ocean Leisure**

### Horizontal Brass Sundial ▼
- *circa 1780*
Brass sundial with octagonal base
engraved with hororary table.
Gnomon with filigree decoration.
- *length 18cm*
- **£380**          • **Talbot**

### Medicine Cabinet ▼
- *circa 1850*
A mahogany medicine cabinet
with a full set of bottles, scales,
pestle & mortar and pill boxes.
- *height 22cm*
- **£1,375**          • **Mathias**

### Miniature Telescope ▲
- *circa 1820*
One-inch miniature reflecting
telescope – probably Scottish –
with brass body on tripod base.
- *diameter 30cm*
- **£1,500**          • **Talbot**

### Barometer ▲
- *circa 1820*
A fine mahogany stick barometer
by Dolland of London. Silver dial
graduated in inches with a
concealed mercury tube.
- *length 90cm*
- **£5,000**          • **T. Phillips**

### Japanned Barometer ▲
- *circa 1720*
A rare black japanned stick
barometer in the manner of Isaac
Robelou, London.
- *height 93.5cm*
- **£9,000**          • **Norman Adams**

## Reading Glass ▽

- *circa 1760*
Glass with hand-painted horn cover, floral arrangement to front with putti and books on reverse.
- *length 12cm*
- £450 • Talbot

## Sundial ▽

- *18th century*
Signed silver sundial by Le Maire-Tils, Paris. In original leather case and in the butterfield style.
- £2,000 • T. Phillips

## Dispenser's Scales ▷

- *circa 1930*
Scales in chromed steel on a mahogany base.
- *height 31cm*
- £65 • Antiques Warehouse

## Travelling Circumferentor ▽

- *late 18th century*
Miniature travelling circumferentor in original oak travelling box.
- £2,200 • T. Phillips

## Barograph ◀

- *circa 1880*
Barograph in oak and glass case, with drawer to rear.
- *height 23cm*
- £995 • Mathias

## Wheel Barometer ▲

- *circa 1760*
A rare early George III mahogany wheel barometer in a case of clock form.
- *height 1.13m*
- £60,000 • Norman Adams

## Rolling Rule >

- *circa 1940*
An English polished and
lacquered brass parallel rolling
rule with original box.
- *length 45cm*
- £79            • Ocean Leisure

## Microscope ▲

- *circa 1830*
Brass monocular microscope on a
tripod base by Andrew Pritchard,
162 Fleet Street, London.
- *height 49cm*
- £1,900 • Howard & Hamilton

## Sextant ▼

- *19th century*
Brass sextant in good condition
with original brass and mahogany
compartmentalized case, with all
filters and lenses.
- *height 25cm*
- £680    • Howard & Hamilton

## Dividers ▼

- *circa 1900*
A finely tooled pair of dividers by
MDS Ltd London, in fitted
leather-and velvet-lined box.
- *length 25cm*
- £200    • Howard & Hamilton

## Dip Circle ▲

- *circa 1890*
All brass dip circle on tripod base
with screw-adjustable feet.
- *height 27cm*
- £380  • Howard & Hamilton

## Microscope ▲

- *circa 1950*
A monocular steel laboratory
microscope with built-in mains
electric illuminator and range of
magnification on a rotating lens
nosepiece.
- *height 36cm*
- £135                    • Finchley

## Expert Tips

*The original barometers
were stick barometers, and these
and the early aneroid
barometers of the 19th century
are most attractive to the
collector. Wheel – or 'banjo' –
barometers came into popular
use in the late 18th century and
were mass-produced in the
19th. Even the early ones are
still reasonably priced.*

## Telescope ◄

- *circa 1840*
19th-century leather and brass
three-draw telescope with slide
lens cover.
- *length 30cm*
- £440  • Howard & Hamilton

# Collector's Items

**The important rule for the collector of 'collectables' is to take care of the ephemera of today – they may be the antiques of tomorrow.**

Rarity and condition are the two factors which make collectable items collectable. The great advantages with collectables is that they do not need to be especially old and they do not need to cost a great deal of money. Take almost any disposable item commonly in use at the moment, and you can be certain that someone is building a collection of it and that, in a few years, it will be much in demand. The most collectable of these essentially ephemeral items are those which are in some way ground-breaking or revolutionary. The first SLR cameras, for instance, or the first refillable fountain pens. It is not too difficult to spot the collectables of the future using this as a criterion – what about the first truly mobile phones, or lap-top computers? The important thing is that everything is collectable and that you have the opportunity to collect something that you really like and really know about – and discover that there are any number of other people interested in the same thing.

Start gathering the antiques of tomorrow today!

## Advertising & Packaging

**Stilton Cheese Dish** ▲
- *circa 1955*
A stilton cheese dish, designed by Gilroy to advertise Guinness.
- *height 16cm*
- **£50** • **D. Huxtable**

**Polish Box** ▼
- *circa 1930*
A metal polish box with a secondary use as a string dispenser.
- *height 15cm*
- **£35** • **D. Huxtable**

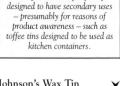

**Johnson's Wax Tin** ▼
- *circa 1950*
A tin of Johnson's Wax polish.
- *diameter 10cm*
- **£4.50** • **Magpies**

**Belgian Biscuit Tin** ◄
- *circa 1939*
A Disney biscuit tin from Belgium, with cartoon characters.
- *length 32cm*
- **£120** • **D. Huxtable**

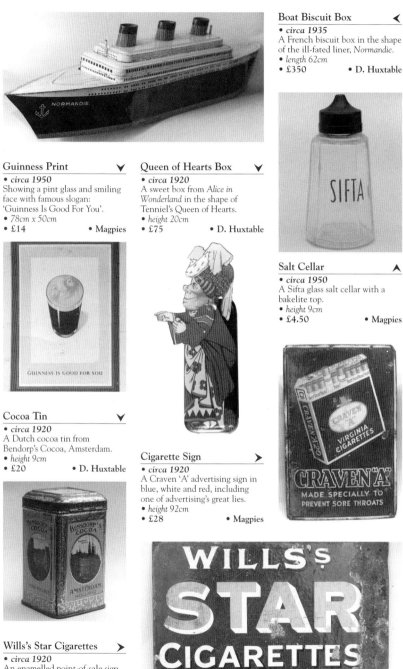

**Boat Biscuit Box** ◄
- *circa 1935*
A French biscuit box in the shape of the ill-fated liner, *Normandie*.
- *length 62cm*
- **£350**  • D. Huxtable

**Guinness Print** ▼
- *circa 1950*
Showing a pint glass and smiling face with famous slogan: 'Guinness Is Good For You'.
- *78cm x 50cm*
- **£14**  • Magpies

**Queen of Hearts Box** ▼
- *circa 1920*
A sweet box from *Alice in Wonderland* in the shape of Tenniel's Queen of Hearts.
- *height 20cm*
- **£75**  • D. Huxtable

**Salt Cellar** ▲
- *circa 1950*
A Sifta glass salt cellar with a bakelite top.
- *height 9cm*
- **£4.50**  • Magpies

**Cocoa Tin** ▼
- *circa 1920*
A Dutch cocoa tin from Bendorp's Cocoa, Amsterdam.
- *height 9cm*
- **£20**  • D. Huxtable

**Cigarette Sign** ►
- *circa 1920*
A Craven 'A' advertising sign in blue, white and red, including one of advertising's great lies.
- *height 92cm*
- **£28**  • Magpies

**Wills's Star Cigarettes** ►
- *circa 1920*
An enamelled point-of-sale sign in brown and orange.
- *height 28cm*
- **£42**  • Magpies

161

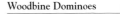

## Woodbine Dominoes ◀

- *circa 1920*
A metal box of Wills's Woodbine
Dominoes with a full set of
bakelite playing pieces.
- *length 16cm*
- £24                    • Magpies

## Gramophone Needle Box ▲

- *circa 1920*
A tinplate box for 200 Columbia
gramophone needles.
- *length 4cm*
- £4.50                  • Magpies

## Jackson's Pastilles ▼

- *circa 1940*
A Jackson's Night-Cough
Pastilles tin, with illustration of a
sleeping street.
- *diameter 8cm*
- £5.50                  • Magpies

## Soapless Shampoo ▲

- *circa 1920*
Sachets of Butywave Soapless
Shampoo, wisely unused.
- *height 12cm*
- £4                     • D. Huxtable

## Cocoa Tin ◀

- *circa 1930*
A French cocoa tin, emanating
from the French West Indies,
proclaiming Banania Cocoa with
a suitably impressed maiden on
the front panel.
- *height 16cm*
- £120                   • D. Huxtable

## Biscuit Tin ▲

- *circa 1930*
Huntley & Palmer's bell-shaped
biscuit tin with floral decoration.
- *height 15cm*
- £22                    • Magpies

## Disney Biscuit Tin ▶

- *circa 1939*
A Belgian biscuit tin showing
various Disney characters.
- *length 30cm*
- £120        • D. Huxtable

### Lux Soap Flakes  ▲
- *circa 1960*

An unopened box of Lever
Brothers' Lux soap flakes.
- *height 28cm*
- £10          • D. Huxtable

### Toothpaste Lid  ▼
- *circa 1900*

A Woods Areca Nut toothpaste
lid by W. Woods, Plymouth.
- £20          • Magpies

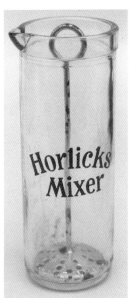

### Biscuit Tin  ▼
- *circa 1910*

A biscuit tin in the shape of a
book, made by Hoffman Suisse.
- *height 36cm*
- £90          • D. Huxtable

### Horlicks Mixer  ▲
- *circa 1950*

A Horlicks promotional glass jug
with a metal mixer.
- *height 15cm*
- £10          • Magpies

### McVitie Biscuit Box  ▲
- *circa 1910*

A 'Billie Bird' biscuit box by
McVitie.
- *height 32cm*
- £120          • D. Huxtable

### Talcum Powder  ▶
- *circa 1950*

A 'Jolly Baby' talcum powder
container, with voluptuous cover.
- *height 15cm*
- £40          • D. Huxtable

### Battery Advertisement  ◀
- *circa 1960*

An Oldham Batteries metal
advertising sign, incorporating
the 'I told 'em – Oldham' slogan.
- *height 37cm*
- £28          • Magpies

# Aeronautica

### BOAC Sales Leaflet ◄
• *circa 1970*
Advertising standard
merchandise of the era. With
colour pictures.
• *length 20cm*
• £10                    • Cobwebs

### Model Kit ▲
• *circa 1940*
'Robot Bomb' balsa-wood model
of a jet-propelled bomb used
against England by the Germans
in France during World War II.
• £10                    • Cobwebs

### Aero Club Badge ▼
• *circa 1920*
Brooklands club badge in pressed
steel with coloured enamels. The
club was established in the 1920s.
• *height 10cm*
• £600                    • CARS

### Aerial ABC Gazetteer ▲
• *date August 1929*
Light brown in colour with black
and white print. In mint
condition.
• *22cm x 14.5cm*
• £40                    • Cobwebs

### Fighter Plane Model ▼
• *circa 1980*
Model of a battle-camouflaged
Tornado fighter plane. On a steel
frame with rubber feet.
• *height 10cm*
• £30                    • Cobwebs

### Spanish Airline Leaflet ◄
• *circa 1922*
In good condition, but with a
folding crease down the centre.
• *15.5cm x 12cm*
• £25                    • Cobwebs

### Expert Tips

*The most enduringly collectable
aeronautical artefacts tend still
to be those of World War II
and, most particularly, those
relating to the Battle of
Britain, 1940.*

### Qantas Empire Airways ►
• *circa 1930*
A Qantas flying-boat map of the
Sydney to Singapore route. Good
condition.
• *length 24.5cm, width 12cm*
• £50                    • Cobwebs

## Expert Tips

*The difference between a model and a toy is one of accuracy of scale, but also of durability. Toy aircraft tend to have been played with hard, and good, early examples fetch good prices.*

### Route Map  ∨
- *circa 1930*
Period Airways route map from Southampton to Alexandria.
- *22cm x 14cm*
- **£50**                    • Cobwebs

### Daily Graphic  ∨
- *date 1924*
Daily Graphic airship flight certificate from the 1924 British Empire Exhibition.
- *20.5cm x 13.5cm*
- **£25**                    • Cobwebs

### Model Airplane  ➤
- *circa 1940*
A brass twin-engined aircraft on a beechwood base.
- *height 10cm*
- **£70**                    • Cobwebs

### Four Cannon Shells  ∨
- *circa 1942*
Four fighter-plane cannon shells, converted into a desk pen holder and mounted on oak and brass. The result of a dogfight between British and German fighter planes.
- *15cm x 15cm*
- **£45**                    • Cobwebs

### Model Messerschmitt  ∨
- *circa 1940*
Hand-made model of a Messerschmitt ME110 fighter plane on perspex and beaten steel base, with Nazi insignia modelled into base of stem.
- *wingspan 31.5cm*
- **£350**              • Sean Arnold

### Aircraft Timetable  ∧
- *date 1926*
An Imperial Airways Ltd summer timetable, second edition, in good condition.
- *15cm x 11cm*
- **£40**                    • Cobwebs

### Pan-Am Ticket  ∧
- *date 1949*
Pan-American Clipper ticket, sponsored by the Bulova watch company, in half green and half white with black and white print.
- *diameter 11cm*
- **£20**                    • Cobwebs

## Qantas Ticket ➤

- *circa 1941*
Flying-boat hotel ticket, from
Australia to Singapore, with
Qantas Empire Airways.
- *16.5cm x 11cm*
- **£15**　　　　• Cobwebs

## Route Map ◄

- *circa 1937*
Empire flying-boat route map
from England to Egypt. Mint
condition.
- *21.5cm x 12.5cm*
- **£30**　　　　• Cobwebs

## German Flying Boat ▼

- *circa 1929*
A black and white photograph of
the six-engined German Dorrier
Dox flying boat, off Calshot Spit,
in Southampton Water.
- *21.5cm x 15cm*
- **£15-20**　　　　• Cobwebs

## Princess Flying Boat ▼

- *circa 1950*
Photograph of the *Princess*, the
biggest flying boat ever made.
- *119.5cm x 15cm*
- **£25**　　　　• Cobwebs

## Brooklands Flying Club ▲

- *circa 1920*
A Brooklands trophy, in pressed
steel with an alloy finish.
- *height 11.5cm*
- **£1,500**　　　　• CARS

## Comet Model Plane ▼

- *circa 1940*
A balsa-wood model kit of the B-
4 Superfortress. Made by the
Comet model factory, Chicago,
Illinois. In mint condition.
- **£10**　　　　• Cobwebs

## Brass Model Plane ◄

- *circa 1940*
Chrome-plated brass model of a
four-engined plane set on a
beechwood base with brass plate.
- *height 10cm*
- **£70**　　　　• Cobwebs

## Souvenir Programme ▲

- *date 1930*
Illustrated souvenir programme
from the British Hospitals' Air
Pageant, 1930. In good condition.
- *21.5cm x 14cm*
- £40                          • Cobwebs

## Promotional Magazine ➤

- *circa 1917*
Whitehead aircraft company
promotional magazine. In good
condition with black and white
and colour prints.
- *19cm x 12cm*
- £30                          • Cobwebs

## Airship Safety Award ▼

- *circa 1959*
An American 'Aviation Safety
Award' with brass engraving set
in a plaque of beechwood.
- *16cm x 13cm*
- £25-30                       • Cobwebs

## Aerial Timetable ➤

- *date 1927*
'International Aerial Time Table'
in good condition and in colour
print, with a fascinating cover
picture of unlikely flyers.
- *21.5cm x 14cm*
- £50                          • Cobwebs

## Aircraft Propellor ▲

- *circa 1920*
A four-bladed wooden coarse-
pitched, wind-generator
propellor, in mahogany with
lamination and holes in the
centre intact.
- *length 61cm*
- £165                         • Cobwebs

## Model Airplane ▼

- *circa 1940*
Chrome model, twin-engined
unidentified American plane.
- *height 10cm*
- £65                          • Cobwebs

## Concorde Postal Cover ◄

- *circa 1978*
Commemorating the first flight
from London to New York, with
colour print showing an early
Concorde in blue sky.
- *19cm x 11.5cm*
- £15                          • Cobwebs

# Bicycles

## Arnold Schwin Parckard ➤

- *circa 1930*
American lady's bicycle, with
pedal back brake, maroon finish,
single-speed. Very good
condition.
- *66cm wheel*
- £550        • **Bridge Bikes**

## Raleigh Roadster ▲

- *circa 1950*
Single-speed post-war bike.
Good rideable condition, with
Westwood rims and rod
brakes.
- *66cm wheel*
- £50        • **G Whizz**

## Expert Tips

*There is no doubt that fear for
the ozone layer and the
increasing villification of the
motorcar has led to an upsurge
in the popularity of the bicycle.
They need to be in good
condition and working.*

## Raleigh Rocky II ➤

- *date 1986*
Raleigh Rocky II with fifteen
Shimano gears.
- *153cm frame*
- *66cm wheel*
- £200        • **G Whizz**

## Italian Legnano ▲

- *circa 1940*
Lady's cycle, single-speed, unique
rod brakes running through
handlebars, full chain cover.
- *66cm wheel*
- £100        • **Bridge Bikes**

## Humber Gents ▼

- *circa 1940*
Gent's bike with enclosed chain,
three-speed hub, rod brake.
- *156cm frame*
- *71cm wheel*
- £150        • **Bridge Bikes**

## Rival of Norwich ◄

- *circa 1930*
Lady's roadster. Unusual make
and very collectable.
- *155cm seat tube*
- *63cm wheel*
- £50        • **G Whizz**

### BSA Ladies Junior ◄
- *circa 1950*

Single-speed, cable brake.
Original wicker basket attached
to the front of the bike.
- *61cm wheel*
- £200 • Bridge Bikes

### Dutch Torpedo ◄
- *circa 1946*

Classic old Dutch bike, probably
post war, torpedo coaster brake.
All original.
- *158cm frame*
- *69cm wheel*
- £80 • G Whizz

### Unique French Bike ▲
- *circa 1930*

Independently made. Consists of
one lady's frame welded on top of
a men's frame. Steel and painted
red with Frexel brakes.
- *height 1.4m*
- £500 • Bike Park

### Ladies GPO Bike ➤
- *circa 1960*

Rare post-office bike fitted with
35cc petrol engine, yellow finish,
hub brakes. Post-office carrier
attached to the front.
- *66cm wheel*
- £750 • Bridge Bikes

### Lady's Single Speed ▼
- *circa 1930*

Rudge Whitworth large black
single speed. With lap frame
dynamo. For restoration.
- *138cm frame*
- *69cm wheel*
- £100 • Bridge Bikes

### Triumph Lady's Roadster ▲
- *circa 1977*

Unusual fork crown. Good
running order. Black enamel
finish with some pitting.
- *153cm frame*
- *66cm wheel*
- £40 • G Whizz

### Kirk Revolution
### Mountain Bike ▲
- *date 1991*

Unique one-piece magnesium
frame. 21-speed shimano C10
components. Original condition.
- *146cm frame*
- *66cm wheel*
- £150 • G Whizz

# Bottles

### Silver Scent Bottle ▲
- *circa 1886*
An English, decorative silver
scent bottle with scrolls and a
cut-glass stopper.
- *height 5.5cm*
- £250 • John Clay

### Schiaparelli Bottle ▲
- *circa 1938*
A Schiaparelli perfume bottle of
twisted and fluted design with red
finial top and beaded base.
- £180 • Linda Bee

### Saville London 'June' ▼
- *circa 1930*
A novelty perfume bottle in the
form of a sundial.
- £125 • Linda Bee

### French Glass Perfume ▼
- *date 1860*
Mazarin blue glass perfume bottle
with floral gilding and large
octagonal stopper.
- *height 16cm*
- £145 • Trio

### European Perfume ➤
- *date 1880*
Perfume bottle of latissimo glass
with engraved silver cover with
glass stopper inside.
- £190 • Trio

### Prince Matchabello 'Beloved' ▲
- *circa 1950*
Enamel crown bottle. With inner
and outer box.
- £220 • Linda Bee

### Bourjois Kobako ▲
- *circa 1925*
A fashionable oriental-style
perfume bottle, designed by
Bourjois of Paris, with bakelite
cover and carved stand.
- £390 • Linda Bee

### Owl Perfume Bottle ▼
- *circa 1895*
A blue perfume bottle with silver owl's head shaped top with glass eyes, by Morden & Co, London.
- £1,700 • S. & A. Thompson

### Lancome Tresor ▼
- *circa 1950*
Original Tresor with cut glass bottle stand.
- £195 • Linda Bee

### Bourjois 'Evening in Paris' ▲
- *circa 1935*
A novelty perfume bottle in perspex wheelbarrow.
- £250 • Linda Bee

### Perfume Set ▲
- *circa 1890*
A late 19th-century perfume set of vaseline and cranberry coloured glass bottles, having silver-plated stoppers with recessed corks, all in original leather case.
- £200 • Trio

### Decanter Bottle ▼
- *circa 1920*
A decanter bottle with handle in original wicker coat.
- *height 23cm*
- £25 • Ranby Hall

### Christian Dior 'Miss Dior' ▼
- *circa 1945*
A Christian Dior perfume bottle of obelisk shape.
- £450 • Linda Bee

### Art Deco Set ◄
- *date 1920*
An Art Deco perfume bottle and powder box, cut and engraved, with enameling.
- £210 • Trio

◀

## Bourjois 'Mais Oui'
- *circa 1938*
A bottle of Boujois 'Mais Oui', in perfect condition with original inner and outer box.
- £175 • Linda Bee

### Jardin des Bagatelle ▼
- *circa 1980*
Window display bottle. With brass mounts.
- £275 • Linda Bee

## Art Deco Set ▲
- *date 1920*
An Art Deco dressing-table set, consisting of a perfume atomiser and a powder box with lid, both in smoked glass.
- £170 • Trio

## Mercury Bottle ▲
- *date 1880*
A very rare perfume bottle in cut red glass with a moulded silver hinged stopper.
- £310 • Trio

## Chanel Tester Kit ▼
- *circa 1950*
A perfume tester kit from Chanel, with five tester bottles including some deleted perfumes.
- £280 • Linda Bee

## Christian Dior 'Miss Dior' ▲
- *circa 1950*
A Christian Dior 'Miss Dior' perfume bottle, unused and in its original packaging.
- £250 • Linda Bee

## Jacinthe De Coty ▲
- *circa 1920*
Bottle with metalic plaque and beaded decoration; the stopper has floral designs.
- £150 • Linda Bee

### Guerlain 'L'Heure Bleue' ▼
• *circa 1940*
Made by Baccarate perfume, with original box.
• £125          • Linda Bee

### Grossmith 'Old Cottage' Lavender Water ▲
• *circa 1930*
A bottle of English lavender water of etched glass.
• £95          • Linda Bee

### Nina Ricci 'Coeur-Joie' ▼
• *date 1946*
Lalique bottle with heart-shaped centre and floral decoration.
• £210          • Linda Bee

### Conical Bottle ▼
• *circa 1866*
A mid-Victorian silver fluted perfume bottle, of conical form, with silver stopper.
• £210          • Trio

### Bohemian Glass Bottle ▲
• *circa 1860*
Floral perfume bottle, in Bohemian glass, with enamelling and large cut stopper.
• £300          • Trio

### Unknown Heart-Shaped Perfume Bottle ▼
• *circa 1940*
With etched glass and bakelite base with dipper.
• £65          • Linda Bee

### French Apothecary's Bottles ▶
• *circa 19th century*
Collection of nine apothecary's bottles including stoppers.
• £655 set          • Ranby Hall

# Cameras

### Reflex Camera ▼
- *circa 1960*
Rolleiflex 2.8f twin lens reflex
camera with built in light meter
and overhead viewfinder.
- £600
- Jessop Classic Photographica

### Cine Camera ▼
- *circa 1960*
Bell & Howell 'Sportster
Standard 8' 8mm cine camera.
- £30
- Mac's Cameras

### Kodak Field Camera ▲
- *circa 1950*
Kodak No.1 Autographic
120mm film field camera with
folding case.
- £70
- Mac's Cameras

### Filma Projector ▲
- *circa 1970*
Filma 240f 8mm sound projector.
Standard 8 sound and silent.
Portable and with outfit case.
- £100
- Mac's Cameras

### 35mm SLR Camera ▲
- *circa 1965*
Leicaflex 35mm SLR with f/2
semi-micron lens.
- £400
- Mac's Cameras

## Expert Tips

*The Leica camera totally
dominated the 35mm market
from the mid 1920s until the
1960s. Virtually any Leica
camera will sell well at auction,
the most avid collectors being
the Japanese.*

### Rollei Camera ▼
- *circa 1975*
Rollei 35S gold 35mm camera. A
specially finished precision
compact camera. Limited edition
of 1500, gold-plated.
- £900
- Jessop Classic Photographica

### Field Camera ◄
- *circa 1930*
Deardorff 10x8-inch camera
made of mahogany with nickel-
plated fittings. Schneider and
Symmar 300mm lens.
- £2,000
- Jessop Classic Photographica

## Purma Roll Camera ➤

- *circa 1932*
Purma 'Special' bakelite 127 roll
camera with telescoping lens.
- £30
- Jessop Classic Photographica

## Leicaflex SLR Camera ▲

- *circa 1970*
Leicaflex 35mm SLR camera with
f2.8/90 Elmarit lens.
- £500
- Mac's Cameras

## Flash-Bulb Holder ▲

- *circa 1949*
Leica Chico flash-bulb holder for
Leica cameras.
- £20
- Jessop Classic Photographica

### Expert Tips

*Mint condition boxed
originals are worth about double
the price of the same camera
showing reasonable wear. But
the latter must be in perfect
working order.*

## Miniature Spy Camera ➤

- *circa 1958*
Minox B sub miniature spy
camera, which takes 8x11mm
negatives. With brushed
aluminium body.
- £180
- Jessop Classic Photographica

## Hollywood Splicer ➤

- *circa 1960*
Hollywood stainless-steel splicer.
8mm x 16mm, in original box.
- £30
- Mac's Cameras

## Roll Film Camera ▲

- *circa 1935*
Coronet midget 16mm camera
made in five colours, blue being
the rarest. Made in Birmingham.
- £350
- Jessop Classic Photographica

## Mamiya 120 Camera ▼

- *circa 1970–1980*
Mamiya C33 first professional
120 camera with interchangeable
lens. 6x6 image.
- £170      • Mac's Cameras

## Magazine Camera ▲
- *circa 1960*
A Bell & Howell "Speedster" 16mm magazine camera with film auto load.
- £90
- Mac's Cameras

## 16mm Cine Camera ▲
- *circa 1960*
AGFA 16mm cine camera and telephoto lens with 100ft spool. All metal body.
- £90
- Mac's Cameras

## Pentax Roll Film Camera ▲
- *circa 1969*
Pentax 6x7 roll film camera. This has been a very popular professional camera for the last thirty-one years.
- £900
- Jessop Classic Photographica

## Brownie Six-20 Camera ▲
- *circa 1960*
A model 'C' Brownie Six-20 camera. Made in England by Kodak Ltd.
- £30
- Mac's Cameras

## Pentax Asahi ▼
- *circa 1970*
Pentax Asahi 'Sportmatik' 500 camera with a 55mm fixed lens f1.8. All metal body.
- £100
- Mac's Cameras

## Leica M3 35mm Camera ▼
- *circa 1954*
Leica M3 with 50mm f2 standard lens. One of the most highly regarded cameras ever made. Used by many photographers.
- £1,000
- Jessop Classic Photographica

## 35mm Range Finder ▼
- *circa 1957*
Minolta super A 35mm range finder interchangeable lens camera with standard lens.
- £200
- Jessop Classic Photographica

## Leica with 40cm f5 lens ➤

- *circa 1936*
Leica with a 40cm f5 Telyt lens.
This lens was used in the 1936
Berlin Olympic Games.
- £4,000
- Jessop Classic Photographica

## 6x7cm Roll Film Camera ▲

- *circa 1965*
Koni Omega rapid 6x7cm roll
film camera with interchangeable
lenses of Japanese origin.
- £300
- Jessop Classic Photographica

## Rolleiflex Camera ▼

- *circa 1950*
German Rolleiflex camera with
flip-top view finder and Carl Zeiss
twin lenses. 120 film.
- £70
- Mac's Cameras

## Light Meter ▲

- *circa 1950–1960*
Sixtus light meter with folding
bakelite case. No batteries
required.
- £30
- Mac's Cameras

## Editor with Viewer ▲

- *circa 1970*
8mm Crown editor with
magnified and backlit viewer.
All-metal body and hand-
operated spools.
- £30
- Mac's Cameras

### Expert Tips

*The rarity and quality of a
particular camera model is more
important in assessing its value
than when it was made. Rare
and limited editions of post-war
Japanese cameras can command
astronomical prices.*

## Stereo Plate Camera ▼

- *circa 1926*
Rollei Heidoskop camera. It takes
two parallel pictures to create a
3D image.
- £700
- Jessop Classic Photographica

## Cine Camera ◄

- *circa 1960*
Standard 8 Bolex cine camera
with a fixed zoom lens. All-metal
body with a detachable pistol grip.
- £100
- Mac's Cameras

### Light Exposure Meter ➤

- *circa 1960*
1 Kophot light exposure meter by
Zeiss in a folding burgundy
leather case.
- £30
- Mac's Cameras

### Field Camera ▲

- *circa 1954*
MPP micro precision 5x4 press
camera. Made in Kingston-upon-
Thames, Surrey.
- £300
- Jessop Classic Photographica

### Pyramid Tripod ➤

- *circa 1960*
Camera base with wooden legs and
adjustable tubular metal stands.
- £15
- Mac's Cameras

### Robot Camera ▲

- *circa 1940*
Luftwaffen Eigentum German
Airforce robot camera. With
built-in clockwork spring motor.
- £300
- Jessop Classic Photographica

### Brownie Box Camera ▼

- *circa 1960*
Brownie Box camera, for 127
film, made in Canada by Kodak
Eastman Co Ltd.
- £30
- Mac's Cameras

### Cine Camera ▲

- *circa 1960*
A standard 8 film Bolex 8mm
cine camera and a selection of
Kern lenses with leather cases
and original instructions.
- £100
- Mac's Cameras

### Slide Projector ▲

- *circa 1960*
Aldis 35mm slide projector with
original box.
- £30
- Mac's Cameras

## Expert Tips

*George Eastman's invention of
the dry plate, in 1879, led to the
mass production of cameras.
The first Box Brownie was
produced in 1888 and they
changed almost imperceptibly
for 80 years.*

## Half-Plate Camera ▲
- *circa 1900*

Sands and Hunter tail board 5x4 half plate camera of mahogany and brass construction.
- £400
- Jessop Classic Photographica

## Kodak Roll Film Camera ▲
- *circa 1920*

Kodak VPK series 3 camera using 127 roll film.
- £300
- Jessop Classic Photographica

## Nikon SLR Camera ▲
- *circa 1959*

Nikon F 35mm single lens reflex camera. This is a landmark camera for the 35mm Japanese camera industry.
- £550
- Jessop Classic Photographica

## 35mm Field Camera ➤
- *circa 1950*

A Thagee 35mm field camera made in München Germany. All-metal body.
- £50
- Mac's Cameras

## Expert Tips

*Great innovations in camera technology were made from 1920-40. Collectors particularly seek out models which represent a significant step forward.*

## M.P.P. Plate Holder ▼
- *circa 1960*

M.P.P. plate holder for 5x4 plate camera used by large format cameras.
- £10
- Mac's Cameras

## Light Meter ▼
- *circa 1960*

A pocket-sized Weston Master V Selinium light meter with all-metal body construction. In good condition.
- £40
- Jessop Classic Photographica

## Light Meter ▼
- *circa 1950–1960*

An electro BEWI light meter in metal case.
- £30
- Mac's Cameras

## Quarter-Plate Camera ▲
- *circa 1935*
Baby speed graphic quarter plate camera. Made in America. With original leather straps.
- £400
- Jessop Classic Photographica

## Autographic Camera ▲
- *circa 1920*
A Kodak vest pocket Autographic camera. Made in Rochester NY, USA.
- £30
- Mac's Cameras

## Meopta Cine Camera ▼
- *circa 1958-1965*
A standard 8 Meopta Admira 8mm cine camera with full metal case.
- £30
- Mac's Cameras

## Mickey Mouse Camera ▼
- *circa 1980*
A 110 cartridge system camera with a plastic body in the form of Mickey Mouse. With viewfinder placed on forehead.
- £50
- Jessop Classic Photographica

## Brownie 'Flash' Camera ▲
- *circa 1970*
A Brownie 'flash' 20 camera with interchangeable flash. With built-in filters. All plastic body in very good condition.
- £30
- Mac's Cameras

## Expert Tips

*Wet-plate cameras were manufactured from 1840–1890 and are very rare. The craftsmanship of the case, as well as the manufacturer's name, define the value.*

## Square Roll Film Camera ▼
- *circa 1953*
First six V 120 6x6cm square roll film camera. One of the first to be made in Japan, inspired by earlier German designs.
- £100
- Jessop Classic Photographica

## Cartridge System Camera ◄
- *circa 1975*
A 110 cartridge system camera modelled as a caricature of a British Airways Aeroplane. In good condition.
- £60
- Jessop Classic Photographica

## Polaroid Camera ▲
- *circa 1960*
The first Polaroid instant film camera – the 900 Electric Eye Land Camera.
- £90
- Mac's Cameras

## Press Camera ▲
- *circa 1930*
A 9x12 VN press camera with sports finder, ground-glass screen.
- £250
- Finchley Fine Art Galleries

## Colorflex SLR ▲
- *circa 1960*
Agfa SLR with built in light meter and interchangeable prism.
- £90
- Mac's Cameras

## Magic Lantern ▼
- *circa 1900*
Lancaster magic lantern used for projective hand-painted glass slides.
- £300
- Jessop Classic Photographica

## Canon Ixus Camera ▼
- *circa 2000*
18 ct. gold limited edition with certificate of authenticity and remote control.
- £400
- Mac's Cameras

## Exacta Varex Camera ▼
- *circa 1950*
A sought-after first model Exacta Varex, f/2 Biotar.
- £70
- Mac's Cameras

## Brownie Box Camera ▼
- *circa 1960*
Brownie box camera flash model 'B', with filters.
- £30
- Mac's Cameras

## Nikkorex Camera ▼
- *circa 1970*
A standard 8 format Nikkorex cine camera with zoom. All-metal body.
- £70
- Mac's Cameras

# Chess Sets

## Ivory Chess Set ◄
- *circa 1845*

A rare 19th-century French design ivory chess set.
- *height 10cm (king)*
- £8,500    • G.D. Coleman

## Boxwood and Ebony Staunton Chess Set ▲
- *late 19th century*

Mahogany green baize-lined lift-top box with Jacques of London green paper label to the inside lid.
- *height 19cm (king)*
- £950    • G.D. Coleman

## Tortoiseshell & Ivory Chess Set ◄
- *circa 19th century*

Interlaced vine decoration on light mahogany base.
- *height 19cm*
- £650    • Shahdad

## Mythological Chess Set ►
- *circa 1920*

Unusual French decorated lead chess set on a mythological classical theme.
- *height 13cm (king)*
- £1,800    • G.D. Coleman

## Selenus Chess Set ▲
- *circa 1800*

German carved bone with red and white kings and queens topped by Maltese crosses.
- *height 12cm*
- £2,850    • G.D. Coleman

## Painted Metal Chess Set ▼
- *circa 1920*

King and queen representing mythical gods. White figures show a mottled effect.
- £1,800    • G.D. Coleman

## Portuguese European vs Chinese Chess Set ▲
- *circa 1865*

Fine carved ivory, from Macau.
- *height 10cm (king)*
- £1,850    • G.D. Coleman

## Ivory Chess Set ➤

- *circa 1825*
With red and white pieces. Kings
with Maltese cross and queens
with leaf on ball-shaped head.
- *height 13cm (king)*
- £2,350    • G.D. Coleman

## Games Compendium ◄

- *circa 1890*
Late Victorian oak compendium
including chess, backgammon,
cards and dominoes.
- £895    • J. & T. Stone

## Indian Folding Chess and Backgammon Set ▼

- *circa 1840*
Fine Indian ivory and horn inlaid
sandlewood board, with chess
inlaid on the outside and
backgammon on the inside.
- *45 x 50 x 5cm*
- £4,500    • G.D. Coleman

## Morphy Chess Set ◄

- *circa 1880*
Late 19th-century metal figural
'Morphy' chess set.
- £1,850    • G.D. Coleman

## Spanish 'Pulpit' Bone Chess Set ▼

- *early 19th century*
Rare set. One side natural colour,
the other stained dark brown.
- *height 12cm (king)*
- £8,500    • G.D. Coleman

## Ivory Calvert-Style Chess Set ▲

- *early 19th century*
Carved and turned in natural and
red-stained ivory.
- *height 7.5cm (king)*
- £950    • G.D. Coleman

## Ivory Chess Set ▲

- *circa 1880*
Late 19th-century Indian ivory
export chess set with exquisitely
carved figures.
- *height 7.5cm (king)*
- £680    • G.D. Coleman

### Mah Jong Game Set ➤
- *circa 1930*
A mah jong bone game set in an oak case with drawers and complete with all original pieces.
- £180 • G.D. Coleman

### Ivory Bears Chess Set ▲
- *circa 1820*
Early 'Bears of Berne' chess set.
- £14,000 • G.D. Coleman

### Chinese Macau Ivory ▲
- *circa 1840*
Red and white pieces. Made for European market, slightly oriental features. Queen has oriental headdress and the king has a crown.
- £1,850 • G.D. Coleman

### Chess Board ▼
- *circa 1910*
An English Edwardian inlaid wood chess board.
- *42 x 42cm*
- £180 • G.D. Coleman

### Ivory Burmese Chess Set ◄
- *19th century*
White and red very ornate set. Kings and queens have ornate crowns and castles have waving flags on their battlements.
- £1,850 • G.D. Coleman

## Expert Tips

*The very earliest chess sets were made in India in 600AD or earlier. By 1000AD, the game had spread through Europe and as far as Scandinavia.*

### English Chess Set ▼
- *circa 1835*
An English ivory 'Lund'-style chess set in red and white.
- *height 7.5cm*
- £620 • G.D. Coleman

### German Chess Set ◄
- *circa 1880*
Rare German decorated wood, plaster and metal large figural chess set. Comes in original two layer decorated card-lidded box.
- *height 13.5cm*
- £5,850 • G.D. Coleman

## Quartz Chess Set ◄

- **19th century**
An Indian rock crystal (quartz) export chess set with red and white colours.
- **£1,250**   • G.D. Coleman

## Staunton Chess Set ▲

- **circa 1880**
Ivory Staunton chess set by Jaques of London with 'Carton Pierre' casket and chess board.
- **£2,500**   • G.D. Coleman

## Russian Ivory Chess Set ▼

- **19th century**
Carved and turned in mammoth ivory. One side natural, the other side with unusual pewter effect.
- *height 8.2cm (king)*
- **£850**   • G.D. Coleman

## 'Bauhaus' Wooden Chess Set ▲

- **early 20th century**
Chess set and board (not photographed).
- *height 10cm (king)*
- **£380**   • G.D. Coleman

## Expert Tips

*The modern era of chess dates from the 16th century, when the moves of the game began to take their present form. Philidor, a Frenchman who played in the 1700s, is widely regarded as the first world champion.*

## Wooden Chess Set ▼

- **19th century**
Very rare. All pieces are in the form of 'The Bears of Berne'. Made of Swiss natural wood, some stained darker.
- **£2,850**   • G.D. Coleman

## Staunton Ivory Set ▲

- **circa 1865**
Magnificent rare set by Jaques of London. With gold and red leather case and board.
- *height 14cm (king)*
- **£16,500**   • G.D. Coleman

## Ivory Monobloc Set ➤

- **circa 1835**
Finely carved. One side in rare stained green, the other natural.
- *height 10.5cm (king)*
- **£2,850**   • G.D. Coleman

## Ivory Rooks ▼
• *circa 1820*
A pair of early 19th-century ivory rooks, with flag-bearing sentries, from a John Company chess set.
• **£350 (pair)** • **G.D. Coleman**

## Folding Game Board ▼
• *19th century*
A Victorian papier mâché folding chess and backgammon board in the form of a two-volume book, with backgammon board on the inside and chess outside.
• **£750** • **G.D. Coleman**

## Ceramic Chess Set ➤
• *circa 1880*
Late 19th-century Wedgwood-style ceramic chess set made after a Flaxman design.
• **£2,750** • **G.D. Coleman**

## Indian 'Pepys' Chess Set ▲
• *circa 19th century*
Ivory. Design known as 'Pepys' after famous English diarist.
• *height 18cm (king)*
• **£2,350** • **G.D. Coleman**

## East Prussian Chess Set ▲
• *circa 1795*
Very rare. Made of Baltic amber and wood.
• *height 10cm (king)*
• **£7,950** • **G.D. Coleman**

## English Chess Set ▼
• *circa 1972*
Silver and silver-gilt chess set designed by Cy Enfield to commemorate the Fischer-Spassky chess match at Reykjavik.
• *21 x 14 x 3cm*
• **£595** • **G.D. Coleman**

## Selenus Chess Set ▼
• *circa 1800*
German carved bone red and white Kings and Queens topped by Maltese crosses.
• **£2,850** • **G.D. Coleman**

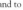
# Commemorative Ware

### Vase ▼
- *date 1937*
Single-handled vase to
commemorate the coronation of
King George VI and Queen
Elizabeth. Designed and signed by
Charlotte Rhead.
- *height 18.5cm*
- **£325**       • **Hope & Glory**

### Gilt Bronze ▼
- *circa 1837*
Bronze of a young Queen
Victoria, on armorial bronze
acanthus-leaf base.
- *height 32cm*
- **£1,500**       • **The Armoury**

### Shaving Mug ▲
- *date 1911*
Shaving mug, probably
continental, commemorating the
coronation of King George V and
Queen Mary.
- *height 10.5cm*
- **£80**       • **Hope & Glory**

### Carlton Ware Mug ▲
- *circa 1981*
Carlton Ware mug with double
heart handle, commemorating
the marriage of the Prince of
Wales and Lady Diana Spencer.
- *height 11cm*
- **£50**       • **Hope & Glory**

## Expert Tips

*Because very few
commemorative pieces are
thrown away, good condition is
essential to maintain value.*

### Royal Horse Guard ▼
- *date 1915*
'The Blues' made by Copeland to
commemorate the centenary of
the Battle of Waterloo.
- *height 39cm*
- **£1,700**       • **The Armoury**

### Chain and Breast Star ▼
- *circa 1900*
Imperial Russian order of St
Andrew, made by Albert Kiebel,
of St Petersburg for King
Ferdinand of Bulgaria.
- **£65,000**       • **The Armoury**

### Three Egg Cups ◄
- *date 1911*
Bone-china egg cups
commemorating the coronation
of King George V.
- *height 6.5cm*
- **£33 (each)**       • **Hope & Glory**

### Coronation Mug ▼
- *date 1911*
Coronation mug of King George
V and Queen Mary.
- *height 7cm*
- £24      • **Magpies**

### Loving Cup ▲
- *date 1937*
A bone china loving cup, by
Shelly, to commemorate the
proposed coronation of King
Edward VIII.
- *height 11.5cm*
- £275      • **Hope & Glory**

### Poole Pottery Vase ▼
- *date 1977*
Vase commemorating the silver
jubilee of Queen Elizabeth II,
showing the lion and unicorn.
- *height 25cm*
- £125      • **Hope & Glory**

### Musical Teapot ◄
- *circa 1953*
Teapot in the form of a coach,
commemorating the coronation
of Queen Elizabeth II. Plays the
National Anthem.
- *height 13cm*
- £240      • **Hope & Glory**

### Winston S. Churchill
### Toby Jug ▼
- *circa 1941*
With anchor handle, by Fieldings,
representing Churchill's second
appointment as First Lord.
- *height 15cm*
- £190      • **Hope & Glory**

### Pottery Mug ►
- *circa 1969*
A mug from the Portmerion
pottery to commemorate the first
landing of men on the moon by
Apollo II.
- *height 10cm*
- £70      • **Hope & Glory**

### Snuffbox ►
- *date 1895*
Victorian silver table snuffbox,
inscribed as presented by HRH
Albert Edward of Wales.
- *length 14cm*
- £2,850  • **S. & A. Thompson**

## Cup & Saucer ◀
- *circa 1910*
Cup and saucer with letter attesting to the fact that they were used by King Edward VII at 4.45pm on the afternoon of his death.
- **£1,200** • **The Armoury**

## Commemorative Plate ◀
- *circa 1937*
For the proposed coronation of Edward VIII. Made by Paragon with the Royal Coat of Arms.
- *diameter 27cm*
- **£450** • **The Armoury**

## Jubilee Mug ▲
- *date 1935*
Armorial mug celebrating the Silver Jubilee of King George V and Queen Mary.
- *height 7cm*
- **£24** • **Magpies**

## Slipware Charger ▶
- *circa 1977*
Charger by Mary Wondrausch to commemorate the silver jubilee of Queen Elizabeth II.
- *diameter 46cm*
- **£390** • **Hope & Glory**

## Coronation Mug ▼
- *circa 1953*
To commemorate the coronation of Queen Elizabeth II.
- *height 8.5cm*
- **£16** • **Magpies**

## Jigsaw Puzzle ▲
- *circa 1934*
With original box showing the young Princess Elizabeth and Princess Margaret in front of Windsor Castle.
- *28 x 34cm*
- **£75** • **Hope & Glory**

## Boer War Mug ▲
- *circa 1902*
Mug commemorating the end of the Boer War on the front, with the back celebrating the coronation of King Edward VII.
- *height 8cm*
- **£125** • **Hope & Glory**

## Four Castles Plate ▲
- *date 1901*
Black transfer on earthenware
plate to commemorate the death
of Queen Victoria, such items are
quite scarce.
- *diameter 24.5cm*
- £240          • Hope & Glory

## Bone China Plate ▼
- *circa 1900*
By Royal Worcester to
commemorate the relief of
Mafeking. Transfer shows Baden-
Powell.
- *diameter 23.5cm*
- £140          • Hope & Glory

## Victorian Mug ▲
- *circa 1878*
Mug commemorating the visit of
Edward, Prince of Wales to India
on the occasion of Queen
Victoria being made Empress.
- *height 10.5cm*
- £150          • Hope & Glory

## Dutch Delft Plaque ▼
- *circa 1945*
To commemorate the liberation
of Holland. Showing mother,
child and aeroplane.
- *height 20cm*
- £150          • Hope & Glory

## Chocolate Tin ▲
- *circa 1953*
Royal blue enamelled tin with
fleur de lys motif,
commemorating the coronation
of Queen Elizabeth II.
- *height 7cm*
- £5          • Magpies

## Expert Tips

*The market for commemorative
items is driven by emotion.
They start off overpriced and,
as the individual becomes less
well known, may lose value.*

## Officer on Horseback ▲
- *circa 1910*
German. Napoleonic period.
Probably Dresden.
- *height 38cm*
- £2,500          • The Armoury

## Pottery Loving Cup ▶
- *date 1897*
Loving cup by Brannum pottery,
commemorating the Diamond
Jubilee of Queen Victoria.
- *height 14cm*
- £240          • Hope & Glory

### Whisky Decanter ▼
• *date 1911*
Spode decanter made for Andrew Usher & Co, distillers, Edinburgh, commemorating the coronation of George V.
• *height 25cm*
• £160      • Hope & Glory

### Pair of Perfume Flasks ▲
• *circa 1840*
Hand-decorated porcelain perfume flasks by Jacob Petit, commemorating the marriage of Queen Victoria and Prince Albert.
• *height 31cm*
• £3,750      • Hope & Glory

### Children's Plate ▼
• *date 1847*
Showing the young Edward, Prince of Wales, on a pony. Entitled 'England's Hope'.
• *diameter 16.5cm*
• £340      • Hope & Glory

### Coronation Mug ▼
• *date 1902*
Copeland mug commemorating the coronation of King Edward VII and Queen Alexandra. This mug shows the correct date of August 9th, 1902. Most commemorative ware gives the date as June 26th, from when the event was postponed due to the King's appendicitis.
• *height 7.5cm*
• £160      • Hope & Glory

### Wedgwood Mug ▼
• *circa 1937*
A Wedgwood mug commemorating the coronation of King George VI, designed by Eric Ravilious.
• *height 11cm*
• £475      • Hope & Glory

### Ceramic Plaque ▲
• *circa 1911*
Plaque, by Ridgways, to commemorate the coronation of George VI and Queen Mary.
• *16 x 21cm*
• £85      • Hope & Glory

### Teapot ➤
• *circa 1897*
Commemorating the Diamond Jubilee of Queen Victoria. Copeland bone china with gold decoration. Portrait of Victoria in relief.
• *height 14cm*
• £525      • Hope & Glory

## Scottish Ceramic Jug  ▲

- *circa 1887*
To commemorate the Golden
Jubilee of Queen Victoria.
- *height 21cm*
- £195          • Hope & Glory

## Bronze Gilt  ▲

- *circa 1840*
Of Napolean crossing the Alps.
After 'David'.
- £475          • The Armoury

## Jubilee Mug  ➤

- *date 1935*
Ceramic mug celebrating the
Silver Jubilee of King George V
and Queen Mary.
- *height 7cm*
- £24          • Magpies

## Bronze Plaque  ▼

- *circa 1820*
An oval bronze plaque showing
the Duke of Wellington.
- *length 26cm*
- £450          • The Armoury

## Ink Well  ▼

- *circa 1915*
Hand grenade casing used as an
ink well to commemorate the
First World War.
- *height 10.5cm*
- £80          • Hope & Glory

## Small Children's Plate  ▲

- *circa 1838*
Made at the time of Queen
Victoria's coronation.
Staffordshire earthenware with
transfer printing.
- *diameter 12cm*
- £290          • Hope & Glory

## Moulded Jug  ▲

- *circa 1863*
Jug with fixed, hinged silverplate
cover, commemorating the
wedding of Edward, Prince of
Wales to Princess Alexandra.
- *height 18cm*
- £175          • Hope & Glory

# Ephemera

## Thor  ▼
• *date January 1970*
*The Mighty Thor*, no. 172, original price one shilling, from Marvel Comics.
• £10                    • Gosh

## Famous Crowns Series  ▼
• *date 1938*
Set of 25 cards, by Godfrey Phillips Ltd. Illustration shows an Italian crown.
• £8                    • Murray Cards

## Strange Tales  ▶
• *date 1967*
Strange Tales No.161– *Doctor Strange – The Second Doom*. Published by Marvel Comics.
• £15
• Book & Comic Exchange

## Titanic Series  ▲
• *date 1999*
Set of 25 large scale cards of the Titanic, produced by Rockwell Publishing at the time of James Cameron's film.
• £10                    • Murray Cards

## Star Trek  ▲
• *date 1970*
Star Trek No.7 March 1970. Published by Gold Key.
• £50
• Book & Comic Exchange

## Superman Series  ▼
• *date 1968*
Set of cards, issued as series 950 by Primrose Confectionery Co, with sweet cigarettes. Illustration shows 'Space Nightmare'.
• £15                    • Murray Cards

## Kensitas Flower Series  ▼
• *date 1933*
An unusual series of 60 cigarette collecting items with silk flowers enclosed in envelopes. By J Wix & Sons.
• £168                    • Murray Cards

## Ray Lowry Cartoon  ▼
• *date 1992*
An original cartoon drawing by Ray Lowry.
• £65                    • Gosh

### Amazing Spiderman ▼
• *date February 1966*
Amazing Spiderman no. 333 –
*The Final Chapter!* – published by
Marvel Comics.
• £50                    • Gosh

### Opera Series ▲
• *date 1895*
Set of six opera cards, collected
with products of The Liebig
Extract Meat Co, France.
• £80                    • Murray Cards

### Monte Hale ▼
• *date 1952*
Monte Hale Western comic. Issue
no. 76, price 10 cents.
• £15
• Book & Comic Exchange

### Searle Lithograph ▼
• *circa 1960*
A Ronald Searle lithograph from
'Those Magnificent Men in Their
Flying Machines'.
• £420                   • Gosh

### The Incredible Hulk ▲
• *date September 1968*
The Incredible Hulk, issue no.
107, by Marvel Comics.
• £13.50                 • Gosh

### Fantastic Four ▼
• *date March 1966*
Issue no.48 – *The X-Men!* –
published by Marvel Comics.
• £225                   • Gosh

### Romantic Story ▼
• *date September 1958*
No. 40 – *Love's Tender Moments* –
published by Charlton.
• £17.50                 • Gosh

### Billiard Series ▲
• *circa 1905*
Set of 15 cards of *double entendre*
billiard terms, from Salmon &
Gluckstein.
• £825                   • Murray Cards

### Political Cartoon ▼
• *date 1997*
A political cartoon – *Springs in
Spring* – by John Springs.
• £150                   • Gosh

## Taddy's Clown Series  ▲

- *date 1920*

One of 20 known sets of Taddy's 'Clowns' – the most prized of British cigarette cards, with completely blank backs.

- £13,000
- Murray Cards

## Whitbread Inn Signs Series  ▲

- *date 1974*

Set of 25 cards of Isle of Wight pubs. This one shows The Railway Inn, Ryde.

- £80
- Murray Cards

## Star Spangled Comics  ▲

- *date May 1942*

Star Spangled Comics issue no. 8 by DC Comics.

- £185
- Gosh

## Herbie  ▼

- *date January 1965*

Herbie issue no.13 – *Private Gold Man's New Coat* – published by ACG Comics.

- £15
- Gosh

## Guardian Strip  ▼

- *date 1997*

A strip cartoon for *The Guardian*, called 'If', by Steve Bell.

- £135
- Cartoon Gallery

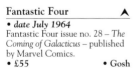

## Spawn  ▼

- *date May 1992*

Spawn magazine, issue no. 1, published by Image.

- £12.50
- Gosh

## Esquire Magazine  ▲

- *date 1959*

A publication of *Esquire* magazine for March 1959.

- £8
- Book & Comic Exchange

## Fantastic Four  ▲

- *date July 1964*

Fantastic Four issue no. 28 – *The Coming of Galacticus* – published by Marvel Comics.

- £55
- Gosh

## London Standard Strip  ▲

- *date 1997*

A London *Evening Standard* strip of 'Bristow' by Frank Dickens.

- £60
- Gosh

## Stan Eales Cartoon ▲
- *date* 1998

A cartoon by Stan Eales of a man standing on the ledge of a burning building.
- £250    • Cartoon Gallery

## Blakes 7 ▲
- *date* October 1981

Blake 7 magazine issue no. 1, published by Marvel UK.
- £8-12
- Book & Comic Exchange

## The Dandy ▼
- *date* April 1973

The Dandy, issue no. 1640, published by D.C. Thompson.
- £1    • Gosh

## Strange Tales ▼
- *date* March 1964

Strange Tales issue no. 118 – *The Human Torch* – published by Marvel Comics.
- £17    • Gosh

## Playboy ◄
- *date* May 1969

May 1969 issue of Playboy magazine, in good condition.
- £6    • Radio Times

### Expert Tips

*Most magazines launched run to only one issue, so that factor is no rarity. Condition must be excellent.*

## Marvel Masterworks ▲
- *date* 1997

Spiderman volume 1.
- £25    • Gosh

## Cricket Series ▲
- *circa* 1896

Wills's first set of 50 cricketing cigarette cards. Illustration shows Dr W G Grace of Gloucestershire.
- £3,250    • Murray Cards

## Soho International ▲
- *date* 1971

Volume 1, No. 1.
- £10
- Book & Comic Exchange

## National Costumes Series ▼
• *date 1895*
Wills's cigarette cards set of 25. This card shows a Venetian beauty.
• **£4,125**    • **Murray Cards**

## X-Men ▼
• *date January 1969*
X-Men magazine, issue no. 52 – *Armageddon Now!* – published by Marvel Comics.
• **£20**    • **Gosh**

## Buffy the Vampire Slayer ▶
• *date 1999*
Mail order only. Premium Darkhorse publication.
• **£10**
• **Book & Comic Exchange**

## Famous Film Scene Series ▲
• *date 1935*
Set of 48 cigarette cards, by Gallaher Ltd. Shows Laurel & Hardy from "Babes in Toyland."
• **£36**    • **Murray Cards**

## Watchmen ▲
• *date 1987*
The collected edition of a comic original in 12 issues, retelling the super-hero story.
• **£14.95**    • **Gosh**

## Radio Times Cartoon ▼
• *date 1998*
A topical cartoon for *Radio Times* by Kipper Williams.
• **£120**    • **Cartoon Gallery**

## Mayfair Magazine ▼
• *date 1970*
Volume 3, no.1. British edition.
• **£20**
• **Book & Comic Exchange**

## The Observer Cartoon ▼
• *date 1997*
Political cartoon by Chris Riddell, from *The Observer*.
• **£225**    • **Cartoon Gallery**

### King of Europe Series ▾
• *date 1999*
Set of 15 cards by Philip Neill
comemorating Manchester
United FC's historic treble in
1999. Illustration shows a
caricature of David Beckham.
• £6 (set)    • **Murray Cards**

### Star Wars, Episode I Series ▾
• *date 1999*
Set of 20 cards collected through
Kentucky Fried Chicken.
• £6    • **Murray Cards**

### Original Cartoon ▾
• *date 1998*
A cartoon titled 'Great Moments
in Science' by Hunt Emerson.
• £100    • **Cartoon Gallery**

### X-Men ▲
• *date December 1977*
X-Men issue no. 108 – *Twilight of
the Mutants* – published by
Marvel Comics.
• £12    • **Gosh**

### Amazing Spiderman ▲
• *date May 1988*
Issue no. 300 of *The Amazing
Spiderman* by Marvel Comics.
• £18    • **Gosh**

### Curious Beaks Series ▲
• *date 1929*
Set of 50 cigarette cards from
John Player & Sons. Illustration
shows Australian Jacana.
• £40    • **Murray Cards**

### Films and Filming ▾
• *date February 1975*
Published by Hanson Books.
• £5
• **Book & Comic Exchange**

### Independent Cartoon ▾
• *date 1997*
A political cartoon from *The
Independent*, by Chris Priestley.
• £200    • **Cartoon Gallery**

### Wolverine ▾
• *date September 1982*
Issue No. 1 by Marvel Comics.
• £7.50    • **Gosh**

## Vogue △
- *date November 1946*
A November 1946 copy of *Vogue*
by Conde Nast.
- £10
- **Radio Times**

## Builders of the British Empire Series △
- *circa 1929*
Set of 50 cards by J A
Pattreiouex. Illustration shows
General Gordon.
- £135          • **Murray Cards**

## Studio International Art △
- *date April 1964*
Issue of the art magazine.
- £6
- **Book & Comic Exchange**

## Film Fun ➤
- *date 1957*
Issue no. 1971. Published by The
Amalgamated Press.
- £1.50          • **Gosh**

## Famous Monsters No.46 △
- *date 1967*
Famous Monsters of Filmland.
- £5-10
- **Book & Comic Exchange**

## Witchblade △
- *date November 1996*
Issue no. 10. Published by Top
Cow and signed by the artist.
- £20
- **Book & Comic Exchange**

## Beatles Series ▽
- *circa 1998*
A set of 10 cards in a limited
edition of 2,000. The illustration
shows Paul McCartney.
- £5          • **Murray Cards**

## Batman in the Sixties ▽
- *date 1997*
T.V. series spin-off magazine,
published by DC Comics.
- £15          • **Gosh**

## Optical Illusions Series ▲
• *date 1923*
Set of 25 cigarette cards from Ogdens.
• £65 • Murray Cards

## Daily Telegraph Strip ▲
• *date 1998*
An original 'Alex' cartoon strip for *The Daily Telegraph*. By Peattie & Taylor.
• £165 • Cartoon Gallery

## Hawkman ▲
• *date July 1961*
Hawkman issue no. 36 – *The Brave and the Bold* – published by DC Comics.
• £90 • Gosh

## Vogue ▼
• *date March 1967*
Volume 124, No. 4 of Conde Nast's *Vogue* magazine.
• £15
• Book & Comic Exchange.

## Knockout ▼
• *date 1954*
Issue no. 806 of Knockout comic, by The Algamated Press.
• £1 • Gosh

## Vogue ▼
• *date July 1949*
A July 1949 edition of *Vogue* magazine by Conde Nast.
• £10 • Radio Times

## Playboy ▲
• *date November 1968*
A 1968 issue of *Playboy* magazine with election cover.
• £8 • Radio Times

## Man's World ▲
• *date 1967*
Man's World Volume 13. no.1.
• £3-5
• Book & Comic Exchange

## The Topper ▲
• *date April 1957*
Issue no. 220 by DC Thompson.
• £1.50 • Gosh

## Aircraft of the Royal Air Force ▲
- *date 1938*
Set of 50 cigarette cards from Players. Illustration shows Hawker Hurricane.
- £45    • Murray Cards

## Sunday Times Cartoon ▲
- *date 1997*
A cartoon for *The Sunday Times* by Nick Newman.
- £120    • Cartoon Gallery

## Roses Series ▲
- *date 1912*
Set of 50 cigarette cards from Wills. Illustration shows a Mrs Cocker Rose.
- £50    • Murray Cards

## Akira Comic ▼
- *date 1988*
Akira issue no. 2, by Epic publishers. Signed by the translator Frank Yonco.
- £10
- Book & Comic Exchange

## Boys' Ranch ▼
- *date June 1951*
Boys' Ranch issue no. 5 – *Great Pony Express Issue* – published by Home Comics.
- £45    • Gosh

## Noted Cats Series ▼
- *date 1930*
Set of 24 cards by Cowans Confectionery, Canada. Shows a Persian male cat.
- £132    • Murray Cards

## Notable MPs ▼
- *date 1929*
Series of 50 cigarette cards of politicians, from Carreras Ltd. Illustration shows caricature of David Lloyd George.
- £45    • Murray Cards

## Custard Drawing ▼
- *date 1999*
A drawing of the character Custard, by Bob Godfrey, taken from the TV series 'Roobarb'.
- £130    • Cartoon Gallery

## Children of Nations Series ▼
- *circa 1900*
Set of 12 cards by Huntley & Palmer biscuit manufacturers, for sale in France.
- £66    • Murray Cards

## Konga ▼
• *date 1960*
An issue of Konga magazine, published by Charlton Comics.
• £15                    • Gosh

## Incredible Hulk ▼
• *date 1969*
Incredible Hulk, issue no. 112 – *The Brute Battles On!* – published by Marvel Comics.
• £12
• Book & Comic Exchange

## Types of Horses ▼
• *date 1939*
Set of 25 large cigarette cards from John Player & Sons. Illustration shows a Cob horse.
• £85                    • Murray Cards

## Waterloo Series ▲
• *circa 1914*
Set of 50 cigarette cards from Wills, never issued because of fear of offending French during First World War.
• £4,750              • Murray Cards

## Expert Tips

*The French have been producing collectable cards – on products other than cigarettes – since the mid-19th century. Their point-of-sale power was unassailable.*

## Daredevil ➤
• *date June 1964*
Daredevil issue no. 2, published by Marvel Comics.
• £135                    • Gosh

## Batman ▼
• *date May 1942*
Very early Batman magazine – issue no. 10, by DC Comics.
• £220                    • Gosh

## Land Rover Series ▼
• *date 2000*
Set of seven cards, showing seven seater. Illustration shows 86-inch seven-seater.
• £3                    • Murray Cards

## Magical World of Disney ◀
• *circa 1989*
Set of 25 cards, from Brooke Bond tea. Illustration shows Mickey Mouse.
• £5                    • Murray Cards

## Original Cartoon ▼
- *date 1997*
A drawing by Ed MacLachlan for NET magazine.
- £140 • Cartoon Gallery

## Dope Fiend Funnies ▼
- *date 1974*
Published by Cosmic Comics.
- £8
- Book & Comic Exchange

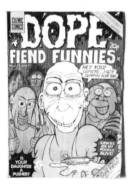

## Daily Telegraph Cartoon ▼
- *date 1998*
A cartoon for *The Daily Telegraph* by Matt.
- £100 • Cartoon Gallery

## Film Directors ▲
- *date 1992*
A set of 20 famous film directors, issued by Cecil Court Collectors Centre.
- £6 • Murray Cards

## Sandman Comic ▲
- *date 1989*
Issue no. 1 of Sandman Comic, from D.C. Comics.
- £20
- Book & Comic Exchange

## 'X Files' Series ▲
- *date 1996*
Set of 72 spin-off cards, from the X Files TV series, by Topps Chewing Gum, USA.
- £12 • Murray Cards

## Guardian Cartoon ▼
- *date 1999*
A cartoon for *The Guardian* newspaper, by Steve Bell.
- £250 • Cartoon Gallery

## American Indian Chiefs ▼
- *date 1888*
Set of 50 cards, by Allen & Ginter of Virginia, USA. Illustration shows Sitting Bull.
- £1,500 • Murray Cards

## New Statesman Cover ▼
- *date 1999*
Cartoon by Chris Riddell, used on cover of *New Statesman*.
- £250 • Cartoon Gallery

## Vanity Fair Series ➤
- *circa 1902*
Set of 50 cigarette cards of *Vanity Fair* caricatures from Wills. Illustration shows George Wyndham, MP.
- **£225**   • **Murray Cards**

## Private Eye Strip ▲
- *date 1997*
YOBS cartoon strip, from *Private Eye*, by Tony Husband.
- **£120**   • **Cartoon Gallery**

## Highland Clan Series ▲
- *date 1907*
Set of 25 cigarette cards from Players. Illustration shows a representative of the Murray clan.
- **£80**   • **Murray Cards**

## Racing Yachts Series ▲
- *date 1938*
Set of 25 cards, from paintings by Charles Pears. Illustration shows X.O.D. class.
- **£80**   • **Murray Cards**

## The Invincible Iron Man ▼
- *date June 1968*
Issue no. 2 of *The Invincible Iron Man – Enter the Demolisher!* – published by Marvel comics.
- **£24**   • **Gosh**

## Imperial Dog Collection Series ▼
- *date 1999*
Set of six cards by Imperial Publishing. Illustration shows an English bulldog.
- **£3**   • **Murray Cards**

## Modeling with Millie ▼
- *date December 1964*
*Modeling with Millie* magazine, issue no. 36 – *The Greatest Love Story!* – published by Marvel.
- **£10**   • **Gosh**

## History of the VC ▼
- *date 1980*
Set of 24 cards, from Doncella cigars, commemorating winners of the Victoria Cross.
- **£18**   • **Murray Cards**

### Expert Tips

*All prices shown are for complete sets of cards, not for parts of sets. Individual cards can be valuable – some collectors spend a lifetime completing a set.*

# Kitchenalia

## Bell Weight ▼
- *circa 1890*

A Victorian, two pound, solid brass kitchen weight in very good condition.
- *height 11cm*
- £22 • Magpies

## Glass Cloche ▼
- *circa 1860*

A French glass cloche from the mid 19th-century.
- *diameter 55cm*
- £150 • Gabrielle de Giles

## Pie Funnel ▲
- *circa 1890*

Roe's patent 'Rosebud' ceramic pie funnel, with name on obverse and baking instructions on reverse.
- *height 8cm*
- £26 • Magpies

## Scales ▲
- *circa 1940*

Berkel cast iron scales with red enamel finish, spirit level and adjustable foot. Weighs up to 2lb. Made in England.
- *height 50cm*
- £95 • After Noah

## Chocolate Jug ▼
- *circa 1946*

Cadbury's salt glaze chocolate jug, hand painted with the Cadbury's name and logo.
- *height 15cm*
- £22 • Magpies

## Chamber-Stick ▼
- *circa 1890*

A late Victorian blue enamel chamber candlestick, with no chips to the enamel.
- *diameter 14cm*
- £12.50 • Magpies

## Stone Sink ◄
- *circa 1890*

A late Victorian stone sink, with brown glaze to the interior and decorative glaze to the exterior.
- *length 95cm*
- £120 • Curios

## Miniature Saucepans ◄
- *circa 1890*
Late Victorian tinned copper oval, two-handled skillet, high-sided frying pan with long-handled lid and milk saucepan, all in miniature.
- £225    • Elizabeth Bradwin

## Butter Dish ▲
- *circa 1920*
A 20th-century fruitwood butter dish with a moulded glass insert, circular in form and in very good condition.
- *diameter 13cm*
- £9.50    • Magpies

## Cream Maker ▼
- *circa 1890*
Fluted glass-bodied cream maker with metal top and turning handle attached to wooden spatula within.
- *height 26cm*
- £33    • Magpies

## Coffee Pot ▲
- *circa 1930*
Domino coffee pot with white dots on a blue glaze ground. With scrolled handle, lid and upward-pointing spout. Made in England by T.G. Green.
- *height 16cm*
- £38    • Magpies

## Spice Tin ◄
- *circa 1890*
Spice container made of tinplate with six compartments and a domed lid.
- *diameter 19cm*
- £38    • Magpies

## Coffee Pot ▲
- *circa 1935*
Characteristically '30s chrome coffee pot with ceramic handle and spout.
- *height 19m*
- £45    • H. Hay

## Copper Pan ➤
- *circa 1870*
Large 19th-century copper deep boiling pan, without lid. With two handles.
- *height 19cm*
- £135    • Castlegate

## Jam-Making Equipment ➤
• *circa 1880*
Miniature, late Victorian open,
two-handled jam pan, copper
jelly mould and copper, deep,
lidded two-handled pot.
• £255    • Elizabeth Bradwin

## Hot Water Can ▲
• *circa 1880*
A hexagonal Benham & Froude
brass hot water can designed by
Dr Christopher Dresser with
turned wooden knob.
• *height 23cm*
• £675    • D. Pickup

## Cookie Cutters ▲
• *circa 1952*
Set of 12 metal, shaped cookie
cutters in original box.
• *length 22cm*
• £7.50    • Magpies

## Dutch Copper Kettle ▼
• *19th century*
Dutch copper kettle designed for
a cooking range, the lower
section to be inserted into the
fire. With lid, handle and spout.
• *height 43cm*
• £110    • Rosemary Conquest

## Jelly Mould ▼
• *circa 1890*
A miniature, Victorian jelly
mould in white china with flower
and leaf motif.
• *diameter 8cm*
• £26    • Magpies

## Coffee Roaster ▼
• *circa 1890*
Coffee roaster with drum
container and turning handle,
with brazier. In mild steel.
• *height 52cm*
• £135    • Rosemary Conquest

## Moulds ◄
• *circa 1900*
A group of classically shaped
moulds, for moulding mousses,
jellies, patés etc. May be sold
separately.
• £14.50 each    • Magpies

## Copper & Brass Urn ▲
- *circa 1820*
Copper and brass urn with brass
tap and double-ring handle,
banding and finial on a brass
pedestal foot.
- *height 48cm*
- £250 • **Rosemary Conquest**

### Expert Tips

*In order to retain their value, it
is important that items of
kitchenalia should not be purely
decorative. They must be
complete and in working order.*

## Herb Chopper ▼
- *circa 1880*
A Victorian double-handled herb
chopping knife.
- *length 24cm*
- £15 • **Magpies**

## Fish Kettle ➤
- *circa 1900*
French copper fish kettle of three
interlocking pieces.
- *length 53cm*
- £150 • **Youlls**

## Cordial Syphon ▼
- *circa 1934*
Fluted, etched glass cordial
syphon with brass top.
- *height 30cm*
- £20 • **Magpies**

## Knife Sharpener ➤
- *circa 1890*
A Victorian patent knife
sharpener with a cast-iron frame.
- *height 34cm*
- £475 • **Drummonds**

## Salt Tin ▲
- *circa 1930*
White enamel tin for salt, with
black lettering and detailing and
domed lid.
- *height 26cm*
- £18 • **Magpies**

## Flat Iron ◄
- *circa 1890*
Victorian cast-iron flat iron for
use with cooking range.
- *length 13cm*
- £14 • **Magpies**

### Butcher's Block ➤

• *circa 1860*
A 19th-century butcher's block
and table with fluted pillars to
the front and two cupboards.
• *height 84cm*
• **£1,625**        • **Drummonds**

### Butcher's Block ▲

• *circa 1910*
Well worn English butcher's
block with steel mounts.
• *height 75cm*
• **£170**        • **Myriad**

### Watering Can ▼

• *circa 1880*
Decorative brass watering can
with lattice design, hinged lid
and two handles.
• *height 27cm*
• **£45**        • **Magpies**

### Toaster ◄

• *circa 1930*
A manually-operated toaster
made of chrome and painted
metal, with bakelite knobs.
• *height 20cm*
• **£55**        • **H. Hay**

### Teapot ▼

• *circa 1930*
Dartmouth Pottery teapot, with
small white dots on a blue ground.
• *height 17cm*
• **£38**        • **Magpies**

### Copper Funnel ▼

• *circa 1900*
A Victorian copper funnel with
removable sieve.
• *height 12cm*
• **£18**        • **Magpies**

### Steel Footman ◄

• *circa 1800*
Steel footman, for cooking, with
cabriole legs on spade feet.
• *height 30cm*
• **£200**        • **Albany**

## Miniature Cooking Utensils ◄
- *circa 1890*
Miniature tinned copper frying pan, skillet, saucepan, ladle and flat strainer spoon.
- £225 • Elizabeth Bradwin

## Aluminium Kettle ▼
- *circa 1955*
A Picquot, Art Deco aluminium kettle, with wooden handle.
- *height 16cm*
- £68 • H. Hay

## Copper Kettle ▼
- *circa 1890*
A typical Victorian hearth kettle, in copper.
- *height 28cm*
- £55 • Castlegate

## Oak Tray Set ▶
- *circa 1910*
Set of four Edwardian oak trays, in diminishing sizes for stacking. Painted black with gilded scrolling and copper mounts.
- £280 • Youlls

## Copper Jug ▼
- *19th century*
Copper jug with brass handle and banding, with large spout.
- *height 43cm*
- £125 • Rosemary Conquest

## Preserving Pan ▶
- *circa 1880*
Victorian brass preserving pan with iron hooped handle.
- *height 15cm*
- £38 • Magpies

## Sugar Sifter ▲
- *circa 1930s*
Sugar sifter by T.G. Green, with blue and white banding.
- *height 28cm*
- £58 • Magpies

## Novelty Egg Cups ◄

- *circa 1930s*
A group of novelty egg cups,
showing cockerel, duck, owl and
elephant.
- **from £9**          • Magpies

## Biscuit Barrel ▲

- *circa 1930s*
A novelty Crown Derby biscuit
barrel, in the shape of a dog, with
black and white detailing, a red
nose, brown collar and eyes and a
yellow hat doubling as a top.
- *height 24cm*
- **£185**          • Beverley

## Teapot ▼

- *circa 1932*
A 'Domino' teapot by T.G.
Green, decorated with white dots
on a blue ground.
- *height 12cm*
- **£55**          • Magpies

## Marmalade Jar ▲

- *circa 1900*
A late Victorian, two-tone
stoneware jar for storing
marmalade or preserves.
Originally with cork stopper.
- *height 21cm*
- **£11**          • Magpies

## Mortar & Pestle ▼

- *circa 1900*
A mortar and pestle, by Mason's,
with turned wooden pestle and
white ceramic mortar with crest.
For grinding spices.
- *height 10cm*
- **£35**          • Magpies

## Expert Tips

*Much kitchenalia is to be found
in boot fairs, jumble sales or
junk shops. The advantage of
junk shops is that they will
probably have bought up the
entire contents of a house for an
agreed price and with the
intention of acquiring one or
two good items – anything that
the vast range of other items
fetches is 'found' money for
them and good value for you.*

## Watering Can ▲

- *circa 1860*
19th-century brass watering can
with banding and hinged flap.
- *height 39cm*
- **£115**          • Castlegate

## Bread Knife ➤

- *circa 1900*
A late Victorian bread knife with
a stainless steel, serrated blade
and a fruitwood handle carved
with the word 'Bread'.
- *length 31cm*
- **£12**          • Magpies

## Scales ➤

- *circa 1940*
Berkel cast iron scales with red enamel finish and spirit level. Weighs up to 2lbs. Made in London.
- *length 50cm*
- £95                    • After Noah

## Chamber Stick ▲

- *circa 1910*
An Edwardian, enamelled chamber candlestick with floral decoration on a white ground with black, enamel rim.
- *diameter 14cm*
- £14.50                    • Magpies

## Cocoa Tin ▼

- *circa 1890*
A Dutch cocoa tin, inscribed 'Cacao C.J. Van Houten & Zoon. Weesp (Holland)', with profusely decorated panels.
- *height 31cm*
- £110          • Rosemary Conquest

## Rectangular Bread Bin ▼

- *circa 1930*
A rectangular bread bin, enamelled in white, with black lettering and detailing and blue enamelled handles.
- *height 30cm*
- £34                    • Magpies

### Expert Tips

*Genuine, practical kitchen and scullery implements tend to be very plain and unfussy. Too much decoration may indicate a later copy.*

## Water Jug ◄

- *circa 1880*
Copper water jug with large splayed lip and tubular handle.
- *height 30cm*
- £46                    • Magpies

## Copper Kettle ▼

- *circa 1870*
A Victorian copper kettle with slender, hooped handle.
- *height 31cm*
- £105                    • Castlegate

## Fish Kettle ◄

- *circa 1880*
A large, 19th-century copper fish kettle, with rounded ends and two handles.
- *height 19cm*
- £135                    • Castlegate

## Tin Opener ◀

- *circa 1900*
A cast iron 'Bull's Head' late
Victorian tin opener, with steel
blade, in good condition.
- *length 16cm*
- **£14.50**          • **Magpies**

## Biscuit Tin ▶

- *circa 1880*
Victorian brass biscuit tin with
applied copper cherubs around
the body and lid.
- *height 23cm*
- **£390**          • **Barham**

## Ham Stand ▲

- *circa 1900*
Late Victorian, white china ham
stand, printed 'G. Rushbrook
(Smithfield)'.
- *height 20cm*
- **£42**          • **Magpies**

## Coffee Bin ▼

- *circa 1880*
Coffee bin with gilded lettering
and design on a red ground.
- *height 51cm*
- **£140**     • **Rosemary Conquest**

## Glue Pot ▲

- *circa 1890*
Black, cast iron late 19th-century
cauldron used for melting glue.
With looped handle and cast iron
insert, also with handle.
- **£22**          • **Magpies**

## Cheese Cutter ▲

- *circa 1910*
An Edwardian oak, brass and
marble cheese cutter.
- *length 33cm*
- **£295**          • **Castlegate**

## Brass Fish Scale ▶

- *circa 1900*
A Victorian / Edwardian brass
fish scale, showing weight of up
to 100lbs, with sprung
mechanism and steel fittings.
- *length 25cm*
- **£55**     • **Andrew Coulson**

## Butcher's Block ➤
• *circa 1890*
A French bow-fronted butcher's block table with drawers and cupboards below.
• *length 36cm*
• £2,850          • Drummonds

## Toaster ⋀
• *circa 1959*
Early classic chrome toaster, by Morphy Richards. Immaculate condition.
• *height 19cm*
• £58          • H. Hay

## Copper Jug ⋁
• *circa 1890*
Water jug in hammered copper, with large splayed lip and armorial frieze.
• *height 26cm*
• £33          • Magpies

## Flour Tin ⋁
• *circa 1920*
White enamel flour tin with black lettering and detailing and black enamel on the two handles.
• *height 28cm*
• £28          • Magpies

## Flour Jar ⋀
• *circa 1950*
A white ceramic flour jar with red banded decoration around middle and on the finial top and broad red band to base.
• *height 16cm*
• £32          • Magpies

### Expert Tips
*Even if your kitchenalia isn't worth much, it can still be useful. Redundant graters, for instance, with just the insertion of a candle, make excellent patio lights.*

## Ovaltine Mug ⋁
• *circa 1950*
Mug promoting the bedtime drink, Ovaltine. These mugs were produced in association with their long-running radio show.
• *height 11cm*
• £15          • Magpies

## Bottle Opener ◄
• *circa 1920*
A highly collectable Edwardian novelty bottle-opener in the shape of a lady's shoe, made of copper on cast iron.
• *length 12cm*
• £27          • Magpies

# Luggage

### Crocodile Case ▼
- *circa 1928-29*
Crocodile case from Garrards of London, made from skin of animal shot by Captain SJ Bassett in Zanzibar in 1926. With padded satin lining.
- *37cm x 25cm*
- £1,500 • Holland & Holland

### Picnic Case for Two ▼
- *circa 1910*
English Edwardian leather picnic case, fully fitted with custom-made accoutrements, including chrome finished hip flask, food storage containers, original Thermos flask, complete bone-handled set of stainless steel cutlery and china crockery.
- *width 28cm*
- £550 • Mia Cartwright

### Picnic Hamper ▲
- *circa 1940*
Made from leather, cane and canvas, with iron fittings and large rope handles at either end.
- *length 75cm*
- £480 • Myriad Antiques

### Suitcases ▲
- *1910*
Classic English leather suitcases with brass catches and locks and leather carrying-handles and lined interiors.
- £70 & £150 • Henry Gregory

### Leather Trunk ◄
- *circa 1910*
Small Edwardian trunk of heavy-duty leather with wooden base slats and reinforced corners, sturdy brass catches and locks and two leather restraining straps with fitted loops. Carrying handles are fitted to the middle and to each end. The interior is lined with cotton ticking, compartmentalized and fitted with restraining straps.
- *length 79cm*
- £70-£150 • Henry Gregory

## Expert Tips

*Leather luggage to look out for is generally made in London and most reliably by military outfitters. Good luggage is extremely heavy and more for decoration than modern use.*

### Victorian Hat Case ▼
- *circa 1870*
Victorian hat case in hide leather with brass fittings and red quilted interior. Designed to carry two top hats and an opera hat.
- *height 87cm*
- *width 85cm*
- £475 • Mia Cartwright

### Hat Box ◄
- *circa 1920*
Luxury leather hat box, holding several hats, with canvas lining and original travel sticker and initials 'K.C.' to front. Made in Northampton.
- *width 83cm*
- £375 • Matthews

## Gladstone Travelling Bag ◀

- *circa 1870*
All leather Gladstone bag with brass attachments, two straps and double handles.
- *length 69cm*
- £480  • Henry Gregory

## Square Travelling Case ▲

- *circa 1910*
Leather and canvas square case with brass fittings, with inner tray and ticking lined.
- *height 40cm*
- £110  • Henry Gregory

## Cartridge Case ▼

- *circa 1910-20*
Army and Navy case used for carrying cartridges. Hide leather, brass fittings and blue felt interior.
- *height 13cm*
- £650  • Mia Cartwright

## Official Mail Bag ▲

- *circa 1920*
English leather mail bag.
- *length 45cm*
- £155  • Matthews

## Leather Hat Box ▼

- *circa 1890*
Hide leather. Initials 'P. C.' inlaid on lid. Hat included in the red silk quilted interior. Beautiful condition.
- *width 82cm*
- £350  • Mia Cartwright

## Military Boot Trunk ▲

- *circa 1870-80*
Late Victorian English boot trunk, all in leather with fitted and compartmentalized interior and carrying handles on the front and both ends. Made by Peel & Co, Victoria, for Captain A. Pepys, whose name is inscribed. Possibly for the Crimea.
- *length 66cm*
- £875  • Mia Cartwright

## Travelling Wardrobe ▲

- *circa 1900*
Leather and brass trunk with canvas drawers and interior fittings. French.
- *length 1.2m*
- £900  • Henry Gregory

## Leather Suitcase ▶

- *circa 1910*
Square leather travelling case with brass fittings.
- *depth 40cm*
- £110  • Henry Gregory

# Mechanical Music

## Polyphon Table Model Style 45 ▲
- *circa 1900*
Two-comb, Polyphon Sublime Harmony Piccolo, in superb carved walnut case with floral marquetry. With ten discs.
- £4,950 • Keith Harding

## Twelve-Air Musical Box ➤
- *circa 1890*
Exceptionally good Nicole Frères 12-air, two-per-turn, forte-piano musical box, serial number 46094. Outstandingly beautiful case with exquisite marquetry on lid and front. Excellent tone and good musical arrangements of a popular operatic and light classical programme.
- £5,500 • Keith Harding

## Miniature Musical Box ▼
- *circa 1890*
Two-air music box with the rare tunecard of AMI RIVENC. In fruitwood case inlaid with parquetry. Geneva.
- £750 • Keith Harding

## Musical Ballerina ◄
- *circa 1890*
Automaton ballerina, rotating and dancing arabesques. On red plush base. By Rouillet et Decamps.
- £4,500 • Keith Harding

## Swiss Musical Box ▲
- *circa 1850*
Swiss musical box of eight tunes. Inlaid with song bird and foliage decoration.
- £3,250 • Pendulum

## Portable Gramophone ▲
- *circa 1920*
A Japanese portable gramophone, by Mikkephone, with unusual flattened horn speaker and carrying-case with strap.
- *width 30cm*
- £200 • TalkMach

## Cylinder Piano ▲
- *circa 1860*
Small upright domestic piano. Rosewood case with red-cloth frontal, by Hicks of London and Bristol. With 10 tunes.
- £3,300 • Keith Harding

### Mandoline Music Box ➤

* *circa 1880*
Music box by Nicole Frères, in
marquetry rosewood. Plays twelve
operatic airs which are listed on
original card.
* **£3,950**      * **Keith Harding**

### Portable Gramophone ▲

* *circa 1910*
English portable gramophone
with lockable case and shaped
arm with speaker attached.
* *width 34cm*
* **£250**      * **TalkMach**

### HMV Gramophone ▼

* *circa 1915*
An His Master's Voice
gramophone in mahogany case,
with cast-iron components,
straight arm and speaker below.
* *height 35cm*
* **£280**      * **Ronan Daly**

### Child's Gramophone ▲

* *circa 1940*
A German child's gramophone,
in tinplate.
* *width 17cm*
* **£125**      * **TalkMach**

### Table Model Polyphon ◄

* *circa 1890*
One of the most popular disc
musical boxes, housed in a walnut
case with floral marquetry lid.
Supplied with ten discs.
* **£3,500**      * **Keith Harding**

### Coin-Operated Polyphon ▲

* *circa 1900*
Upright, coin-operated polyphon
in walnut case with ten discs.
* *height 1.3m*
* **£9,500**      * **Keith Harding**

### Bremond Mandoline Musical Box ◄

* *circa 1890*
A large cylindered musical box in
a veneered rosewood case with
kingwood banding.
* *cylinder 41.5cm*
* **£3,950**      * **Keith Harding**

## Musical Box  ◄
- *circa 1865*
Forte Piano by Nicole Frères of
Geneva, with eight operatic airs.
- **£4,995**  • **Keith Harding**

## Phonograph  ▲
- *circa 1900*
An English 'Puck' phonograph
with large speaker.
- *height 35cm*
- **£250**  • **TalkMach**

## Art Nouveau Polyphon  ▼
- *circa 1900*
A rare autochange polyphon,
from Leipzig, Germany, with
16 22-inch discs and orchestral
bells in an Art Nouveau,
mahogany case.
- **£9,500**  • **Keith Harding**

## Musical Decanter  ▲
- *circa 1835*
A very rare musical decanter of
Prussian shape, with a Swiss
movement. Plays two tunes.
- **£1,250**  • **Jasmin Cameron**

## Lecoultre Musical Box  ▲
- *circa 1890*
Musical box in a rosewood case,
with original key. Plays six dance
tunes, listed on original card.
- **£2,400**  • **Keith Harding**

## Chiming Table Clock  ►
- *circa 1875*
Large chiming clock, in fruitwood
with gilt brass mounts. Plays
Westminster chimes on gongs,
Whittington on bells.
- **£3,500**  • **Keith Harding**

## Musical Box  ◄
- *circa 1895*
Nicole Frères key-wind musical
box, playing eight Scottish airs.
Rosewood lid with good
marquetry in wood and enamel.
- **£3,950**  • **Keith Harding**

### Edison Phonograph ▼
- *circa 1920*
American Edison phonograph
with metal swan-neck horn
formed on a sprung support.
- *height 96cm*
- £2,900    • Keith Harding

### Musical Banjo Player ▼
- *circa 1890*
In the form of a busker dressed in
period costume.
- *height 48cm*
- £6,800    • Keith Harding

### Key Wound Musical Box ➤
- *circa 1880*
In plain fruit wood case with no
end flap over the controls. Plays
four airs, 22cm cylinder and
square head comb screws.
- £2,400    • Keith Harding

### Columbia Gramophone ▲
- *circa 1930*
Columbia portable gramophone
with collapsable arm and record
store in the lid.
- *height 16cm*
- £175    • Ronan Daly

### Phonograph ▼
- *circa 1900*
America Edisson phonograph.
- *height 42cm*
- £250    • TalkMach

### Nicole Frères Box ▼
- *circa 1875*
Playing a programme of eight
Sankey and Moody hymns.
Rosewood veneered lid with
boxwood lines and ebony
cartouche with marquetry in
coloured woods.
- £3,500    • Keith Harding

### Coin-Operated Polyphon ◄
- *circa 1880*
Polyphon in walnut case, the
door centred with a brass lyre
backed with red material.
Supplied with ten discs.
- £5,500    • Keith Harding

## Victorian Cased Musical Box ◄
- *circa 1875*
A 19th-century musical box, with marquetry designs, playing six airs.
- *length 41cm*
- £2,000          • Lesley Bragge

## Child's Record Player ▲
- *circa 1940*
A German child's musical box in pink and green tinplate.
- *width 17cm*
- £125          • TalkMach

## Phonograph ▼
- *circa 1900*
A Columbia 'Grapaphone' cylinder player.
- *height 48cm*
- £350          • TalkMach

## Table Polyphon ▲
- *circa 1900*
A lockable table polyphon with a serpentine walnut case, 58-tooth comb. The polyphon is supplied with ten discs and winding handle.
- £2,600          • Keith Harding

## Portable Street Barrel Organ ▲
- *circa 1905*
Signed Thibouville Lamy but probably made by Marenghi of Paris. Seventeen-key action, playing six tunes – including Champagne Charlie – through three ranks of pipes. With rosewood veneered case and leather carrying strap.
- £9,500          • Keith Harding

## Rabbit Musical Box ▼
- *circa 1890*
Rabbit in cabbage musical box. By Rouillet et Decamps. Rabbit first raises his head and then turns his head and disappears.
- £2,800          • Keith Harding

### Expert Tips

*Modern 'marriages' of horn gramophones of dubious origins tend to cast the 'elbow' – attaching the horn to the machine – in aluminium. Only Columbia, among the original manufacturers, habitually used aluminium for this purpose.*

## Musical Autometer ►
- *circa 1880*
With mechanically moving mill, train and ship at sea, all under a glass dome. The musical box plays two tunes.
- *height 39cm*
- £2,800          • Keith Harding

### English Organette ➤
• *circa 1910*
By J.M. Draper, England.
Fourteen notes, with three stops,
flute, expression and principal
which operate flaps over the reed
box to control the tone.
• £950          • Keith Harding

### Phonograph Cylinders ▲
• *circa 1900*
Three phonograph cylinders, two
from Edison and one from Bell, in
their original packaging.
• £25 – £45          • TalkMach

### Concert Roller Organ ▲
• *circa 1900*
Twenty-key organette by
Autophone Company, N.Y.
Played by 'cobs' or barrels. Ten
cobs supplied.
• £1,750          • Keith Harding

### Polyphon Table Model ▲
• *circa 1890*
Rare, style 48, with two combs.
Sublime Harmony accompanied
by Twelve Saucer Bells. Supplied
with eight discs in a walnut case.
• £5,800          • Keith Harding

### Faventia Spanish Street
Piano ▼
• *circa 1900*
Two barrels, each playing six
tunes. With red-grained finish, on
original green and yellow cart.
• £1,495          • Keith Harding

### English Gramophone ◄
• *circa 1915*
An English gramophone by
HMV, 'His Master's Voice Junior
Monarch'.
• *height 36cm*
• £3,500          • Keith Harding

## Expert Tips

*The Edison Gem and Edison
Standard phonographs were
produced in vast quantities.
Condition needs to be very good
to excite the collector.*

### Dog Model Gramophone ◄
• *circa 1900*
By the Gramophone and
Typewriter company. Model
number 3. With original brass
horn and concert soundbox.
Completely overhauled.
• £1,950          • Keith Harding

## Paperweights

### American "Cherries" ▲
- *late 19th century*
American glass paperweight with central cherry pattern on a white latticino ground.
- *diameter 7cm*
- £620        • G.D. Coleman

### Clichy Blue Swirl ▼
- *date 1848*
A rare Clichy swirl glass paperweight in blue and white with central pink and white cones.
- *diameter 7cm*
- £1,350        • G.D. Coleman

### St Louis Paperweight ➤
- *circa 1855*
A St Louis glass paperweight with a mauve, dahlia flower pattern with green leaves.
- *diameter 8cm*
- £1,350        • G.D. Coleman

### Paul Ysart Paperweight ▼
- *circa 20th century*
Quality paperweight by Paul Ysart with a PY signature cane.
- *diameter 8cm*
- £480        • G.D. Coleman

### Baccarat Blue Primose ▼
- *circa 1850*
Baccarat glass paperweight showing a blue primrose and leaves on a clear ground with star cut base. Good condition.
- *diameter 5.5cm*
- £1,250        • G.D. Coleman

### Baccarat Scrambled ▲
- *circa 1850*
Paperweight of a type called 'End of Day', since they were made by glass workers after hours with leftovers from the floor.
- *diameter 8cm*
- £580        • G.D. Coleman

### Green Jasper ▲
- *circa 1860*
Mid 19th-century St Louis paperweight with flowers on a green jasper ground.
- *diameter 6cm*
- £380        • G.D. Coleman

## Rainbow Hand Coolers ◀

- *late 19th century*
Two rare hollow blown St Louis
rainbow striped hand coolers.
- *length 6cm*
- £780 • G.D. Coleman

## St Louis Magnum ▼

- *circa 1850*
Rare, magnum sized glass
paperweight, decorated with a
bouquet on a cigar background.
Unrecorded, so probably a one-off
design and size.
- *diameter 10cm*
- £5,560 • G.D. Coleman

## Baccarat Millefiore ▼

- *date 1847*
Closepack. Signed 'B 1847'.
- *diameter 6cm*
- £1,500 • G.D. Coleman

## Clichy Green Swirl ▲

- *circa 1850*
Clichy paperweight with green
and white swirls and central pink
and white canes.
- *diameter 7cm*
- £1,350 • G.D. Coleman

## Clichy Swirl ▼

- *circa 1850*
Clichy swirl paperweight in green
with central flower.
- *diameter 6cm*
- £1,200 • G.D. Coleman

## Baccarat Millefiori ▶

- *circa 1850*
Millefiori closepack designed
paperweight with various
coloured and patterned canes.
- *diameter 6cm*
- £1,500 • G.D. Coleman

## French Suphide ▶

- *date 1840*
Paperweight commemorating the
interment of Napoleon at Les
Invalides, Paris. The sulphide
with various Napoleonic
emblems, inscription and date.
- *diameter 8cm*
- £250 • G.D. Coleman

# Photographs

### Coronation Photograph ▲
• *12th May 1937*
George VI coronation photograph, by Dorothy Wilding. Autographed by the King and Queen Elizabeth.
• £2,000          • The Armoury

### Silver Gelatin Print ▲
• *20th century*
Photograph 'Andy, Bob & Elvis' by Nat Finkelstein.
• *length 11.5cm*
• £550
• Photographers' Gallery

### Colour Fresson Print ▼
• *Date 1996*
New York colour Fresson print by Delores Marat.
• *length 45cm*
• £800
• Photographers' Gallery

### Cyanotype Photograph ▼
• *20th century*
Plate entitled 'Large Anenome' by Sheva Fruitman.
• *length 15cm*
• £325
• Photographers' Gallery

### C-Type Colour Print ▲
• *20th century*
Adam Barfos,'Conference Building Elevators', from his International Territory series.
• *length 50cm*
• £1,000
•Photographers' Gallery

### Silver Gelatin Print ▲
• *Date 1951*
'Maidens in Waiting, Blackpool'. One of a series by Bert Hardy.
• £500
• Photographers' Gallery

### French Photograph Album ➤
• *circa 1890*
Brass-bound album with several plates of photographs.
• *length 23cm*
• £165          • Castlegate

## Coronation Photograph ◄
- *Date 1949*
Framed family group photograph of King George VI, Queen Elizabeth and Princess Margaret, with autographed letter by Princess Margaret.
- £300                • The Armoury

## Signed C-Type ▲
- *20th century*
Untitled photograph by Nigel Shafran, from 'Ruthbook', featuring blue hippo on radiator sill with green ground. Signed limited edition of 20.
- *length 40cm*
- £450
- **Photographers' Gallery**

## C-Type Print ▲
- *Date 1996*
'Making the Bed', c-type print, by Elinor Carrucci. Limited edition of 15.
- *length 50cm*
- £750
- **Photographers' Gallery**

## Audrey Hepburn ▼
- *Date 1953*
Audrey Hepburn on Paramount Lot. Signed modern silver-gelatin print by Bob Willoughby.
- *length 30cm*
- £400
- **Photographers' Gallery**

### Expert Tips

*Pictures of famous subjects are collectable, but the price should reflect the quantity of prints in circulation and the age of the print; new prints from old negatives command less interest.*

## Silver Gelatin Print ▲
- *Date 1965*
'March Climax, Trafalgar Square' London photograph by John 'Hoppy' Hopkins.
- *length 40cm*
- £350
- **Photographers' Gallery**

## Signed C-Type ▼
- *Date 1999*
'Corridor of Hydrotherapy Treatment Rooms, Mishkov Sanatorium' by Jason Oddy.
- *length 50cm*
- £775
- **Photographers' Gallery**

## Signed Print ▲
- *Date 1955*
'Dreaming of Home' by Thurston Hopkins. Signed, modern silver-gelatin print.
- £800
- **Photographers' Gallery**

## Signed Modern Print ▲
- *Date 1931*
'Renée, Paris. January 1931' by Jacques-Henri Lartigue. Signed modern silver gelatin print.
- *length 50cm*
- **£3,000**
- **Photographs' Gallery**

## Gelatin Print ▲
- *Date 1999*
'Striped Wall and Cyclist' by Marcus Davies.
- *length 40cm*
- **£350**
- **Photographers' Gallery**

## Expert Tips

*Beware of celebrity signatures unless well authenticated.*

## Children of George V ➤
- *1st June 1902*
Autographs and photograph of the children of George V at York House, St James's Palace.
- **£450**          • **The Armoury**

## Signed Saxaphone Print ▼
- *Date 1965*
'Dexter Gordon' by John 'Hoppy' Hopkins. Signed modern silver gelatin print.
- *length 50cm*
- **£350**
- **Photographs' Gallery**

## Signed Gelatin Print ▼
- *Date 1953*
'Chet Baker' by Bob Willoughby.
- *length 40cm*
- **£600**
- **Photographers' Gallery**

## Signed C-Type ▲
- *Date 1998*
'Kitchen' by Sheva Fruitman, from the 'Barrytown' series.
- *length 17.5cm*
- **£550**
- **Photographs' Gallery**

## Silver Gelatin Print ▲
- *Date 1951*
'Paris 1951' by Ed Van der Elsken. Estate print.
- *length 30cm*
- **£650**
- **Photographers' Gallery**

## Signed Gelatin Print ◄
- *Date 1965*
'Ringo' by John 'Hoppy' Hopkins.
Featuring John Lennon.
- *length 30cm*
- £350
- **Photographers' Gallery**

## Signed C-Type ▲
- *Date 1965*
'Hulme' by Shirley Baker.
- *length 40cm*
- £250
- **Photographers' Gallery**

## C-Type Print ◄
- *20th century*
Signed recto by Julian Germain
from 'Soccer Wonderland' series.
- *length 30cm*
- £300
- **Photographers' Gallery**

## Colour Landscape ▼
- *20th century*
Untitled print from 'Moving
Landscape' series by Chrystel Lebas.
Edition of ten, signed verso.
- £450
- **Photographers' Gallery**

## Signed C-Type ▲
- *Date 1998*
Signed limited edition of three,
'Lina', by Annelies Strbar.
- *length 17.5cm*
- £1,320
- **Photographers' Gallery**

## Silver Gelatin Print ▲
- *20th century*
'Monsieur Plitt Teaching Tupy to
Jump over the Brook' by Jacques-
Henri Lartigue.
- *length 75cm*
- £1,850
- **Photographers' Gallery**

## Signed Gelatin Print ▶
- *Date 1958*
'Swimming Pool, Welch, West
Virginia' by O.Winston Link.
- *length 50cm*
- £1,350
- **Photographers' Gallery**

## Signed Modern Print  ◄

- *Date 1938*
'Good Reputation Sleeping' by Manuel Alvarez Bravo.
- *length 20cm*
- **£1,250**
- **Photographers' Gallery**

## Silver Gelatin Print  ▼

- *Date 1991*
'Kazaksthan', signed print by Sebastiao Salgado.
- *length 35cm*
- **£2,500**
- **Photographers' Gallery**

## Signed Gelatin Print  ▲

- *Date 1957*
'US 6th Fleet in the Mediterranean' by Bert Hardy.
- *length 50cm*
- **£400**
- **Photographers' Gallery**

## Silver Gelatin Print  ▲

- *Date 1934*
'Cafe Soho, London' by Wolfgang Suschitzky. Signed verso.
- *length 40cm*
- **£300**
- **Photographers' Gallery**

## Silver Gelatin Print  ▲

- *Date 1967*
'Manchester' by Shirley Baker.
- *length 30cm*
- **£200**
- **Photographers' Gallery**

## Solarized Portrait  ►

- *circa 1935*
One of an edition of 50 prints of 'Dorothy Hill, Solarized Portrait, New York 1935' by Lee Miller, estate stamped verso.
- **£300**
- **Photographers' Gallery**

## Silver Gelatin Print  ▲

- *Date 1966*
A pair of portraits, this showing Queen Elizabeth II, the other of Prince Philip.
- **£950**          • **Jim Hanson**

### Cibachrome Print ▾

- *20th century*
Untitled from 'The Wild West' series by David Levinthal. Edition limited to 25.
- *length 25cm*
- £500
- **Photographers' Gallery**

### C-Type Print ▶

- *20th century*
Untitled girl in hammock photograph by Nat Finkelstein.
- *length 30cm*
- £550
- **Photographers' Gallery**

### Estate Print ▲

- *20th century*
'Asleep on the job' by Weegee. Silver gelatin print.
- *length 27.5cm*
- £500
- **Photographers' Gallery**

### Silver Gelatin Print ◀

- *date 1957*
'Vali Reflected in the Mirror' by Ed Van der Elsken.
- *length 42cm*
- £650
- **Photographers' Gallery**

### Signed Gelatin Print ▾

- *Date 1953*
'Nude, Eygalieres, France' by Bill Brandt. Signed recto.
- *length 50cm*
- £1,500
- **Photographers' Gallery**

### Paris Print ▾

- *Date 1951*
'Claudy and Vali in Claudy's Hotel Room' by Ed Van der Elsken.
- £2,050
- **Photographers' Gallery**

### Photograph Album ◀

- *circa 1890*
Brass-mounted book with mother-of-pearl and rosewood inlay.
- *length 23cm*
- £295                    • Castlegate

# Posters

**Jungle Book Poster**  ▲
- *circa 1967*
Released by Buena Vista with credits to voice talents.
- *length 1m, width 69cm*
- **£300**   • **Reel Poster Gallery**

**Andy Warhol's 'Bad'**  ▲
- *circa 1977*
Artwork by John Van Hamersveld. With caption.
- *length 1m, width 69cm*
- **£325**   • **Reel Poster Gallery**

**2001: A Space Odyssey**  ▼
- *circa 1968*
Entitled 'The Ultimate Trip' and signed by Kaplan.
- *length 1m, width 69cm*
- **£3,000**   • **Reel Poster Gallery**

**Coca-Cola Card Sign**  ▼
- *circa 1940*
A Coca-Cola card sign with caption 'Have a Coke'.
- *height 65cm*
- **£115**   • **Dodo**

**Stand-Up Card Sign**  ▶
- *circa 1940*
A Hartley's three-dimensional stand-up card sign.
- *height 53cm*
- **£160**   • **Dodo**

**Goldfinger Poster**  ▲
- *circa 1964*
Original French poster by Jeism Mascii. Released by United Artists. Captions in French.
- *length 79cm, width 61cm*
- **£500**   • **Reel Poster Gallery**

**Anatomy of Murder**  ▲
- *circa 1959*
Graphic artist style by Saul Bass. Photographs by Sam Leavitt.
- *length 1m, width 76cm*
- **£850**   • **Reel Poster Gallery**

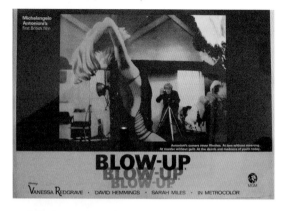

## Blow-Up ◄
- *circa 1967*
Framed behind glass, in style A.
Designed by Acy R. lehman.
- *length 1m, width 76cm*
- **£500**  • Reel Poster Gallery

## Embossed Tin Sign ▼
- *circa 1910*
An embossed tin sign advertising
Turnbull's Scotch Whisky.
- *height 46cm*
- **£120**  • Dodo

## Monsoleil Lithograph ▲
- *circa 1930*
An large original Monsoleil
lithograph.
- *height 1.54m*
- **£380**  • Dodo

## Casablanca ▲
- *circa 1961*
Original Italian 1961 re-release.
Art by Campejgi Silvano.
Showing stars' names and the
Islamic skyline.
- *length 2m, width 1.4m*
- **£7,500** • Reel Poster Gallery

## Barbarella Poster ▼
- *circa 1968*
Argentinian poster showing Jane
Fonda. Conservation backed.
- *height 1.07m, width 71cm*
- **£500**  • Reel Poster Gallery

## Le Mépris ▲
- *circa 1963*
Starring Brigitte Bardot. Linen
backed poster with artwork by
George Allard.
- *length 79cm, width 61cm*
- **£600**  • Reel Poster Gallery

## Clint Eastwood Poster ▲
- *circa 1973*
Showing Clint Eastwood as Dirty
Harry. Three-panel layout with
pistol reaching out to viewer.
- *length 2.06m, width 1.04m*
- **£950**  • Reel Poster Gallery

### Card Sign ➤
- *circa 1900*
A Kenyon & Craven's card sign advertising jams and marmalade.
- *height 40cm*
- £245　　　• Dodo

### Curse of Frankenstein ▲
- *circa 1957*
Japanese, paper-backed and signed by Christopher Lee.
- *length 76cm, width 51cm*
- £950　　• Reel Poster Gallery

### Embossed Tin Sign ▲
- *circa 1910*
An embossed tin sign showing an advertisement for alcohol.
- *height 31cm*
- £175　　　• Dodo

### Showcard ▾
- *circa 1950*
A showcard advertising Twinsol pure wool socks.
- *height 65cm*
- £20　　　• Radio Times

### Un Homme et une Femme ▾
- *circa 1966*
A montage of photo images from the film, in Eastman colours.
- *length 79cm, width 61cm*
- £1,250　• Reel Poster Gallery

### Star Wars Poster ▲
- *circa 1977*
With Polish translation and paper-backed. Artwork by Jakub Enol.
- *length 97cm, width 69cm*
- £425　　• Reel Poster Gallery

### Pseudonym Autonym ▲
- *circa 1890*
An Aubrey Beardsley original poster. English but printed in France.
- *length 50cm*
- £380　　　• Victor Arnas

### Get Carter ▼
- *circa 1971*
With photographic captions from the film by M.G.M.
- *length 1m, width 69cm*
- **£425**    • **Reel Poster Gallery**

### 'Reine de Joie' Poster ▼
- *circa 1890*
An original poster showing a large man with a lady in a red dress on his lap.
- *length 30cm*
- **£800**    • **Victor Arnas**

### Le Mans ▲
- *circa 1971*
French poster showing Steve McQueen. Artist Rene Fenacci.
- *length 61cm, width 41cm*
- **£150**    • **Reel Poster Gallery**

### Jess II Bandito ▲
- *circa 1939*
Showing actor Tyrone Power. Released by 20th Century Fox.
- *length 2m, width 1.4m*
- **£1,800**  • **Reel Poster Gallery**

### Sleeping Beauty ▼
- *circa 1959*
A paper-backed poster of Walt Disney's *Sleeping Beauty* showing various characters from the story and the title 'Awaken to a World of Wonders!'.
- *length 76cm, width 51cm*
- **£300**    • **Reel Poster Gallery**

### Planet of the Apes ▼
- *circa 1968*
A linen-backed, cartoon style Romanian poster with title 'Planeta Maimutelor'.
- *length 97cm, width 69cm*
- **£950**    • **Reel Poster Gallery**

### Psycho ◄
- *circa 1960*
Showing Alfred Hitchcock on a blank background. Printed in England by W.E. Berry and released by Paramount Pictures. In style B.
- *length 1m, width 76cm*
- **£5,000**  • **Reel Poster Gallery**

## Radio, TV & Sound Equipment

### American Radio ▼
• *circa 1930*
Designed by Harold Van Doren.
Skyscraper influence, produced
by AirKing. Then the largest
U.S. Bakelite moulding produced.
• *height 30cm*
• £3,000          • Decodence

### HMV TV/Radiocode ▼
• *circa 1937*
Model 900 with mirror lid. A
very popular set despite its 80-
guinea cost, speakers extra at £5.
• *height 96cm*
• £1,500          • Vintage Wireless

### German Radio ▲
• *circa 1950*
A rare post-war German bakelite
mains radio.
• *height 58cm*
• £175          • TalkMach

### English Radio ▲
• *circa 1950*
Kiather Brandes BM 20, rare
green bakelite radio, made of two
exact halves. Made in many
colours, some quite unique.
• *height 22cm*
• £500          • Decodence

### Red Radio ▼
• *circa 1965*
A very Sixties round plastic red
portable radio, giving medium
wave reception.
• £80          • Whitford Fine Art

### Murphy Console ▼
• *circa 1938*
Model A56V. A good-quality
middle of the range set costing
£30, vision and TV sound only.
• *height 86cm*
• £1,000          • Vintage Wireless

### Wooden Radio ◄
• *circa 1940*
Fully working wooden radio from
the Second World War.
• *height 30cm*
• *width 53cm*
• £105          • Radio Days

## Ekco Table Model ▲
- *circa 1939*
Model TA201. Original price 22 guineas. Vision only (sound was obtained by tuning a suitable radio to the TV channel).
- *height 50cm*
- £600 • **Vintage Wireless**

## 'KB' Wooden Radio ▲
- *circa 1940*
Fully working radio. One of many produced in Great Britain during the Second World War.
- *height 46cm*
- *width 53cm*
- £125 • **Radio Days**

## Bush TV ▼
- *circa 1949*
22 Model. Most desired of all British Bakelite TVs.
- *height 39cm*
- £300 • **Decodence**

## TV/Radio & Gramophone ▼
- *date 1938*
R.G.D. (Radio Gramophone Developments) model RG. Top of the range radiogram. Image viewed through mirror in the lid.
- *height 92.5cm*
- £3,250 • **Vintage Wireless**

## CKCO Model AD75 ▲
- *circa 1940*
Wartime English bakelite radio designed by Wells Coates to meet marine needs.
- *height 35cm*
- £700 • **Decodence**

## Expert Tips

*The Second World War was the golden age of radio production in the UK. The government needed the medium for morale purposes and insisted on economical manufacture.*

## Marconi Mastergram ▼
- *date 1937*
Model 703 TV/radio/auto-radiogram. Same chassis as HMV equivalent and originally costing 120 guineas.
- *height 97.5cm*
- £3,000 • **Vintage Wireless**

## Silver Tone Bullet 6110 ◄
- *circa 1938*
Modern design push-button radio with enormous rotating turning scale. Designed by Clarence Karstacht.
- *height 17cm*
- £1,100 • **Decodence**

## Baird Televisol ➤
* *circa 1930*
'The world's first television',
actually a mechanical system as
opposed to the later electronic
tubes. Viewed through small lens.
* *height 54cm*
* £5,000  • Vintage Wireless

## Cossor TV/Radio ▲
* *date 1939*
Cossor model 1210. When new
cost 48 guineas. Top of the range
of Cossor models, it used the
largest diameter tube.
* *height 1.21m*
* £1,000  • Vintage Wireless

## TV/Radio & Gramophone ▲
* *circa 1937*
HMV model 902. Very rare set,
less than five examples known to
exist. Cost 120 guineas new.
* *height 1.22m*
* £3,000  • Vintage Wireless

## Wooden Radio ▲
* *circa 1930*
Valve radio with wooden case.
* *height 30cm*
* *width 54cm*
* £85  • Radio Days

## HMV TV/Radio ▲
* *circa 1938*
Model 904. Same chassis as
Marconi model 706.
* *height 45cm*
* £1,800  • Vintage Wireless

## Console TV/Radio ▼
* *date August 1939*
HMV model 1850, cost 57
guineas new. Top of the range of
four models when introduced.
* *height 1.22m*
* £1,500  • Vintage Wireless

## Cossor Table Model ◄
* *date 1938*
Costing 23 guineas when new,
the cheapest pre-war set with
sound. A rare set.
* *height 44cm*
* £1,000  • Vintage Wireless

### Invicta Table Model ▼
- *date 1939*
Model TL5, made by Pye of
Cambridge. This is the only
known model of Invicta.
- *height 47.5cm*
- £800        • Vintage Wireless

### Philips Radio ▼
- *circa 1931*
Hexagonal with oxidised bronze
grill. Sought after for its unusual
appearance.
- *height 43cm*
- £500        • Decodence

### Crystal Set ▲
- *circa 1910*
An English Edwardian crystal set
in mahogany case with brass
fittings. In good condition.
- *height 30cm*
- £585        • TalkMach

### Grille Radio ▲
- *circa 1945*
Chunky automobile fender grille
radio. Made by Sentinel. Very
desirable.
- *height 19cm*
- £1,000        • Decodence

### JVC Television ▼
- *circa 1968*
A JVC 'Space Helmet' television
of spherical form on a square
plinth. Monochrome reception.
- *height 60cm*
- £200        • TalkMach

### Portable Radio ▼
- *circa 1955*
A small portable radio with
original leather protective case.
Medium and long waves.
- *height 11cm*
- £45        • TalkMach

## Expert Tips

*Most radios need to be in full
working order; if they are not,
then they need to be remarkably
unusual or celebrity-connected
to be collectable.*

### Mains Radio ➤
- *circa 1950*
A very small, red-cased mains
radio by Packard Bell of the
U.S.A., with large central dial
and minimal controls.
- *height 14cm*
- £140        • TalkMach

## Rock & Pop

**Beatles Album**  ▲
- *circa 1966*
'The Beatles Yesterday and Today'. Original USA stereo with 'Butcher' cover.
- £825  • **More Than Music**

**Andy Warhol Magazine**  ▲
- *date December 1966*
Set of postcards and flip-book magazine incorporating Velvet Underground flexidisc.
- £950  • **Music & Video**

**Collage Postcard**  ➤
- *date 9th November 1978*
'Que serait la vie sans les soirs?', signed by Genesis P. Orridge and dedicated to Mark Penny.
- £950  • **Music & Video**

**'The Beautiful Freaks'**  ▼
- *circa 1969*
Oz magazine issue no. 24, with cover by Robert Crumb.
- £30
- **Book & Comic Exchange**

**Beatles First No. 1**  ▼
- *circa 1963*
A copy of the 'Red A' label demo 45rpm recording of 'From Me to You' and 'Thank You Girl' – The Beatles first No. 1.
- £695  • **More Than Music**

**Powder Compact**  ▲
- *circa 1963*
A circular powder compact featuring a Dezo Hoffman black and white shot of The Beatles.
- £475  • **More Than Music**

**Set of Beatles Badges**  ▲
- *circa 1964*
With 'I Love Paul', 'I Love John', 'I Love Ringo' & 'I Love George'. Tin badges with pin.
- £195 (set)
- **More Than Music**

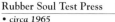

### David Bowie CD ◄
- *circa 1996*
Sampler of 'David Bowie's BBC
Sessions 1969-1972', released by
Worldwide Music.
- £400     • Music & Video

### John Lennon Autograph ∨
- *circa 1969*
Lennon autograph 'To Mandy
Love From John Lennon', on a
page of his book, 'John Lennon In
His Own Write'.
- £65     • Music & Video

### Rubber Soul Test Press ∨
- *circa 1965*
A Parlophone test press features
side two of 'Rubber Soul' with
white label and track listing.
- £2,250     • More Than Music

### The Move Demo ∧
- *date 1965*
The only surviving demo by The
Move, with one vocal per member
and featuring 'Winter Song'.
- £7,000     • Music & Video

### No New York ►
- *circa 1978*
Produced by Brian Eno and
recorded ar Big Apple Studio, NY
Cover by Steve Keisler.
- £65     • Music & Video

### The Beatles Live at BBC ∨
- *circa 1995*
The only existing maquette for
the proposed HMV box set, 'Live
at the BBC', permission for which
was withdrawn by Apple.
- £5,025     • Music & Video

### 'The Beatles' ►
- *circa 1964*
The JD 33rpm 'Deutsher
Schallplattenclub' edition with
red club label. Limited run.
- £575     • More Than Music

### 'At Home With Screamin' Jay Hawkins' ➤
- *circa 1958*

Album by the late Jay Hawkins – known for the epic single 'I Put a Spell on You'.
- £499  • Music & Video

### Beatles Parlophone A Label Demo ⋀
- *date 1967*

A green 'A Label' demo disc, featuring 'Hello Goodbye' and 'I am the Walrus'.
- £800  • More Than Music

### John Lennon Jug ⋀
- *circa 1987*

One of a limited edition of 1,000 Royal Doulton mugs, modelled by Stanley James Taylor.
- £750  • More Than Music

### Mojo Magazine ⋀
- *circa 1995*

Issue no. 24 showing The Beatles. Published in three colours – this one with a red background.
- £20
- Book & Comic Exchange

### 'Best of the Beach Boys' ⋁
- *circa 1966*

Special disc jockey producer copy of 'The Best of the Beach Boys' LP, by EMI Records, London.
- £184  • Music & Video

### Rolling Stones Album ◄
- *date 1975*

Japanese five LP, 62-track promo of 'The Great History of The Rolling Stones'. Box comes with large book and OBI. Individually printed inner sleeves.
- £347  • Music & Video

### Wings Album ◄
- *circa 1979*

'Back to the Egg' promo. Only picture disc manufactured for the MPL Christmas Party 1979.
- £1,250  • Music & Video

## Expert Tips

*The most desirable objects are personal items belonging to the stars – such as clothes and instruments – preferably accompanied by a photograph of the star using or wearing them.*

## Record Sleeve ▲
• **date 1975**
Wings 'Listen to What the Man Said' and 'King Alfred's Rubbish', autographed by Paul and Linda McCartney.
• **£675**     • **More Than Music**

## John's Children ▲
• *circa 1967*
Copy of 'Desdemona' by John's Children, featuring Marc Bolan and banned by the BBC.
• **£100**     • **Music & Video**

## Iron Maiden Dish ▼
• *circa 1983*
A picture disc of Iron Maiden's 'Peace of Mind' album, illustrated on both sides.
• **£40**     • **Music & Video**

## The Verve ▼
• *circa 1992*
Mint condition copy of 'Voyager 1', recorded live in New York, by The Verve.
• **£65**     • **Music & Video**

## Mojo ▲
• *circa 1995*
Mojo issue no. 24 showing The Beatles. Published with three different covers, this one with a blue background.
• **£20**
• **Book & Comic Exchange**

### Expert Tips

*Brian Epstein, The Beatles' manager, was famously dismissive of the value of merchandising. As a result, 'official' souvenirs proliferate and prices are unpredictable.*

## Beatles Sketch ▼
• *circa 1967*
An original sketch of Paul McCartney from The Beatles' film 'Yellow Submarine'.
• **£300**     • **Music & Video**

## Elvis 68 ◄
• *circa 1988*
A copy of the NBC TV 'Comeback Special' commemorative Elvis Presley promotional album.
• **£125**     • **Music & Video**

## Brute Force Album ▼
- *circa 1971*
'Extemporaneous', recorded at Olmstead studios, with design and photography by Hal Wilson. Published by Jingle House Music.
- £499          • Music & Video

## Mojo ▼
- *circa 1995*
Mojo issue no. 24 – They're Back! – published with three different covers – this one in black and white.
- £20
- Book & Comic Exchange

## Straight No Chaser ▶
- *date December 1988*
Issue no.1 of the jazz magazine entitled 'Straight No Chaser' issue no. 1 dated December 1998.
- £10
- Book & Comic Exchange

## Black Sabbath Album ▲
- *date 1971*
Vertigo records album 'Masters of Reality', produced by Roger Bain for Tony Hall Enterprises.
- £85          • Music & Video

## Coil Album ▲
- *circa 1988*
Album entitled 'Gold is the Metal with the Broadest Shoulders', by Coil. Deluxe limited edition, no. 29 of 55.
- £500          • Music & Video

## Sex Pistols Press Pack ▼
- *circa 1976*
'Glitterbest' press pack for 'Anarchy in the UK' album. Twenty pages on white, pink and yellow stock, hand stamped.
- £482          • Music & Video

## John and Yoko ▼
- *circa 1968*
Album cover for 'Two Virgins' in limited mono version, available by mail order only.
- £3,250          • More Than Music

**Beatles Archive Footage** ◄
• *date 1964*
Two four-minute standard 8, silent, black and white reels. Of 'London and Kennedy Airports' and 'The Beatles Triumphant Appearance in the U.S.A'. In original box.
• **£195 each** • **More Than Music**

**Untied Diaries Box Set** ▼
• *date 1988*
Untied Diaries edition 30, with 32 cassettes individually recorded and packaged. This is different from the vinyl version.
• **£900**        • **Music & Video**

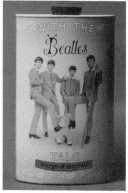

**Heavy Metal** ▼
• *circa 1977*
Issue no. I of Heavy Metal magazine, pursuivant on the cult film of the same name.
• **£20**
• **Book & Comic Exchange**

**Beatles Talc Powder** ▲
• *date 1964*
Talcum powder tin with different studies of the loveable mop-tops on either side. By Margo of Mayfair.
• *height 18cm*
• **£450**        • **More Than Music**

**Beatles Dress** ▲
• *circa 1964*
Official Dutch Beatles' cotton dress in mustard with polka dots. With the makers' card tag.
• **£395**        • **More Than Music**

**Portrait by Joe Meek** ▲
• *circa 1966*
'Pat as I see Him' – pen and ink on envelope by producer Joe Meek of his boyfriend.
• **£5,950**        • **Music & Video**

## Expert Tips

*The more recent the star, the more memorabilia will have been made to support them. There is very little Buddy Holly ephemera about, but a great deal on the Spice Girls.*

**Harrison Autobiography** ▲
• *date 1980*
Rare, unsigned hardback copy of first edition of Beatle George Harrison's autobiography 'I Me Mine', with dust cover. Published by Simon Schuster.
• **£75**        • **More Than Music**

## Set of Four Beatles Figures ➤
• **date 1964**
Ceramic 'Noddinghead' figures, by Car Mascot. Complete with original box.
• £1,000  • **More Than Music**

## Peter Wyngarde ▲
• *circa 1970*
Cult 1960s-70s TV actor Peter Wyngarde's departure into music. Recorded at Olympic Sound Studios, Surrey.
• £120  • **Music & Video**

## Mail Art ▲
• *circa 1977*
A double-sided postcard collage by Genesis P. Orridge, featuring an industrial sea-side scene and the Queen of England.
• £300  • **Music & Video**

## Oz Magazine ▼
• **date 1970**
A copy of issue no. 28, the famous School Kids' Issue.
• £80
• **Book & Comic Exchange**

## Beatles Fan Badge ◄
• *circa 1964*
Official Beatles' Fan Club badge, featuring faces of the Fab Four with their names beside them for identification (for true fans).
• £45  • **More Than Music**

## Knebworth Park ▲
• **date 5th July 1974**
Official programme for Pink Floyd's open-air concert at Knebworth Park, in performance with other bands.
• £65  • **Music & Video**

### Expert Tips
*Stars who regularly present signed artefacts to charities do not help the value of their fans' collections.*

## Psychic TV ◄
• *circa 1982*
A trophy cast in solid brass with an incription around the head and the base and recipient companies on shaft.
• £500  • **Music & Video**

## Official Carded Beatles Accessories ➤
- *date 1964*

Sales cards containing Beatles cufflinks and tie-pin, with the group's heads cast in brass.
- **£245 (left), £175 (right)**
- **More Than Music**

## Official Carded Jewellery Box ◄
- *date 1964*

Oval leather and brass accessories, with The Beatles' faces featured on the lid of the box.
- **£225** • **More Than Music**

## The Who Album ▼
- *date 1965*

The Who's 'My Generation' album, by Brunswick, with original band line up on cover. Poor condition.
- **£40** • **Music & Video**

## Official Corgi Toy ▲
- *date 1968*

Die-cast metal yellow submarine with revolving periscope and one yellow and one white hatch. From the movie.
- **£375** • **More Than Music**

## Official Brooch ▲
- *date 1964*

Official Nicki Byrne-designed Beatles brooch, with guitar and drum interwoven with the group's name and ceramic plaque showing their image, all on the original sales card.
- **£250** • **More Than Music**

## Expert Tips

*There was much more scope for worthwhile artwork on the vinyl album covers of the 60s and 70s than on the subsequent cassette and compact disk covers. This is reflected in the prices of original artwork of the period.*

## Beatles Sneakers ◄
- *circa 1964*

Official 'Wing Dings' Beatles sneakers, with images and signatures of the group on the shoes and the original box. In excellent condition.
- **£795** • **More Than Music**

# Scripophilly & Paper Money

## Queen Victoria Letter ▼
- **19th August 1954**
To M. le Comte de Mensdorff Pouilly. Written in German and sent from Windsor Castle.
- **£600** • **Jim Hanson**

## French Revolution Note ▼
- **31st October 1793**
A five livre note dating from the French revolution. Extremely fine condition.
- **£8.50** • **C. Narbeth**

## Scottish Pound Note ▼
- **circa 1958**
An ordinary Scottish note of one pound sterling value, issued by the Bank of Scotland. In extremely fine condition.
- **£12** • **C. Narbeth**

## Confederate States Bank Note ▲
- **date 1862**
A Confederate States American Civil War bank note of $100 value with a milkmaid vignette. Fine condition.
- **£25** • **C. Narbeth**

## Ten Shilling Note ▲
- **circa 1920**
A United Kingdom ten shilling note. A third issue 'B' note, issued by John Bradbury, in very fine condition.
- **£165** • **C. Narbeth**

## English Pound Note ▲
- **circa 1914**
Signed by John Bradbury and overprinted for the Dardenelles campaign during WW1. Very rare and in very fine condition
- **£2,500** • **C. Narbeth**

## Expert Tips

*When collecting banknotes, always go for perfect condition and uncirculated notes if the issue is reasonably prolific. If the notes are rare, however, then the condition is not as critical.*

## 1,000 Marks Note ▼
- **date 1910**
A German Reichsbank 1,000 mark note in very fine condition.
- **£2** • **C. Narbeth**

## Stanley Matthews Programme ▼
- **April 1965**
An original programme for Stanley Matthews' farewell performance at Stoke City, signed by Sir Stanley.
- **£250** • **Star Signings**

## Guinea Bank Note ▼
- **date 1825**
Commemorative one guinea bank note for George IV's historic state visit to Scotland. Issued by the Leith Banking Company of Edinburgh.
- **£650** • **C. Narbeth**

### 500 Rouble Note ◄
- *date 1912*
A large Russian 500 rouble note, showing a portrait of Peter the Great. In extremely fine condition.
- £5       • C. Narbeth

### Boer War Note ▼
- *date 1900*
A South African Boer War note of five pounds, issued from Pretoria, the Boer capital. In very fine condition.
- £28       • C. Narbeth

### Hungarian Pengo Note ▲
- *date 1946*
100,000 billion pengo note – reflecting the world's highest ever inflation in post-war Hungary. In extremely fine condition.
- £3.50       • C. Narbeth

### Three Pence Note ▲
- *circa 1960*
A British Armed Forces three pence note, mainly for use by the British Army of the Rhine in Germany.
- £12.50       • C. Narbeth

### Letter from Edward VII ▼
- *18th January 1910*
A crested letter and photo regarding his private affairs. Addressed to his sister-in-law, the Duchess of Connaught and sent from Sandringham.
- £650       • Jim Hanson

### Siege of Khartoum Note ▲
- *circa 1884*
A 20 piastre note from the siege of Khartoum, Sudan. Hand-signed by General Gordon and in very fine condition.
- £275       • C. Narbeth

### Squad Photograph ▲
- *date 1966*
Signed, commemorative photograph of the England 1966 World Cup winning team, featuring Alf Ramsey, the team manager, Bobby Moore, the captain and players Nobby Stiles and Martin Peters, with signatures of the entire winning team. A full squad photograph is also included.
- £2,500       • Star Signings

### Chinese Cash Note ►
- *circa 1858*
A Chinese 2,000 cash note issued during the Taiping Rebellion. In very fine condition.
- £65       • C. Narbeth

## Egyptian Bank Note ◄
- *circa 1960*
Note of 10 pounds' value with a cartouche of King Tutankhamen. Uncirculated.
- **£22**
- **C. Narbeth**

## Signed Photograph ▼
- *date 1996*
A signed photograph of Diana, Princess of Wales and her two sons. In a leather presentation frame with crowned 'D' symbol.
- **£5,000**
- **Jim Hanson**

## Spanish Note ▲
- *date 1928*
A Banco de España note of 50 pesetas value, showing a cartouche of Velasquez. In extremely fine condition.
- **£2.50**
- **C. Narbeth**

## Five Pound Note ▲
- *circa 1952*
A Bank of England five pound note. Uncirculated.
- **£100**
- **C. Narbeth**

## Expert Tips

*The Scandinavians are avid collectors of banknotes. The first European banknotes were produced in Sweden in 1661.*

## American 15 Shilling Note ▼
- *circa 1773*
A colonial 15 shilling note, from Pennsylvania, with a prominent signature.
- **£48**
- **C. Narbeth**

## Five Pound Note ▼
- *circa 1838*
From Newcastle-upon-Tyne, with a nautical cartouche, and in fine condition.
- **£38**
- **C. Narbeth**

## Mafeking 10 Shilling Note ▲
- *date 1900*
Issued during the siege of Mafeking, January - March 1900 by Baden-Powell. In extremely fine condition.
- **£250**
- **C. Narbeth**

## American Bank Note ◄
- *date 1850*
Five dollar bank note from an obsolete US bank – the Citizens' Bank of Louisiana. Extremely fine bank note.
- **£14**
- **C. Narbeth**

### Tibetan Note ◄
- *circa 1950*
A 100 strang denomination note from Tibet, serial numbers applied by hand by Buddhist monks. One seal represents the monetary authority and the other that of the Dalai Lama. Uncirculated.
- £22 • C. Narbeth

### Letter from George V ▼
- *19th October 1873*
Written by the future king, then aged eight, from Marlborough House, to Lady Julia Lockwood.
- £650 • Jim Hanson

### Austrian 1,000 Kronen ▲
- *date 1919*
An Austrian tausend Kronen note in mint condition.
- £3.50 • C. Narbeth

### Swedish Kronor ▲
- *date 1940*
A Swedish five kronor note. Extremely fine.
- £9.50 • C. Narbeth

### African Republic Note ▲
- *circa 1974*
A 500 franc note from the Central African Republic, showing President Bokassa in a military pose. In mint condition.
- £70 • C. Narbeth

### Expert Tips
*Check that the four corners of a note are sharp; hold it up to the light to check for creases; if it curls in the palm of the hand, it has been ironed.*

### Five Reichsmark Note ▲
- *circa 1942*
Dated from the Second World War and showing a Hitler Youth in the Horst Wessel mould.
- £10 • C. Narbeth

### Fifty Mark Note ▼
- *circa 1933*
A German 50 mark note. Extremely fine condition.
- £3.50 • C. Narbeth

### Ugandan Bank Note ►
- *circa 1973*
An Idi Amin Ugandan bank note of five shillings' value. Extemely fine note.
- £4.50 • C. Narbeth

## Sewing Items

### Sewing Table ▼
- *circa 1840*
A lyre-ended chinoiserie sewing table of the 19th-century.
- *height 65cm*
- £750          • North West 8

### Needle Case ▼
- *circa 1890*
Ivory and mother-of-pearl needle case with hinged lid and silver cornucopia.
- *length 7.5cm*
- £149          • Fulton

### Regency Table Cabinet ▲
- *circa 1815*
Shaped late-Regency table cabinet in rosewood, with mother of pearl inlay and fitted sewing tray.
- *width 32.5cm*
- £1,800          • Hygra

### Tunbridge Ware ▲
- *circa 1800*
A turned and painted early Tunbridge-ware sewing companion.
- *height 6cm*
- £450          • Hygra

### Small Sewing Machine ▼
- *circa 1900*
An American 'Little Comfort', handle-driven sewing machine.
- *height 17.5cm*
- £350          • TalkMach

### Work Table ▼
- *circa 1850*
Scandinavian birchwood work table. With turned, adjustable central column.
- *height 1.1m*
- £995          • Old Cinema

### Compartmentalised Thread Box ◄
- *circa 1810*
A straw-work thread box.
- *width 44cm*
- £180          • Hygra

## Small Sewing Machine ➤
- *circa 1900*
A 'Stitchwell' hand-driven sewing machine.
- *height 14cm*
- £150
- TalkMach

## Sewing Box ▲
- *circa 1820*
Concave-shaped rosewood sewing box standing on ball feet with brass inlay.
- *width 28.5cm*
- £850
- Hygra

## Tunbridge-Ware Box ▲
- *19th century*
Shaped Tunbridge-ware sewing box standing on turned feet. Van Dyke parquetry pattern with native and imported hardwood.
- *width 21cm*
- £900
- Hygra

## Penwork Sewing Box ▼
- *circa 1800*
A shaped Regency penwork sewing box with original embossed brass drop handles, standing on embossed paw feet.
- *width 24cm*
- £850
- Hygra

## Sewing Table ▼
- *circa 1820*
Mahogany sewing table of the Regency period. Full width cedar and pine lined drawer with original decorative brass knobs.
- *height 73cm*
- £1,850
- J. Collins

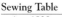

## Commemorative Sewing Machine ▲
- *circa 1875*
An English 'Princess of Wales' commemorative sewing machine by Newton & Wilson. In its original box.
- *height 34cm*
- £250
- TalkMach

## Expert Tips

*The acknowledged father of the modern sewing machine, Elias Howe, started manufacture in the USA in 1846 and in the UK in 1849. Isaac Singer was active at about the same time, and invented the pedal-driven machine.*

## Sewing Box ▲
- *circa 1875*
An exceptional Victorian straight-grain walnut sewing box, with gilded brass decoration and original blue, shot-silk interior.
- *height 34cm*
- £995
- J. & T. Stone

## Sewing Box ▼

• *circa 1800*
Early 19th-century sewing box in pollarded oak and rosewood inlay. Retaining its original lift-out tray.
• *width 28cm*
• **£480**                    • **Hygra**

## Chinese Sewing Box ▼

• *circa 1820*
Sewing box in Chinese lacquer. The box stands on four carved wooden feet. Chinese-made for export to England.
• *width 42.5cm*
• **£1,200**                    • **Hygra**

## Miniature Singer ➤

• *circa 1935*
A cast-iron Singer sewing machine of the Art Deco period, hand-driven and with a raised action and bobbin board.
• *height 13cm*
• **£400**                    • **TalkMach**

## Necessaire ▲

• *circa 1780*
An 18th-century tortoiseshell and silver necessaire.
• *height 7.5cm*
• **£1,200**                    • **Hygra**

## Expert Tips

*Thomas Saint patented the world's first sewing machine in 1790, in England.*

## Carpet Sticher ◄

• *19th century*
An American hand-powered carpet stitcher made by the Singer factory.
• *length 59cm*
• **£285**                    • **Mathews**

## Bobbins ▲

• *circa 1930*
Selection of three fruitwood bobbins with beaded decoration and carved stems.
• *length 19cm*
• **£4 each**                    • **Mathews**

## Sewing Basket ▲

• *Early 19th century*
A fine and delicate Anglo-Indian sewing basket, with fretted ivory panels framed with Sadeli mosaic.
• *width 20cm*
• **£1,200**                    • **Hygra**

# Snuff Boxes & Smoking Equipment

**Monkey Snuff Box** ▲
- *circa 1800*
Finely carved snuffbox in the shape of a monkey.
- *height 7cm*
- £950          • A. & E. Foster

**Horn Snuff Mull** ▲
- *circa 1810*
Extremely rare silver-mounted horn snuff mull. Made by Robert Kaye of Perth, Scotland.
- *length 15cm*
- £1,750          • Nicholas Shaw

**Cigar Cutter** ➤
- *circa 1880*
Ivory and silver cigar cutter. Monogrammed. No marks.
- *length 15cm*
- £420          • S. & A. Thompson

**Spitfire Ashtray** ∨
- *circa 1950*
Spitfire brass trophy ashtray. On marble base. Spitfire with pivot support.
- *height 15cm*
- £90          • Henry Gregory

**Match Strike** ∨
- *circa 1900*
Glass circular match strike with incised banding around outer edge for striking.
- *height 12cm*
- £98          • Magpies

**Wooden Snuffbox** ➤
- *circa 1860*
Handcarved Scottish snuffbox.
- *length 6cm*
- *height 6cm*
- £1,250          • The Lacquer Chest

**Cigarette Box** ▲
- *circa 1940*
Silver cigarette box with 18ct gold sides. Smooth with a small lip. By Boucheron, Paris.
- £2,000          • Henry Gregory

**Goat Head Snuff Box** ▲
- *late 19th century*
Snuff box in the shape of a goat's head. Pewter fittings. Brown and blue glaze with grey horns.
- *height 13cm*
- £1,100          • Elizabeth Brodwen

### Regimental Humidor ◄
• *circa 1930*
Unusual oak and brass-bound regimental humidor with brass emblem and motto. Original partitioned interior with plated presentation plaque. By Edward & Sons, London.
• *length 15cm*
• £900 • Henry Gregory

### Mr Punch Cigarette Lighter ▼
• *circa 1920*
Silverplated with registered design mark on base. Lighter is underneath character's hat. Of English make.
• *height 16.5cm*
• £290 • Barham

### Cigarette Display Case ▲
• *circa late 19th century*
Shop counter cigarette display box. Box contains four sections for single cigarette sales.
• *width 27.5cm*
• £80 • Ian Spencer

### Monkey Snuff Box ▲
• *circa 1800*
Finely carved coquilla nut snuff box representing a monkey. French.
• £895 • A. & E. Foster

### Miners Snuff Box ▼
• *mid 19th century*
Lead-lined. Half-hinged lid shaped for the back pocket.
• £60 • Ocean Leisure

### Mastiff Snuff Box ▲
• *late 19th century*
Continental coloured bisque snuff box in the shape of a mastiff, with pewter fittings and a hinged flap.
• *height 8cm*
• £630 • Elizabeth Bradwin

### Cloisonné Opium Pipe ▲
• *circa 1900*
Brass body with floral enamelling on a carved wooden base.
• £265 • Finchley

## Expert Tips

*Solid rolls of tobacco were carried by early snuff-takers, together with snuff rasps for making the powder. Rasps became decorative and elaborate during the eighteenth century.*

# Telephones

### Series 700 Telephone ▲
- *circa 1967*
British Telecom, acrylic with rotary dial, flexicord and handset extension. Resprayed in silver.
- £85 • **After Noah**

### Danish Telephone ▲
- *circa 1935*
A Danish magneto telephone based on an L.M. Ericsson design. Can't be used on today's system.
- £270 • **Old Telephone Co**

### Upright Dial Telephone ➤
- *circa 1908*
Made from 1908 by Telefon Fabrik Automatic of Copenhagen.
- £510 • **Old Telephone Co**

### Viscount Telephone ▼
- *circa 1986*
A British Telecom-supplied telephone in burnt orange with cream flexcord extension.
- £20 • **Retro**

### Bakelite Telephone ▼
- *circa 1950*
A GPO model telephone cast in bakelite with rotary dial.
- £125 • **H. Hay**

### Swiss Telephone ▲
- *circa 1950*
A Swiss wall-mounted telephone with bell-ring displayed to top and hook connection.
- £100 • **Decodence**

### Elvis Presley Telephone ▲
- *circa 1980*
'Jailhouse Rock' shown with guitar and period clothes. Touch tone handset.
- £99 • **Telephone Lines**

### Betacom 'Golphone' ➤
• *mid 1980*
Model GFI. Made in Hong Kong
with golf-bag handset and push
buttons, mute tone and redial.
• £18                    • Retro

### Belgian Wall Phone ➤
• *circa 1960*
A Belgian wall phone repainted
in red. Made in Antwerp by Bell
Telephones, a subsidiary of the
American Bell Telephones.
• £180        • Old Telephone Co

### Danish Telephone ▼
• *circa 1930*
Telephone with dial and hand-
raised cradle, made in Denmark
for the Danish telephone
authority.
• £350        • Old Telephone Co

### 500 Series Telephone ◄
• *circa 1978*
Made by Northern Telecom,
Stromberg-Carlson. Originally
supplied for an American airforce
base but resold in 1994. Unused
and in original sealed box.
• £95         • Old Telephone Co

### 300 Series Telephone ▼
• *circa 1955*
A 300 series black bakelite office
telephone with original handset,
cord and draw.
• £230        • Old Telephone Co

### Audioline 310 Telephone ▲
• *circa 1980*
Red Audioline 310, with
oversized keypad with numbers
also in red, push-button controls
and black flexicord extension.
• £30                    • Retro

### R2D2 Telephone ▲
• *circa 1980*
A telephone in the form of the
character R2D2, from the 'Star
Wars' films. His head moves and
lifts up when the phone rings.
• £99         • Telephone Lines

## 200 Series Telephone ◄
- *circa 1940*
English cream telephone with original undermounted bell box. Rare in any colour but black.
- £550　　　　　• Decodence

## Post Office Telephone ◄
- *circa 1935*
GPO series 300. Made by Ericsson with bakelite body, rotary dial and address drawer.
- £295　　　　　• After Noah

## Candlestick Telephone ▼
- *circa 1923*
Candlestick telephone 150 with original no.1 solid back transmitter.
- £600 (with bell set 25)
- £780 (with bell set 1)
- Old Telephone Co

## Mickey Mouse Telephone ▲
- *circa 1980*
British-made showing Mickey Mouse standing on faux-wooden base with push-button dial.
- £189　　　　　• Telephone Lines

## Bakelite Telephone ▲
- *circa 1955*
A British-made green, bakelite telephone, made for the GPO, model number 332. Shows original label on all-metal rotary dial, cheese-dish address drawer and gold-coloured, fabric-covered, interwoven flex. Green is a particularly rare colour.
- £500　　　　　• Telephone Lines

## Belgian Desk Telephone ▲
- *circa 1960*
A Belgian ivory desk telephone. Most of these were made in black, making this very collectable.
- £190　　　　　• Old Telephone Co

## Belgian Telephone ➤
- *circa 1940*
Copper-bodied telephone by the Bell Company, with pleasant ring and carrying handle.
- £89　　　　　• Telephone Lines

## Ivory Telephone ➤

- *circa 1930*

A GPO telephone in ivory, rare for the period. Shows all-metal rotary dial with original central label and number / letter display.

- £395 • H. Hay

## Danish Telephone ▲

- *circa 1935*

A variation on the D30, with two exchange lines coming in. Supplied with a separate bell set.

- £420 • Old Telephone Co

## Desk Telephone ▲

- *circa 1960*

A Belgian desk telephone in black plastic, with black rotary dial and white base on rubber feet.

- £150 • Old Telephone Co

## Magneto Telephone ▼

- *circa 1925*

A classic design by L. M. Ericsson, Stockholm, made from around 1896. Also known as Eiffel Tower.

- £850 • Old Telephone Co

## 300 Series Telephone ▲

- *circa 1954*

By Siemens Brothers, Woolwich. Rarest colour in this series. Used for shared or party lines.

- £600 • Old Telephone Co

## Darth Vader Telephone ◄

- *circa 1980*

Telephone in the form of Darth Vader, from 'Star Wars', with moving head.

- £99 • Telephone Lines

## Expert Tips

*Ascertain from the dealer, when effecting your purchase, whether the telephone you are buying can be used on a modern system and, if so, what conversion equipment is necessary.*

## Trimphone ◄

- *circa 1970*

Silver-painted British 'Trimphone' made for the GPO, with push-button dialling. With distinctive ringing tone.

- £85 • After Noah

## GPO Desk Phone  ◄
- *circa 1957*
Standard GPO desk phone, made from 1937–1959, with original drawer, handset and cord.
- £230    • Old Telephone Co

## Skeleton Telephone  ▼
- *circa 1895*
Highly collectable handset telephone by L.M. Ericsson and Co Metal body with enamelling.
- £600    • Telephone Lines Ltd

## 200 Series Telephone  ▲
- *circa 1938*
Almost the rarest colour in the 200 series. Made by Siemens Brothers of Woolwich.
- £1,100    • Old Telephone Co

## Danish Telephone  ▲
- *circa 1920*
Made in Copenhagen to a Swedish design and also known as the corporation telephone.
- £330    • Old Telephone Co

## Star Trek Telephone  ➤
- *circa 1994*
Modelled on Star Trek's 'Enterprise' with sound effects and push-button dial to base.
- £89    • Telephone Lines Ltd

## Danish Telephone  ▲
- *circa 1966*
By Kristian Kirks, Telefon Fabrikka of Horsens, for the Jydsk (Jutland) telephone authority.
- £150    • Old Telephone Co

### Expert Tips

*Condition is all-important in the value of collectable telephones. Bakelite, in particular, is easy to chip and crack and difficult to retain in its original colour.*

## British 'Pulpit'  ➤
- *circa 1897*
By Ericsson National Telephone Co with wood construction and outside terminal receiver.
- £1,600    • Telephone Lines Ltd

### Queen's Silver Jubilee ◄
- *circa 1977*
Very rare and limited edition, unused with type 64d bell set. Introduced to commemorate the 25th year of Elizabeth II's reign.
- **£150**      • **Old Telephone Co**

### Ericofon Telephone ◄
- *circa 1955*
Designed in 1953 by Ralph Lysell and Hugo Blomberg. In white and red with dial underneath.
- **£70**      • **Telephone Lines Ltd**

### Bakelite Pyramid Phone ▲
- *circa 1930*
Series 200 with chrome rotary dial, cloth flex and address drawer.
- **£295**      • **After Noah**

### Model 1000 ▲
- *circa 1962*
Made by GEC of Coventry and was intended as a replacement for the 300 series but not adopted.
- **£160**      • **Old Telephone Co**

### 300 Series Telephone ▼
- *circa 1957*
A rare 328 telephone made by Plessey, Ilford, Essex. With bell-on and bell-off push buttons.
- **£650**      • **Old Telephone Co**

### Candlestick Telephone ▲
- *circa 1927*
Type 150, in bakelite, featuring a replacement microphone. Made by Ibex Telephones.
- **£460**      • **Old Telephone Co**

## Expert Tips

*Telephones do not have to work in order to be collectable. Very early ones are intrinsically valuable as are some of the antiques of the future – early mobiles and car-phones.*

### Genie Telephone ►
- *circa 1978*
BT special range, a much sought-after designer telephone in white with metal dial.
- **£39**      • **Telephone Lines Ltd**

# Walking sticks

## Brass-Headed Stick ▼
- *date 1880*
Cast brass head of Mr Punch in good detail with plain brass colbar and malacca shaft.
- £300 • Michael German

## Large Victorian Stick ▼
- *date 1918*
Large Victorian curved ivory dog-head handle. Carved in fine detail with snarling open mouth, drooping ears and glass eyes. Silver collar marked with Brigg, London. Shaft is made of ebony.
- £1,400 • Michael German

## Gilt Metal, Hardwood Stick ▲
- *date 1890*
Ebonized cane of hardwood. Large American gilt metal. Tall handle with original owner's initials and decorated with floral scrolls.
- £440 • Michael German

## Victorian Stick ▲
- *date 1860*
Stick with carved handle in the shape of a grotesque dog head. Glass eyes, open mouth with human ears. Gilt collar on a natural hardwood shaft.
- £400 • Michael German

## Country Walking Stick ▼
- *date 1910*
Country walking stick with antler handle and silver band.
- £125 • The Reel Thing

## Rare Porcelain Handled Stick ▼
- *date 1837*
Rare porcelain cane. Handle painted with a portrait of Queen Victoria at her coronation. VR cypher and dated 1837 on reverse of handle. Gilt metal collar on ebony shaft. Painted on a gilt and blue background.
- £250 • Michael German

## Drinking Cane ◄
- *date 1880*
Late 19th-century drinking cane complete with glass spirit flask, stopper and small glass goblet. Decorated with copper mounts. Has a country Briar wood shaft. Made in Austria and of good quality.
- £240 • Michael German

## Rare Victorian Telescope Cane ◀

- *date 1870*
Rare Victorian telescope cane with pullout laquered brass pivot and scope. For use by naturalists (birdspotting). Upper section of cane in lacquered brass, rest of shaft in ebony. Of English make.
- £1,400 • Michael German

## Steel- and Gold-Handled Stick ▼

- *circa 1870*
Steel crook-handle walking stick. Inlaid with gold floral and geometric designs. Of Spanish, Toledo make. The shaft is of snake wood.
- £750 • Michael German

## Victorian Silver ▲

- *date 1895*
Late 19th-century Victorian silver parrot-head walking stick. Showing glass eyes on an ebonized shaft. Silver hallmark with finely chased feather relief.
- £420 • Michael German

## Ladies Cane ▲

- *date 1880*
Small silver club-shaped handle with bands of enamel blue flowers. Ebony shaft. Sterling marked. Made in USA.
- £550 • Michael German

## Snake- and Hand-Headed Stick ▼

- *date 1850*
Mid 19th-century walking stick with folk art cane shaft. It is decorated with two snakes entwining themselves along the shaft with a hand clutching the snake heads at the top.
- £550 • Michael German

## Porcelain-Handled Stick ▲

- *circa 19th century*
Porcelain-handled stick portraying a woman's head. Decorated with flowers and insects on a white background. Probably continental malacca shaft. Made in the early 19th century.
- £1,200 • Michael German

## Sailor's Walking Stick ▲

- *circa 1800*
English walking stick. Used by early 19th-century sailors. Decorated with a characteristic Turk's head knot.
- £950 • A & E Foster

# Coins & Medals

**Coins are probably the most collected antiques of all, existing in sufficient quantities to provide for both large and small collections.**

Nothing traces the ascent of civilisation as accurately and as thoroughly as the coin. The study of coin development from its beginnings, in about 640BC, to the present day is richly endowed with history. Ancient Greek and Roman coins are usually very expensive and Oriental coinage is best left to the expert, but general world coinage provides a fascinating field of study and is much more accessible to the new collector.

Coins and medals of all types have the advantage of telling the collector exactly what they are – provided that he can read the relevant script or language. It is then a matter of historical knowledge and common sense to work out what

may make an item a rarity. The value of coins is dependent on their design, legend, mintmark, date, current demand and condition, the latter graded from 'FDC' or fleur de coin, meaning 'in mint condition', to 'F', meaning 'fair', which means that, despite hard usage, the main features of the coin are still recognisable.

Medals are divided between campaign medals and those awarded for individual bravery and depend for value on condition, rarity and the circumstance and individual involved – the action and the deed.

The Napoleonic Wars, the Crimean War, the Indian Mutiny and other Victorian engagements are ones to look out for.

## Copper Medal ➤
• *date 1799*
A copper William Pitt the Younger medal by Hancock, struck at a time when Pitt was enjoying great popularity due to victories over Napoleon in Egypt, notably the Battle of the Nile.
• *diameter 52mm*
• £40　　• **Malcolm Bord**

## Regimental Brooches ▲
• *19th-20th century*
A selection of brooches representing regiments of the British Army, the Royal Navy and the Royal Air Force, in gold, enamel and diamonds.
• £200-2,000　• **The Armoury**

## George III Coin ▼
• *date 1798*
A silver George III emergency-issue dollar coin, minted during the War of Independence, with an oval countermark.
• *diameter 39mm*
• £600　　• **Malcolm Bord**

## General Service Medal ▼
• *date 1962*
A Northern Ireland service medal, awarded to L/CPL R. Scott, Scots Guards. With purple and green ribbon.
• £42　　• **Gordon's Medals**

## Expert Tips

*If your collection is worth a significant amount of money it is a good idea to have it catalogued and the significant items photographed for the police and insurers. It is a very bad idea to keep such lists and photographs near the collection.*

### Commemorative Coin ▼

• *date 1935*
A gold coin commemorating the Silver Jubilee of King George V. The coin shows the King and Queen Mary with Windsor Castle on reverse.
• *diameter 31mm*
• £250      • Malcolm Bord

### Half-Sovereign Coin ▼

• *date 1817*
A gold King George III half-sovereign coin.
• *diameter 19mm*
• £250      • Malcolm Bord

### Iron Cross ▶

• *date 1939*
A Second World War German Iron Cross Second Class, awarded for bravery and / or leadership. Ring stamped with swastika and with red and white ribbon.
• £38      • Gordon's Medals

### Military Cross ▼

• *date 1918*
In original case of issue and inscribed on reverse '2nd Lieut. S.G. Williams 1st Battalion, Devonshire Regiment'.
• £325      • Gordon's Medals

### Gold Sovereign Coin ▼

• *date 1553*
Queen Mary fine sovereign coin of thirty shillings. With Queen enthroned and Tudor Rose on reverse. Date in Roman numerals.
• *diameter 44mm*
• £5,000      • Malcolm Bord

### Breast Badge ▲

• *date 1933*
Knights Bachelor breast badge, silver gilt with red enamel background. From the Royal Mint with original box. Sword shown between two spurs.
• £220      • Gordon's Medals

### Gold Guinea Coin ▲

• *date 1794*
A gold George III guinea coin. This issue is known as the 'Spadge Guinea'.
• *diameter 19mm*
• £200      • Malcolm Bord

## Imperial Iron Cross ➤
• *date 1914*
A World War I Imperial Iron
Cross, Second Class with crown,
'W' mark, dated and with
Friedrich Wilhelm crest.
• **£20**     • **Gordon's Medals**

## Austrian Coin ▼
• *date 1936*
Gold Austrian 100-schilling coin
with Madonna on obverse and
Austrian shield on reverse.
• *diameter 32mm*
• **£450**     • **Malcolm Bord**

## German Coin ▼
• *date 1698*
A gold German six-ducat
Nuremberg coin.
• *diameter 44mm*
• **£6,000**     • **Malcolm Bord**

## Silver Penny ▲
• *circa 1025*
A short cross-type silver penny
from the court of King Cnut.
• *diameter 32mm*
• **£100**     • **Malcolm Bord**

### Expert Tips

*Bars on Victorian medals,
indicating the actions within a
campaign, add to the value.*

## George III Guinea Coin ▼
• *date 1813*
A gold George III guinea coin.
This coin is known as the
'Military Guinea'.
• *diameter 19mm*
• **£800**     • **Malcolm Bord**

## Crimean Medal ▲
• *date 1854*
Crimean Medal with Sebastapol
bar. Officially impressed 'E. Moss
of the Coldstream Guards'. With
yellow and pale blue ribbon –
Prince Albert's colours.
• **£145**     • **Gordon's Medals**

## George III Crown ◄
• *date 1750*
A silver George III crown coin,
with the early head portrait.
• *diameter 38mm*
• **£750**     • **Malcolm Bord**

## Five-Pound Coin ▲
- *date 1902*
A very rare gold Edward VII five-pound coin.
- *diameter 35mm*
- £700  • Malcolm Bord

## South African Medal ▲
- *date 1899-1902*
QSA (Queen's South African) Medal from the Boer War, with bars for OFS and Transvaal. Showing Queen Victoria and Britannia on reverse.
- £65  • Gordon's Medals

## White Metal Medal ▼
- *date 1852*
A white metal medal by Allen & Moore, commemorating the death of the Duke of Wellington.
- *diameter 50mm*
- £30  • Malcolm Bord

## Garter Breast Star ▼
- *circa 1810*
A fine Georgian Order of the Garter breast star. An articulated example, with facet-cut silver, gold and enamel.
- £15,000  • The Armoury

## 100-Franc Coin ▼
- *date 1904*
Gold Monaco 100-franc coin. Showing the head of Prince Albert I of Monaco.
- *diameter 34mm*
- £250  • Malcolm Bord

## Naval General Service Medal ▲
- *date 1861*
General Service medal, with Algiers bar, awarded to Midshipman F.H. Le Mesurier.
- £825  • Gordon's Medals

## Prize Medal ▲
- *date 1760*
Silver Wilhelmus de Wykeham medal from Winchester School.
- *diameter 33mm*
- £100  • Malcolm Bord

### Expert Tips
*The inscription of the name of the recipients could legitimately have been added at a later date. Regimental rolls will confirm whether the recipient is genuine.*

# Decorative Arts

**The market for decorative arts has consolidated and expanded over the last 20 years and shows no sign of easing up.**

The decorative arts – or the applied arts, – although difficult to define, have undergone a collecting revolution over the past two decades. Originally, activity largely centred around artefacts of European Art Nouveau and Art Deco but has since expanded across the Atlantic. There is now intense interest in European decorative arts in Japan, which has helped the values considerably, particularly in the case of works by Gallé, Daume and Lalique.

Riding on the same wave of collecting enthusiasm are the English potters, with Clarice Cliff in the van and Susie Cooper, William Moorcroft and the Poole Pottery lagging not far behind. The metal artefacts of Dr Christopher Dresser find an excellent market if you happen upon one at anything less than an astronomical price.

This is an area which is shifting and expanding all the time. There are no rules, but as long as you like what you buy, you won't be the loser.

## Figures & Busts

### Marble Plaque ∨
- *circa 1820*
Marble plaque with relief showing Hermes, Aphrodite and Paris.
- *height 112cm*
- **£19,500**  • Westland & Co

### Marble Bust ∧
- *circa 1865*
An early Victorian marble bust of J. E. Boehm, statuary white, in excellent condition.
- *height 58.5cm*
- **£3,850**  • Newland

### Stone Statue ∨
- *circa 1920*
A French stone statue of the torso and thighs of a woman, with attention to form.
- *height 190cm*
- **£3,600**  • Drummonds

### Sienna Marble Group ◄
- *circa 1890*
Group of two tigers fighting, signed by Angelo Vannetti.
- *height 50.8cm*
- **£25,000**  • Westland & Co

Figures & Busts

## Terracotta Bust ▼

• *circa 1890*
Bust of Marie Antoinette with
head inclined to sinister. Raised
on a spreading square plinth.
• *height 65cm*
• £950          • Westland & Co

## French Statue ▼

• *circa 1890*
A statuary marble and alabaster
statue of La Poete de la Danse.
• *height 57cm*
• £2,500          • Westland & Co

### Expert Tips

*There are no set guidelines for
this area of collecting. Buying
quality always proves a good
investment and if you are
fortunate enough to combine
quality with decorative appeal,
you can't go wrong.*

## Terracotta Roundel ▲

• *circa 1890*
A French terracotta roundel of a
horse's head. Dated ' '92'.
• *diameter 99cm*
• £3,500          • Westland & Co

## Stone Torso ▲

• *circa 1880*
A classical reconstructed stone
torso of a woman, with loincloth
and shell fastening.
• *height 86cm*
• £950          • Westland & Co

## Bust of Bacchus ▼

• *20th century*
A plaster bust of Bacchus, with
head inclined to dexter.
• *height 67cm*
• £950          • Westland & Co

## Statue of Neptune ▼

• *circa 1765*
A finely carved stone figure of
the god Neptune in traditional
pose, with broken hand.
• *height 205cm*
• £4,850          • Drummonds

## Marble Bust ◄

• *circa 1800*
Large marble bust of Lorenzo di
Medici, patron of Michelangelo.
• *height 62cm*
• £9,500          • Westland & Co

269

# Lighting

## Italian Candelabra ▼
- *circa 1900*
A metal hour-glass base, with
wire and enamel flower
decoration with pierced finial of
acanthus and trellis design.
- *height 106cm*
- £950    • Rosemary Conquest

## Ormolu Chandelier ▲
- *circa 1790*
A fine late 18th-century Baltic
glass and ormolu chandelier, with
suspended pendants and swags
linking six curved branches.
Converted to electricity.
- *height 102cm*
- £40,000    • Norman Adams

## Pair of Candelabra ▼
- *circa 1825*
Pair of Regency, cut glass and
ormolu, two-branch candelabra
with long faceted drops.
- *height 36cm*
- £9,000    • Norman Adams

## Elephant Oil Lamps ▼
- *circa 1900*
Pair of continental, miniature oil
lamps mounted on porcelain,
elephant bodies with all original
fittings and leather covers.
- *height 22cm*
- £670    • Elizabeth Bradwin

## Expert Tips

*Always check that lamps
converted to electricity adhere to
current safety standards. Some
of them were converted a long
time ago.*

## Pewter Candelabra ▼
- *date 1885*
A candelabra of English pewter
with a shaft of pierced, organic
form on a square, splayed base.
The branches with cup sconces.
- *h eight 28cm*
- £2,500    • Kieron

## Puppy Oil Lamp ▲
- *circa 1910*
A continental oil lamp mounted
on the ceramic model of a
begging puppy, with glass eyes,
on a moulded, circular base.
New shade and frame.
- *height 32cm*
- £650    • Elizabeth Bradwin

## Bronze Lamps ▼
- *circa 1830*
Pair of bronze lamps with
acanthus-leaf decoration.
- *height 51cm*
- £1,850    • Lynda Franklin

## Neogothic Candlesticks ▲
- *circa 1860*
Pair of brass candlesticks, with twisted stem on domed circular base and pierced frieze about sconce.
- *height 31cm*
- £650 • Westland & Co

## Paris Light Shade ▲
- *circa 1860*
A ceramic Paris light shade with floral decoration around the body, gilding to the rim and suspended by a triple gilt chain.
- *height 53cm*
- £1,280 • P.L. James

## Elephant Oil Lamp ▼
- *circa 1880*
Oil lamp modelled on four, outward-looking elephants, with enormous reservoir and detachable top for use as planter.
- *height 34cm*
- £790 • Elizabeth Bradwin

## Cherub Candelabra ▼
- *circa 1785*
Louis XVI marble, bronze and ormolu candelabra.
- *height 44cm*
- £18,000 • Norman Adams

## Candlesticks ◄
- *date 1853*
A pair of Victorian figural candlesticks made by Charles & George Fox, London.
- *height 87cm*
- £10,000 • Nicholas Shaw

## Ormolu Candelabra ▲
- *circa 1840*
Pair of four-branch, ormolu candelabra with flame finial convertable to fifth candle dish. the shafts have snake designs emerging from acanthus-leaf decoration. The whole on an architectural tripod base.
- *height 62cm*
- £3,850 • O.F. Wilson

## Mercury Oil Lamp ▲
- *circa 1820*
Important statue of Mercury holding aloft an oil lamp, with associated tools suspended from it on silver chains. Fashioned in bronze and silver by Giovacchino Belli of Rome, after a model by Giam Bologna.
- *height 70cm*
- £17,500 • Bazaart

## Elephant Oil Lamp ▲
- *circa 1880*
Continental lamp supported by a fluted, porcelain column surmounted by three elephant heads. Original fittings.
- *height 31cm*
- £580 • **Elizabeth Bradwin**

## Alabaster Figural Lamps ▲
- *circa 1830*
A pair of French alabaster figure lamps showing cherub figures on a cylindrical base.
- *height 87cm*
- £10,000 • **Norman Adams**

## Cut-glass Candelabra ▲
- *circa 1785*
Fine and rare pair of George III cut-glass candelabra on Wedgwood bases.
- *height 83cm*
- £40,000 • **Norman Adams**

## Pair of Candlesticks ▼
- *19th century*
Turned wood gilt, single-spike candlesticks, on a triangular base with champfered corners and carved lion's-claw feet.
- *height 90cm*
- £700 • **Lynda Franklin**

## Pair of Candlesticks ▼
- *circa 1750*
Pair of Italian carved wood and silver candlesticks, with floral assymetric designs on three heavily scrolled feet.
- *height 67cm*
- £1,900 • **O.F. Wilson**

## Pair of Candelabra ▲
- *circa 1825*
A pair of Regency, cut glass and ormolu candelabra with two branches. The cut glass is formed in long-faceted drops. On cut-glass base and stem.
- *height 36.5cm*
- £10,000 • **Norman Adams**

## French Candelabra ▲
- *circa 1880*
French candelabra with cranberry glass reservoir, three branches and chain link to gilded ceiling rose.
- *height 103cm*
- £425 • **Rosemary Conquest**

## Ecclestastical Candelabra ▼

- *circa 1900*

An ecclesiastical candelabra of two sections, the upper half forming a triangular section with five candle-spikes.

- *height 165cm*
- **£295** • **Youlls Antiques**

## French Candelabra ▼

- *circa 1880*

A pair of French table candelabra with brass fittings and stand, profusely decorated in hanging, faceted crystals.

- *height 50cm*
- **£750** • **Rainbow**

---

## Expert Tips

*Cleaning candlesticks of excess wax is best achieved by immersing them in boiling water, which is more efficient and less damaging than using a sharp tool. Ensure, however, that you put the plug in the sink, as otherwise the wax will solidify in the drain.*

## Stoneware Lamps ▲

- *circa 1850*

A pair of mid 19th-century continental stoneware, urn-shaped lamps, with double handles on square base.

- *height 75cm*
- **£3,500** • **Norman Adams**

## Gothic Candlesticks ▲

- *circa 1860*

A fine pair of 19th-century bronze, Gothic candlesticks with architectural and Gothic tracery with hexagonal bases on matching, white marble hexagonal plinths.

- *height 58cm*
- **£1,200** • **Lynda Franklin**

---

## Art Nouveau Table Lamp ▼

- *circa 1895*

A silver oxidised cast brass lamp fitted with an overlay glass shade.

- *height 32cm*
- **£1,600** • **Turn On**

## French Chandelier ▼

- *circa 1880*

A double tier French chandelier with twelve branches, faceted crystals and rewired bronze.

- *diameter 70cm*
- **£1,650** • **Rainbow**

## French Wall Lights ▼

- *circa 1880*

A set of four French wall lights with bronze fittings and crystals.

- *height 30cm*
- **£1,200** • **Rainbow**

## Altar Candlesticks ▼

• *circa 1780*
Italian silvered wooden altar
candlesticks, turned and profusely
carved with tripod feet.
• *height 84cm*
• £3,000
• M. Wakelin & H. Linfield

## Brass Lantern ▼

• *circa 1835*
A fine William IV lacquered brass
lantern in neo-Elizabethan style,
with six etched glass panels and
pierced floral decoration.
• *height 114cm*
• £35,000    • Norman Adams

## Pair of Candlesticks ▲

• *early 19th century*
Pair of wooden mahogany and
brass candlesticks.
• *height 37cm*
• £1,250    • P.L. James

## Brass Desk Lamp ▲

• *circa 1895*
Arts and crafts handbeaten brass
lamp with a shell-shaped shade.
• *height 42cm*
• £895    • Turn On

## Oil Lamp ▼

• *19th century*
A Victorian oil lamp on a brass,
Corinthian column, with green
glass reservoir vessel and all
original fittings.
• *height 81cm*
• £480    • Ranby Hall

## French Chandelier ▼

• *circa 1900*
Brass-bodied French chandelier
with four lights with blue crystal
tear drops and heavily cut prisms.
• *height 67cm*
• £500    • Rosemary Conquest

## Verdegris Lantern ◄

• *circa 1890*
A copper and glass lantern with a
curved quadrant chapeau.
• *height 1m*
• £1,000    • David Ford

## French Bag Chandelier  ▼
- *circa 1880*
An Empire style French bag
chandelier with eight branches
and bronze and crystal chains.
- *diameter 75cm*
- £1,200      • Rainbow

## Brass Lantern  ▲
- *circa 1895*
A late Victorian brass lantern
with a tulip-shaped shade on a
brass column, the whole on
tripod feet.
- *height 36cm*
- £750      • Turn On

## French Chandelier  ▲
- *circa 1870*
A French chandelier with twelve
branches and bronze and faceted
hanging crystals.
- *diameter 60cm*
- £1,250      • Rainbow

## Library Lamp  ▼
- *circa 1895*
Cast brass library table lamp
fitted with an iridescent green
glass shade. The light is
adjustable for height.
- *height 33cm*
- £895      • Turn On

## French Candelabra  ▲
- *circa 1840*
A pair of French four-light crystal
candelabra in original condition.
- *height 60cm*
- £2,900      • Judy Fox

## Malachite Candelabra  ▲
- *circa 1880*
A fine malachite candelabra with
six lights, decorated in gilt on a
green base, heavily gilded, with
an imperial crest.
- *height 1.32m*
- £43,000      • Emanouel

## Six-Light Candelabra  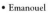
- *circa 1820*
Empire bronze and gilt with a
pair of angels holding the light
branches.Decoration to the base.
- *height 78cm*
- £22,000      • Emanouel

# Metalware

### Bronze Carp ◄
- **19th century**
A Japanese signed gilt and shakudo bronze model of a carp, naturalistically formed.
- *length 36cm*
- £5,800 • Gregg Baker

### Helen of Troy on Horse ▲
- *circa 1900*
French, Art Nouveau, patinated bronze, ormolu and ivory model, showing Helen of Troy mounted on a horse. Anonymous artist.
- *height 41cm*
- £5,250 • Gavin Douglas

### Japanese Rooster ►
- **18th century**
An iron suzuribako with a rooster and poem, signed by Myochin.
- *height 22cm*
- £1,950 • Gregg Baker

### Bronze Flower Vessel ▼
- **17th century**
Rikka-form vase cast with a central band of geometric design with 'arrow vase'-style handles. Edo period, Japan.
- *height 21cm*
- £6,000 • Gregg Baker

### Cherub Candelabra ▲
- *circa 1785*
A pair of Louis XVI bronze and ormolu cherub candelabra on marble bases.
- *height 60cm*
- £25,000 • Norman Adams

### Alloy Bowl ▲
- **12th century**
Bell metal-alloy bowl of the Ghaznavid period, with circular geometric designs to the exterior.
- *diameter 27.5cm*
- £600 • Oasis

## Expert Tips

*Beware of polishing bronzes. They have a patina which, when they are overcleaned, disappears to become a brassy colour. This will halve or quarter the value, particularly of a good bronze.*

### Iron Wall Plaque ►
- *circa 1890*
A burnished cast-iron belle epoque wall plaque of extravagant foliate design.
- *height 56cm*
- £1,250 • Westland & Co

## Bronze Candlestick ▲
- **12th-13th century**
Seljuk period candlestick with
Arabic design, standing on three
legs, with some patination.
- *height 26.5cm*
- £300                    • Oasis

## Empire Cassolettes ▼
- *circa 1800*
Patinated bronze and ormolu
cassolettes, shown with one cover
turned over, with ormolu panel of
musical nymphs in high relief.
- *height 34cm*
- £7,750        • Gavin Douglas

## The Snake Charmer ▼
- *circa 1925*
Gilt bronze of a snake charmer,
set on an onyx chamfered base.
Signed by Rudolph Marcuse.
- *height 54cm*
- £3,600        • Gavin Douglas

## Bronze Bustard ▲
- *circa 1880*
A good bronze model of a
bustard, signed by Q. Vesnal,
founder and Pascal, sculptor.
- *height 11cm*
- £900        • Elizabeth Bradwin

## French Gasolier ▲
- *circa 1880*
A 19th-century French neo-
Gothic wrought-iron gasolier,
with some restoration.
- *height 73.5cm*
- £2,400        • Westland & Co

## English Door Knobs ▲
- *circa 1890*
Pair of English beehive door
knobs with brass mounts and
turned decoration.
- *length 19cm*
- £85                    • Myriad

## Gamekeeper Bronze ▲
- *circa 1870*
A signed French bronze by
Dubucand. Gamekeeper carrying
a dead fox with a dog by his side.
- *height 24cm*
- £1,650        • Elizabeth Bradwin

### Bronze Figures ▲
- *circa 1850*
A patinated bronze group of
Baccanalian revellers, on red
marble base, by Marc Chal.
- *height 41cm*
- £2,450 • Gavin Douglas

### Chinese Bronze Censer ▲
- *circa 1800*
Censer with dog of Fo, pierced
floral decoration to lid and body,
with dragon-head handles.
- *height 33cm*
- £500 • Namdar

### French Vases ▼
- *circa 1795*
A pair of French directoire
patinated bronze and ormolu
vases, with scrolled handles.
- *height 35cm*
- £8,250 • Gavin Douglas

### Islamic Incense Burner ▼
- *13th century*
Bronze incense burner in the
form of a bird with a hinged beak.
- *height 6cm*
- £2,200 • Shiraz

### Chinese Canton ▲
- *18th century*
A metal brazier decorated with
flowers and foliage on turquoise
enamel ground. Qianlong period.
- *height 43cm*
- £3,800 • Guest & Gray

### Fleur De Lys ▲
- *circa 1850*
One of a set of burnished fleur de
lys with star-shaped piercing.
- *height 54.4cm*
- £750 • Westland & Co

## Expert Tips

*Bronzes are notoriously easy to
fake. Only experience in
handling will make you sure of
the piece you are buying.*

### Bronze Hounds ◄
- *circa 1880*
A French bronze by J. Moigniez; a
rare model of two hounds tugging
at a hare.
- *height 14cm*
- £1,320 • Elizabeth Bradwin

## The Reader ▲
- *circa 1775*
Patinated bronze, ormolu and
black marble in the form of an oil
lamp with a figure of a muse
reading from scroll. By Boizot.
- *height 40cm*
- **£6,250** • Gavin Douglas

## Lion and Unicorn ▲
- *circa 1840*
A fine pair of early Victorian
burnished cast-iron lion and
unicorn.
- *height 43cm*
- **£2,500** • Westland & Co

## Model of a Hound ▼
- *circa 1860*
Bronze of a recumbant hound.
Unsigned, probably French.
- *height 12.5cm*
- **£1,200** • Elizabeth Bradwin

## Pair of Casolettes ▼
- *circa 1810*
Pair of patinated bronze and
ormolu campana-shaped
cassolettes with scrolled handles.
Bultic or Russian origin.
- *height 44cm*
- **£9,750** • Gavin Douglas

## Islamic Bronze ◄
- *12th century*
Three Islamic bronzes from the
Salyough period. A tall-necked
jar with handle, a small bottle
with tear-drop design and a
small pot.
- **£400-600 each** • Shiraz

## Brass Coffee Pot
## and Cover ▲
- *circa 1880*
A coffee pot from Bokhara, with
elaborately swirled engraving and
a pierced cover.
- *height 36cm*
- **£400** • Sinia

## Bronze Figures ▲
- *19th century*
Patinated bronze of a young girl
lifting a struggling child. Signed
'J. Petermann Fondeur, Bruxelles'.
- *height 38cm*
- **£5,200** • Ranby Hall

## Bronze Group ▼

• *circa 1895*
Art Nouveau bronze of the Muse of Knowledge imparting her science to a blacksmith. Signed by L. Chalon.
• *height 90cm*
• £9,750          • Gavin Douglas

## Bronze Sumo Wrestlers ▼

• *19th century*
On a bronze, four-legged base with variegated motifs.
• *height 31cm*
• £1,850          • Gregg Baker

## Bronze Venus de Milo ▲

• *19th century*
Standing on a stopped marble plinth on gilt mounted feet. With foundry stamp, Delafontaine AD.
• *height 81cm*
• £2,400          • Ranby Hall

## Leda and the Swan ▲

• *circa 1910*
A Danish erotic bronze of Leda and the Swan by R. Tegnar. Made at the Siot foundry, numbered.
• *height 42cm*
• £3,750          • Gavin Douglas

## Live-Cast Baby Alligator ➤

• *circa 1900*
Possibly live-cast. Cold-painted Vienna bronze from the Bergman foundary. Nickel-plated on bronze.
• *height 32cm*
• £2,200     • Elizabeth Bradwin

## Bronze Koro ▼

• *19th century*
Japanese koro in the form of a boar with a raised head.
• *height 17cm*
• £3,200          • Gregg Baker

## Bronze Vase ▼

• *19th century*
A Japanese vase of lobed form decorated with a coiled dragon.
• *height 42cm*
• £3,200          • Gregg Baker

## Bronze Group of Mice ◄
- *19th century*
Bronze group with mice, grapes and pomegranate on a table, with the lid of the pomegranate lifting to reveal an incense burner. Signed by Sessei Chu.
- *height 24cm*
- **£3,400**          • **Gregg Baker**

## Bronze Greyhound ▼
- *circa 1776-1884*
By Jean Francois Theodore Gechten. Greyhound with prey on a naturalistic oval base.
- *height 36cm*
- **£6,650**          • **Ranby Hall**

## Bronze Figure ▲
- *19th century*
A French patinated bronze figure of a goddess, on an onyx base.
- *height 45cm*
- **£2,000**          • **Lynda Franklin**

## Japanese Vase ▼
- *circa 1868-1912*
Bronze vase with two-tone patination and fern decoration.
- *height 35.5cm*
- **£2,000**          • **Robert Brandt**

## Persian Vase and Cover ▲
- *circa 1880*
Bulbous body with long tapered neck, with floral cartouches and gilding.
- *height 46cms*
- **£1,600**          • **Sinia**

## Bronze of Young Girl ▲
- *circa 1902*
Art Nouveau bronze with two-tone patination. Foundry stamped and signed by Rudolph Marcuse.
- *height 25cm*
- **£1,550**          • **Gavin Douglas**

## Bronze Figure ▲
- *circa 1809-1852*
Fine bronze of a man carrying a
basket of fruit with his axe and
his hat in his belt. Signed by
Charles Camberworth.
- *height 71cm*
- £5,750        • Gavin Douglas

## French Coat Hooks ▲
- *circa 1880*
A pair of French coat hooks in
twisted brass with acanthus-leaf
mounts and ceramic knobs.
- *length 16cm*
- £116        • Myriad

## Islamic Dish ▼
- *circa 1890*
Brass, copper and silver dish with
organic designs, the rim with
Islamic cursive script.
- *diameter 26cm*
- £300        • Sinia

## Steel Bucket Grate ▼
- *circa 1840*
An English steel bucket grate
with 'C' scrolling terminating in
lion-paw feet.
- *height 65cm*
- £2,800        • Riverbank

## Bronze Lions ▼
- *circa 1820*
A pair of Italian Grand Tour
bronze lions on faux marble
plinths with wreath mount.
- *height 31cm*
- £1,800        • Riverbank

## Coffee Pot and Cover ▲
- *circa 1880*
Coffee pot with engraved floral
and geometric designs and
enamel jewel inset.
- *height 34cm*
- £400        • Sinia

## Bronze Florentine Singer ▲
- *circa 1880*
A bronze, by Paul Dubois,
showing a young man in medieval
costume playing a lute. From the
F. Barbedienne foundry.
- *height 63cm*
- £3,750        • Gavin Douglas

### Brazier Stand ▼
- *19th century*

A modelled cast-iron brazier stand in neo-classical manner with ram's head and cloven-hoof decoration.
- *height 1.11m*
- £3,500
- Westland & Co

### Pair of Candelabra ▲
- *circa 1886*

Patinated bronze ormolu and porphyry three-branch candelabra. Signed by Henry Dawson.
- *height 61cm*
- £10,000 • Gavin Douglas

### Chinese Incense Burner ▼
- *late 18th century*

A pewter Chinese incense burner of a Chinese boy holding an urn from a Western market.
- *height 44cm*
- £3,500 • Robert Brandt

### Persian Silver Beaker ▲
- *circa 1900*

From Kirmanshah, Iran. Showing domestic and rural scenes. Profusely decorated and embossed.
- *height 10cm*
- £150 • Namdar

### Brass Water Jug ▼
- *circa 1890*

From Damascus with silver inset cursive Islamic script.
- *height 25cm*
- £450 • Sinia

### Bronze Hawk ▼
- *19th century*

A Japanese bronze model of a hawk on a bronze branch.
- *height 47cm*
- £2,600 • Gregg Baker

### Pair of Fire Dogs ◀
- *circa 1820*

Coollatin House, County Wicklow with corinthian column with acanthus-leaf and ball finials.
- *height 84cm*
- £6,800 • Riverbank

# Furniture

**The market for antique furniture goes from strength to strength and is spreading across the world.**

The most used antiques of them all and, obviously, a vast field of study, antique furniture varies considerably in style depending on the period and the country in which it was made. Most collectors tend to concentrate on one area or one period, bookcases and cabinets, for instance, or Victorian furniture. Fakes, reproductions and updated pieces abound in this field more than any other, and it is important to be able to tell when a piece is 'right'.

A methodical approach to examination is important to be able to judge whether there has been any restoration – or whether distressing is evident in a place which would not have been distressed during the course of natural usage or wear.

There is no substitute for experience. The more used you are to handling and examining the real thing, the more likely you are to identify the 'wrong' one. The best reason for buying a piece of furniture is a genuine liking for it, so there is some satisfaction and pleasure in the possession in any event. However, the better informed you are about the main buying criteria – style, materials, method of construction, period, manufacturer – the more likely you are to make a wise purchase and the more you will enjoy the experience of owning it.

## Beds

### Louis XVI Bed ➤
- *circa 1880 (1774-1793)*
A mahogany Louis XVI-style bed with brass moulding and mounts.
- £1,550  • Old Cinema

### Chippendale Bed ▲
- *18th century*
A Chippendale mahogany bed reconstructed to current size with modern cream silk canopy insert.
- *width 1.82m*
- £6,500  • Mora & Upham

### Expert Tips

*Four-poster beds became unfashionable in the 18th and 19th centuries, and many were dismantled. Most of the beds on the market today are made up from the discards.*

### Oak Bedroom Suite ▼
- *circa 1785*
A French suite consisting of bed, bedside table, washstand, armoire, chest and much more.
- £25,000  • Sleeping Beauty

### Louis XV Walnut Bed ▲
- *circa 1890*
A five-foot Louis XV solid walnut bed. Heavily carved with swags and roses.
- £2,250  • Sleeping Beauty

## Oak Bed ➤
- *19th century*

Oak bed with carved rosettes and finial decoration on tapered fluted legs.
- £980          • Drummonds

## French Renaissance Bed ▲
- *circa 1860*

A heavily carved solid walnut Renaissance bed with finials and turned and fluted posts.
- *length 2m*
- £4,500          • Sleeping Beauty

## Spanish Bedstead ▲
- *circa 1860*

A Spanish hand-forged iron bedstead with large ornate cast-brass ornamentation.
- £1,695          • Sleeping Beauty

## Pair of Marquetry Beds ▲
- *circa 1870*

Italian, fine-quality beds with oval figurative panels and floral borders in the manner of Maggiolina.
- *height 1.33m*
- £9,500          • Browns Antiques

## Expert Tips

*The side irons of metal beds are essential, providing a frame on which to fit the base and mattress. Duplicates are almost impossible to find, so do not buy a bed where the irons are missing or don't fit properly.*

## French Brass Bedstead ◄
- *circa 1885*

French all-brass bedstead with beautiful cast ornamentation and finials.
- £2,500          • Sleeping Beauty

## Victorian Bedsteads ▼
- *circa 1880*

A pair of Victorian brass and cast-iron bedsteads.
- *length 1.95m*
- £1,295          • Sleeping Beauty

## Louis XVI Bed ▼
- *circa 1890*

A French mahogany bow-fronted bed with inlaid panels, adorned with ormolu mounts.
- £4,200          • Sleeping Beauty

### Louis XV-Style Suite ▲
- *circa 1890*

Painted French bedroom suite of dressing table, armoire and bedside table with original marble.
- **£12,000** • Sleeping Beauty

### Four-Poster Bed ▲
- *18th century*

A four poster carved bed with twisted columns.
- *height 2.16m*
- **£2,450** • Drummonds

### Louis XV-Style Bed ▼
- *circa 1890*

A rare six-foor wide walnut framed bed with heavily carved roses on foot board.
- *width 1.78m*
- **£6,500** • Sleeping Beauty

### French Renaissance Bed ▶
- *circa 1860*

Ebonized four-poster bedstead with heavily carved turned posts with canopy and carved footboard.
- *length 1.9m*
- **£8,500** • Sleeping Beauty

## Expert Tips

*Plaques bearing a maker's name are a mark of quality in brass beds. Among these are Maple and Co, Heal and Son and R. W. Winfield; the latter made beds for royal households and the plaque bears a coat-of-arms.*

### French Bed ▲
- *circa 1885*

A French Chapeau Grendarme with ornate brasswork and large castings.
- *length 1.5m*
- **£1,895** • Sleeping Beauty

### Victorian Brass Bed ▼
- *circa 1860*

An early Victorian all-brass bedstead with barley-twist posts.
- *length 2.2m*
- **£18,000** • Sleeping Beauty

### Polished French Bedstead ◀
- *circa 1870*

A small, double polished bedstead with floral rosettes.
- *height 1.1m*
- **£500** • After Noah

## Bonheurs du Jour

### Lady's Desk ∨

- *circa 1870*

A 19th-century English bonheur
du jour in lacquered bamboo,
with splayed legs on an 'H' frame
stretcher.
- *height 1.24m (to top)*
- £1,250          • North West 8

### Make-Up Table ➤

- *circa 1910*

An Edwardian lady's make-up
table in rosewood, with inlay, two
drawers and two side cabinets,
the whole on tapered legs with
castors.
- *height 88cm*
- £750          • Antiques Pavilion

### Burr-Walnut Bonheur du Jour ∧

- *circa 1860*

A Victorian burr-walnut bonheur
du jour with boxwood inlay, gilt
ormolu mounts and cabriole legs.
The interior in rosewood with
leather inset to the writing
surface. Shows three mirrors.
- *height 1.42m*
- £3,800          • Judy Fox

### Walnut Bonheur du Jour ∨

- *circa 1860*

An English marquetry inlaid
walnut bonheur du jour with
ornately carved mounts and
cabriole legs.
- *height 1.2m*
- £3,800          • Furniture Vault

### Burr Walnut Bonheur ∨

- *circa 1870*

Boxwood seaweed inlay with
ormolu mounts and gallery mirror.
- *height 1.4m*
- £3,800          • Judy Fox

### Inlaid Bonheur ◄

- *circa 1860*

A two-drawer, Victorian bonheur
du jour, the upper section with
cupboard doors inlaid with floral
decoration and pillared mirror.
- *height 80cm*
- £1,100          • Tower Bridge

## George III Mahogany Dressing Table ◄
- *circa 1810*

An early nineteenth century dressing table and chest of drawers with sliding mirror and pot cupboard.
- *height 90cm*
- **£5,850**    • Old Cinema

## French Bonheur du Jour ▼
- *circa 1880*

A French, rosewood bonheur du jour with gilt ormolu mounts and cabriole legs. The pull-out writing surface is inlaid with green tooled leather and the cupboard door panels show Sèvres plaques.
- *height 1.36m*
- **£4,800**    • Judy Fox

## Mahogany Bonheur ▼
- *circa 1880*

By Maples, with fine satin string inlay and shielded mirror.
- *height 1.21m*
- **£1,760** • Antique Warehouse

## Walnut Bonheur du Jour ▲
- *circa 1860*

A mid 19th-century walnut and cherry wood inlaid bonheur with ormolu surrounds and handles and Bombay-shaped front, sides and back, all raised on four cabriole legs.
- *height 75cm*
- **£6,500**    • L. & E. Kreckovic

## Expert Tips

*A plus factor when buying a bonheur du jour is having a maker's name, such as Waring and Gillow, on the piece. However, some 19th-century cabinet makers stamped their names onto pieces they were restoring.*

## Art Nouveau Bonheur ▶
- *circa 1900*

An Edwardian bonheur du jour in the Art Nouveau style, with typical inlay. Shows a raised set of small drawers with mirror and green leather inlay to the writing surface, above three drawers, all supported on tapered legs.
- *height 90cm*
- **£2,250**    • Tower Bridge

# Bookcases

## Chippendale Bookcase  ▼

- *circa 1900*
In mahogany with swan-neck
pediment inscribed 'T. Wilson,
66 Great Queen St, London'.
- *height 2.42m*
- £4,900      • Furniture Vault

## Bureau Bookcase  ▼

- *circa 1790*
George III mahogany with brass
fittings and a leather fitted desk.
- *height 2.27m*
- £4,800      • Chris Newland

## Breakfront Bookcase  ➤

- *circa 1810*
Mahogany with astragal glazed
doors, cupboard and drawers.
- *height 2.52m*
- £24,500      • Chambers

## Rosewood Bookcase  ▲

- *circa 1830*
A late-Regency open bookcase
with carved pilasters and three
adjustable shelves.
- *height 1.07m*
- £2,950      • M. J. Bowdery

## Secretaire Chest  ▼

- *19th century*
A mahogany secretaire chest with
swan-neck pediment.
- *height 1.04m*
- £1,450      • Castlegate

## Breakfront Bookcase  ◀

- *circa 1835*
Flame mahogany bookcase with
unusual glazed upper doors.
- *height 1.92m*
- £16,500      • Paul Andrews

### Biedermeier Bookcase ➤
- *circa 1900*
Swedish birchwood bookcase in
the Biedermeier style with gilt
mounts, ebonized pillars and a
moulded top.
- *height 1.24m*
- £4,500    • Rupert Cavendish

### Victorian Bookcase ▲
- *circa 1850*
A two-door glazed secretaire
bookcase in mahogany with
architectural pillars.
- *height 2.22m*
- £2,250    • Castlegate

### Oak Bookcase ◄
- *circa 1910*
An oak bookcase originally from
a post office, more lately from an
author's library.
- *height 1.33m*
- £1,450    • Julia Bennet

### Bureau Bookcase ▼
- *circa 1790*
A simple oak bureau bookcase
with four graduating drawers and
two pull-out candle holders.
- *height 2.15m*
- £3,800    • Chris Newland

### Secretaire Bookcase ▲
- *circa 1830*
William IV bookcase set in
mahogany with brass fittings.
- *height 2.1m*
- £4,250    • F. Beck

### Breakfronted Bookcase ▲
- *circa 1810*
One of a pair of bookcases, with
glazed doors above moulded
double doors.
- *height 2.36m*
- £24,500    • Chambers

## Bureau Bookcase  ▼
- *circa* 1770
Two solid mahogany panelled
doors. The bureau has fitted
interior with oak-lined drawers.
- *height 2.27m*
- £19,500    • J. de Haan

## Victorian Bookcase  ▲
- *circa* 1870
Good-quality bookcase made in
mahogany with rounded edges.
- *height 2.3m*
- £2,600    • Chris Newland

## Victorian Cabinet  ▼
- *circa* 1910
Mahogany bookcase with fine
glazed doors, raised on slender
turned feet. By Maple & Co.
- *height 98cm*
- £1,485    • Ranby Hall

## Secretaire Bookcase  ▼
- *circa* 1780
Faded mahogany with two glazed
doors and a fitted interior.
- *height 2.29m*
- £28,500    • M. Wakelin

## Breakfront Bookcase  ◄
- *circa* 1840
Mahogany with boxwood styling
and inlay and ebonized moulding,
with three glazed doors.
- *height 2.16m*
- £7,950  • Antique Warehouse

## Breakfront Bookcase  ►
- *circa* 1930
A fine neo-classical breakfront
bookcase in elm.
- *height 2.3m*
- £9,500    • Westland & Co

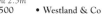

## Secretaire Bookcase ▼

- *circa 1790*
George III inlaid mahogany
bookcase with removable cornice.
- *height 2.75m*
- £18,500 • J. Collins

## Victorian Bookcase ▲

- *circa 1880*
Flame mahogany bookcase with
two glazed doors over two drawers
and figured mahogany doors.
- *height 2.43m*
- £3,875 • Antique Warehouse

### Expert Tips

*Glazing with astragals, the
glazing bars used to cover the
joins between small panes of
glass, persisted well after glass
factories had become capable of
producing large panes. Small
panes mean quality.*

## Secretaire Bookcase ➤

- *circa 1780*
A very fine English Sheraton
astragal-glazed secretaire
bookcase.
- *height 2.37m*
- £18,000 • P. L. James

## Breakfront Bookcase ▼

- *circa 1825*
A fine Hepplewhite-period
mahogany breakfront bookcase.
- *height 2.83m*
- £220,000 • Norman Adams

## Mahogany Bookcase ▼

- *circa 1835*
William IV mahogany bookcase
on swept bracket feet showing
empire pediment.
- *height 2.02m*
- £4,850 • Ranby Hall

## Gentleman's Bookcase ◄

- *circa 1710*
Rare thuyawood and rosewood
Anglo-Dutch gentleman's
bookcase, with original mounts.
- *width 1.6m*
- £18,500 • Luther & Goodwin

## Oak Bookcase ▼

- **19th century**
Light oak bookcase with glazed
doors above two drawers and two
doors, all with original mounts.
- *height 2.25m*
- **£1,295**    • Old Cinema

## Walnut Bookcase ▼

- **19th century**
Three-tiered bookcase with
Gothic bars and two drawers.
- *height 1.96m*
- **£850**    • Tower Bridge

## Breakfront Bookcase ➤

- **circa 1825**
A George IV figured mahogany
breakfront bookcase.
- *height 2.52m*
- **£100,000**    • Norman Adams

## Open Bookcase ▼

- **circa 1820**
Simulated rosewood bookcase
with two shelves on turned feet
and brass castors.
- *height 1.3m*
- **£1,650**    • M. J. Bowdery

## Breakfront Bookcase ➤

- **circa 1830**
A 19th-century English Gothic
country house burr elm and
amboyna breakfront bookcase
with cabinet.
- *height 1.17m*
- **£9,800**    • Luther & Goowin

## Globe Werniker ▲

- **circa 1915**
Six-stack, oak Globe Werniker
bookcase with lifting glass panels.
- *height 2m*
- **£950**    • Oola Boola

### Mahogany Bookcase ➤

- *circa 1900*
Fine astragal-glazed doors raised
on ogee bracket feet.
- *height 99cm*
- £780            • Ranby Hall

### Secretaire Bookcase ◣

- *circa 1795*
A rare small Sheraton period
secretaire in satinwood and
coromandel.
- *height 1.94m*
- £60,000      • Norman Adams

### George III Bookcase ➤

- *circa 1800*
Bookcase with lion-shaped brass
handles. Bureau with three
graduating drawers, ivory handles.
- *height 2.27m*
- £4,200         • Chris Newland

### Breakfront Bookcase ▼

- *circa 1870*
A very fine coromandel
breakfront bookcase, with four
glazed doors.
- *height 2.65m*
- £22,000              • Butchoff

### Mahogany Bookcase ◣

- *circa 1820*
Waterfall mahogany bookcase.
- *height 1.92m*
- £6,000              • T. Morse

### Mahogany Bookcase ◣

- *circa 1900*
A mahogany bookcase with two
glazed-over two-panelled doors.
- *height 2.3m*
- £2,200                • Fulton

# Boxes

## Rosewood Tea Caddy ▼
• *late 19th century*
Simple, rosewood tea caddy comprising two compartments for different blends. Decorated with brass on the clasp and lid. This caddy incorporates a magnificent cut-glass sugar bowl.
• *width 25cm*
• £220                    • Ian Spencer

## Hexagonal Tea Caddy ▲
• *circa 1785*
Late 18th-century, George III hexagonal, gilded, rolled-paper single tea caddy of unusual open design.
• *height 15cm*
• £2,450
• J. & T. Stone

## Ivory Sewing-Box ▼
• *circa 1830*
Magnificent early 19th-century vizagapatnum engraved and etched ivory sewing box with side drawer and sandalwood interior, in the form of a house with chimney finial and monogrammed cartouche.
• *height 14cm*
• £2,250          • J. & T. Stone

## Tortoiseshell Tea Caddy ▲
• *date 1830*
Very rare early 19th-century Regency pressed tortoiseshell two-compartment tea caddy, with ribbed and bowed front panels, domed top, silver stringing and insignia plate
• *height 18cm*
• £8,950          • J. & T. Stone

## Penwork Tea Caddy ➤
• *circa 1825*
Exceptional, Regency penwork double tea caddy, decorated with chinoiserie scenes of a festive parade inside and out. The caddy has matching side handles, brass lion feet and a cut crystal sugar bowl.
• *height 18cm*
• £8,950
• J. & T. Stone

## Thoya Wood Tea Caddy ▼
• *date 1775*
George III, 18th-century thoya tea caddy of outstanding quality, heavily decorated with oval shell patinae with matched inner lid, burr walnut and satin wood banding.
• *height 14cm*
• £2,250          • J. & T. Stone

## Victoria Wooden Dressing Case ▼
• *circa 1864*
Very unusual, Victorian, wooden dressing case with 11 extensively engraved silver-topped jars and containers marked with 1864. Two secret drawers. Signed by W. H. Toole.
• £9,950
• J. & T. Stone

## Expert Tips

*Price is generally determined by quality and materials used, as well as age and rarity. In general, boxes made from wood or papier mâché are widely available and most affordable.*

## Sovereign Sorter ▼

• *early 20th century*
Originally used by shopkeepers
to sort sovereigns and half
sovereigns. Mahogany with
brass fittings and escutcheon
to the lower drawer.
• *height 27.5cm*
• £650          • Ian Spencer

## Tortoiseshell Tea Caddy ▼

• *date 1810*
Early 19th-century very rare
green tortoiseshell tea caddy
with two compartments.
Showing ivory stringing, canted
corners, silver escutcheon, initial
plate and silver ball feet.
• *height 13cm*
• £8,950
• J. & T. Stone

## Two Compartment
## Tea Caddy ➤

• *date 1820*
Early 19th-century fine
Regency japanned penwork
two-compartment tea caddy of
elongated octagonal form, with
tented top and brass-loop handle.
Figures painted on the sides of the
box and pagoda pattern on lid.
• *height 17cm*
• £7,950
• J. & T. Stone

## Mother-of-Pearl
## Tea Caddy ▲

• *date 1840*
A mid 19th-century, Victorian
mother-of-pearl and abalone tea
caddy with two compartments
and original key.
• *height 17cm*
• £995          • J. & T. Stone

## Dressing Table Set ▲

• *circa 1930*
Art Deco turquoise shell dressing
table set in original silk-lined
leather box. Set comprises two
wooden hair brushes with
handles, two clothes brushes and
bottles and pots of cut glass in
various shapes and sizes, with
a mirror and tray in the lid.
• £1,450
• J. & T. Stone

## Sarcophagus Tea-Caddy ▼

• *circa 1835*
A fine quality yew-wood William
IV tea caddy. Concave lid with
panelled front, decorated with
quarter cotton reel edging and
solid, rosewood ring handles.
Whole is raised on a stepped
cotton reel base with squat brass
feet. Fine condition with original
patination throughout.
• *width 28.5cm*
• £975          • J. Collins

## Ten-sided Tea Caddy ▲

• *date 1790*
Late 18th-century ten-sided,
George III tea caddy. Quite
unusual, blonde tortoiseshell
with ivory stringing. The tea
caddy has two compartments,
silver top and handle with
escutcheon and monogrammed
initial plate and finial.
• *height 14cm*
• £5,950          • J. & T. Stone

## Crocodile Box  ➤
• *circa 1900*
Deep grained, crocodile box
with padded, velvet interior
and nickel mounts.
• *16x9cm*
• £480    • Holland & Holland

## Tortoiseshell Tea Caddy  ▲
• *date 1775*
Rare 18th-century oval
tortoiseshell single tea caddy
with ivory and engraved silver
stringing. Unusual construction
with tortoiseshell base.
• *height 11cm*
• £9,950    • J. & T. Stone

## Japanese Iron Box  ▲
• *circa 19th century*
Iron kogo (box) formed as a
kabuto (helmet). The top of
the kogo is decorated with gilt
mons. Signed by Yoshiatsu.
• *height 6cm*
• £1,450        Gregg Baker

## George III Tea Caddy  ▼
• *circa 1790*
George III, decagonal ivory tea
caddy with mother-of-pearl
inlay. Made in England.
• *height 10cm*
• £3,950        • J. de Haan

## Jewellery Box  ▼
• *circa 1900*
Fine, silverplated crocodile
jewellery box with padded velvet
interior. Plaque made in London.
• *24x18cm*
• £565    • Holland & Holland

## Straw Work Tea-Caddy  ◄
• *circa 1780*
Very rare single compartment tea
caddy, with decorative designs
following the neoclassical style.
• *width 16cm*
• £4,500    • Sign of the Hygra

## Wooden Tea Caddy  ▲
• *date 1790*
High quality, 18th-century
Georgian single compartment
wooden tea caddy with shell
patinae and checker stringing.
With brass top handle.
• *height 11.5cm*
• £1,250    • J. & T. Stone

## William IV Jewellery Box  ▲
• *circa 1835*
A very good quality William IV
coromandel brass-bound jewellery
box. The rectangular lid has a
central brass plaque, lock and
key and opens to reveal a
removable mirror. Mahogany
lined interior and sprung drawer.
• *height 18cm*
• £820        • J. Collins

### Travelling Dressing Case ◀
- *circa 1934*
An early 20th-century, fine-quality, Art Deco, crocodile-skin, gentleman's travelling dressing case. Made by Cartier of London. Hallmarked silver, inscribed 'Sir W. Rollo'.
- £3,995 • J. & T. Stone

### Sewing Box ▲
- *date 1832*
Exceptional, tortoise-shell sewing-box with extensive mother-of-pearl floral inlay. With pull-out lower drawer and a note from the original owner.
- *height 14cm*
- £4,950 • J. & T. Stone

## Expert Tips

*Tunbridgeware originated around Tunbridge Wells 300 years ago and is a form of veneered decoration made entirely from the contrasting grains and colours of local woods. Tunbridgeware boxes are much in demand.*

### Russian Hatbox ▼
- *circa 1900*
An early 20th-century Russian hatbox made of birchwood, with a leather strap.
- *diameter 36.9cm*
- *height 22.5cm*
- £490 • Rupert Cavendish

### Tortoiseshell and Silver Perfume Box ▼
- *circa 1918*
Original and complete. The box contains an inset of floral panel decorations. Made in England.
- *height 7.5cm*
- £1,270
- Sue & Allan Thompson

### Gold Japanese Kogo ▲
- *circa 19th century*
Japanese, gold lacquered 19th-century kogo (box) in the form of a very unusual piebald puppy. The box is a container for incense.
- *height 6cm*
- £1,650 • Gregg Baker

### Tunbridgeware Tea Caddy ▲
- *circa 1860*
Mid 19th-century, rectangular tea caddy. A view of Eridge Castle is shown on the lid. The box is made from rosewood with a keyhole in the panel of the box.
- *height 12cm*
- £625
- J. de Haan

### English Tortoiseshell Tea Caddy ▲
- *circa 1850*
Mid 19th-century English bow-front tortoiseshell tea caddy. Contains a mother-of-pearl floral inlay to the front panel. A fine quality piece.
- *height 33cm*
- £2,875
- J. de Haan

# Bureaux

### Walnut Bureau ◄

- *circa 1720*
18th-century bureau with five outer drawers and typical inner compartments.
- *height 82cm*
- £3,200 • Antiques Pavilion

### Rolltop Bureau ▲

- *circa 1860*
French with bronze mounts and authentification stamp.
- *height 1.2m*
- £15,500 • M. Mathers

### Cherrywood Secretaire ▼
- *circa 1810*
French secretaire with griffin feet and lion brass fittings.
- *height 1.41m*
- £4,800 • Sieff

### Bookcase Bureau ▲

- *circa 1860*
Chippendale-style twin-cylinder roll-top secretaire/bookcase.
- *height 2.5m*
- £18,650 • Antique Warehouse

### George I Bureau ▲
- *circa 1720*
Walnut bureau with good colour and patination. Original brass mounts and fitted interior.
- *height 1m*
- £7,995 • Red Lion

### Oak Bureau ►
- *circa 1820*
Ornately carved oak bureau with original drop-handles.
- *height 82cm*
- £975 • Antiques Pavilion

## Oak Bureau  ▼
- *circa 1780*

With flap enclosing pigeonhole
and small drawers, on tapered legs.
- *height 98cm*
- £1,100     • Gur & Sprake

## Bureau Bookcase  ▼
- *circa 1820*

Mahogany with fitted interior
and four drawers on bracket feet.
- *height 2.31m*
- £2,995  • Antique Warehouse

## Cylinder Bureau  ➤
- *circa 1880*

Victorian oak bureau with
stringing and chequered inlay.
- *height 1.51m*
- £2,995  • Antique Warehouse

## Oak Escritoire  ▲
- *circa 1650*

A very rare William and Mary
escritoire of small size with superb
colour and patina.
- *height 1.55m*
- £11,500     • Red Lion

## Expert Tips

*Until relatively recently,
bureaux other than walnut ones
were fairly inexpensive and,
therefore, not worth the trouble
and expense of faking. This is
not the case with walnut
bureaux, which were extensively
and painstakingly faked, often
with great ingenuity– as when
older but less valuable oak
bureaux were veneered.*

## French Cylinder Bureau  ▼
- *late 19th century*

Gilt metal mounted with four
drawers and fitted interior.
- *height 1.29m*
- £18,500     • Ranby Hall

## Biedermeier Secretaire  ▼
- *circa 1820*

Biedermeier-style birchwood
secretaire/bureau on square feet.
- *height 1.42m*
- £9,800     • Cavendish

## George III Bureau ◄
- *early 19th century*
Mahogany bureau with sloping
lid enclosing fitted interior.
- *height 1.06m*
- £5,500        • Old Cinema

## George II Escritoire ▼
- *circa 1785*
George II kingwood and
marquetry escritoire on stand.
- *height 1.21m*
- £20,000        • Norman Adams

## Bureau Bookcase ▲
- *circa 1730*
George II burr oak bureau with
walnut crossbanding. Fitted
interior with drawers below.
- *height 2.06m*
- £14,500        • Red Lion

## Bureau Bookcase ▲
- *circa 1800*
Oak and mahogany crossbanded
bureau bookcase on plinth feet.
- *height 2.14m*
- £4,950        • Red Lion

## Bookcase Bureau ➤
- *circa 1810*
A Regency secretaire bookcase,
in mahogany.
- *height 2.21m*
- £4,950        • Old Cinema

## Secretaire/Bureau ◄
- *circa 1825*
North European elm-wood
secretaire commode. Pull-out first
drawer over two other drawers.
- *height 94cm*
- £950        • Mark Constantini

### Mahogany Bureau ◄
- *circa 1780*
An 18th-century mahogany
bureau without leather inlay.
- *height 1.02m*
- £3,800    • Mora & Upham

### George III Bureau ▼
- *early 19th century*
Mahogany inlaid bureau with
fitted interior shaped upon
slightly splayed feet.
- *height 1.45m*
- £2,200    • Old Cinema

### Roll Top Bureau ▼
- *circa 1880*
Burr walnut with serpentine front,
fitted interior and three drawers.
Standing on scrolled feet.
- *height 2.26m*
- £8,250  • Antique Warehouse

### Campaign Chest ▲
- *circa 1840*
English mahogany secretaire
campaign chest with pull-out
flap, fitted compartments and
brass mounts.
- *height 1.10m*
- £4,200       • Riverbank

### Cylinder Bureau ▼
- *circa 1800*
A fine early 19th-century George
III mahogany cylinder bureau on
original castors.
- *height 1.41m*
- £10,500    • Westland & Co

## Expert Tips

*The earliest bureaux
were made in two parts, a
bureau on top and a chest
base below, each with its own
carrying handles. Ones to
look out for are transitional
examples, made in one piece
but still with the accoutrements
of two.*

### Military Chest ►
- *19th century*
Campaign/military chest in
camphor wood with brass handles.
- *height 1.06m*
- £3,500       • Tower Bridge

### Cylinder Bureau ➤
- *circa 1890*
Mahogany bureau with boxwood
and satinwood crossbanding.
- *height 1.12m*
- £7,000      • Judy Fox

### Oak Bureau ▲
- *circa 1750*
Shaped interior with drawers and
pigeon holes, on bracket feet.
- *height 1.35m*
- £2,450      • M.J.Bowdery

### English Country Bureau ▲
- *18th century*
Crossbanded in mahogany with
swan brass handles and shell inlay.
- *height 1.02m*
- £3,575      • I.& J.L.Brown

### Georgian Bureau ▲
- *circa 1810*
Mahogany bureau with green
leather inset and fitted interior.
- *height 1.06m*
- £1,400      • Zai Davar

## Expert Tips

*All other elements being equal,
the smaller the bureau the more
valuable it is likely to be.*

### Fall Front Bureau ◄
- *circa 1735*
George II red walnut bureau with
well fitted breakfront interior.
- *height 1.03m*
- £5,750      • J. Collins

# Cabinets

## Oriental Cabinet ▽
- *19th century*
A lacquered cabinet on a stand with a well fitted interior of ten compartments.
- *height 1.36m*
- £2,600     • Ranby Hall

## Continental Vitrine ▽
- *circa 1830*
A walnut-panelled vitrine with gilt mounts and lyre feet.
- *height 1.6m*
- £1,350     • Travers

## Mahogany Side Cabinet ▲
- *circa 1790*
A cabinet of the Sheraton period, of crossbanded satinwood with ebony and boxwood stringing.
- *height 89.5cm*
- £8,500     • J. Collins

## Pier Cabinet ▲
- *circa 1865*
A Victorian ebonised two-door pier cabinet inlaid with amboyna.
- *height 1.06m*
- £2,600     • Judy Fox

## Walnut Pier Cabinet ▽
- *circa 1860*
Cabinet with a mirror-fronted door panel and gilt-metal mounts.
- *height 1.08m*
- £1,980
- Ranby Hall

## Lacquered Cabinet ▽
- *circa 1770*
A good, small English table-top cabinet with chinoiserie scenes.
- *height 69cm*
- £3,800     • P. L. James

## Side Cabinet ➤
- *circa 1860*
A Victorian, walnut-veneered serpentine side cabinet.
- *height 1.08m*
- £1,980     • Ranby Hall

## Normandy Vitrine ➤
- *early 19th century*
A French vitrine with glazed doors, floral decoration and designs to the top. The whole standing on scrolled feet.
- *height 2.5m*
- £5,200  • Lynda Franklin

## Mizuya Kitchen Cabinet ▲
- *Edo period (1830)*
A Japanese Mizuya kitchen cabinet with a lacquered hinoki frame and keyaki drawer fronts.
- *height 1.66m*
- £3,400  • Gordon Reece

## Specimen Cabinet ➤
- *circa 1890*
Double-doored mahogany cabinet, with eight tiers of drawers. From the British Museum.
- *height 1.38m*
- £1,700  • Castlegate

## Circular Side Cabinet ▼
- *19th century*
A side cabinet in mahogany, of circular form with shelving.
- *height 68cm*
- £960  • Ranby Hall

## Scottish Cabinet ▲
- *circa 1840*
An unusual Scottish pokerwork cabinet, fully decorated and resting on bun feet, complete with key and shelving and made of Scots pine.
- *height 1.8m*
- £4,500  • Martin-Taylor

## Display Cabinet ▲
- *19th century*
A cabinet with waved pediment, central carved cartouche and overglazed doors. With S-shape drawers and ormolu fittings to front and sides.
- *height 2.47m*
- £6,850  • Ranby Hall

## Dutch Display Cabinet ➤
- *19th century*
A bombé-fronted Dutch marquetry display cabinet.
- *height 1.6m*
- £12,500  • P. L. James

## Japanese Lacquered Cabinet  ▲
- *19th century*
A fine Japanese lacquered cabinet on an English stand.
- *height 1m*
- £9,850　　　• P. L. James

## Japanned Display Case  ▲
- *19th century*
In Queen Anne style, with pagoda scenes, lattice-work and floral decoration. The whole on an X-frame stretcher and bun feet.
- *height 2.06m*
- £5,850　　　• Ranby Hall

### Expert Tips
*Pre-mid-18th century glazed doors may be indentified by their small, rectangular panes of glass and astragal mouldings. After 1750, glass became easier to cut.*

## Breakfronted Cabinet  ▼
- *circa 1890*
A satinwood cabinet decorated in marquetry by F. J. Genin, Paris.
- *height 1.77m*
- £4,950　　　• Browns

## Biedermeier Cabinet  ▼
- *circa 1815*
Swedish mahogany with top drawer and lower cupboard.
- *height 86cm*
- £3,400　　• Rupert Cavendish

## Victorian Credenza  ▼
- *circa 1870*
An ebonised credenza with ormolu mounts, showing painted porcelain plaques.
- *height 1.19m*
- £3,850　　• Kenneth Harvey

## Marquetry Cabinet  ▲
- *circa 1920*
An 18th-century style Dutch marquetry vitrine on a bombé chest base and standing on bracket feet.
- *height 2m*
- £2,250　　　• Canonbury

## Demi-Lune Vitrine  ▲
- *circa 1900*
An Edwardian inlaid mahogany single-door vitrine with compartment beneath and on square tapered spade feet.
- *height 1.7m*
- £2,700　　　• Judy Fox

## Biedermeier Cabinet ➤
- *19th century*
A substantial mahogany side
cabinet, inlaid with figured and
oval, floral panel designs.
- *height 1.59m*
- £3,650 • **Ranby Hall**

## Chinese Style Cabinet ▲
- *19th century*
Chippendale-style library display
cabinet with astragal-glazed doors
above three cupboards with
chinoiserie design of figures,
flowers and pagodas.
- *height 2.35m*
- £11,500 • **Ranby Hall**

## Corner Cabinet ▲
- *circa 1920*
A glazed cabinet with carved
decoration, on three cabriole legs.
- *height 1.78m*
- £2,950 • **Kenneth Harvey**

## Regency Cabinet ▼
- *circa 1830*
Regency flame-mahogany side
cabinet. On bun feet.
- *height 98cm*
- £1,350 • **Victoria Harvey**

## Display Cabinet ▼
- *circa 1900*
Edwardian display cabinet with
ebony stringing, on swept feet.
- *height 2.2m*
- £2,750 • **Ian Spencer**

## Hanging Corner Cabinet ▼
- *circa 1790*
Moulded concave and sectioned
cornice. Well grained doors.
- *height 1.05m*
- £2,650 • **J. Collins**

## Corner Cupboard ▼
- *circa 1800*
A George III mahogany cupboard
with exceptional patina. With
shelves and two drawers within.
- *height 1.03m*
- £995 • **Castlegate**

## Japanese Chest-Cupboard ▼
- *circa 1830*
A late Edo period Japanese chest-cupboard with three zelkova drawers above slatted cupboard fronts and two larger drawers below, all in an elm frame.
- *height 91cm*
- **£2,800**          • **Gordon Reece**

## Satinwood Cupboard ▶
- *circa 1785*
An English, satinwood, bedside cabinet for storing the chamber pot, with inlaid detailing to the front and top, the whole on square, tapered legs.
- *height 77cm*
- **£1,850**          • **O. F. Wilson**

## George II Escritoire ▲
- *circa 1750*
A kingwood and marquetry writing cabinet on stand.
- *height 1.21m*
- **£120,000**
- **Norman Adams**

## Japanese Chest ▲
- *circa 1830*
An Edo chest with looking cabinet. The whole in Paulownia wood with original fittings.
- *height 59cm*
- **£1,900**          • **Gordon Reece**

## Victorian Display Cabinet ▼
- *19th century*
A black ebonised and amboyna display cabinet.
- *height 1.06m*
- **£1,100**          • **Old Cinema**

## Edwardian Vitrine ▼
- *circa 1890*
Mahogany, Sheriton-style vitrine with floral marquetry.
- *height 1.8m*
- **£5,200**          • **Judy Fox**

## Display Cabinet ▼
- *circa 1905*
An unusually small, English Edwardian, mahogany, inlaid, bow-fronted cabinet, well proportioned with solid wood stretcher and tapered legs on spade feet.
- *height 1.66m*
- **£2,950**   • **S. & A. Thompson**

### Expert Tips

*Some cabinets have been cut down to suit modern size preferences. Look carefully at the underside of the bases and top surfaces, and check for joins that should not be there.*

## Collector's Cabinet ▲
- *circa 1900*
Steel and glass collector's cabinet with brass mountings.
- *height 1.25m*
- £1,500 • David Ford

## Bedside Cupboard ▲
- *circa 1820*
A mahogany French Empire cupboard with ormolu and gilt mountings and a marble top.
- *height 77cm*
- £1,950 • O. F. Wilson

## Chinese Herbal Cabinet ➤
- *19th century*
A red lacquered herbalist's cabinet with Chinese characters.
- *height 2.12m*
- £1,850 • Riverbank

## Hanging Corner Cabinet ▲
- *circa 1740*
The cabinet has two double panelled doors with starburst marquetry inlay designs.
- *height 1.14m*
- £1,575 • Red Lion

## George II Pot Cupboards ▲
- *circa 1750*
A pair of burr-walnut pot cabinets.
- *height 70cm*
- £1,675 • C. Preston

## Continental Cabinet ▼
- *circa 1800*
Unusual mahogany cabinet with a shaped panel door and moulded square taper legs.
- *height 1.54m*
- £1,495 • M. J. Bowdery

## Breakfront Cabinet ◄
- *date 1866*
A mahogany cabinet by Gillow, signed Thos Whiteside. With architectural and leaf decoration.
- *height 98cm*
- £6,850
- Chambers

### Mahogany Side Cabinets ▼
- *circa 1880*
Matched pair of mahogany side
cabinets with marble tops.
- *height 84cm*
- £1,150          • Ranby Hall

### Corner Cabinet ▶
- *circa 1910*
One of a pair of Edwardian
mahogany cabinets with glazed
upper part and a cupboard base.
- *height 2.16m*
- £750          • Canonbury

### Oak Corner Cabinet ▲
- *circa 1780*
A full standing cupboard with
patina and original mounts.
- *height 2.09m*
- £3,975          • Red Lion

### Italian Walnut Cabinet ▲
- *circa 1880*
A cabinet in the Bambocci
manner, decorated with figural
uprights and panelled doors.
- *height 91.5cm*
- £2,400          • Westland & Co

### French Pearwood Cabinet ▼
- *circa 1830*
Carved pearwood cabinet from
Normandy. Good colour with
diamond-shaped panels and
chamfered columns on both sides.
- *height 1.23m*
- £2,750          • Town & Country

### Corner Cupboard ▼
- *circa 1780*
A rare George III, chinoiserie-
patterned, Japanned, standing
corner cupboard.
- *height 2.03m*
- £40,000          • Norman Adams

### Secretaire/Cabinet ▼
- *19th century*
A boulle-work ebonised secretaire
with rosewood interior and
various compartments.
- *height 1.36m*
- £2,750          • Ranby Hall

# Canterburies

## Music Stand ◄
- *circa 1920*

Regency-style painted, wrought-iron music canterbury with profuse floral pierced decoration and splayed legs.
- *height 68cm*
- £1,275          • Browns

## Victorian Canterbury ▼
- *circa 1850*

Burr walnut with turn supports on original porcelain castors.
- *height 55cm*
- £1,400          • Judy Fox

## Victorian Canterbury ▲
- *circa 1875*

Burr walnut Victorian canterbury with ornate pierced gallery top and pierced divisions, the whole raised on turned feet.
- *height 87cm*
- £1,495          • Fulham

## Victorian Canterbury ▼
- *circa 1880*

Mahogany wood with turned supports and legs and one drawer.
- *height 56cm*
- £1,025 • Antiques Warehouse

## Brass Magazine Rack ▲
- *circa 1915*

An Edwardian brass magazine rack, with carrying handle.
- *height 80cm*
- £245          • Castlegate

### Expert Tips

*The legs of canterburies are particularly vulnerable. Check them for evidence of repair or replacement.*

## Mahogany Canterbury ▲
- *circa 1815*

A fine-quality English mahogany canterbury with turned columns and legs with brass castors.
- *height 54cm*
- £2,800          • Tredantiques

## Walnut Canterbury ➤
• *circa 1900*
An Edwardian walnut canterbury
with frame surmounted by finials
mounted by turned and reeded
columns and a frieze drawer raised
on turned legs.
• *height 50cm*
• **£1,750** • **Hatchwell**

## Mahogany Canterbury ▲
• *circa 1810*
A mahogany canterbury with two
drawers, finials and turned legs
with original brass castors.
• *height 52cm*
• **£2,200** • **Chambers**

## Walnut Canterbury ▼
• *circa 1910*
An Edwardian canterbury with
frame surmounted by finials
mounted with turned and reeded
columns.
• *height 52cm*
• **£1,650** • **Hatchwell**

## Burr Walnut Canterbury ▼
• *circa 1850*
Canterbury with turned supports
and legs, standing on original
porcelain castors.
• *height 55cm*
• **£1,400** • **Judy Fox**

## Double Music Stand ▼
• *19th century*
English mahogany stand with lyre
motif and carved triangular base.
• *adjustable height*
• **£2,300** • **Judy Fox**

## Folio Stand ◄
• *1820*
Early 19th-century mahogany
folio stand.
• *height 56cm*
• **£4,000** • **Walpole**

# Chairs

## Tapestry Armchair ▼
- *circa 1680*
A rare French hardwood
armchair with tapestry cover.
- *height 1.21m*
- £6,500 • Raffety & Walwyn

## Grotto Harp Stool ▼
- *circa 1850*
A grotto stool with scallop shell
seat on acanthus cabriole legs and
claw feet. The whole in gilt.
- *height 65cm*
- £1,600 • Lynda Franklin

## Regency Bergère ➤
- *circa 1810*
A very good, large Regency
bergère.
- *height 96cm*
- £6,200 • Christopher Preston

## Biedermeier-Style Chair ▲
- *circa 1915*
A pair of Swedish masur birch
chairs in cream ultra-suede.
- *height 93cm*
- £4,900 • Rupert Cavendish

## Sheraton Chair ▲
- *circa 1780*
An English green-painted chair
decorated with floral designs.
- *height 90cm*
- £4,600 • O.F. Wilson

## Bamboo Chair ▼
- *circa 1830*
A Regency single chair painted to
simulate bamboo.
- *height 87cm*
- £175 • O.F. Wilson

## Hall Chair ▼
- *circa 1850*
An English mahogany mid 19th-
century hall chair, with scrolled
arms and an extensively turned
frame, the whole resting on bun
feet. The chair is in perfect
condition, and reupholstered,
with a red and gold Gothic
pattern.
- *height 98cm*
- £1,800 • Gabrielle de Giles

## Oak Armchairs  ◄
- **19th century**
A pair of 19th-century oak armchairs with leather upholstery.
- *height 1.07m*
- **£2,750**                    • Browns

## Rocking Chairs  ►
- *circa 1885*
A pair of arts and crafts ladder-back rocking chairs.
- *height 85cm*
- **£480**                    • Riverbank

## Elbow Chair  ▲
- *circa 1835*
Mahogany elbow chair with scrolled arm rests, turned front and sabre back legs.
- *height 81cm*
- **£400**                    • Castlegate

## Bergére Library Chair  ▼
- **19th century**
An English-made solid rosewood chair with scrolled top rails, turned legs and scrolled lappets.
- *height 97cm*
- **£8,950**
- **M. Wakelin & H. Linfield**

## Hepplewhite Chair  ▲
- *circa 1780*
A fine single chair in mahogany with carved cabriole legs.
- *height 91cm*
- **£1,950**                    • J. de Haan

## Egyptian Armchair  ▲
- *circa 1840*
An unusual Egyptian Mouhraby inlay walnut armchair.
- *depth 85cm*
- **£5,800**                    • Martin-Taylor

## Library Chair  ◄
- **19th century**
A superb quality chair with reeded legs terminating in casters. Signed 'Gillows'.
- height 93cm
- **£3,850**                    • Browns

Chairs

## Hepplewhite Armchairs ▼
- *circa 1770*
A pair of shield-back Hepplewhite armchairs with the decoration restored as new.
- *height 83cm*
- £3,850 • P.L. James

## Gothic Painted Chairs ▼
- *19th century*
A pair of Victorian Gothic red-painted chairs with turned legs, Gothic tracery and a pierced backrest with finials.
- *height 89cm*
- £640 • Myriad

## Gilt Wood Chair ▲
- *19th century*
George I-style chair in carved gilt wood with green upholstery.
- *height 85cm*
- £4,000 • Browns

## Gothic Armchairs ▲
- *19th century*
Pair of Gothic armchairs with fine tracery.
- *height 1.1m*
- £4,850 • Christopher Preston

## Expert Tips

The Victorians introduced suites of sofas, armchairs, chairs without arms and, sometimes, footstools. It is rare to find these pieces together; even pairs of armchairs are uncommon.

## Arts and Crafts Chair ▼
- *circa 1860*
An early arts and crafts English chair in the style of Pugin.
- *height 83cm*
- £1,500 • Riverbank

## French Empire Chairs ▼
- *circa 1830*
One of a set of six mahogany chairs with scrolled arms.
- *height 72cm*
- £5,950 • O.F. Wilson

## French Leather Armchair ▼
- *circa 1880*
A French button leather armchair with turned legs.
- *height 69cm*
- £975 • Youlls

315

## Writing Chair ▲
• *circa 1840*
A fine 19th-century Portuguese carved rosewood writing chair.
• *height 98cm*
• **£20,000**     • **Norman Adams**

## Provincial Fauteuil ▲
• *circa 1820*
An oversized French provincial walnut open armchair, with escargot feet, covered in moleskin.
• *width 1.15m*
• **£1,950**     • **French Country**

## Red Walnut Chairs ▼
• *circa 1730*
A fine pair of red walnut chairs with cabriole legs.
• *height 96cm*
• **£9,500**   • **Raffety & Walwyn**

## Victorian Chairs ▼
• *circa 1885*
Set of four rosewood chairs with cabriole legs and pierced leaf decoration.
• *height 85cm*
• **£950**                • **Castlegate**

## French Bergère ◄
• *19th century*
A pair of French bergères painted with scroll and shell motifs on scrolled feet.
• *height 1.03m*
• **£2,550**     • **Lynda Franklin**

## Bedroom Chair ▲
• *circa 1880*
A French gold bedroom chair with original upholstery.
• *height 90cm*
• **£190**        • **Lacquer Chest**

## Piano Chair ▲
• *circa 1860*
A mahogany balloon back revolving piano chair.
• *height 80cm*
• **£550**         • **North West 8**

## Expert Tips
*Beware overstuffed drop-in seats. If these have been pushed hard onto the frame, they may have put pressure on the rail joints, causing them to split.*

Chairs

### Irish Desk Chairs ➤
- *19th century*
A pair of mahogany chairs with
carved decoration to backrest.
- *height 93cm*
- £1,125      • Old Cinema

### Bergère Chair ▲
- *circa 1815*
A Regency, mahogany bergère
chair, with buttoned upholstery
cushions and turned legs
terminating in casters.
- *height 1.03m*
- £1,850      • Terence Morse

### Ladies Armchair ▼
- *circa 1910*
A Hepplewhite-style armchair in
painted satin wood, with turned
legs and stretchers.
- *height 87cm*
- £1,000      • Browns

### Mahogany Rocking Chair ▲
- *circa 1860*
With new upholstery, scrolled
arms and turned legs.
- *height 1.04m*
- £725      • Castlegate

### French Armchair ▼
- *circa 1880*
Brass inlaid with gilt decoration
on turned and fluted legs.
- *height 1.1m*
- £1,550      • Youlls

### Turner's Chair ▲
- *circa 1660*
A 17th-century turner's chair in
ash, with profuse turning
demonstrating the maker's skills.
- *height 1.28m*
- £4,500      • M.J. Bowdery

### Library Chair ▲
- *circa 1840*
A Victorian library buttoned
slipperback chair on casters.
- *height 87cm*
- £1,850 • Christopher Preston

## George II Chairs ⌄

- *circa 1740*
Set of four oak chairs with spoon backrest and cabriole front legs.
- *height 98cm*
- £950                    • Albany

## Ladder-Back Chair ⌄

- *circa 1730*
A single elm chair with turned legs and nipple decoration.
- *height 97cm*
- £125                    • Castlegate

## Hepplewhite Chairs ❯

- *circa 1780*
A set of eight mahogany shield-back dining chairs.
- *height 92.5cm*
- £60,000            • Norman Adams

## Set of Chairs ⌃

- *circa 1900*
A set of four painted and gilded Northern Italian chairs with shell and mushroom motifs, on cabriole legs.
- *height 85cm*
- £1,450            • Andrew Bewick

## French Fauteuil ⌃

- *circa 1770*
With terrecotta highlights, light blue cloth and floral designs.
- *height 91cm*
- £2,200                • O.F. Wilson

## Bergère Library Armchair ⌄

- *circa 1830*
Mahogany with turned legs and wickerwork to back and sides.
- *height 91cm*
- £990                    • Castlegate

## Egyptian Design Chair ⌄

- *circa 1920*
Pair of English elbow chairs with hand-worked tapestry covers.
- *height 94cm*
- £4,950
- M. Wakelin & H. Linfield

## Chippendale Armchairs ➤

- *circa 1760*
A pair of Chippendale period
mahogany armchairs with
generously proportioned seats.
- *height 95cm*
- £26,000 • Norman Adams

## Country Armchair ▲

- *circa 1840*
An ash and elm country armchair
with good patination, with turned
arm supports and legs.
- *height 91cm*
- £195 • Castlegate

## Upholstered Armchair ▲

- *circa 1890*
An upholstered armchair with
original green patterned material.
- *height 91cm*
- £725 • Lacquer Chest

## Balloon Back Armchair ▼

- *circa 1885*
With scrolled arms, on turned
feet with original casters.
- *height 92cm*
- £395 • Castlegate

## Drawing Room Chairs ▼

- *circa 1840*
Set of six with moulded backs
and carved vertical central splat.
- *height 81cm*
- £3,750 • J. Collins

## Gothic Hall Chairs ▲

- *circa 1840*
A pair of Gothic chairs with
period architectural back with
the letters 'A.S.'.
- *height 92cm*
- £495 • Castlegate

## Child's Rocking Chair ▲

- *circa 1900*
A turned child's rocking chair in
ash and elm.
- *height 85cm*
- £145 • Castlegate

## Mahogany Chairs ▲

• *circa 1755*
Set of six chairs with caned seats, pierced back and sabre back legs.
• *height 82cm*
• **£3,750**          • **Lesley Bragge**

---

### Expert Tips

*The more chairs in a set, the greater the value. Thus a pair will be worth more than twice the value of a single chair, but a set of eight will be worth perhaps 20 times the value of a single chair. The most valuable sets will include one or two carvers.*

---

## Child's Rocking chair ▼

• *circa 1790*
An 18th-century turned ash and elm child's rocking chair.
• *height 51cm*
• **£265**          • **Castlegate**

## Country Dining Chairs ▼

• *circa 1885*
Set of four arts and crafts elm chairs with tapered legs.
• *height 90cm*
• **£550**          • **Castlegate**

## Winged Armchair ▶

• *circa 1880*
An armchair raised on ebonized cabriole legs with pad feet.
• *height 1.3m*
• **£1,850**          • **Ranby Hall**

## Empire-Style Chair ▲

• *circa 1900*
Pair of Swedish, mahogany chairs with sabre back legs and gilded decoration to the backrest.
• *height 84cm*
• **£2,300**          • **Rupert Cavendish**

## Lacquered Chair ▲

• *19th century*
By Hitchcock, Connecticut.
With fruit and leaf decoration.
• *height 83cm*
• **£1,400**          • **Lynda Franklin**

## American Rocker ▼

• *circa 1880*
With profuse turned decoration and tartan upholstery.
• *height 1.03m*
• **£395**          • **Castlegate**

### George III Armchairs ▶

- *circa 1790*
A pair of beech, shield-back
armchairs with fine original
painted decoration.
- *height 97.5cm*
- **£30,000**   • **Norman Adams**

### Mahogany Chair ▲

- *circa 1760*
A mahogany chair of the
Chippendale period with carved
scrolling decoration, pierced back
splat and generous seat.
- *height 98cm*
- **£1,650**   • **Riverbank**

### Leather and Walnut Chair ▲

- *circa 1885*
Leather chair with stud work,
turned arms, on an X-frame base.
- *height 89cm*
- **£680**   • **Youlls**

### Victorian Chairs ▲

- *circa 1860*
A very attractive pair of walnut
single chairs with carved and
pierced backs, on cabriole legs
with escargot feet.
- *height 87cm*
- **£575**   • **M.J. Bowdery**

### French Painted Chair ▲

- *circa 1790*
A painted chair with portcullis
back and octagonal, tapered legs.
- *height 92cm*
- **£1,250**   • **Riverbank**

### French Armchairs ▼

- *circa 1890*
A pair of ornately carved French
painted armchairs with original
cream paint, on cabriole legs.
- *height 92cm*
- **£2,850**   • **Tredantiques**

### George III Armchair ▼

- *circa 1790*
A mahogany open armchair with
moulded serpentine toprail,
pierced, carved decoration to the
back splat and a generous
upholstered seat, the whole on
bun feet.
- *height 89cm*
- **£1,250**   • **Westland & Co**

### Hepplewhite Period Chair ▼
- *circa 1780*
In mahogany with pierced backrest and turned legs.
- *height 88cm*
- £520 • Castlegate

### Neo-Gothic Armchair ▼
- *19th century*
Impressively carved chair, with Gothic tracery, twisted and fluted decoration and solid-wood seat, the whole on turned legs.
- *height 1.31m*
- £1,750 • The Old Cinema

### Mahogany Dining Chairs ➤
- *19th century*
Six chairs with moulded camel back and good patination.
- *height 96.5cm*
- £7,500 • J. Collins

### French Fauteuils ▲
- *circa 1755*
A pair of open-arm gilt wood chairs, stamped 'Iocob'.
- *height 88cm*
- £5,500 • Michael Davidson

### Library Chair ▲
- *circa 1810*
A deep button-backed library chair with original upholstery.
- *height 1.06m*
- £2,200 • Riverbank

### Set of Dining Chairs ▼
- *circa 1780*
A set of six 18th-century fruitwood dining chairs, set on turned, candlestick legs, with classical motifs throughout.
- £3,200 • Sieff

### Leather Desk Chair ▼
- *circa 1885*
Leather and mahogany chair with brass stud work, on tapered legs.
- *height 99cm*
- £260 • Youlls

---

### Pair of Fauteuils ➤

- *circa 1820*
A pair of early 19th-century
French mahogany fauteuils with
original tapestry.
- £1,900  • Sieff

### Chinese Chairs ▲

- *circa 1820*
A rare pair of tall-backed Chinese
hardwood chairs.
- *height 82cm*
- £680  • P.L. James

### Chippendale Chair ▲

- *circa 1780*
With a pierced vase-shaped splat,
solid seat and square chamfered
legs with stretchers.
- *height 95cm*
- £1,450  • M.J. Bowdery

### George III Elbow Chair ▲

- *circa 1800*
In mahogany, with lyre-shaped
centre splat and turned supports.
- *height 85cm*
- £795  • M.J. Bowdery

### Victorian Low Chair ▲

- *19th century*
A walnut low chair with carved
decoration and turned legs
terminating in casters.
- *height 76cm*
- £695  • Old Cinema

### Mahogany Library Chair ▼

- *circa 1810*
An English library armchair with
turned front legs.
- *height 94cm*
- £2,750  • Riverbank

### Elbow Chair ▼

- *circa 1800*
An elbow chair in elm with
remains of the original paint.
- *height 97cm*
- £850  • Lacquer Chest

323

### Painted Cane Chair ▼
- *19th century*
French 19th-century painted cane with carved ribbon decoration and turned legs.
- *height 91cm*
- £380 • Lynda Franklin

### Windsor Chair ▼
- *circa 1760*
An 18th-century, cabriole leg Windsor chair with excellent colour and a wide seat.
- *height 1.02m*
- £1,800 • Red Lion

### William IV Chairs ▶
- *circa 1835*
Set of rosewood dining chairs, six plus two. Carvers with scrolled arms. All with well carved midrail and turned, fluted legs.
- *height 96cm*
- £12,500 • Chambers

### Victorian Library Chair ▼
- *circa 1850*
A mahogany Victorian library chair, with scrolled arms and turned front legs.
- *height 79cm*
- £1,150 • Old Cinema

### Folding Campaign Chair ▼
- *circa 1870*
A folding campaign chair in green upholstery.
- *height 82cm*
- £330 • Lacquer Chest

### Danish Oak Chair ▲
- *circa 1880*
A Danish oak chair upholstered in fine quality needlework.
- *height 99cm*
- £1,150 • Ranby Hall

### Horseshoe Chairs ▲
- *circa 1820*
A pair of Chinese horseshoe chairs in elmwood with rattan seats.
- *height 82cm*
- £2,500 • Gordon Reece

## Venetian Chair ▲

- *circa 1875*
Set of six 19th-century Venetian chairs with interlaced backs and original silk covers.
- *height 91cm*
- **£6,000**
- **M. Wakelin & H. Linfield**

## Sheraton Chairs ▲

- *circa 1780*
A set of eight singles and two carvers with Sheraton decoration.
- *height 80cm*
- **£15,000**          • P.L. James

## Windsor Chair ▼

- *circa 1800*
A rare ash and elm windsor chair with crinoline stetcher.
- *height 1.01m*
- **£1,795**          • Red Lion

## Regency Chairs ▼

- *circa 1820*
A set of well restored Regency chairs including six singles and two armchairs.
- *height 80cm*
- **£12,800**          • P.L. James

## Oak Chair ➤

- *circa 1780*
A country oak chair with turned decoration on a solid seat.
- *height 91cm*
- **£195**          • Lacquer Chest

## Leather Library Chair ▲

- *circa 1825*
A rosewood library chair with moulded and shaped arms reminiscent of the lyre form.
- *height 1.02m*
- **£10,500**
- **M. Wakelin & H. Linfield**

## Spanish Hall Chairs ▲

- *circa 1850*
A pair of decorative Spanish walnut hall chairs with well carved mushroom engravings to the front panels.
- *height 80cm*
- **£2,000**          • Gabrielle de Giles

## Walnut Armchairs ▲

• *circa 1880*
A pair of finely carved French walnut armchairs with original leather upholstery and profusely turned stretchers. The chairs are carved with leaf patterns adorning the bottom and tops of the arms. The whole rests on lion-paw feet.
• *height 94cm*
• **£3,200**     • **Tredantiques**

---

## Expert Tips

*Beware of 'scrambling', where unscrupulous dealers – or innocent householders – add to a set of chairs by taking some of them apart and replacing parts with new members, making up new chairs from old parts.*

---

## French Walnut Chairs ▼

• *19th century*
A pair of walnut chairs with carved leaf decoration and scrolling designs, on cabriole legs.
• *height 83cm*
• **£1,450**     • **Lynda Franklin**

## Gilt Armchairs ▼

• *circa 1880*
A pair of French armchairs with carved detail on frame and arms.
• *height 1.03m*
• **£2,500**     • **Canonbury**

## Child's Highchair ▼

• *circa 1800*
A bergère highchair with turned front and splayed rear legs. Easily converted to a table and chair, with a central screw to table base.
• *height 94cm*
• **£1,350**     • **John Clay**

## Victorian Sofa Chairs ▶

• *19th century*
A pair of Victorian sofa chairs.
• *height 40cm*
• **£1,650**     • **Fiona McDonald**

## Windsor Chair ▲

• *circa 1760*
Windsor chair in ash and elm with comb back and cabriole legs.
• *height 1.08m*
• **£5,800**     • **Raffety & Walwyn**

## Sheraton Armchair ▲

• *circa 1795*
A Sheraton period painted and gilded armchair.
• *height 88.5cm*
• **£8,000**     • **Norman Adams**

## Queen Anne Chair  ▼
• *circa 1700*
A very rare Queen Anne
transitional chair with excellent
colour and patina.
• *height 1.02m*
• £3,450          • Red Lion

## Queen Anne Armchair  ▲
• *circa 1710*
Very stylish and of bold
proportions with repairs to frame.
• *height 83cm*
• £1,975          • Red Lion

## Oak Armchair  ▼
• *circa 1840*
With button back, turned fluted
front legs and carved decoration.
• *height 85cm*
• £850          • John Clay

## Country Chairs  ▼
• *circa 1800*
A pair of country chairs with
carved back splat, in oak with
upholstered seats and turned
front legs on pad feet.
• *height 1m*
• £1,250          • Lacquer Chest

## Italian Gondola Chairs  ▲
• *circa 1780*
A pair of 18th-century Venetian
gondola chairs, in wood, part-
covered in leather with silver
damask upholstery and
extravagant baroque lines.
• *width at base 94cm*
• £4,250          • French Country

## Louis XV Armchair  ▼
• *circa 1880*
French walnut armchair with
carved floral decoration.
• *height 87cm*
• £1,050          • The French Room

## Mahogany Dining Chairs  ➤
• *19th century*
Set of six English dining chairs
with hide seats.
• *height 79cm*
• £2,950          • Westland & Co

327

### Windsor Side Chairs ▼
- *circa 1810*
A pair of comb-back windsor side chairs with turned legs.
- *height 87cm*
- £145 • Castlegate

### Invalid's Chair ▼
- *circa 1910*
An invalid's chair with original green upholstery.
- *height 1.36m*
- £190 • Lacquer Chest

### George I Oak Chairs ▶
- *circa 1720*
A solid pair of George I oak chairs with good colour.
- *height 99cm*
- £595 • Red Lion

### Louis XVI Bergère ▲
- *19th century*
A Louis XVI-style bergère with gold leaf on tapered, reeded legs.
- *height 1.06m*
- £1,395 • Red Lion

### Simulated Bamboo Chairs ▲
- *circa 1820*
Set of six Regency simulated and painted bamboo chairs.
- *height 84cm*
- £1,200 • North West 8

### French Dining Chairs ▼
- *circa 1885*
A set of eight French Empire-style dining chairs.
- *height 91cm*
- £4,500 • North West 8

## Expert Tips

*Large sets of chairs have often been broken up, and carvers manufactured from them. Check the wood match on the arms of the carver and, particularly, the size of the seat. The carver should be at least two inches wider than the other chairs.*

### Mahogany Hall Chair ▲
- *circa 1820*
English Regency period, of unusual shape, with sabre legs.
- *height 80cm*
- £4,650 • O.F. Wilson

## Occasional Chair ▼
- *circa 1890*
Louis XVI-style chair with caned
seat and back.
- *height 90cm*
- £225                    • Youlls

## Walnut Nursing Chair ▼
- *circa 1860*
A Victorian walnut nursing chair
with floral carving, on cabriole
legs and scroll feet.
- *height 91cm*
- £525                    • Albany

## Fauteuil Chairs ▶
- *19th century*
A pair of carved and gilt
armchairs with upholstered arms.
- *height 1m*
- £4-5,000               • Browns

## Fauteuil ▲
- *circa 1760*
A pair of walnut and beachwood
French chairs with floral tapestry.
- *height 1.15m*
- £28,000         • O.F. Wilson

## Biedermeier Style Chairs ▲
- *circa 1885*
A pair of Swedish birchwood
chairs covered in damask fabric.
- *height 85cm*
- £2,900    • Rupert Cavendish

## William IV Armchair ▼
- *circa 1835*
Excellent William IV armchair in
red leather upholstery with
carved decoration on turned feet.
- *height 94cm*
- £2,600          • Old Cinema

## Mahogany Elbow Chair ▼
- *circa 1835*
With scrolled arm rests, turned
front legs and sabre back legs.
- *height 81cm*
- £400                • Castlegate

# Chaises Longues & Day Beds

### Mahogany Chaise Longue ➤
- *circa 1830*
Fine mahogany William IV
covered chaise longue.
- *length 1.47m*
- **£8,500** • **Butchoff**

### Victorian Chaise Longue ▲
- *19th century*
With pierced and scrolling leaf
decoration, on cabriole legs.
- *height 96cm*
- **£1,675** • **Castlegate**

### Walnut Settee ➤
- *circa 1860*
English, canvas with button back,
standing on cabriole legs.
- *length 2.2m*
- **£4,950** • **S. & A. Thompson**

### William IV Day Bed ◄
- *circa 1835*
William IV rosewood daybed.
- *length 1.84m*
- **£5,500** • **Butchoff**

### Expert Tips

*The condition of the framework
of a chaise longue is all-
important. The condition of the
upholstery is also important, but
only in so far as it is very
expensive to replace. The
novelty of springs led restorers
of the late 19th and early 20th
centuries to use them rather
than taut webbing in
reupholstery. A bad idea.*

### Mahogany Day Bed ➤
- *circa 1830*
Cuban mahogany day bed with
bronze engraving on the lower
side panel. In excellent
condition.
- *length 1.9m*
- **£1,900** • **Pillows**

### English Chaise Longue ➤
- *circa 1820*
A Regency green watered silk
faux rosewood chaise longue with
carving.
- *length 1.88m*
- **£2,900** • **Mora & Upham**

### Victorian Chaise Longue ◄
- *circa 1880*
Mahogany frame, cabriole legs
and acanthus-leaf decoration.
- *length 84cm*
- £1,550        • Castlegate

### French Chaise Longue ◄
- *circa 1890*
A French Third Republic chaise
longue in mahogany, with brass
mounts. The whole raised on
turned legs with brass castors.
- *length 2.11m*
- £2,300        • Ian Spencer

### French Chaise Longue ▲
- *circa 1900*
Mahogany walnut Louis XVI
style meridienne.
- *length 1.73m*
- £1,650        • French Room

### Victorian Chaise Longue ➤
- *circa 1870*
Recently upholstered. Original
marble castors and brass fittings.
- *length 2.13m*
- £1,900        • Gabrielle de Giles

## Expert Tips

*Repainting of the framework of
a chaise longue is perfectly
acceptable as long as it is very
well done. It is preferable to
much Victorian overpainting.*

### French Day Bed ▼
- *early 19th century*
Early 19th-century French daybed
in fruitwood.
- *length 1.9m*
- £2,250        • Julia Bennett

### French Day Bed ◄
- *circa 1890*
Painted and upholstered and
adorned with circular engravings
on both uprights. With decorated
frieze, fluted legs and grey/cream-
coloured upholstery.
- *length 1.79m*
- £2,500        • Victoria Harvey

### Louis XVI Chaise Longue ➤
- *circa 1890*
Double-ended chaise longue in
the Louis XVI style.
- *length 1.7m*
- £2,700        • North West 8

# Chests of Drawers & Commodes

## Bow Chest ▼
- *circa 1850*
A Victorian mahogany bow-fronted chest of drawers.
- *height 89cm*
- £1,650          • C. Preston

## Chest on Stand ▼
- *circa 1710*
A fine chest on original stand with exceptional patina.
- *height 1.32m*
- £7,000          • Raffety

## Oak Chest ▼
- *circa 1820*
A 19th-century oak chest of drawers with brass, swan-necked handles and bracket feet.
- *height 1.04m*
- £750          • Fulham

## Channel Islands Tallboy ▲
- *circa 1800*
Beautifully faded mahogany with shell inlay and original brass.
- *height 2.05m*
- £14,500
- M. Wakelin & H. Linfield

## Mahogany Tallboy ▲
- *circa 1825*
A Swedish tallboy of unusually narrow form, with gilded mounts and lion's-paw feet.
- *height 1.36m*
- £4,500          • Cavendish

## Linen Press ▼
- *circa 1860*
Victorian mahogany linen press with oval panel doors.
- *height 2.31m*
- £4,450          • Ranby Hall

## Expert Tips

*It is highly advantageous to the value of a chest of drawers to have its original handles. Check inside a drawer to see if there are any holes from handles of a previous incarnation.*

## Step Commode ▼
- *circa 1830*
William IV commode in the form of library steps, with hinged compartment, on four turned legs.
- *height 79cm*
- £950          • Castlegate

Chests of Drawers & Commodes

## Chest of Drawers ▼
• *circa 1725*
George I figured walnut chest of drawers with slide and original handles on moulded bracket feet.
• *height 83cm*
• £16,000 • **Norman Adams**

## Bombé Chest ▼
• *circa 1780*
European bombé-fronted chest of drawers and linen press.
• *height 2.2m*
• £6,500 • **L. & E. Krekovic**

## Marriage Coffer ➤
• *circa 1724*
A Swedish coffer in pale oak with original paint and iron strapwork.
• *length 1.53m*
• £3,800 • **Riverbank**

## Chest on Chest ▲
• *circa 1760*
Mahogany chest on chest, the top with moulded cornice.
• *height 1.79m*
• £4,200 • **Old Cinema**

## Chest on Stand ▲
• *circa 1770*
Oak chest with walnut veneer, with drawers of graduated sizes, on later oak base with serpentine stretchers and turned legs.
• *height 1.5m*
• £3,900 • **Angel**

## Tallboy ▼
• *circa 1760*
A George III mahogany tallboy, with chamfered corners, with slide, on bracket feet.
• *height 1.8m*
• £6,500 • **Terence Morse**

## Inlaid Commode ▼
• *circa 1890*
A late 19th-century, inlaid Louis XV-style serpentine commode with fruitwood and satinwood marquetry and ormolu mounts, on splayed legs.
• *height 85cm*
• £1,250 • **Youlls**

## Oak Chest of Drawers  ▲

• *circa 1880*
A graduated oak chest of drawers with pearl escutcheons and circular brass handles.
• *height 84cm*
• £750                    • Fulham

## Linen Press  ▼

• *circa 1864*
Flame mahogany linen press with moulded decoration to the doors.
• *height 2.31m*
• £4,450                  • Ranby Hall

## Directoire Commode  ▶

• *circa 1790*
A directoire French commode.
• *height 83cm*
• £16,500
• M.Wakelin & H. Linfield

## Bachelor Chest  ▼

• *circa 1705*
An unusual, small Queen Anne walnut bachelor chest, with original mounts.
• *height 81cm*
• £80,000        • Norman Adams

## Bow-Fronted Commode  ◀

• *circa 1800*
A lift-top commode on splayed feet with replacement mounts.
• *height 66cm*
• £420                    • Albany

### Expert Tips

*Early veneer was hand-cut and will not be of a regular thickness. Machine-cut veneer will be thinner and uniform. You can see the thickness on the edges of the drawers.*

## Dressing Chest  ▲

• *circa 1760*
A dressing chest, in mahogany, with top drawer fitted with original mirror and shaving box.
• *height 82cm*
• £3,250 • Christopher Preston

## China Trade Chest  ▲

• *circa 1820*
A China trade chest of amboyna, with military-style handles.
• *height 1.01m*
• £14,500
• M. Wakelin & H. Linfield

## Oak Trunk ◄

- *date* 1770
A Westphalian decorated oak
trunk, with date to front.
- *height* 75cm
- £2,650 • C. Preston

### Campaign Chest ▼

- *circa* 1850
Mahogany military chest in two
parts, the whole on bun feet.
- *height* 1.09m
- £1,425 • Ranby Hall

## Small Chest of Drawers ▲

- *circa* 1830
A mahogany chest of drawers,
with a rectangular breakfront top
with 'B' moulded edge.
- *height* 94.5cm
- £3,200 • J. Collins

### Mahogany Chest ▼

- *circa* 1820
An early 19th-century, well-
figured mahogany chest with
shaped apron and splayed feet.
- *height* 1.15m
- £1,895 • M. J. Bowdery

### Wellington Chest ▲

- *circa* 1830
A flame mahogany Wellington
chest with original brass mounts
and bracket feet.
- *height* 1.4m
- £3,800 • Castlegate

### George III Chest ►

- *circa* 1800
A large chest of drawers, with
original brass handles.
- *height* 1.2m
- £1,100 • Castlegate

## Tall Chest of Drawers ▲

- *circa* 1775
A Hepplewhite-period, mahogany
serpentine chest of drawers.
- *height* 1.53m
- £20,000 • Norman Adams

### French Commode ◄
• *19th century*
A French, mahogany commode of exceptional quality with violet-veined marble slab top with turned architectural side columns and brass inlay. The whole on turned, bun feet.
• *height 85cm*
• **£3,850** • **Ranby Hall**

### Secretaire Tallboy ►
• *circa 1790*
A Sheraton period, mahogany secretaire tallboy.
• *height 1.88m*
• **£28,000** • **Norman Adams**

### Walnut Tallboy ▲
• *circa 1730*
A tallboy of good colour and proportions, with engraved brass handles and cabriole legs.
• *height 1.58m*
• **£9,500** • **Red Lion**

### Mahogany Chest ▲
• *circa 1820*
A mahogany chest of two over three drawers, with round brass handles and shaped apron.
• *height 1m*
• **£795** • **Fulham**

### Miniature Chest of Drawers ▼
• *circa 1850*
A mid-19th century miniature chest of drawers in figured mahogany, with bowed top drawer above three smaller drawers and turned architectural columns, the whole on bun feet.
• *height 72cm*
• **£1,150** • **Walpole**

### Pine Chest of Drawers ▲
• *circa 1880*
A Victorian painted pine chest of drawers with white porcelain handles and plinth base.
• *height 98cm*
• **£395** • **Old Cinema**

### Chest on Chest ◄
• *circa 1790*
A George III, mahogany chest on chest, with slide, dental cornice and original handles, all raised on bracket feet.
• *height 1.97m*
• **£5,800** • **Ranby Hall**

## Oak Coffer ◄
- **17th century**
A 17th-century oak coffer with organic and geometric carving, on bracket feet.
- *height 99cm*
- **£1,200**          • **Angel**

## Oak Chest of Drawers ▼
- *circa 1680*
A 17th-century oak chest of drawers with applied geometric moulding, the whole on stile feet.
- *height 84cm*
- **£7,750**          • **Angel**

## Italian Commode ▲
- *circa 1750*
Serpentine-fronted commode with profuse painted decoration.
- *height 86cm*
- **£7,500**     • **Lynda Franklin**

## Wellington Chest ▼
- *circa 1870*
A Victorian, seven-drawer Wellington chest, in mahogany.
- *height 1.28m*
- **£2,900**        • **Old Cinema**

## Chest of Drawers ▲
- *circa 1790*
A mahogany, serpentine-fronted chest of drawers with satinwood cross-banding and splayed feet.
- *height 91cm*
- **£5,850**          • **Harvey**

## Wellington Chest ▲
- *circa 1860*
An exceptionally large, Victorian walnut Wellington chest.
- *height 2m*
- **£5,500**          • **Harvey**

## Mule Chest ➤
- *circa 1700*
Oak mule chest with original lozenge carving and two drawers.
- *length 1.04m*
- **£1,650**        • **Red Lion**

### Burgundy Chest  ➤

- *circa 1870*
Chest with linen-fold side panels
and Gothic pilasters and tracery.
- *height 72cm*
- £2,850        • Old Cinema

### Serpentine Chest  ▲

- *circa 1770*
A mahogany, serpentine chest of
drawers with cant and reeded
corners and original brass swan
handles, all on bracket feet.
- *height 81cm*
- £18,500        • Chambers

### Oak Chest of Drawers  ▼

- *circa 1710*
Chest with four tiers of drawers
with engraved brass mounts.
- *height 89cm*
- £1,850        • Red Lion

### Two-Part Chest  ▼

- *circa 1750*
Rare, George I, walnut, two-part
chest of drawers on bracket feet.
- *height 1.02m*
- £3,975        • Red Lion

### Chest of Drawers  ▲

- *circa 1850*
Flame mahogany chest of drawers
with brass drop handles.
- *height 1.1m*
- £795        • Fulham

### Chest on Chest  ▲

- *circa 1770*
A George III mahogany chest on
chest with carved, chamfered
decoration on splayed feet.
- *height 1.87m*
- £8,500        • Harvey

### Regency Chest  ◄

- *circa 1825*
Mahogany chest of drawers with
turned and reeded pillars and
circular brass handles.
- *height 1.08m*
- £875        • Fulham

## Oak Chest of Drawers ◄

- *circa 1680*
A 17th-century oak chest of
drawers, with moulded decoration
and brass mounts.
- *height 90cm*
- £2,500                    • Angel

## Georgian Chest ▼

- *circa 1790*
With pierced, latticed brass
mounts, on bracket feet.
- *height 78cm*
- £950                    • Albany

## Oak Chest on Stand ▲

- *circa 1740*
Chest with four tiers of drawers
above stand with hoof foot.
- *height 1.36m*
- £4,975                    • Red Lion

## Flame Mahogany Chest ▼

- *circa 1885*
Round-cornered chest of drawers
with bun feet.
- *height 86cm*
- £650                    • Fulham

## Georgian Tallboy ▲

- *circa 1820*
A late Georgian mahogany,
seven-drawer tallboy with oval
brass handles and replacement
pediment, on shaped, bracket feet.
- *height 2.09m*
- £2,850                    • Old Cinema

## French Commode ▲

- *circa 1890*
A French commode chest with
range marble top, ormolu mounts
and floral inlay designs.
- *height 89cm*
- £1,480                    • Ranby Hall

## Sword Chest ➤

- *circa 1620*
A continental sabre or sword
chest on shaped legs.
- *length 1.44m*
- £3,650                    • Red Lion

### Lacquer Commode ➤
- *circa 1860*
English bombé commode,
chinoiserie painted and lacquered.
- *height 92cm*
- £8,000          • David Ford

### Italian Commode ▲
- *circa 1895*
Venetian amboyna commode on
splayed legs with scrolled feet.
- *height 92cm*
- £4,850          • Lamberty

### Large Chest of Drawers ▲
- *circa 1800*
A George III chest of drawers
with original brass handles on
splayed, bracket feet.
- *height 1.2m*
- £1,100          • Castlegate

### Bombé Commode ▲
- *circa 1876*
An Italian, bombé serpentine
commode in figured burr walnut
and mounted on cabriole legs.
- *height 83cm*
- £4,250
- M.Wakelin & H. Linfield

### Italian Commode ▲
- *circa 1785*
A double bow-fronted Italian
commode, made in the 18th
century and painted in the early
19th, with découpage decoration.
(Découpage is the art of using
paper cutouts to decorate
furniture and accessories such as
boxes and trays, after they have
been sanded and painted. The
finished object which has been so
decorated looks and feels, after
the application of a protective
sealant, like fine enamel).
- *height 78cm*
- £5,850          • Browns

### Chest on Chest ▼
- *circa 1760*
Figured mahogany chest on chest
with original brass handles.
- *height 2.1m*
- £10,400          • Chambers

## Expert Tips
*Furniture with a wax finish
should be polished no more
frequently than every few weeks
or so. To be properly protective,
the surface needs time to harden
between polishes.*

### Miniature Chest ◄
- *circa 1880*
A Cuban mahogany miniature
chest of drawers with rounded
corners and plinth base.
- *height 75cm*
- £1,650          • Walpole

## Oak Chest of Drawers ◄
- *circa 1895*

A Jacobean-style chest of drawers with geometric lozenge moulding to drawers and brass drop handles, all on bracket feet.
- *height 96cm*
- £1,850 • Fulham

## Rosewood Veneer Chest ▲
- *circa 1830*

In mahogany, with brass stringing and carved leaf decoration.
- *height 1.02m*
- £1,250 • Castlegate

## Night Table ◄
- *circa 1780*

A mahogany night table with lift top and serpentine front.
- *height 76cm*
- £1,950 • Chambers

## Queen Anne Chest ▼
- *circa 1710*

In elm, fruitwood and oak, crossbanded on bracket feet.
- *height 99cm*
- £3,200 • Angel

## German Chest ▲
- *circa 1825*

By Biedermeier, in birchwood, with four deep drawers with ebonized shield escutcheons.
- *height 96cm*
- £4,500 • Cavendish

## Walnut and Oak Chest ▲
- *circa 1710*

A walnut and oak chest of drawers with cross-banded top and drawers.
- *height 92.5cm*
- £4,850 • M. J. Bowdery

## Mule Chest ►
- *circa 1750*

A mid 18th-century oak mule chest with two drawers, on bracket feet.
- *height 75cm*
- £1,495 • Old Cinema

# Davenports

## Burr Walnut Davenport ▼
- *circa 1850*
Decorated with boxwood
marquetry with Wellington door-
closing mechanism.
- *height 84cm*
- £5,400 • Judy Fox

## Mahogany Davenport ▲
- *circa 1860*
With swivel top, brass gallery and
fitted interior.
- *height 85cm*
- £1,950 • Youlls

## William IV Davenport ▶
- *circa 1830*
In Rosewood, sitting on carved
bun feet with castors. With tan
leather writing surface and brass
heart insignia on the rail.
- *height 90cm*
- £2,950 • F. Beck

## Regency Davenport ▼
- *circa 1810*
Rosewood davenport with
drawers on the side, side pillars
and a mustard green inlay.
- *height 85cm*
- £1,950 • Tower Bridge

## Burr Elm Davenport ▼
- *circa 1880*
Burr elm davenport with lift top
and brass gallery.
- *height 85cm*
- £8,700 • Butchoff

## Walnut Davenport ◀
- *circa 1860*
With secret pen tray, cabriole
legs, leaf decoration and brass
gallery. The whole on bun feet.
- *height 84cm*
- £1,650 • Castlegate

## Chinese Davenport ▼
- *circa 1830*
An exported small Chinese davenport with chinoise decoration. On bun feet.
- height 92cm
- £5,500  • Martin-Taylor

## Ebony Davenport ▲
- *circa 1830*
With maple-wood fitted interior and new black-leather top.
- height 92cm
- £7,500  • R. Hamilton

## Victorian Davenport ▼
- *19th century*
Davenport with inkwells, geometric inlay designs and side drawers with ceramic handles.
- height 79cm
- £1,280  • Castlegate

## Expert Tips
*Davenports became popular during the Regency period and earlier examples, which are unusual, are relatively plain in design.*

## Piano Pop-up Davenport ◄
- *circa 1860*
Burr walnut with fitted interior and sliding writing surface with red leather inlay. Has carved supports on bun feet.
- height 90cm
- £4,250  • Judy Fox

## Rosewood Davenport ▼
- *19th century*
Original leather insert with well turned side columns.
- height 84cm
- £2,850  • Ranby Hall

## Walnut Davenport ➤
- *19th century*
With lockable pen and pencil compartment and walnut gallery.
- height 81cm
- £1,550  • Old Cinema

# Desks

## Pedestal Desk ➤

• *circa 1850*
A superb example of a mid 19th-century burr walnut pedestal desk with all original brass handles, raised on bun feet.
• *height 75cm*
• **£5,750**        • **Browns**

## Chippendale Desk ▲

• *circa 1770*
A good Chippendale-period reading desk, with tooled leather inlaid surface supported by narrow, four-drawer pillars.
• *height 82cm*
• **£7,500**        • **P. L. James**

## Expert Tips

*There are many kneehole desks in circulation which did not start out in life in that role. Some have been converted from chests of drawers; to establish this check that the drawers look complete and that the veneers match. Desks with kneeholes but drawers on only one side should be avoided. It is most probable that they are converted from washstands.*

## Partners' Desk ➤

• *circa 1745*
Victorian partners' desk in mahogany. Pedestals can be reversed. Smaller than usual.
• *length 1.51m*
• **£4,250** • **Antique Warehouse**

## Pedestal Desk ▲

• *circa 1930*
A continental art deco pedestal desk made in birch with two panelled cupboards with four sliding shelves and three drawers with locks and keys.
• **£1,600**        • **Chris Newland**

## Walnut Secretaire ▼

• *circa 1870*
A rare, open-fronted secretaire with walnut birch and ebony stringing. With lockable cabinet.
• **£3,250**        • **Chris Newland**

## Victorian Partners' Desk ◄

• *circa 1880*
A 19th-century mahogany desk with reversible full hide leather pedestals.
• *length 1.76m*
• **£4,950** • **Antique Warehouse**

## Partners' Desk ◄
- *circa 1840*
A mid-19th-century figured mahogany desk with frieze drawers. Replacement leather inlay. On shaped plinth base.
- *height 78cm*
- **£2,000** • Spencer

## Lady's Desk ▼
- *circa 1880*
A rosewood lady's desk, with boxwood inlay, decorated with penwork to a floral design, with leather insert. Standing on eight tapering legs, with splayed feet and castors.
- *height 94cm*
- **£3,600** • Judy Fox

## Lady's Writing Desk ▲
- *circa 1890*
Walnut gothic style lady's writing desk with two doors enclosing open shelves with leather inset writing top.
- *height 67cm*
- **£695** • Fulham

## Kneehole Desk ▼
- *circa 1740*
A rare kneehole desk in solid cherrywood with good patina.
- *height 89cm*
- **£2,750** • Red Lion

## Reading Table ▲
- *circa 1785*
A George III satinwood reading table of simple lines, with prop-up reading and writing surface and two drawers with original ceramic handles, on tapering legs with brass castors.
- *height 74.5cm*
- **£15,000** • Norman Adams

## Expert Tips

*Tooled leather panels came in at the end of the 19th century. Good replacement panels are not detrimental.*

## Partners' Desk ➤
- *circa 1780*
A large, mahogany partners' desk with frieze drawers and plain curved brass handles, all raised on shaped bracket feet.
- *height 77cm*
- **£2,600** • Spencer

## Cylinder-Top Desk ◄
- *circa 1870*
Victorian cylinder-top desk with various compartments, pull-out writing flap and drawers.
- *height 1.26m*
- **£3,500** • **Old Cinema**

## William IV Desk ▲
- *circa 1825*
Mahogany drop-leaf pembroke desk with one dummy drawer on back and real one on front. On a turned base.
- *height 73cm*
- **£2,600** • **L. & E. Kreckovic**

## Writing Desk ▼
- *circa 1920*
Mahogany Hepplewhite writing desk with brass-bound and leather top on carved cabriole legs.
- *height 73cm*
- **£695** • **Fulham Antiques**

## French Cylinder Desk ▼
- *circa 1780*
Walnut cylinder desk on square legs with drawers above and below and pull-out writing flap.
- *height 1.27m*
- **£5,500** • **Kenneth Harvey**

## Roll-Top Desk ▲
- *circa 1880*
A rare English Victorian roll-top desk in solid mahogany, signed Hobb & Co, with fitted locks and handles.
- *height 1.2m*
- **£1,950** • **Chris Newland**

### Expert Tips

*Large desks were cut down when smaller desks became fashionable. Look for the repositioning of drawer handles.*

## Birch Desk ▲
- *circa 1830*
Unusual satinwood, birch and ebony line-inlaid desk with a rising lid and well fitted interior.
- *height 95cm*
- **£1,450** • **M.J. Bowdery**

## Oak Desk ▶
- *circa 1850*
Partners' desk with four drawers to each pedestal and three-drawer frieze. Original brass handles.
- *height 74cm*
- **£3,800** • **Terence Morse**

### Tambour Desk ➤
- *circa 1890*
American mahogany desk with
writing slides, original handles
and self-locking drawers. Stamped
'Buddha - 1012 McFarland St,
Normal, Oklahoma'.
- *width 1.55m*
- £12,750        • C. Preston

### Library Desk ▲
- *circa 1810*
George III period mahogany desk
on tapered legs with castors. The
top divides and opens to reveal a
chart and map compartment.
- *length 1.24m*
- £11,500        • John Bly

### Pedestal Desk ▲
- *circa 1900*
A well restored pedestal desk
embossed in brown leather with
brass handles.
- *height 77cm*
- £1,850        • Chris Newland

### George II Davenport ▼
- *circa 1785*
A Regency mahogany davenport
desk with swivel top.
- *height 84cm*
- £10,000        • Norman Adams

### Partners' Desk ▲
- *19th century*
A substantial mahogany partners'
desk with green, tooled leather
inlay, original brass drop handles
and prominent bun feet.
- *height 79cm*
- £1,600        • Fulton

## Expert Tips

*Original carving always stands
proud of the outline of a desk or
other piece of furniture; it is not
recessed. In the same way,
18th-century beading was
carved from wood left on a piece
of furniture for that purpose,
making the grain pattern true,
unlike Victorian beading which
is easy to spot because it was
carved separately and then glued
into place.*

### Kneehole Desk ◄
- *circa 1760*
An 18th-century mahogany
kneehole desk with original,
circular brass drop handles and
central, two-door cupboard.
- *height 79cm*
- £3,500        • Mora & Upham

## Chinese Writing Table ◄
- *late 19th century*
Rosewood bombe/serpentine-shaped writing table.
- *height 1.16m*
- £1,950                    • John Clay

## French Desk ▲
- *circa 1850*
A 19th-century French painted beech and pinewood desk, with curved drawer on central opening and bracket feet.
- *width 1.92m*
- £3,000          • Oonagh Black

## Walnut Desk ▼
- *circa 1840*
A figured walnut pedestal desk with rounded corners and heavy moulding. Original knob handles.
- *height 78cm*
- £5,500          • Ian Spencer

## Fruitwood Country Desk ▲
- *19th century*
In fruitwood with cabriole legs and three drawers.
- *height 77cm*
- £1,835     • I. & J. L. Brown

## Mahogany Desk ▲
- *circa 1920*
Early 20th-century mahognay desk in the George III manner. The top is inlaid with calf leather and decorated with gold tooling.
- *height 79cm*
- £1,500      • Westland & Co

## Expert Tips

*Handles and feet are the most obvious and the easiest aids in dating a piece of furniture. Unfortunately, they are also the easiest parts to alter.*

## Lady's Writing Table ►
- *circa 1880*
A Victorian mahogany lady's writing table with seven drawers and ebonized stringing. Standing on tapered legs.
- *length 1.22m*
- £1,995 • Antique Warehouse

Desks

## Cylinder Bureau ◄
• *circa 1865*
A French Second Empire
mahogany and gilt-mounted
cylinder bureau.
• *height 129cm*
• £18,500          • Ranby Hall

## English Painted Desk ▲
• *circa 1880*
An English satinwood painted
desk with original decoration to
front and back and standing on
tapered legs.
• £4,750          • Penny Fawcett

## French Desk ▲
• *circa 1840*
French mahogany and ormolu
mounted desk with five drawers
to each pillar and one central
drawer beneath a new leather top
and inlay.
• £8,800          • M. Mathers

## Regency Desk ▼
• *circa 1810*
An early 19th-century mahogany
desk with a red leather top and
nine drawers – in two pillars of
four with one central – on front
and three dummy drawers on
back. Ebony inlay around drawers
with castors.
• £15,000          • P. Lipitch

## Carlton House Desk ▲
• *circa 1910*
Fine Sheraton revival English
mahogany Carlton House desk.
Signed, with brass handles.
• *height 1m*
• £9,500          • Browns

### Expert Tips

*Damage such as minor repairs
to bandings and mouldings,
releathering of writing surfaces,
replaced castors and replaced
handles are acceptable if not
desirable, since absolutely
pristine pieces are becoming
rarer – and much more rarified
in price.*

## Gothic Revival Desk ➤
• *circa 1870*
Carved oak and burr walnut with
black tooled leather and single
drawers over end legs.
• *height 1.07m*
• £1,500          • M. Constantini

349

# Dining tables

### 'D'-End Dining Table ◄
- *circa 1810*
Mahogany 'D'-end dining table of the Regency period, to seat six persons comfortably. The table retains its original loose leaf.
- *length 1.95m (extended)*
- £8,750 • J. Collins

### Extending Dining Table ▲
- *circa 1835*
French extending mahogany dining table with original brass locks and castors. Has oak supports.
- *length 4.5m (extended)*
- £18,000 • Julia Boston

### Tilt-Top Dining Table ▼
- *circa 1875*
Circular tilt-top dining table on triform carved feet with ceramic castors.
- *diameter 1.18m*
- £950 • Fulham

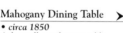

### Mahogany Dining Table ►
- *circa 1850*
A four-pillar mahogany table with royal patented wind-up mechanism and five leaves.
- *length 1.76m*
- £5,000 • John Bly

### Extending Table ▲
- *circa 1840*
Cuban mahogany-top extending table, with tapered legs and brass tips. Comes complete with original mahogany chairs.
- *width 1.8m*
- £3.750 • Abbey Green

## Expert Tips

*To establish whether or not leaves are a perfect match with the table, the grain should be examined from the underside. Any reeding or moulding should be critically examined as well, to see if it was added after the leaf was trimmed to fit.*

### Three-Pillar Table ►
- *circa 1795*
A Scottish mahogany three-pillar dining table from the Sheraton period. The pedestals have turned stems on splayed legs.
- *length 3.2m*
- £200,000 • Norman Adams

## Five-Leaf Table ▼

• *circa 1830*
A circular, figured Cuban
mahogany dining table with five
leaves on reeded legs, extending
to seat twelve people.
• *diameter 145cm*
• **£9,800** • **Luther & Goodwin**

## Extending Table ▲

• *circa 1920*
Swedish birchwood extending
table with ebonized feet.
• *length 2.63m (extended)*
• **£4,900** • **Cavendish**

## Drop-Leaf Table ◄

• *circa 1825*
George IV mahogany drop-leaf
dining table on six turned legs..
• *width 1.67m*
• **£4,300** • **L. & E. Kreckovic**

## Expert Tips

*Drop-leaf tables rarely have tops
which are inlaid or crossbanded.
This form of decoration will
almost always have been added
at a later date.*

## Walnut Dining Table ►

• *circa 1880*
Burr-walnut oval Victorian tilt-
top dining table on pillared
triform base with carved feet and
ceramic castors.
• *height 87cm*
• **£1,750** • **Fulham**

## Tip-up Table ▼

• *circa 1825*
Mahogany tip-up dining table
from the William IV period.
• *width 1.4m*
• **£2,500** • **L. & E. Kreckovic**

## French Farmhouse Table ◄

• *circa 1890*
Large table with pine top and
turned and tapered walnut legs.
• *length 2.4m*
• **£2,000** • **Gabrielle de Giles**

Furniture

## Doors

### Metal-Studded Door ∨
• *circa 1885*
Substantial Gothic oak, metal-studded door, with six panels and Gothic tracery.
• £2,450          • Drummonds

### Teardrop Loft Door ∨
• *circa 1870*
Game-larder or loft door of possible French origin.
• *height 2.34m*
• £1,475     • Annette Puttnam

### Pine Overdoor ∧
• *circa 1890*
Carved pine overdoor in the George I style.
• *height 77.5cm*
• £450          • Westland & Co

### Double Doors ∧
• *circa 1910*
A pair of six-panelled mahogany doors with brass furniture.
• *height 2.8m*
• £3,500          • Ian Spencer

### Italian Double Doors ∨
• *circa 1790*
A pair of giltwood and ivory painted double doors, centred by jasper panels.
• *height 2.95m*
• £15,000     • Westland & Co

### Carved Oak Doorway ∨
• *circa 1850*
A finely carved oak doorway in the Venetian renaissance manner.
• *height 2.49m*
• £3,200     • Westland & Co

### Baroque-Style Overdoor ◄
• *circa 1890*
A carved wood overdoor in the baroque manner.
• *height 1m*
• £1,600          • Westland & Co

## Overdoor ◄

- *circa 1890*

A fine French carved Beaux Art overdoor with scrolls centred by a female mask with wings.
- *height 59cm*
- £7,500     • Westland & Co

## French Doors ▼

- *circa 1900*

Two pairs of French doors with Art Nouveau polychrome glass.
- *height 2.32m*
- £950 (pair)   • Westland & Co

## Walnut Doorway ▲

- *circa 1885*

Carved walnut doorway in the Renaissance manner.
- *height 2.62m*
- £18,000    • Westland & Co

## Four Pairs of Doors ▲

- *circa 1890*

Four pairs of carved neoclassical carved doors together with matching frames.
- *height 2.46m*
- £5,500      • Westland & Co

## Pine Door Surround ▼

- *circa 1790*

A large and imposing carved pine door surround, with wrought-iron fanlight and fluted pilasters.
- *height 3.53m*
- £15,500     • Westland & Co

## Oak Door ▲

- *circa 1920*

Panelled oak door with carved and pierced roundel of birds and foliate designs.
- £2,500           • John Bly

## Folding Bronze Doors ▲

- *circa 1930*

A very substantial and unusual pair of 1930s double folding bronze doors with twenty-eight raised and fielded panels. The doors show some patination.
- *height 2.64m*
- £6,500     • Westland & Co

# Dressers

## Cupboard ▽
- *18th century*
Housekeeper's cupboard with
original handles and brassware.
- *height 1.95m*
- £5,800 • Riverbank

## Display Case ▽
- *19th century*
Queen Anne-style with lattice
work and floral decoration.
- *height 2.06m*
- £5,850 • Ranby Hall

## Storage Cupboard ▲
- *circa 1820*
Northern Swedish cupboard with
typical rural profile doors. Good
carving to the top and base.
- *height 2.01m*
- £3,200 • Aberg

## Charles II Cupboard ▲
- *circa 1680*
Oak court cupboard with heraldic
central panel.
- *height 1.64m*
- £3,850 • Angel

## Buffet de Corps ▽
- *circa 1790*
Rare dresser in yew wood with
three tiers of shelves above a base
with three drawers.
- *height 2m*
- £5,950 • Red Lion

## Walnut Dresser ▽
- *circa 1890*
Aesthetic movement dresser,
with panels of birds, highlighting,
amboyna back and acorn finials.
- *height 1.72m*
- £1,250 • Travers

## Louis XVI Dresser ◀
- *18th century*
Swedish, Gustavian dresser
painted in off-white.
- *length 2m*
- £7,500 • Cavendish

## James II Oak Cupboard ◄
- *Date 1687*
Overhanging cornice with carved frieze and 'RS' initialled.
- *height 2m*
- **£7,950**          • Old Cinema

## Cupboard/Dresser ◄
- *circa 1800*
Excellent quality oak press cupboard/dresser with two doors above three tiers of drawers.
- *height 1.95m*
- **£5,750**          • Red Lion

## Shropshire Dresser ▲
- *circa 1800*
Oak dresser with cupboard base and dummy drawers.
- *height 2.09m*
- **£5,500**          • Castlegate

## Poland Oak Sideboard ▼
- *late 19th century*
Bach carved with 'Mirth Becomes A Feast' above panels.
- *length 2.3m*
- **£5,000**          • Old Cinema

## Mahogany Cupboard ▲
- *circa 1870*
A figured mahogany, oval-panelled cupboard with boxwood inlay to drawers and brass handles. The whole raised on bracket feet.
- *height 1.2m*
- **£1,450**          • Ian Spencer

## Regency Chiffonier ▲
- *circa 1820*
Rosewood with pleated silk panels and gilt-leaf decoration.
- *height 1.25m*
- **£1,450**          • Travers

## Mahogany Cupboard ➤
- *circa 1820*
Mahogany cupboard of Regency period with tapered legs.
- *height 81cm*
- **£1,450**          • J. Collins

## Oak Dresser △

- *circa 1790*
With cupboards, shelving and
drawers. Replacement knobs.
- *height 1.89m*
- £1,750 • Albany

## French Cupboard △

- *18th century*
Cupboard in oak serpentine frieze
with floral carving.
- *length 1.69m*
- £1,200 • Lynda Franklin

## Welsh Deuddiarw ▽

- *circa 1740*
Rare cupboard with small
proportions. Cupboards above
two drawers and cupboards below.
- *height 1.8m*
- £5,950 • Red Lion

## French Buffet d'Accord ▽

- *circa 1800*
Cherrywood buffet with carved
panelled doors, a chapeau cornice
and escargot legs.
- *height 2.47m*
- £7,500 • Oonagh Black

## Cherrywood Cabinet △

- *circa 1720*
French provincial cabinet with
moulded frieze and square feet.
- *height 2.17m*
- £3,750 • Albany

## Expert Tips

*Before buying a dresser, check
that all the drawers match each
other in terms of appearance
and manufacture (dovetailing
etc.). Replacement parts are
very detrimental to desirability.*

## Chiffonier ▽

- *circa 1830*
A late Regency, two-door
mahogany chiffonier.
- *height 1.26m*
- £1,650 • Castlegate

## Cabriole Leg Dresser ◁

- *circa 1760*
Base in good original condition
with replaced handles.
- *height 83cm*
- £5,950 • Red Lion

Dressers

## Painted Sideboard ➤

- *18th century*
French sideboard with carved
floral design and scrolled feet.
- *height 96cm*
- **£2,750**     • Lynda Franklin

## Mahogany Sideboard ▲

- *circa 1900*
Mahogany sideboard with
rosewood crossbanding and
boxwood and ebony stringing.
- *height 93cm*
- **£4,800**     • David Pickup

## Oak Sideboard ◄

- *19th century*
Mirror-backed dental cornice
with architectural details above.
- *height 1.96m*
- **£3,495** • Antique Warehouse

## Bombay Front ▼

- *circa 1820*
Anglo-Indian Bombay-front
cabinet, carved in rosewood.
- *height 1.13m*
- **£3,400** • L. & E. Kreckovic

## Pedestal Sideboards ➤

- *circa 1880*
Twin sideboards with mirror back
and floral carving.
- *length 2.14m*
- **£3,595** • Antique Warehouse

## Pine Dresser ◄

- *circa 1830*
Cabriole-leg pine dresser with
serpentine frieze and two shelves
above base, with two drawers.
- *length 1.04m*
- **£2,150**     • Red Lion

## Housekeeper's Dresser ▲

- *circa 1800*
A rare early 19th-century
housekeeper's dresser with two
doors above a three-door base.
- *length 2.02m*
- **£4,750**     • Red Lion

### Expert Tips

*Marriages of bases and racks are
very common and should be
avoided. Usually the colour and
patina will give the marriage
away, but use your judgement as
to the proportions of the piece.*

### Ash Sideboard ➤
- *circa 1915*
An English sideboard of
substantial construction.
- *height 1.02m*
- £1,295      • Castlegate

### French Pine Cabinet ▼
- *circa 1830*
Cabinet with quarter columns
and serpentine top with steel
hinges, all on block feet.
- *height 1.83m*
- £1,000      • Albany

### Potboard Dresser ▼
- *circa 1750*
Dresser from West Wales with
unusually small proportions.
- *height 1.74m*
- £7,750      • Angel

### Oak Potboard ▲
- *circa 1820*
Well proportioned oak potboard
dresser from South Wales.
- *length 2.02m*
- £5,975      • Red Lion

### Sideboard ▲
- *circa 1820*
Mahogany sideboard with cellaret
cupboard, raised on spade feet.
- *height 1.54m*
- £2,000      • Ian Spencer

### Arts & Crafts Buffet ▼
- *circa 1905*
English walnut buffet carved with
strapwork decoration.
- *height 93cm*
- £10,000      • David Pickup

### Early Victorian Sideboard ◄
- *19th century*
Mahogany pedestal sideboard
with moulded decoration.
- *height 1.6m*
- £3,850      • Ranby Hall

# Dumb Waiters & Whatnots

## Bamboo Table ∨
- *early 20th century*
Bamboo and rattan table by
Maple in original condition.
- *height 66cm*
- **£240** • **Christopher Howe**

## Walnut Whatnot ∨
- *circa 1890*
Three-tier walnut whatnot set on
castors with four turned columns.
- *height 98cm*
- **£550** • **Frederick Beck**

## Hanging Shelves ∧
- *circa 1830*
Mahogany hanging shelves with
turned columns.
- *height 71cm*
- **£475** • **Lynda Franklin**

## Walnut Whatnot ∧
- *circa 1883*
Walnut canterbury whatnot with
boxwood and satinwood stringing
and turned supports.
- *height 1.15m*
- **£2,450** • **Judy Fox**

## Buffet Table ∨
- *circa 1860*
Good-quality marble-topped
whatnot in mahogany with three
tiers on brass castors.
- *height 1m*
- **£7,400** • **Christopher Howe**

## Buffet Table ∨
- *circa 1830*
Mahogany two tier buffet table in
original condition.
- *height 1m*
- **£240** • **Christopher Howe**

## French Trolley ∨
- *circa 1930*
Nickel-plated trolley on castors
with removable top.
- *height 84cm*
- **£600** • **Christopher Howe**

## Mahogany Dumb Waiter ▲
- *circa 1850*
Three-tier mahogany dumb waiter supported by reeded columns and set on brass castors.
- *height 1.22m*
- **£2,190** • **Frederick Beck**

## French Tea Table ▲
- *circa 1885*
French two-tier tea table japanned on maple wood with bronze carrying handles.
- *height 83cm*
- **£3,500** • **R. Hamilton**

## Pot Cupboard ▼
- *William IV*
Unusual flared mahogany pot cupboard.
- *height 82cm*
- **£850** • **V. Harvey**

## Mahogany Buffet ▼
- *circa 1850*
A mid 19th-century English three-tiered buffet or dumb waiter, in mahogany, with turned supports. Each tier has a gallery and the whole is supported on original ceramic castors with brass brackets. There are two shallow drawers to the base, with carved button handles, and carved acorn finials to the top.
- *height 1.2m*
- **£1,800** • **Judy Fox**

## Book Etagère ▲
- *circa 1820*
An Anglo-Indian book étagère in coromandel wood with two base drawers and three shelves.
- *height 1.21m*
- **£7,250** • **R. Hamilton**

## Dumb Waiter ▲
- *18th century*
All mahogany with folding tiers. Turned column on a tripod base with drop levers.
- *height 1.08m*
- **£3,850** • **Chambers**

### Expert Tips

*As the whatnot changed in function, it changed in appearance. The invention of the wood-carving machine in 1845 led to elaborate decoration for very little money.*

# Lowboys

## Victorian Lowboy ∨

- *circa 1900*
Walnut lowboy on cabriole legs with acanthus-leaf motif.
- *height 77cm*
- **£1,295** • **Antique Warehouse**

## Reproduction Lowboy ➤

- *circa 1930*
Reproduction of a four-drawer, 18th-century, walnut lowboy, with crossbanded marquetry and raised on cabriole legs with pad feet.
- *height 75cm*
- **£395** • **Fulham**

## Mahogany Lowboy ∧

- *circa 1740*
An 18th-century, Chippendale period, well-figured mahogany lowboy with three drawers, two small below one large, with original brass mounts, the whole raised on cabriole legs with pad feet. The piece has an unusually shaped kneehole and apron, reflecting its original purpose as a dressing-table.
- *height 71cm*
- **£3,500** • **L. & E. Kreckovic**

## Dutch Lowboy ∨

- *circa 1750*
A fine, Dutch, 18th-century lowboy, with serpentine front and quarter drawers each side of the two main drawers. Original handles and fine marquetry decoration.
- *height 77cm*
- **£8,250** • **Chambers**

## George I Lowboy ∨

- *circa 1720*
A fine George I lowboy in figured walnut, with three drawers with original mounts.
- *height 72.5cm*
- **£40,000** • **Norman Adams**

## Regency Tallboy ◄

- *circa 1820*
An English 19th-century tallboy, in walnut, with three drawers and brass mounts, the whole on cabriole legs.
- *height 72cms*
- **£2,700** • **Moore &Upham**

Furniture

## Mirrors

### Toilet Mirror ▾
- *circa 1725*
A George I walnut toilet-mirror with one drawer.
- *height 77.5cm*
- £10,000  • Norman Adams

### Carved Mirror ▾
- *circa 1785*
Carved and painted mirror with floral swags, vines and wheat.
- *height 133cm*
- £3,750  • Paul Andrews

### Mantel Mirror ▶
- *circa 1890*
A three division, over- mantel mirror with decorated frieze.
- *length 142cm, height 87.5cm*
- £2,250
- Through the Looking Glass

### Three Part Mirror ▲
- *circa 1910*
A Majorellel mirror, leather backed with glass behind door.
- *height 18cm*
- £2,800  • Cameo Gallery

### Regency Mirror ▲
- *circa 1890*
A simple gilt Regency mirror.
- *diameter 50cm*
- £1,100
- Through the Looking Glass

### Easel Mirror ▾
- *circa 1725*
A rare George I, gilded, carved gesso easel mirror.
- *height 78cm*
- £16,000  • Norman Adams

### English Mirror ▾
- *circa 1890*
An English round mirror in a rectangular gilt frame.
- *height 55cm*
- £650
- Through the Looking Glass

362

## Venetian Mirror ▲

- *circa 1890*
A highly ornate, oval Venetian etched-crest mirror.
- *height 1.32m*
- £2,850
- Through the Looking Glass

## Venetian Mirror ▲

- *circa 1850*
An fine etched and engraved Venetian mirror.
- *height 148cm*
- £3,300 • Paul Andrews

### Expert Tips

*Test for the use of stucco with a needle on the reverse of the frame. It will penetrate wood but not stucco.*

## Regency Mirror ▼

- *circa 1820*
A convex Regency gilt mirror with an eagle above.
- *height 115cm*
- £3,650
- Through the Looking Glass

## Toilet Mirror ▼

- *circa 1780*
A Chinese export lacquered toilet mirror.
- *height 68cm*
- £3,850 • P.L. James

## Italian Mirror ➤

- *circa 1890*
Small, rectangular giltwood and fretted Florentine mirror.
- *height 55cm*
- £850
- Through the Looking Glass

## Victorian Gilt Mirror ▲

- *circa 1890*
Gilt mirror with shelf scrolls hatch, broken pediment and heart-shaped mirror.
- *height 100cm*
- £850
- Through the Looking Glass

## Toilet Mirror ▲

- *circa 1760*
An unusual Chippendale-period carved mahogany toilet mirror.
- *height 60cm*
- £15,000 • Norman Adams

## Console and Mirror ▲
- *circa 1830*
Scandinavian-made, with crested detail to the head of mirror.
- *height 320cm*
- £10,500 • Ranby Hall

## Sheraton Mirror ▲
- *circa 1800*
A gilded, carved wood and papier mâché rectangular mirror.
- *height 151cm*
- £14,500 • Norman Adams

## Toilet Mirror ➤
- *circa 1810*
Restored George III walnut parcel-gilt toilet mirror
- *height 68cm*
- £1,250 • P.L. James

## Irish Mirrors ▲
- *circa 1800*
A pair of Irish mirrors.
- *height 70cm*
- £3,800 • P.L. James

## Carved Console ▲
- *circa 1890*
Continental giltwood console.
- *height 85cm*
- £2,650
- **Through the Looking Glass**

## Expert Tips

*Until 1773, looking glass was blown from cylinders of glass, which, accordingly, limited the size. Thus early mirrors are either small or made of two or three pieces covered by astragal bars at the join.*

## Parcel Gilt Mirror ▼
- *circa 1735*
A fine, George II, parcel-gilt mirror with serpentine frame.
- *height 174cm*
- £60,000 • Norman Adams

## Lacquered Mirror ▼
- *circa 1710*
A fine Queen Anne-style lacquered mirror.
- *height 1.6m*
- £6,850 • P.L. James

## Regency Mirror ➤
- *circa 1830*
A Regency gilt mirror, decorated with balls, vine eglomise and with Corinthian columns.
- *height 82.5cm*
- **£1,350**
- **Through the Looking Glass**

## Chippendale Mirror ▲
- *circa 1760*
A fine Chippendale-period gilded, carved-wood mirror.
- *height 2.32m*
- **£125,000** • **Norman Adams**

## George II Wall Mirror ▲
- *circa 1760*
A walnut, fret-cut mirror with gilded motif and inner slip.
- *height 91.5cm*
- **£875** • **J. Collins**

## English Mirror ▼
- *circa 1890*
An English carved giltwood mandalin and flute top mirror.
- *height 72.5cm*
- **£650**
- **Through the Looking Glass**

## Regency Dressing Mirror ▼
- *circa 1820*
A mahogany dressing mirror with three drawers outlined with boxwood stringing.
- *height 65cm*
- **£950** • **J. Collins**

## George III Mirror ▼
- *circa 1770*
A good, oval Chippendale mirror.
- *height 1.33m*
- **£16,500** • **P.L. James**

## Console and Mirror ▼
- *circa 1830*
A mahogany console and mirror, with architectural pillars supporting the pediment.
- *height 250cm*
- **£4,850** • **Ranby Hall**

## French Mirror ∨
- *circa 1895*
A French winged-dragon gilt, bevelled mirror.
- height 115cm
- £875
- Through the Looking Glass

## Trumeau Mirror ∨
- *circa 1885*
A slim, gilt continental trumeau mirror, showing pastoral scene.
- height 123cm
- £1,600
- Through the Looking Glass

## George II Mirror ∧
- *circa 1750*
A matched pair of George II gilded, carved wood mirrors.
- *height 1.38m*
- £90,000   • Norman Adams

## English Mirror ∧
- *circa 1870*
Giltwood mirror with Prince of Wales cartouche.
- *height 86cm*
- £1,550
- Through the Looking Glass

### Expert Tips

*Early glass is thinner at the top of the frame than the bottom, and thinner overall than modern mirror plate.*

## Victorian Mirror ∨
- *circa 1880*
A Victorian gilt convex mirror with balls to the rim.
- *diameter 55cm*
- £1,100
- Through the Looking Glass

## Octagonal Mirror ∨
- *circa 1850*
French cushion gilt with reverse shell base and profuse flowers.
- *height 132cm*
- £2,500
- Through the Looking Glass

## French Oval Mirror ∨
- *circa 1880*
A carved giltwood, oval mirror with floral decoration.
- *height 61cm*
- £1,200
- Through the Looking Glass

## French Mirror ▲

- *19th century*
A French mirror with painted panel and gilt moulded shell and scrolling decoration.
- *height 170cm*
- £2,200 • Lynda Franklin

## Venetian Mirror ▲

- *circa 1850*
An etched and engraved Venetian mirror.
- height 150cm
- £3,700 • Paul Andrews

## Expert Tips

*To check the thickness, and thus the approximate age, of mirror glass, place a pencil, or other pointed object, on to the glass and judge the distance between the point and its image.*

## Chippendale Mirror ▼

- *circa 1770*
A small Chippendale-period mirror, carved and gilded.
- *height 90cm*
- £6,200 • P.L. James

## Chippendale Mirror ▼

- *circa 1760*
A small, cartouche-shaped, carved wood and gilt mirror.
- *height 89cm*
- £8,000 • Norman Adams

## Lacquered Toilet Mirror ▶

- *circa 1790*
Chinese export-lacquered toilet mirror on four-drawer pedestal.
- *height 68cm*
- £3,850 • P.L. James

## Skeleton Dressing Mirror ▲

- *circa 1825*
A dressing mirror, in mahogany, with Dutch drop side screws and acorn finials.
- *height 61cm*
- £475 • J. Collins

## Adam Manner Mirror ▲

- *circa 1875*
Adam manner neo-classical, urn and husks on an oval gilt mirror.
- *height 85cm*
- £1,350
- **Through the Looking Glass**

# Miscellaneous

## Blackamoor Torchères ∨
• *mid 19th century*
Fruitwood torchères with
serpentine tops, figures and
acanthus-leaf body on tripod base.
• *height 91cm*
• £2,850 • Lesley Bragge

## Painted Jardinère ∧
• *late 19th century*
Painted steel body with floral
scrolled handles.
• *height 21cm*
• £90 • Riverbank

## Cane Jardinière ∨
• *late 19th century*
Gilt, cane top with leaf
decoration and cloven feet.
• *height 101cm*
• £550 • Youlls

## Library Steps ∨
• *circa 1900*
Oak library steps with carved
decoration to the sides.
• *height 47cm*
• £500 • Lacquer Chest

## Corner Washstand ∧
• *circa 1800*
Mahogany, two-drawer
washstand, the top with a
rounded splashback.
• *height 86.5cm*
• £1,250 • J. Collins

## Birdcage ∨
• *circa 1940*
A 20th-century birdcage of
rectangular shape with covered
back and sides.
• *height 31cm*
• £22 • Curios

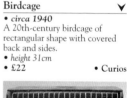

## Regency Bookcarrier ◄
• *circa 1810*
A fine Regency bookcarrier
in the bullock style with a
drawer below.
• *width 43cm*
• £2,350 • P.L. James

## Painted Washstand ▲
• *circa 1800*
Green buff pine with darker green
coaching lines. Large cupboard,
deep drawer and pull-out bidet.
• *height 102cm*
• £2,350      • John Clay

## Library Steps ▲
• *late 19th century*
Three-runged oak library steps
with supporting pole to platform.
• *height 162cm*
• £450      • Riverbank

## Gilt Wood Torchère ▼
• *19th century*
17th-century-style with acanthus-
leaf decoration. On a tripod base
with three carved heads on
scrolled feet.
• *height 146cm*
• £695      • Old Cinema

## Oak Pulpit ▼
• *circa 1890*
A fine Victorian pulpit in the
Arts and Crafts manner.
• *height 143cm*
• £850      • Westland & Co

## Urn Stands ▲
• *circa 1880*
A pair of Oriental stands with
marble tops and pierced flower
decoration.
• *height 92cm*
• £660      • Castlegate

## Victorian Wagonwheel ▲
• *circa 1836-1901*
Metal-banded elm Victorian
wagonwheel.
• *diameter 74cm*
• £75      • Curios

## Mahogany Boot Rack ▲
• *circa 1860*
Fine English mahogany boot rack.
• *height 1.0m*
• £495      • Lacquer Chest

### Plate Drainer ➤
- *circa 1910*
A pine draining board for drying
dishes, with carved ends.
- *width 64cm*
- £150          • Lacquer Chest

### Wine Cooler ▲
- *circa 1810*
Regency, mahogany wine cooler
of oval form, with brass inlay.
- *height 55.5cm*
- £18,000          • Norman Adams

### Mahogany Torchère ▼
- *19th century*
With inlay on a long fluted
pedestal with a tripod base.
- *height 148cm*
- £390          • Youlls

### Regency Jardinière ▲
- *circa 1820*
A Regency painted metal
jardinière of octagonal form with
chinoiserie designs.
- *length 41.5cm*
- £3,250          • O.F. Wilson

### Mahogany Cellaret ▲
- *circa 1790*
A mahogany cellaret with
boxwood stringing and chequered
line inlay.
- *height 66cm*
- £3,250          • J. de Haan

### Mahogany Washstand ▲
- *circa 1860*
Washstand with recesses for wash
bowls, with good patination.
- *height 99cm*
- £780          • Ranby Hall

### Shop Drawers ◀
- *circa 1880*
Mahogany shop-drawer cabinet
with twelve drawers.
- *height 90cm*
- £495          • Lacquer Chest

## Butler's Tray ◀

- *circa 1810*
A mahogany butler's tray and reading stand with turned and tapered legs.
- *height 32cm*
- **£480**　　　　　• P.L. James

## English Washstand ▼

- *circa 1820*
In mahogany with inlay, three drawers and brass handles.
- *height 1.25m*
- **£850**　　　　　• Youlls

## Gothic Stand ▲

- *late 19th century*
A stand of pentagonal form with gothic tracery.
- *height 110cm*
- **£450**　　　　　• Youlls

## Turquoise Jardinière ▲

- *circa 1875*
A jardinière on stand in a turquoise glaze. Probably French.
- *height 116cm*
- **£1,950**　　• Kenneth Harvey

## Edwardian Gong ▲

- *circa 1913*
An oak and horn gong with baton and trophy plaque.
- *height 34cm*
- **£165**　　　　　• Castlegate

## Papier Maché Tray ▼

- *circa 1800*
A red lacquered papier maché tray showing Oriental decoration.
- **£2,850**　　　　• P.L. James

## Victorian Hall Stand ▲

- *circa 1890*
Oak hall stand with ceramic tiles and marble-topped drawer.
- *height 206cm*
- **£950**　　　　　• Old Cinema

## Butler's Tray ▼
• *circa 1780*
A mahogany butler's tray with stand and hinged side flaps.
• *height 32cm*
• £1,250      • Lynda Franklin

## Bamboo Stand ▼
• *19th century*
A 19th-century bamboo stand with tile inset.
• *height 82cm*
• £170      • North West 8

## Marble and Gilt Stand ▲
• *circa 1900*
A French marble stand of doric form with fine ormolu mounts.
• *height 113cm*
• £2,500
• M. Wakelin & H. Linfield

## Papiér Maché Tray ▲
• *circa 1850*
A papiér maché tray standing on a rectangular, wooden stand. In good condition.
• *height 45cm*
• £1,050      • North West 8

## Gueridon Pedestal ▶
• *late 19th century*
A Black Forest gueridon pedestal with an intertwined, tree-like central column.
• *height 77cm*
• £880      • North West 8

## William IV Buffet ▲
• *circa 1835*
A fine buffet with turned legs and supports with a finial top.
• *height 117cm*
• £1,600      • Old Cinema

## Jardinières ▲
• *circa 1840*
A pair of walnut tripod jardinières with scrolled feet and original copper liners.
• *height 107cm*
• £14,500
• M. Wakelin & H. Linfield

**Gothic Hall Stand** ▲
- *late 19th century*
French hall stand with profusely carved tracery and lifting seat.
- *height 242cm*
- £1,400                    • Youlls

**Georgian Whatnot** ▲
- *circa 1780*
A Georgian, mahogany, four-shelved whatnot.
- *height 138m*
- £2,500        • Terence Morse

**Waste Paper Baskets** ▼
- *circa 1910*
Silver plated. With pierced rim and frieze of rabbits below.
- *height 33cm*
- £880           • Lesley Bragge

**Victorian Bucket** ▼
- *circa 1860*
Oak bucket with brass hoops, silver wash, brass handle and name plaque.
- *height 33cm*
- £150                    • Albany

**Towel Rail** ▼
- *19th century*
A good quality mahogany Victorian towel rail with turned decoration.
- *height 95cm*
- £265            • Old Cinema

**Open Wine Cooler** ▲
- *circa 1775*
An Adam-period wine cooler with ram's head handles.
- *height 49.5cm*
- £17,500      • Norman Adams

**Umbrella and Coat Stand** ▲
- *circa 1790*
In patinated mahogany with fine shaped pegs and turned finials. With original zinc liner.
- *height 181cm*
- £2,850
- **M. Wakelin & H. Linfield**

## George III Bucket ▲
- *circa 1790*
A mahogany brass-bound bucket of navette shape.
- *height 33cm*
- £2,350 • J. de Haan

## Lacquered Stand ▲
- *late 19th century*
Stand with mirror and brass candleholders, lacquered with mother-of-pearl and gilt floral decoration.
- *height 125cm*
- £950 • Lynda Franklin

## Whip and Boot Stand ▼
- *circa 1830*
A whip and boot stand in fruitwood with finial tops.
- *height 94cm*
- £450 • Castlegate

## Pair of Knife Boxes ▼
- *circa 1890*
Inlaid mahogany with stepped interiors, marquetry decoration and boxwood stringing.
- *height 68cm (closed)*
- £9,000 • Judy Fox

## Teak Trolley ▶
- *circa 1880*
A three-shelved teak trolley with two large, spoked wheels.
- *height 100cm*
- £300 • Lacquer Chest

## Four Tier Whatnot ▲
- *circa 1825*
A mahogany 'plum pudding' veneered whatnot with a one piece top and an oak lined drawer.
- *height 131cm*
- £3,250 • J. Collins

## Oval Tea Tray ▲
- *circa 1790*
A tray of the Sheraton period, having a wavy edge with the outside inlaid with joined loops.
- *width 71cm*
- £850 • J. Collins

# Screens

## Japanese Fold Screen ◄
- *19th century*

One of a pair of six-fold screens with a Chinese poem in Japanese calligraphy, on buff ground.
- *height 1.72m, length 3.78m*
- **£11,000 (pair)** • **Gregg Baker**

## Paper Screen ◄
- *19th century*

A pair of two-fold paper screens painted in ink on a gold ground.
- *length 53.3cm*
- **£4,800** • **Gregg Baker**

## Silk Screen ▲
- *early 20th century*

Two-fold silk screen painted in ink with birds flying above rose mallow on which are a praying mantis and a cricket.
- *height 1.81m, length 1.17m*
- **£6,800** • **Gregg Baker**

## Silk Screen ▼
- *circa 1850*

Silk screen on a brass stand and crossbar with a gilt wood base.
- *height 1.41m*
- **£750** • **Castlegate**

## Chinoiserie Screen ▲
- *mid 18th century*

An adjustable screen that changes to a side table. On a bronze tripod base.
- *height 1.06m*
- **£2,200** • **Riverbank**

## Expert Tips

*Oriental screens are becoming more collectable all the time, but the best markets are still in Japan and the USA.*

## Two-Fold Paper Screen ▲
- *20th century*

A Taisho period screen painted in ink and colour with hydrangea, peony and poppy.
- *height 1.81m, length 1.62m*
- **£8,600** • **Gregg Baker**

## Japanese Screen ➤
- *18th century*

Lacquer border, textile surround, painted pagodas and figures.
- *length 3.63m*
- **£1,600** • **Lynda Franklin**

## Silk Screen ◄
- *20th century*

Ink and colour on a buff ground with pine trees, bamboo fences, paths and lanterns.
- *height 90cm, length 1.76m*
- **£5,600**  • **Gregg Baker**

### Expert Tips

*Restoration of paper screens involves very expensive processes. Do not buy a screen which needs it.*

## Regency Fire Screen ▼
- *circa 1830*

Needlepoint walnut fire screen.
- *height 71cm*
- **£1,450**  • **Chambers**

## Regency Tapestry Screen ▼
- *circa 1810*

Mahogany ebony inlay with a counter-balanced tapestry screen.
- *height 1.46m*
- **£595**  • **Castlegate**

## Six-Fold Paper Screen ▲
- *18th century*

Ink and colour on a buff ground with clouds in gold leaf.
- *height 77cm, length 1.73m*
- **£8,800**  • **Gregg Baker**

## Mahogany Screen ▲
- *19th century*

Late Georgian with sliding side screens and turned stretchers.
- *height 1.1m*
- **£695**
- **The Old Cinema**

## Four-Fold Paper Screen ▲
- *20th century*

Silver and gold leaf on buff ground with imprint of three fuki.
- *height 171m, length 2.69m*
- **£8,500**  • **Gregg Baker**

## Paper Screen ►
- *18th century*

A pair of screens of the Edo period decorated in ink, colours and gilt on a buff ground. Signed 'Raisai Dogin Show'.
- *height 69cm, length 2.69m*
- **£20,000**  • **Gregg Baker**

# Settees & Sofas

## Wing Sofa ◄
- *circa 1880*
Armchair sofa raised upon ebonised cabriole legs on padded feet.
- *height 1.3m*
- **£1,850**   • **Ranby Hall**

## Canopy Sofa ◄
- *circa 1880*
An unusual ebonized cherry wood and canopy sofa. Bow-backed tortiene carvings and lovely scroll shape overall.
- *width 1.95m*
- **£2,800**   • **Sieff**

## Regency Window Seat ▲
- *circa 1820*
English Regency cane window seat with original gilding and polychrome paints.
- *width 1.52m*
- **£3,700**   • **Mora & Upham**

## Cane Sofa ►
- *19th century*
Cane sofa and two chairs, with studded upholstery backs and tunnel and fluted legs.
- *width 1.4m*
- **£3,400**   • **L. Franklin**

## Victorian Sofa ▲
- *circa 1870*
Walnut sofa on turned legs with carved arm rests.
- *width 1.53m*
- **£2,900**   • **L. & E. Kreckovic**

## Victorian Sofa ►
- *circa 1820*
Howard-style cream-coloured sofa, complete in selling fabric, raised on terracotta castors with brass fittings.
- *width 1.5m*
- **£1,450**   • **Tredantiques**

## Country House Settee ◄
- *circa 1810*
English painted rosewood settee in the George Smith manner. On castors with fleur de lys design.
- *width 2.09m*
- **£4,800**
- • **M. Luther & P. Goodwin**

### Gustavian Suite ➤
• *circa 1880*
Suite of Gustavian-style furniture including a sofa, pair of armchairs and four chairs.
• **£5,600 (suite)**     • **Cavendish**

### Chesterfield Sofa ▲
• *circa 1900*
A two-seater chesterfield with mahogany bun feet and brass castors, covered in hessian.
• *width 1.72m*
• **£1,250**     • **Annette Puttnam**

### Leather Sofa ➤
• *circa 1840*
A 19th-century, two-seater upholstered sofa, in original black leather, with brass castors and mahogany legs.
• *width 2.06m*
• **£3,600**     • **D. Martin-Taylor**

### Three-Seater Sofa ◄
• *19th century*
Upholstery and cushions in good condition.
• *width 1.92m*
• **£1,850**     • **Ranby Hall**

### Silk Sofa ◄
• *circa 1860*
A beige and gold silk-covered sofa with gilt decoration.
• *width 1.2m*
• **£2,200**     • **Mora & Upham**

### Sofa & Two Chairs ▲
• *circa 1860*
A red silk sofa with two chairs. Gilt decoration to frame.
• *width 1.62m (sofa)*
• *width 64cm (chairs)*
• **£1,200 (all)** • **Mora & Upham**

### 'Dolphin' Sofa ➤
• *circa 1820*
North German birchwood and masur birch sofa covered in calico. With noticeable tunnel armrests with dolphin designs. The whole resting on scrolled feet.
• *width 2.1m*
• **£7,500**     • **Cavendish**

### Walnut Settee ➤

• *circa 1870*
A Victorian walnut settee, with back carved into three ovals and serpentine front,. all raised on cabriole legs with china castors.
• *width 2.5m*
• £3,200          • Judy Fox

### French Settee ◀

• *18th century*
An 18th-century French settee painted in grey and standing on eight legs. Upholstered in calico.
• *width 1.9m*
• £1,350          • Gur & Sparke

### Expert Tips

*There is no hard definition of what constitutes a sofa as against a settee. The settee was earlier and was a direct descendant of the wooden settle, which was the earliest form of furniture to accommodate two or more people. The term 'sofa' has come to mean 'a well-upholstered settee'.*

### Swedish Settee ▲

• *circa 1940*
A Swedish settee in brown leather with tapered legs.
• *width 1.95m*
• £2,500          • B. &T. Antiques

### Regency Sofa ◀

• *circa 1810*
An English Regency-period green sofa on eight turned mahogany legs with original brass castors.
• *width 1.9m*
• £3,500          • Ian Spencer

### Day-Bed Sofa ▲

• *circa 1870*
A mid-Victorian satinwood day-bed sofa, in the Regency style, with gilt decoration, scrolled ends and swept feet.
• *width 2.14m*
• £1,895  • Antique Warehouse

### Zebra Striped Sofa ▼

• *circa 1830*
An early 19th-century cowhide sofa painted in zebra stripes with ogee mahogany feet, with double balloon back and serpentine front. A unique design with elegant covers to both back and front.
• *width 1.36m*
• £4,500          • B. & T. Antiques

### French Sofa ◀

• *circa 1815*
A French Restoration, beechwood couch, with serpentine back and front, carved decoration to the apron and central trophy motif to toprail. The upholstery is covered in cream silk material and the whole raised on eight turned and fluted legs.
• *width 1.52m*
• £2,800          • Gur & Sprake

### Three-Seater Sofa ➤
- *circa 1930*
French deco walnut three-seater
sofa with two matching chairs.
- *width 1.8m*
- £2,200 (the set) • Oola Boola

### Bouson-Covered Sofa ⌃
- *circa 1820*
A French 19th-century bouson-
covered sofa with gilt
decoration.
- *width 1.76m*
- £5,000 • Mora & Upham

### Victorian Sofa ➤
- *19th century*
Two-seater, reupholstered
Victorian sofa, the moulded frame
profusely carved in mahogany
with carved feet.
- *width 1.88m*
- £1,350 • Tower Bridge

### Victorian Sofa ⌃
- *circa 1880*
Small Victorian sofa with low
button back, mahogany scrolled
handles and escargot feet.
- *width 1.65m*
- £2,150 • Antique Warehouse

### Calico Sofa ⌄
- *circa 1880*
Sofa by Howard & Sons on
square mahogany tapered legs.
- *width 1.6m*
- £3,500 • David Form

> ## Expert Tips
>
> *The first settees, of the William
> and Mary period, are usually
> found either with very high
> backs, characteristic of the
> chairs of the time, or as
> modified walnut wing chairs, set
> on low, turned walnut legs.*

### Victorian Three-Seater ⌃
- *19th century*
Oak sofa with two matching
chairs with ornate carvings of
birds at the crest of the sofa.
- *width 1.75m*
- £3,200 • Tower Bridge

### Mahogany Sofa ➤
- *circa 1830*
William IV mahogany double-
ended sofa raised on turned legs
with original brass castors.
- *height 85cm*
- £1,650 • Castlegate

# Stools

### French Window Seat ➤
- *circa 1890*
Seat with scrolled carving and
floral decoration on turned legs
with 'X' frame stretcher.
- *length 1.1m*
- £650     • North West 8

### French Giltwood Seat ▲
- *circa 1880*
Louis XV-style serpentine seat
with four, carved cabriole legs.
- *height 44cm*
- £450     • Mark Constantini

### Late-Victorian Stool ▲
- *circa 1890*
A mahogany stool of the late
19th-century, of an 'X'-frame
construction, with bone stringing
and boxwood and rosewood inlay.
- *height 54cm*
- £895     • Judy Fox

### Walnut Stool ▼
- *18th century*
Walnut stool from the William
and Mary period, with 'X' frame
stretcher. Restored in 1900.
- *height 46cm*
- £1,795     • Red Lion

### Biedermeier Stools ◄
- *circa 1825*
A pair of German birchwood
stools covered in horsehair.
- *height 58cm*
- £4,500     • Cavendish

## Expert Tips

*A decorated frieze and well-
turned legs do much to enhance
the value of a stool. Try to make
sure that the legs did not
originally serve a different
purpose.*

### Sabre-Leg Stool ▼
- *circa 1950*
Pair of regency-style stools with
turned supports in fruitwood.
- *height 95cm*
- £1,000     • L. & E. Kreckovic

### Walnut Footstools ◄
- *circa 1850*
A pair of walnut footstools.
Rectangular overstuffed
serpentine seats.
- *height 14cm*
- £950     • J. Collins

### French Stool  ➤
- *circa 1750*
French stool in the Louis XV
style with gilded wooden legs.
- *height 46cm*
- £2,000          • O. F. Wilson

### Victorian Walnut Stool  ▲
- *circa 1870*
A serpentine-fronted, upholstered
walnut stool or window seat,
seating two, with original ceramic
castors. Recovered.
- *height 44cm*
- £3,200          • Judy Fox

### Victorian Stool  ◄
- *circa 1840*
Early Victorian carved stool in
gilt with cabriole legs and salmon
velvet upholstery.
- *height 18cm*
- £265          • Castlegate

### Carved Oak Stool  ◄
- *mid 19th century*
Victorian oak stool with
contemporary needlework to
cover, cabriole legs and original
ceramic castors.
- *height 42cm*
- £16,000          • Norman Adams

### Giltwood Stool  ◄
- *circa 1720*
An early 18th-century giltwood
stool on ornate 'H' frame with
reeded legs.
- *height 90cm*
- £950          • Fulham

### Savanarola Stool  ▲
- *circa 1880*
One of a pair of Savanarola
stools, of 'X' frame form.
- *height 59cm*
- £1,200          • Riverbank

### Rosewood Footstools  ➤
- *late 19th century*
A pair of Victorian stools with
serpentine-shaped cabriole legs.
- *height 22cm*
- £880          • Lesley Bragge

## Cane Stool ▲

- *circa 1900*
An Edwardian Louis XV-style gilt and caned stool on cabriole legs with scrolled feet.
- *height 42cm*
- £295 • French Room

## Leather Stool ▶

- *19th century*
Victorian rosewood stool with leather button upholstery on claw and ball feet.
- *length 1.4m*
- £1,800 • Old Cinema

## French Stool ▼

- *circa 1820*
French mahogany 'X' frame stool with upholstered top.
- *length 52cm*
- £685 • M. J. Bowdery

## Brass Stool ◀

- *circa 1910*
Edwardian brass piano stool of adjustable height with red fabric.
- *height 90cm*
- £175 • Fulham

## Expert Tips

*When examining a stool, check for hessian under the seat. Hessian was never used before 1840 – and it is often used to conceal an alteration.*

## Pair Of Empire Stools ◀

- *circa 1820*
A pair of Swedish stools designed by the architect Sundvall.
- *height 42cm*
- £2,700 • Cavendish

## Pouffe Sculpte Stool ▲

- *19th century*
Walnut pouffe sculpte rectangulaire stool, with shell motif, resting on cabriole legs.
- *height 60cm*
- £950 • Lynda Franklin

## Oak Stepstool ▲

- *circa 1880*
A 19th-century oak, three-stepped stepstool.
- *height 70cm*
- £290 • Lacquer Chest

## Cream Stool ➤
- *circa 1850*
A square Louis XV-style stool.
Painted cream with cabriole legs.
- *height 96cm*
- £2,200          • O. F. Wilson

## Mahogany Stool ▲
- *19th century*
Mahogany stool with tall cabriole
legs. Grotesque design on claws.
- *length 79cm*
- £995          • Old Cinema

## Elm Stool ▲
- *circa 1710*
An early 18th-century English
elm stool on four legs.
- *height 45cm*
- £95          • Castlegate

## Rosewood Stool ▲
- *circa 1860*
Rectangular upholstered top on
four cabouchon and leaf-carved,
moulded cabriole legs,
terminating in scrolled, leaf-
carved toes.
- *height 42cm*
- £950          • J. Collins

## Gilded Stool ▼
- *late 19th century*
A gilded stool with acanthus-leaf
and fluted legs.
- *height 40cm*
- £750          • Lesley Bragge

## Walnut Stool ▼
- *late 19th century*
French walnut stool with button
seat cover and cabriole legs.
- *height 49cm*
- £565          • Lesley Bragge

## Piano Stools ◄
- *circa 1835*
A pair of William IV rosewood
revolving and adjustable stools.
- *height 58cm*
- £2,650          • J. Collins

# Tables

## Pair of Tables ▼
• *circa 1890*
A pair of Regency-style, continental, gilded and painted console tables, with rich, ornate carving and variegated marble.
• *height 92cm*
• **£18,500** • **Rupert Cavendish**

## Urn Table ▼
• *circa 1760*
An unusual Chippendale period mahogany urn table, with fret gallery, inlaid floral side panels and turned, fluted legs.
• *height 61cm*
• **£33,000** • **Norman Adams**

## Swedish Sofa Table ▶
• *circa 1915*
Swedish sofa table in birchwood, with central, ebonised column, folding side flaps and a central drawer.
• *length (flaps up) 90cm*
• **£3,900** • **Rupert Cavendish**

## Marquetry Table ▲
• *circa 1850*
19th-century French marquetry table with floral designs and brass mounts.
• *height 71cm*
• **£1,250** • **Lynda Franklin**

## Tripod Table ▲
• *circa 1820*
A solid, circular mahogany tripod table with one-piece tilt top raised on a well-turned support.
• *height 75cm*
• **£1,650** • **J. Collins**

## French Side Table ▼
• *19th century*
French painted side table with marble inset top and caned platforms on turned and fluted legs with floral swags.
• *height 75cm*
• **£700** • **Youlls Antiques**

## Card Table ▼
• *circa 1880*
French card table, cross-banded with floral marquetry and stringing. Has brass moulding, ormolu mounts and original baize.
• *height 75cm*
• **£3,100** • **Lesley Bragge**

## Expert Tips
*The carving of marine subject motifs, such as dolphins, anchors, tridents and others, were used as a tribute to the victories of Horatio Nelson. Items with such carvings on them, therefore, are unlikely to pre-date 1800.*

### Inlaid Regency Tables ▼
- *circa 1810*
A pair of Regency polescreens converted into tables.
- *height 80cm*
- £3,250          • P.L. James

### French Side Table ▼
- *circa 1880*
Painted French side table with marble top and rosette decoration on turned and fluted legs.
- *height 79cm*
- £350          • Youlls Antiques

### Table de Chevet ▲
- *circa 1790*
Table de chevet in cherrywood with marble shelves.
- *height 72cm*
- £2,200          • O.F. Wilson

### Supper Table ▲
- *circa 1780*
Georgian mahogany tambor-fronted gentleman's supper table on square legs with side flaps.
- *height 70cm*
- £4,000          • Castlegate

### Dining Table ➤
- *circa 1810*
Mahogany D-ended Regency dining table, cross-banded in kingwood with boxwood stringing.
- *length (fully extended) 195cm*
- £8,750          • J. Collins

### Painted Side Table ▼
- *circa 1860*
Painted side table of oval form with inset marble top, set on turned, fluted legs. Oval cupboard at base with oval cane panel.
- *height 75cm*
- £650          • Youlls Antiques

### Gueridon Table ▼
- *circa 1830*
A very good gueridon French table, with an unusual marble top and acanthus scroll legs.
- *height 71cm*
- £6,750 • Christopher Preston

## Coffee Table  ◄
- *circa 1925*
Empire-style table in French
mahogany, with gilt mounts and
curved frame stretchers.
- *length 100cm*
- £2,900   • Rupert Cavendish

## Tilt Table  ▼
- *circa 1790*
Mahogany bird-cage tilt table on
pedestal with three pad feet.
- *height 70cm*
- £1,100   • Youlls Antiques

## Occasional Table  ▲
- *circa 1810*
Regency, mahogany occasional
table in pristine condition.
- *height 72cm*
- £1,650   • J. Collins

## Marquetry Table  ▲
- *circa 1690*
Good William and Mary floral
marquetry table, inlaid with
various woods.
- *height 80cm*
- £8,850   • P.L. James

### Expert Tips

*The majority of tilt-top tables
were rectangular with rounded
corners, oval and circular are
rarer. Beware oval tops which
have been added later.*

## Card Table  ▲
- *circa 1830*
Mahogany envelope card table
with baize to inside on turned
column with platform base.
- *height 71cm*
- £2,200   • John Clay

## Sofa Table  ▼
- *circa 1825*
Regency period mahogany end
support sofa table.
- *height 70cm*
- £11,250   • Ronald Chambers

## Walnut Side Table  ▲
- *circa 1780*
Good French walnut side table
with single drawer and square,
tapered legs.
- *height 72cm*
- £1,100   • Lynda Franklin

## Serving Table ➤

- *circa 1740*
Fine George II carved mahogany
serving table with fluted frieze
above six heavily carved legs with
leaf decoration.
- *height 89cm*
- **£130,000** • **Norman Adams**

## Library Table ▲

- *circa 1810*
Two-drawer, Regency library table
with turned, fluted legs on casters
and brass fittings to drawers.
- *height 76cm*
- **£3,750** • **Browns Antiques**

## Games Table ◄

- *circa 1830*
Fine quality compendium games
table for backgammon, draughts,
chess, cribbage etc.
- *height 73m*
- **£3,250** • **Christopher Preston**

## Pembroke Table ▼

- *circa 1800*
Well-grained, mahogany, one-
piece rectangular top with two
solid leaves and single drawer.
- *height 72.5cm*
- **£1,850** • **J. Collins**

## Marble-Topped Table ▲

- *circa 1740*
Eighteenth century marble-
topped table on turned legs with
ball feet.
- *height 71cm*
- **£1,250** • **Lynda Franklin**

## Rosewood Table ▲

- *circa 1820*
A good Regency rosewood table
with octagonal top and base with
four scroll feet.
- *height 74cm*
- **£3,650** • **P.L. James**

## Italian Table ◄

- *circa 1850*
Italian walnut occasional table
carved with figures of Bacchus,
Pan and other mythological gods.
- *height 74cm*
- **£8,000** • **Ian Spencer**

## Expert Tips

*Look out for signs of woodworm
in walnut – it is particularly
susceptible.*

## Side Tables  ▼

- *circa 1860*

Pair of French, walnut side
cabinets with gilt-metal mounts
and inset marble tops.
- *height 72cm*
- **£1,485**        • **Ranby Hall**

## Card Table  ▼

- *circa 1830*

Regency rosewood, brass inlaid
card table on square base, with
gilt claw casters.
- *height 74cm*
- **£2,300**        • **Castlegate**

## Console Table  ▲

- *circa 1890*

Late 19th-century carved walnut
console table in George I style,
with cabriole legs.
- *height 85cm*
- **£2,450**      • **Browns Antiques**

## Bentwood Table  ▲

- *19th century*

Round table with bentwood legs,
slightly splayed, from ball
decoration.
- *height 54cm*
- **£225**              • **N.W.8**

## Tripod Table  ▼

- *circa 1760*

A Chippendale period mahogany
table with piecrust top.
- *height 70.5cm*
- **£20,000**      • **Norman Adams**

## Tile Table  ▼

- *circa 1890*

Table of bamboo construction,
with legs and stretchers pale and
top darker, with inlaid tile to top.
- *height 47cm*
- **£120**              • **N.W.8**

## Art Deco Coffee Table  ◄

- *circa 1925*

Masur birch and rosewood coffee
table with inlays of satinwood
and cross-banding in 'tiger' birch.
- *length 99cm*
- **£2,700**      • **Rupert Cavendish**

### Gateleg Table ◄
- *circa 1740*
A fine George II almost circular walnut table.
- *height 72cm*
- £40,000 • Norman Adams

### Pier Table ▲
- *circa 1820*
Regency pier table with fluted column supports and pleated panel to rear.
- *height 103cm*
- £1,895 • M.J. Bowdery

### Mahogany Side Table ▼
- *circa 1780*
Small Georgian mahogany side table, with single drawer.
- *height 72cm*
- £1,800 • Terence Morse

### Card Table ▼
- *circa 1790*
George III mahogany card table.
- *height 71cm*
- £3,950 • J. de Haan

### Snap-Top Table ▲
- *circa 1800*
Georgian, mahogany, snap-top occasional table with rectangular top with rounded corners and tripod base with swept feet terminating in casters.
- *height 102cm*
- £800 • Ian Spencer

### Elephant Table ▲
- *circa 1900*
Very detailed, carved table sitting on four elephants' heads, the trunks as legs, with ivory tusks.
- *height 62cm*
- £1,250 • Christopher Preston

### Cherrywood Table ►
- *circa 1760*
French table on cabriole legs.
- *length 180cm*
- £3,200 • Lynda Franklin

### Tilt Table ▼
- *circa 1830*
A Regency lacquered tripod table in chinoiserie style, showing scenes of pagodas and kite flying.
- *height 117cm*
- £2,450          • O.F. Wilson

### Queen Anne Side Table ▲
- *circa 1695*
18th-century walnut side table with single drawer with brass fittings, turned legs on bun feet and turned stretchers.
- *height 67cm*
- £1,750 • Christopher Preston

### Pair of Console Tables ▼
- *circa 1805*
A rare pair of Swedish neoclassical Empire console tables, by Jonas Frisk, Stockholm.
- *height 86cm*
- £16,500 • Rupert Cavendish

### Mahogany Night Table ▼
- *circa 1780*
George III night table with dipped front edge and surrounding gallery.
- *height 78.5cm*
- £2,250          • J. Collins

### Satinwood Table ▼
- *circa 1920*
Two-tier, Edwardian satinwood table on square, splayed legs.
- *height 70cm*
- £2,100          • Terence Morse

### Work Table ▲
- *circa 1880*
An octagonal work table with games top on an eight-sided, fluted base, tapering to base with three legs.
- *height 79cm*
- £950                    • Castlegate

### Centre Table ➤
- *circa 1845*
Rosewood centre table with figural top with gadrooned edge. Carved centre column.
- *height 71cm*
- £3,850          • M.J. Bowdery

### Art Deco Coffee Table ◀
- *circa 1925*
Swedish walnut table with inlays
of heart, burr elm and fruitwood.
- *diameter 100cm*
- £2,700 • Rupert Cavendish

### Games Table ▲
- *circa 1840*
Rosewood games table of
exceptional quality with original
ormolu paw feet.
- *height 74cm*
- £3,800 • Ranby Hall

### Pier Table ▼
- *circa 1790*
A shallow Sheraton period
satinwood pier table.
- *height 86cm*
- £22,500 • Norman Adams

### Side Table ▼
- *19th century*
French oval side table.
- *height 75cm*
- £650 • Youlls Antiques

### Marble Table ▲
- *18th century*
French white marble table with
fine bronze mounts and three
columns on a tri-cornered plinth.
- *height 71cm*
- £2,700 • Lynda Franklin

### Side Table ▼
- *circa 1870*
Mid-Victorian mahogany, two-
drawer side table.
- *height 75cm*
- £1,850 • Browns Antiques

### Shearing Table ▶
- *circa 1850*
Primitive, V-shaped wooden table
for sheep-shearing.
- *height 38cm*
- £520 • Lacquer Chest

## Occasional Table ▼
• *circa 1900*
Occasional table in 18th-century style, with marquetry and boxwood stringing on solid, inlaid stretcher, the whole on four tapered legs.
• *height 75cm*
• **£550**          • **Youlls Antiques**

## Oriental Tables ▲
• *circa 1880*
Set of four hardwood oriental occasional tables.
• *height 47-72cm*
• **£1,450** • **Christopher Preston**

## Pair of Tables ▲
• *circa 1910*
Pair of early 20th-century birchwood and masur birch side tables with top drawer and lower platform, the whole resting on four square tapering legs.
• *height 74cm*
• **£2,900**    • **Rupert Cavendish**

## Folding Table ▼
• *circa 1890*
Late Victorian folding table of simulated bamboo, with turned legs and stretchers.
• *height 70cm*
• **£1,350**       • **Lacquer Chest**

## Serving Table ▼
• *circa 1825*
Good-quality mahogany two-drawer side or serving table on well-turned legs.
• *height 78cm*
• **£1,495**       • **M.J. Bowdery**

## Pembroke Table ▲
• *circa 1800*
A George III mahogany Pembroke table, banded with satinwood.
• *height 71cm*
• **£3,800**       • **Terence Morse**

## Flip-Over Table ➤
• *circa 1905*
Sheraton revival mahogany flip-over table extending to 200cm, with telescopic action.
• *height 72cm*
• **£6,500**       • **Ian Spencer**

## Sewing Table ▲
- *circa 1870*

Victorian walnut writing and sewing table with leaf-decorated, turned cabriole legs and satinwood floral inlay.
- *height 73cm*
- **£1,650**　　　• **Castlegate**

## Games Table ▼
- *circa 1835*

Mahogany, fold-over games table raised on central pedestal.
- *height 75cm*
- **£1,650**　　　• **Ranby Hall**

## Yew Tilt Table ▼
- *circa 1760*

Fine 18th-century yew tilt table with tripod base.
- *height 67cm*
- **£2,250**　　　• **Red Lion**

## Tea Table ▲
- *circa 1800*

George III mahogany tea table with line inlay.
- *height 75cm*
- **£1,745**　　　• **M.J. Bowdery**

## Side Table ▼
- *circa 1690*

Exceptional William and Mary marquetry side table with 'X' stretcher and original bun feet.
- *height 71cm*
- **£4,400**　　　• **Raffety**

## Expert Tips

*Dryness in the atmosphere caused by central heating is furniture's greatest enemy. There are various methods of humidifying the atmosphere; using one of them is essential.*

## Pembroke Table ▼
- *circa 1770*

English mahogany Pembroke table of typical form, veneered with satin and tulipwood, strung with ebony and boxwood. The table has drawers at either end with brass fittings, a side flap and the whole rests on four square tapering legs terminating in brass casters.
- *height 74cm*
- **£4,850**
- **M. Wakelin & H. Linfield**

## Breakfast Table ◄
- *circa 1810*

Regency mahogany breakfast table with tilt top.
- *height 70cm*
- **£12,500**　　　• **J. Collins**

# Wardrobes

## Linen Press ▼
- *circa 1780*
18th-century mahogany linen press with oval door panels, oval brass mounts and moulded cornice, on splayed bracket feet.
- *height 1.6m*
- **£6,800**                • Chambers

## Georgian Linen Press ▼
- *circa 1830*
A mahogany linen press with moulded and cavetto cornice, two short and two full-width mahogany and pine-lined cockbeaded drawers fitted with oval brass decorations.
- *height 2.1m*
- **£3,950**                • J. Collins

## Victorian Compactum ➤
- *circa mid -19th century*
Mahogany compactum, comprising two hanging side cabinets, drawers and shelves.
- *height 2.5m*
- **£3,750**                • Old Cinema

## North Breton Armoire ▼
- *18th century*
With primitive carving, lined with 19th-century fabric.
- *height 1.6m*
- **£2,400**                • Angel

## Oak Cupboard ▼
- *circa 1780*
Oak cupboard with two six-panelled doors above four drawers, on bracket feet.
- *height 1.95m*
- **£4,800**                • Red Lion

## Victorian Compactum ▲
- *circa mid-19th century*
Mahogany compactum comprising two hanging cupboards, two linen presses and five tiers of drawers.
- *height 2.2m*
- **£3,750**                • Old Cinema

## Walnut Armoire ▲
- *circa 1840*
With deep carvings, a simple cornice with shell motif, ornate hinges and a shaped apron.
- *height 2.2m*
- **£3,750**      • Town & Country

### Fruitwood Armoire ▼
- *circa early 19th century*
French fruitwood armoire with
carved doors with rosettes and
fluted centre panel above carved
apron, the whole on scrolled feet.
- *height 2.09m*
- **£2,495**          • Old Cinema

### Gillows Press ▼
- *circa 1805*
A linen press, stamped 'Gillows
of Lancaster', retaining its
original patina and with all
original handles and interior,
with sliding trays, surmounted by
an arched pediment.
- *height 2.3m*
- **£14,500**          • Chambers

### Ash Wardrobe ➤
- *circa 19th century*
Hungarian wardrobe with four
doors above two deep drawers.
- *height 2.8m*
- **£5,995**          • Old Cinema

### Victorian Linen Press ▲
- *circa 1840*
A linen press with secret drawer
and Gothic moulded doors.
- *height 2.35m*
- **£6,800**          • Terence Morse

### Venetian Armoire ▲
- *circa late 17th century*
Venetian armoire with painted
panel doors with dental course
and cast-bronze cherub handles.
- *height 1.95m*
- **£7,500**          • Paul Andrews

### French Oak Armoire ▼
- *date 1844*
Armoire with shaped apron with
date, profuse leaf carving, beading
and scale motif.
- *height 2.2m*
- **£7,400**          • Paul Andrews

### First Empire Linen Press ▼
- *circa 1810*
In flamed mahogany with two
doors above four tiers of drawers,
the columns with fine gilt mounts.
- *height 2.25m*
- **£13,000**          • Pillows

## Linen Press ▲
• *circa 1780*
An 18th-century mahogany linen
press with original fittings.
• *height 2.2m*
• £6,800          • Chambers

## English Cupboard ▲
• *circa 1780*
Very fine cupboard with secret
compartments, heavily cut frieze
and pilaster decoration.
• *height 2.6m*
• £12,800          • Riverbank

## Jersey Wardrobe ▼
• *circa 1800*
An early 19th-century mahogany
wardrobe.
• *height 2.09m*
• £3,500          • Terence Morse

## French Armoire ▼
• *circa 1790*
A Provençale armoire with
serpentine apron.
• *height 1.69m*
• £1,200          • Lynda Franklin

## Dutch Linen Press ▲
• *circa early 19th century*
Mahogany with pilasters and gilt
mounts on plinth feet.
• *height 2m*
• £4,500          • Old Cinema

## Expert Tips

*The size of the panels of these
items render them particularly
vulnerable to splitting. Beware
central heating!*

## Elm Press ▼
• *circa 1820*
English linen-press cupboard on
shaped bracket feet.
• *height 1.8m*
• £2,850          • Angel

## Breakfront Wardrobe ◄
• *circa late 19th century*
Inverted mahogany breakfront
wardrobe with brass mounts, on
shaped bracket feet.
• *height 2m*
• £3,995          • Old Cinema

# Glass

**Glass forms some of the most beautiful artefacts with which to create a collection – and its inherent fragility ensures ongoing rarity value.**

It is only relatively recently that glass has become a popular field for collectors. The probable reasons for this were the fragility of the items in question and the fact that there are considerable difficulties in authentication and attribution.

Drinking glasses were made in large numbers throughout the eighteenth century and are very popular with collectors. Value depends on the rarity of the decoration as well as the shape of the bowl, stem and foot.

Colourful glass of the nineteenth century is increasingly popular with collectors. Many new glassmaking techniques and more varied colours were introduced during this period, and services of glass were introduced in numbers for the first time.

Continental glass is an enormous field, from medieval German and early Venetian to the beautiful colour of Bohemian glass of the nineteenth century, which can fetch staggering prices.

On the other hand, unmarked glass of the nineteenth century is still an excellent buy and can often be less expensive than its modern equivalent.

---

### Engraved Wine Glass ▼
- *circa 1880*
Engraved with grape vines. Bridge cutting to bowl and stem.
- *height 12cm*
- £340          • Jasmin Cameron

### Bohemian Glass ➤
- *circa 1860*
Showing a romantic portrait of a lady with flowers on reverse. With enamel and gilding.
- *height 16cm*
- £360          • Mousa

### Wine Rinser ▲
- *circa 1790*
An early yellow wine rinser with an extreme double lip. Originally part of a dessert set.
- *height 10cm*
- £400          • Jasmin Cameron

### Wine Glass ▼
- *circa 1755*
A mid-18th century bell-bowl baluster wine glass with domed, folded foot.
- *height 16.2cm*
- £270          • Jasmin Cameron

Glass

---

## Russian Drinking Set  ⌄

- *late 19th century*

Five pieces comprising a wine
carafe and four shallow dish
glasses with floral enamel and
gilded decoration.

- £2,600　　　　　• Sinai

## Wine Glass  ⌄

- *circa 1750*

An 18th-century wine glass with
double spiral cables on the stem
and a domed foot.

- *height 16cm*
- £450　　　• Jasmin Cameron

## Bristol Glasses  ➤

- *circa 1885*

A cup, champagne beaker and
wine glass in blue glass.

- £55 (for the 3)
- Mousa

## Engraved Wine Glass  ⌃

- *circa 1850*

Engraved hop and barley with
scale cutting and high knop.

- *height 15cm*
- £425　　• Jasmin Cameron

## Scent Bottle  ⌃

- *circa 1880*

A Bohemian cut-glass scent
bottle with stopper and floral
gilding on a blue ground.

- *height 12cm*
- £210　　　　• Mousa

## French Bottle  ⌄

- *circa 1850*

A French bottle and stopper with
applied brass decoration and lid,
with ornate handles.

- *height 21cm*
- £370　　　　• Mousa

## Rummer  ⌄

- *circa 1810*

A rummer, slightly waisted, with
triple banding around bowl.

- *height 13cm*
- £140　　• Jasmin Cameron

### Bohemian Vase ▼
- *19th century*
With cut and engraved scenes of
deer among woodland.
- *height 44cm*
- £2,600 • Sinai

### Pickle Preserve Jar ▼
- *circa 1825*
With an octagonal body, star base
and star stopper.
- *height 18cm*
- £85 • Jasmin Cameron

### Dessert Service ➤
- *circa 1890*
20-piece enamelled dessert
service with gilded vine and fruit
decoration.
- £4,200 • Sinai

### Port Glass ▲
- *19th century*
A 19th-century port glass with
base knop.
- *height 11cm*
- £65 • Jasmin Cameron

### Bohemian Vases ▲
- *circa 1895*
A pair of green overlay vases with
strong geometric patterns.
- *height 27cm*
- £480 • Mousa

### German Vase ▼
- *circa 1880*
A German vase with scrolling. In
a 17th-century style.
- *height 28cm*
- £200 • Mousa

### Hookah Base ▼
- *circa 1880*
Made for the Middle-Eastern
market. Heavily cut and gilded
with painted enamel flowers.
- *height 26cm*
- £680 • Mousa

## Three Decanters ➤
- *circa 1825, 1770, 1810*
A port decanter, oval spirit
decanter and tapered spirit
decanter.
- *heights 24cm, 23cm, 29cm*
- £420, £360, £420 resp.
- Jasmin Cameron

## Set of Vases ▲
- *circa 1880*
A set of three green matt-glaze
vases, with gilding. Centre-piece
shown with white snake about
stem and base.
- £1,300     • La Bohème

## Bohemian Glass ▼
- *circa 1860*
With enamelled floral panels and
ormolu mounts, with the figures
of three swans.
- *height 20cm*
- £1,100     • Shahdad

## Bohemian Bottle and Dish ▼
- *19th century*
Heavily cut, twisted and fluted
with enamelling and gilding.
- *height 26cm*
- £550     • Sinai

## French Scent Bottle ▲
- *circa 1880*
An opaline scent bottle with
cover and gilded decoration.
- *height 11cm*
- £650     • Sinai

## Wine Carafe ▲
- *circa 1810*
Flat panels, prismatic steps and a
star base with faceting to the lip.
- *height 18cm*
- £235     • Jasmin Cameron

## German Glass Beaker ▲
- *circa 1860*
Showing a painted pastoral scene.
With a heavily cut base.
- *height 12cm*
- £280     • Mousa

## Port Glass ▲
- *circa 1810*
An early 19th-century port glass with knops to stem.
- *height 10cm*
- £110          • Jasmin Cameron

## Bohemian Green Glass ▲
- *19th century*
Pot and cover on a base with gilding and enamelling.
- *height 12cm*
- £1,200          • Sinai

## Bohemian Vases ▼
- *19th century*
With cherubs, enamel flowers and gilding on an ormolu base.
- *height 27cm*
- £2,600          • Sinai

## Venetian Vase ▼
- *18th century*
A Venetian marbelised small vase on a pedestal foot.
- *height 17cm*
- £800          • Shahdad

## Mammoth Wine Glass ▼
- *circa 1850*
With gilded rim and marked JH on the base. Scale cutting to leg.
- *height 28cm*
- £300          • Jasmin Cameron

## Strawberry Cut Jug ▼
- *circa 1825*
An Irish jug with prismatic stars, radial base and fluted handle.
- *height 17cm*
- £180          • Jasmin Cameron

## Venetian Vases ◄
- *19th century*
Two mille fiore double handled vases in perfect condition.
- £400, £500
- Shahdad

## Venetian Bottle Vases ▼
- *circa 1880*
A pair of vases with jewellery to neck and gilt metal bases.
- *height 24cm*
- £480 • Mousa

## Venetian Glasses ▼
- *circa 1900*
Seventy-two pieces with profuse gilding and deep-red glass panels inset within the bowls
- £5,500 • Sinai

## Cordial Wine Glass ◄
- *circa 1770*
A wine glass with red and green coloured bands. Made in Bristol.
- *height 11.7cm*
- £780 • Jasmin Cameron

## German Ewer ▲
- *circa 1870*
A German green glass ewer with armorial and key form design.
- *height 27.5cm*
- £160 • Namdar

## Engraved Port Glass ▲
- *19th century*
A port glass engraved with 'VR' – Victoria Regina.
- *height 12cm*
- £75 • Jasmin Cameron

## Cup and Cover ▲
- *19th century*
With enamelled panel of maidens and a cherub in a classical setting. Gilding and fluted decoration.
- *height 37cm*
- £3,500 • Sinai

## Port Decanters ▲
- *circa 1830*
A pair of engraved decanters with star-shaped bases, faceted neck and lapidary stopper.
- *height 24cm*
- £420 • Jasmin Cameron

### Expert Tips
Good antique hand-blown glass will usually have a distinctive tint caused by the impurities present in production. Later imitations tend to give themselves away by being too pure.

### Engraved Wine Glasses ▼
- *circa 1890*
One of six large engraved glasses
decorated with hops and barley.
- *height 17cm*
- **£640** • **Jasmin Cameron**

### French Glass Vases ▼
- *circa 1880*
A pair of vases with enamelling,
gilding and applied jewels.
- *height 32cm*
- **£1,500** • **Sinai**

### Chamber Pot ▼
- *circa 1880*
A blue glass chamber pot with
floral gilding to bowl and lip.
- *height 16cm*
- **£250** • **Mousa**

### Table Lustres ▲
- *circa 1890*
A pair of Bohemian blue lustre
decorative objects, with
enamelled portraits, cut-glass
crystal and gilded leaf decoration.
- *height 40cm*
- **£1,200** • **La Bohème**

### Bohemian Vase ▲
- *circa 1870*
In red glass with a painted flower
frieze and gilded floral decoration.
- *height 31cm*
- **£380** • **Mousa**

### Engraved Port Glass ▼
- *circa 1860*
One of a set of eight port glasses
with fruited vines and leaves
engraved on the bowl.
- *height 17cm*
- **£360** • **Jasmin Cameron**

### Cordial Wine Glass ▼
- *circa 1755*
An 18th-century cordial glass
with opaque-twist stem.
- *height 11.8cm*
- **£460** • **Jasmin Cameron**

## French Vase ▲
- *circa 1900*
By E. Rousseau, Paris. Showing a
Japanese man with apple blossom.
On a base with bun feet.
- *height 18cm*
- £2,800 • Cameo Gallery

## German Beaker ▼
- *circa 1700*
Engraved with forest, deer,
pastoral subjects and latin script.
- *height 24cm*
- £580 • Mousa

## Nailsea Bottle ▼
- *circa 1865*
A Nailsea factory door porter
with tears.
- *height 12cm*
- £165 • Jasmin Cameron

## Bohemian Glass Goblet ▼
- *19th century*
Glass goblet with cover. Showing
an engraved forest scene.
- *height 52cm*
- £1,200 • Sinai

## Pair of Centrepieces ▶
- *circa 1860*
In green overlay with painted
flower enamels and gilding.
- *height 33cm*
- £1,300 • Mousa

## Wine Goblets ▲
- *circa 1800*
A pair of goblets of ovoid shape
with a raised cut diamond pattern.
- *height 15cm*
- £445 (pair) • Jasmin Cameron

## Six Irish Wine Rinsers ▲
- *circa 1810*
Flat parallel prismatic steps,
sawtooth rim with a double lip.
- *height 19cm*
- £900 (set) • Jasmin Cameron

### Emile Gallé Dish ➤

- *late 19th century*
With fine floral enamelling and
figuration scenes in the panels.
The whole with profuse gilding.
- £8,500 • Sinai

### Ewer and Goblets ⋀

- *19th century*
Bohemian ewer and two goblets
with panels of flowers and profuse
floral gilding.
- £3,200 • Sinai

### Cameo Scent Bottle ➤

- *circa 1860*
An English cameo scent bottle
engraved with flowers and leaves.
- *height 8cm*
- £260 • Mousa

### Red Bohemian Vase ⋁

- *circa 1870*
A red vase with a painted flower
frieze and gilded floral decoration.
- *height 31cm*
- £380 • Mousa

### Port Glass ⋀

- *19th century*
A 19th-century port glass with
knop and domed base.
- *height 11cm*
- £65 • Jasmin Cameron

### German Glass Beaker ⋀

- *circa 1880*
A German green glass beaker
with a coat of arms and coronet.
- *height 10cm*
- £85 • Mousa

### Monteith or Bonnet
### Glasses ⋖

- *circa 1750*
Mid 18th-century glasses.
- *height 8cm*
- £220 • Jasmin Cameron

## Ale / Beer Glass  ▼
- *circa 1850*
A half litre glass on a pedestal, by
Thomas Webb & Co.
- *height 20cm*
- £180   • Jasmin Cameron

## Bohemian Beaker  ▲
- *circa 1880*
Amber glass with three engraved
panels showing seascapes.
- *height 11cm*
- £170   • Mousa

## Goblet and Cover  ▼
- *circa 1860*
Bohemian red glass with deeply
engraved hunting scene.
- *height 51cm*
- £18,500   • Sinai

## Bohemian Goblets  ▲
- *circa 1890*
A pair of blue glass Bohemian
goblets showing running stags in
a forest setting.
- *height 20cm*
- £480 (pair)   • Mousa

## Scent Bottles  ▲
- *circa 1880*
A pair of Bohemian glass scent
bottles with fluted necks and
globular bodies.
- *height 15cm*
- £280   • Mousa

## Port Glass  ▼
- *circa 1840*
A nineteenth-century port glass
with knop and domed base.
- *height 11cm*
- £45   • Jasmin Cameron

## Glass Tankard  ▼
- *circa 1880*
A Bohemian tankard with an
engraving of forest and birds.
- *height 17cm*
- £180   • Mousa

### Expert Tips

*Displayed glass should be
washed and dry-polished
occasionally. A few drops of
vinegar in the rinsing water
helps to produce a sparkling
finish. Tissue paper is ideal for
the final polish.*

## Amethyst Wine Rinser ▲
- *circa 1820*
One of a pair, with a double lip and bulbous shape. A rare colour.
- *height 9cm*
- £450 (pair) • Jasmin Cameron

## German Beaker ▼
- *circa 1890*
A heavy-based beaker with painted hunting scenes.
- *height 12cm*
- £280 • Mousa

## Set of Rummers ▶
- *circa 1820*
On square bases with central frieze of a deep diamond-cut pattern.
- *height 15cm*
- £780 • Riverbank

## Spirit Decanters ▼
- *circa 1835*
With silver collars, linen fold panels and a star base and stopper.
- *height 25cm*
- £490 (pair) • Jasmin Cameron

## Engraved Liqueur Glass ◀
- *circa 1880*
One of six, thumb-cut to bowl with vine and fruit decoration.
- *height 9cm*
- £190 • Jasmin Cameron

## Vase and Cover ▼
- *19th century*
A Bohemian vase and cover in three sections of white, red and gold enamelling. With Eastern panels and flower and leaf designs.
- *height 64cm*
- £3,800 • Sinai

## Bohemian Vase ◀
- *circa 1880*
A Bohemian red glass vase with a painted enamel potrait of a lady. With flowers and profuse floral decoration.
- *height 19cm*
- £260 • Mousa

## Gallé Vase ▼
- *circa 1900*

Black, amber and orange, showing
a harbour scene with lighthouse.
- *height 32cm*
- **£8,500**     • **Cameo Gallery**

## Decanter ▼
- *circa 1870*

A lead crystal locking decanter,
with silver-plated handle.
- *height 16cm*
- **£420**     • **Walpole**

## Champagne Glasses ▲
- *19th century*

Set of eight with honeycomb
bowl, engraved vine and fruits
and a splayed base.
- *height 12cm*
- **£430 (set)**  • **Jasmin Cameron**

## Chemist's Balls ▲
- *circa 1840*

Early 19th-century chemist's glass
balls, with engraved star patterns,
on turned ebonized bases.
- *height 58cm*
- **£2,800**     • **Martin-Taylor**

## Lithyan Vases ▲
- *circa 1860*

A pair of German vases with
spider and cobweb design and
jewellery to base and neck.
- *height 22cm*
- **£480**     • **Mousa**

## English Centrepiece ▼
- *circa 1860*

A light green centrepiece with
painted birds and flowers. Gilding
to scrolled handles, lip and base.
- *height 35cm*
- **£580**     • **Mousa**

## Wine Glass ▼
- *19th century*

One of six unusually patterned
glasses. Trumpet-shaped and set
on a hexagonal stem.
- *height 14cm*
- **£420 (set)**  • **Jasmin Cameron**

## Gallé Scent Bottle ▼
• *circa 1890*
Metal mounts and cracked finish with flowers, praying mantis and moth finial on the stopper.
• *height 10cm*
• **£1,600**      • **Cameo Gallery**

## Red Bohemian Vase ➤
• *circa 1880*
A fluted vase on a pedestal foot. Engraved with forest scenes.
• *height 30cm*
• **£380**      • **Mousa**

## Green Bohemian Glasses ▲
• *circa 1860*
Green Bohemian glasses comprising five pieces with profuse gilt decoration.
• **£10,000**      • **Sinai**

## Bristol Wine Glasses ▲

• *circa 1785*
A pair of tulip-shaped glasses with a peacock-blue tint.
• *height 12cm*
• **£235 (pair)** • **Jasmin Cameron**

## Lamp Base ➤
• *19th century*
A lamp base in gilded bronze and glass with stylized leaf and scrolled decoration.
• *height 55cm*
• **£1,800**      • **Riverbank**

## Claret Jug ▲

• *circa 1870*
A Victorian lead crystal claret jug with silver-plated lid and handle.
• *height 27cm*
• **£275**      • **Barham**

## Shot Glasses ◀
• *circa 1868*
Set of four shot glasses with a lightly engraved rim.
• *height 3.5cm*
• **£120**      • **Jasmin Cameron**

# Jewellery

**An incredible amount of jewellery changes hands every day in auction rooms, dealers' shops, market stalls and boot fairs. Look for quality first.**

The manufacture of jewellery may well be the second oldest profession and, some might argue, in some ways not unrelated to the oldest. One of the most outstanding features of the jewellery market is the simply enormous quantity of it out there and changing hands. A glance at any local paper will reveal the number of antiques fairs, markets and car-boot sales taking place on any given weekend throughout the year and, when one considers that this is going on throughout the country, it boggles the mind as to how much jewellery is being placed before the public quite literally all the time.

There is an enormous diversity of jewellery being collected, from early plastic items through such relatively inexpensive materials as marcasite sets in silver and stained horn, up to the highly prized and precious items that usually dignify the name.

While demand for jewellery is strong in nearly all areas, from Victorian silver to diamond tiaras, the one requirement throughout is for quality. Good design and delicate workmanship can count for a lot more than a bucket-full of poor-quality diamonds.

## Necklace  ▲
- *circa 1850*
With 18ct gold backing and silver front. Five rose-cut diamond flowers suspended from a silver and diamond chain. Three cabachon emeralds hanging delicately from many diamond strands and fringes.
- *length 41cm*
- **£9,500**          • Emmy Abé

### Expert Tips

*If a stone doesn't cut glass, it is not a diamond. If it does, it is not necessarily a diamond.*

## Shell Cameo  ▲
- *circa 1870*
Shell cameo set in 15ct. gold chain mount. Subject showing George and Dragon.
- *height 8cm*
- **£650**          • Rowan & Rowan

## Gold Cross  ▼
- *circa 1810*
Georgian gold cross set with Roman intaglios – sealed gems ornamented with sunken or incised designs. Made in England.
- *length 8cm*
- **£4,800**          • Sandra Cronan

## Perfume Bottle Pendant  ◄
- *date 1880*
Fine grey agate perfume bottle with engraved floral designs to the obverse, a hanging chain and the reverse showing a panel with three lions.
- *length 6cm*
- **£820**
- Sue & Alan Thompson

## Brooch ▾
• *circa 1965*
A 'KJL' brooch, by Kenneth J.
Lane. The brooch is of a
flamboyant, baroque design,
formed as a four-pointed star with
rounded ends, set with a central,
square cut faux cabochon ruby,
and French lapis lazuli.
• *height 8cm*
• £150          • **Hilary Conqy**

## Turquoise Beads ▾
• *circa 1930*
Antique spider web turquoise
beads, from New Mexico, which
have been restrung with new
clasp on a silver chain.
• *length 60cm*
• £499          • **Wilde Ones**

## Brooch/Pendant ➤
• *date 1880*
A French cameo, all carved out of
one piece of sardonyx, showing a
Greek mythological figure in
profile, surrounded by twelve
natural sea pearls with a half-
pearl leaf design surround.
• *height 10cm*
• £1,750          • **Emmy Abé**

## Dragonfly Brooch ▲
• *circa 1880*
Victorian gold dragonfly brooch,
inset with rubies and diamonds
surrounding a natural pearl, all in
gold settings.
• *length 6cm*
• £14,500          • **Sandra Cronan**

## Necklace ▲
• *circa 1940*
A continental necklace of the
Art Deco period, fashioned with
interlinked chrome rings hung
with green bakelite discs.
• £75          • **Hilary Conqy**

## Crystal Beads ▾
• *circa 1940*
A necklace of crystal glass, amber,
faceted beads with the principal
pendant an extremely large,
cushion-cut stone in a pierced,
filigree mounting.
• £35          • **Sugar Antiques**

## Hairslides ▾
• *circa 1910*
Set of three tortoiseshell
hairslides with 9ct. gold
mountings with a solitaire
amethyst and two small pearls to
each piece.
• *2 x 10cmx5cm, 1 x 11cmx7.5cm*
• £900          • **Victor Arnas**

### Expert Tips

*To tell shell cameos
from hardstone, scratch
the back of the piece. With
shell, the scratch will be
apparent; it will have no
effect on hardstone.*

## English Bracelet ◄
- *date 1860*

An English bracelet, silver set with Bristol blue glass and marcasite, in its original domed, morocco box. Pierced floral decoration in the metal of the bracelet and applied to the glass.
- *length 18cm*
- **£500** • **Rowan & Rowan**

## Necklace ▼
- *circa 1885*

Egyptian revival necklace, composed of carved nephrite scarabs, with diamonds and lotus flowers in green and red enamel, mounted in 18 carat gold.
- **£56,000** • **Sandra Cronan**

## Opal Earrings ▼
- *circa 1850*

Austro-Hungarian four-stage drop opal earings, with silver settings.
- *length 6cm*
- **£750** • **Emmy Abé**

## Necklace ►
- *circa 1970*

Turkmen silver choker fertility necklace with pendants. Made in Afghanistan.
- **£65** • **Oriental**

## Mourning Pendant ▼
- *circa 1910*

An Edwardian mourning pendant, with 18 carat gold backing and silver front surrounding glass containing a strand of hair in the form of a feather.
- *length 4cm*
- **£1,250** • **Emmy Abé**

## Zuni Bracelet ►
- *circa 1998*

A Zuni bracelet with three panels of geometric design, showing the four-direction medicine wheel for the protection of the wearer. Made of jet, coral, lapus lazuli and turquoise. By H. Kalfestewa.
- **£1,499** • **Wilde Ones**

## Silver Tiara ▲
- *circa 1910*

Silver and paste belle epoque tiara in original box. French provenance, with Greek key pattern and wreath design.
- *length 15cm*
- **£1,250** • **Rowan & Rowan**

## Czechoslovakian Brooch  ◄
- *circa 1930*
A Czechoslovakian brooch of
blue glass on a plenal base. Of
diamond shape with a large,
central diamond-shaped stone
with a clasp mount.
- *length 7.5cm*
- £40          • Sugar Antiques

## Expert Tips

*Fake stones are
sometimes difficult to spot.
Glass may most easily be
identified by the gas bubbles
which should clearly be seen
under magnification.*

## Wedding Necklace  ▼
- *circa 1930*
Navajo squash-blossom wedding
necklace with naga centrepiece,
representing union, and silver,
handcast beads with turquoise
stones.
- *length 60cm*
- £1,499          • Wilde Ones

## Brooch  ▲
- *circa 1940*
Brooch of glass-encrusted flowers
with blue beads.
*length 7cm*
- £45          • Sugar Antiques

## Coral Necklace  ▼
- *circa 1860*
Whitby jet fossilised coral
necklace. Large anchor links
attached to a jet heart with
applied cameo.
- *length 30cm*
- £750          • Rowan & Rowan

## Bow Brooch  ▼
- *circa 1940s*
Bow brooch with baguettes of
faux sapphire and paste. Signed
by Marcel Boucher.
- *height 6cm*
- £95          • Hilary Conqy

## Brass Necklace  ▲
- *date 1983*
French brass necklace, by
Chanel, with multi-coloured glass
inlays, double-heavy chain and
filigree adornments
- £425          • Hilary Conqy

## Diamond Bracelet  ▶
- *circa 1920*
Art Deco diamond bracelet set
with a rare marquis-shaped
natural fancy blue diamond,
mounted in platinum.
- £155,000      • Sandra Cronan

## Art Deco Brooch ▲

• *circa 1925*
An unusual brooch of the Art Deco period, made in the form of an undulating diamond and onyx scroll, with carved emerald terminals, mounted in platinum. By Boucheron of Paris.
• *length 5.5cm*
• £75,000      • Sandra Cronan

## Pendant and Earrings ▼

• *circa 1880*
A matching set of pendant and earrings, pendant showing enamel figure inside ornate, gold flower and petal surround. The earrings (not shown) are of two cherubs with pearls and flowers.
• £2,500      • Emmy Abé

## Earrings ▲

• *circa 1895*
A pair of late Victorian cultivated pearl and diamond set earrings, formed as flower-head clusters, with twelve diamonds set about a pearl. English.
• £14,500      • Sandra Cronan

## Expert Tips

*Abrasion during cleaning can be injurious to metal and softer stones. The simplest method for cleaning jewellery is by soaking in a strong solution of washing-up liquid.*

## Headdress ◄

• *circa 1970*
Turkmen harem-style metal headdress with chain and plate pendant adornments and plated band with metal teardrop to centre with turquoise inset. Made in Afghanistan.
• £83      • Oriental

## Tab Necklace ▲

• *circa 1936*
Santa Domingo Pueblo tab necklace of red coral, spiny oyster shell and natural matrix turquoise, strung on double-strand original cord.
• *length 46cm*
• £499      • Wilde Ones

## Amethyst Collar ▼

• *circa 1870*
Victorian gold and brilliant-cut faceted amethyst collar. Made in England, in original case.
• £950      • Michelle Rowan

## Art Deco Brooch ▲

• *circa 1925*
An Art Deco brooch of two highly naturalistic parrots, wings spread, fighting over a perch. With diamonds and calibré, buff-topped emeralds, sapphires, rubies and onyx. Mounted on platinum. Made in England.
• £36,500      • Sandra Cronan

## Bead Necklace ▼

• *circa 1940s*
A necklace of turquoise blue beads with glass encrusted flowers interwoven. The pendant is a flower cluster in pink, white blue and yellow.
• *length 45cm*
• £35          • **Sugar Antiques**

## Basket Brooch ▼

• *circa 1925*
An Art Deco basket brooch by Cartier of Paris, of carved onyx with ruby flowers and cabochon emeralds and sapphires, mounted on platinum.
• £9,000          • **Sandra Cronan**

## Art Deco Bracelet ▶

• *circa 1925*
An Art Deco bracelet by Paulcho of Vienna, with enamel plaques, representing water, with floating flowers of craved jade and agate mounted on platinum and gold.
• *length 17cm*
• £100,000          • **Sandra Cronan**

## Expert Tips

*At the end of the nineteenth century, butterflies were popular motifs in jewellery due to their association as good luck symbols, dating back to ancient Egypt.*

## Belt Buckle ▼

• *circa 1955*
A Navajo silver belt buckle with sunburst design, of ovate shape encompassing seven turquoise stones to centre.
• *height 11cm*
• £399          • **Wilde Ones**

## Locket and Collar ▶

• *date 1880*
Victorian silver locket on interlocking silver collar. Of Estruscan revival design, with 18ct. gold ribbon inlay and etching to the silver of the locket.
• *length 23cm*
• £450          • **Rowan & Rowan**

## Amazonite Ring ◀

• *circa 1930*
A Navajo amazonite ring with traditional setting in silver, the whole of an elongated lozenge shape, with beading around the stone and moulded bezel.
• *height 5cm*
• £329          • **Wilde Ones**

## Enamel Cat Brooch ▲

• *circa 1950*
Silver- gilt cat with turquoise enamelled eyes and an enamelled butterfly to the tail.
• *length 6cm*
• £85          • **Sugar Antiques**

## Diamond Ring ▲

- *circa 1970*
Fine diamond ring, the centre set with a one carat, vivid yellow diamond, bordered on either side with two smaller yellow diamonds, surrounded by baguette-cut diamonds. Mounted in platinum. Made by Van Cleef & Arpels of Paris.
- £36,000          • Sandra Cronan

## Stork Brooch ▲

- *circa 1925*
A diamond and gem set stork brooch. His head and shirt are set with cushion-cut diamonds; his waistcoat is carved aquamarine; the cravat pin is cabochon cat's-eye; his cloak is carved garnets; his trousers are carved sapphires; his beak is amethyst and yellow topaz; his eyes are cabochon rubies; his monocle is a diamond and he has pink enamel feet. The whole is mounted on gold.
- *height 7cm*
- £32,000          • Sandra Cronan

## Pearl and Diamond Brooch ▼

- *circa 1860*
Pearl, diamond and black enamel brooch with nine large pearls set in 18ct. gold with five hanging diamond drops. The whole fashioned as three domes, surrounded by 12 diamonds.
- *height 10cm*
- £9,500          • Emmy Abé

## Zuni Pendant ▼

- *date 1998*
Zuni knife wing pin pendant, showing an eagle dancer. An example of inlay jewellery using turquoise, coral, jet and abalone on a silver base. The wings, circular in form, are beaded in silver, with further silver decoration to the ears and hat. Made by D. Iahi.
- £899          • Wilde Ones

## Butterfly Brooch ▲

- *circa 1880*
French 19th-century diamond, emerald and ruby butterfly brooch, with large pearl mounted on the thorax. The main construction is of silver and gold, with filigree to the wings.
- *height 5cm*
- £5,800          • Sandra Cronan

## American Brooch ▲

- *circa 1900*
An American natural pearl and diamond brooch in the form of a chrysanthemum, composed of Mississippi river pearls and an old brilliant-cut 1.1 carat diamond set at the centre.
- £6,800          • Sandra Cronan

## Scarf Clip ▲

- *circa 1880*
Victorian brooch which can also be used as a scarf clip. Made of silver, with paste settings.
- *length 6cm*
- £65          • Sugar Antiques

## Acrylic Rings ▲
- *circa 1965*
Moulded, clear acrylic rings with
panels of colour running
vertically throughout. Designed
by Mary Quant.
- **£20**     • **Themes & Variations**

## Zuni Ring ▲
- *circa 1950*
A Zuni flower design ring
consisting of a central lozenge of
turquoise, surrounded by twelve
smaller stones interspersed with
silver globules.
- *diameter 4cm*
- **£299**     • **Wilde Ones**

## Gold Cross ▼
- *circa 1865*
A 19th-century gold and precious
stone cross, by Robert Phillips of
London.
- *length 8cm*
- **£7,500**     • **Sandra Cronan**

## Coral Necklace ▼
- *circa 1938*
Red coral necklace of the Zuni
tribe, of natural red coral, hand-
drilled and strung. Red is a sacred
colour to the Zuni, bringing good
luck and longevity.
- *length 44cm*
- **£399**     • **Wilde Ones**

## Italian Brooch ◄
- *circa 1650*
Italian 17th-century enamel,
emerald and gold set flower-spray
brooch.
- *height 7.5cm*
- **£8,600**     • **Sandra Cronan**

## Miniature ▲
- *date 1650/1760*
An enamelled oval miniature of
the soldier and statesman George
Monck, 1st Duke of Albemarle,
who was awarded his dukedom for
the part he played in the
restoration of the monarchy. The
miniature is mounted within a
heart-shaped, diamond-set frame.
The enamel is dated 1650 on the
reverse, the frame is circa 1760.
- **£6,800**     • **Sandra Cronan**

## Polychrome Brooch ▲
- *circa 1630*
A very early enamelled gold
brooch depicting St George doing
battle with the Dragon.
- **£6,500**     • **Sandra Cronan**

## Navajo Ring ▲
- *circa 1940*
Turquoise and silver ring with
stones set on circular plate.
Turquoise has four globules of
silver to each side.
- **£199**     • **Wilde Ones**

## Dress Buttons ➤
- *circa 1880*
A set of gold dress buttons, enamelled in blue, by Fabergé, contained in their original box.
- *length 14cm*
- £8,500 • Sandra Cronan

## Masonic Jewel ◄
- *circa 1855*
An engraved masonic treasurer's collar jewel, engraved as a money bag with three interlocking keys and pierced ribbon decoration.
- *height 12cm*
- £350 • Guest & Grey

## Enamelled Brooch ▲
- *circa 1620*
A fine polychrome enamelled plaque brooch depicting the Annunciation to the Blessed Virgin Mary. In a gold frame of later date.
- £8,500 • Sandra Cronan

## Spray Brooch ▼
- *circa 1890*
A French 'tremblant' mounted diamond and emerald flower-spray brooch.
- *height 8cm*
- £16,500 • Sandra Cronan

## Pearl and Diamond Necklace ▲
- *circa 1875*
An articulated French pearl and diamond necklace, mounted in silver and gold.
- £56,000 • Sandra Cronan

## Mourning Brooch ▲
- *circa 1870*
A Victorian pinchbeck mourning brooch or scarf pin, with hair arrangement in the pattern of a flower, behind glass
- *diameter 4.5cm*
- £75 • Sugar Antiques

## Bracelet ➤
- *circa 1910*
A French platinum bracelet mounted with sapphires, diamonds and carved jade and moonstone.
- *length 16cm*
- £6,800 • Sandra Cronan

## Diamond Bracelet  ▲
- *circa 1920s*
A bracelet incorporating 6.5 carat diamonds in total, with five large cushion-cut settings with interspersed links. A symmetrical pattern very popular in the 1920s.
- *length 11cm*
- £7,900　　　　• Emmy Abé

### Expert Tips

*Always examine the wear at the links, especially at the joints of curved bracelets, not only for the imminence of breaks, but also for the presence of lead, used in earlier repairs.*

## Art Deco Bracelet  ▼
- *circa 1925*
An early and highly unusual French Art Deco bracelet with ruby, sapphire and emerald beads. The clasp is set with rubies and diamonds and the whole presents a twisted, interwoven appearance.
- £21,000
- Sandra Cronan

## Marcasite Necklace  ▲
- *circa 1950*
A marcasite* necklace with bow and flower design.
- £55　　　　• Sugar

*\* strictly a pale yellow metal consisting of iron pyrites in crystalline form, but tending now to refer to any cut and polished form of steel used for making jewellery.*

## Coro Duet  ▼
- *circa 1940s*
Sterling silver coro duet brooch with removable fur clip, featuring green and black enamel stylised owls with green crystal eyes in paste settings.
- *height 5cm*
- £120　　　　• Hilary Conqy

## Navajo Bracelet  ▼
- *date 1920*
Sterling silver Navajo bracelet with three main and two smaller, square turquoise panels. There is additional silver cast work between the settings. A traditional Navajo design.
- £699　　　　• Wilde Ones

## Dress Clip  ▼
- *circa 1925*
A French silver dress clip of the Art Deco period, with a carved bakelite centre within a paste setting, showing an impersonal woman's face, swathed in elaborate silver head-dress and gathered veil.
- *height 4.5cm*
- £150　　　　• Hilary Conqy

## Fob Seals  ▲
- *date 1840*
Two 18 carat gold English fob seals, ornately decorated with pineapples and foliage. With carved agate stones.
- *height 3.5cm*
- £300 each • Rowan & Rowan

# Marine Items

**Marine antiques, apart from being very well made, appeal to the romantic souls of an island race.**

Not surprisingly, the sea is a particular obsession with the British. Chronometers and timekeepers, sextants, compasses and barometers always find a ready market. This is not only for sentimental reasons. All these instruments were and, to a lesser extent, still are essential to the lives of sailors. You cannot navigate without being able accurately to tell the time and the importance of being able to gauge the barometric pressure is paramount. As a result, no economies were made on these instruments. If money needed to be saved, it came off the ship's biscuits, not the clock. These items were made of brass and generally boxed in brass-bound mahogany. They tend to have been very well cared for.

Life aboard a sailing ship has been described as 'long periods of boredom interspersed by brief moments of terror', and it was during the long periods that many models of ships, scrimshaw on whalebone and tusk, shellwork pictures and the like were created. Modern ecological thinking has steadied the price of items made from whale over recent years.

## Two Day Chronometer ▼
- *circa 1950*
A fine presentation condition chronometer by Hamilton, USA. In mahogany brass-bound case.
- **£3,900**
- **Langfords Marine**

## Model of Life Boat ➤
- *circa 1860*
Clinker-built Pakefield lifeboat. With copper and brass fittings.
- *length 1.4m*
- **£4,800**
- **Langfords Marine**

## 'Prisoner of War' Model ▲
- *circa 1800*
Napoleonic 'Prisoner of War' model. Made of beef bone. All relevant deck detail with standing and running rigging. Warrior figurehead. Contained within a glass dome.
- *length 32cm*
- *height 30cm*
- **£8,800**
- **Langfords Marine**

## Marine Mug ▼
- *circa 1930*
A rare marine store-dealer mug by Royal Doulton. Dickensware, showing Mr Micawber from *David Copperfield*, a novel with strong nautical associations.
- *height 13cm*
- **£239** • **Ocean Leisure**

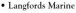

### Parallel Rule ➤
• *circa 1800*
A 12-inch ebony parallel rule, for
use in navigation. Unusual, with
cut out polished brass straps.
• £49          • Ocean Leisure

### Compass ▲
• *circa 1900*
A dry-card compass in a brass
drum case with pull-off cover.
Knurled edge. Original condition.
• £120          • Ocean Leisure

### Luggage Labels ▲
• *circa 1930*
Cunard White Star luggage
labels. Labels read 'Not Wanted
on Voyage', indicating that trunks
should be stored in the hold, and
'First Class', 'Cabin Class' and
'Tourist Class', in descending
order of the social desirability of
the owners.
• £29          • Ocean Leisure

### Porthole ▼
• *date 1901-1910*
Polished seven-inch diameter
porthole made of brass with hinge
and locking nut and six bevelled
screw holes.
• *diameter 17cm*
• £69          • Ocean Leisure

### Proportional Dividers ▼
• *circa 1941*
A pair of polished brass
proportional dividers with steel
points, for navigation. Stamped
Luco Art Metal Co Ltd.
• £129          • Ocean Leisure

### Hand Bearing Compass ▲
• *circa 1930*
An ex-Royal Navy hand bearing
compass, gimballed and
contained in its original chest,
stamped 'small landing compass
no.124/C'.
• £189          • Ocean Leisure

## Expert Tips

*Many arcane nautical
instruments give the impression
to the uninitiated of being very
old, when in fact they may still
be in production. Ships logs, for
instance, which trail behind a
ship or boat and spin, thereby
measuring distance, always look
ancient because of the effect of
salt water on brass.*

### Diorama ◄
• *circa 1880*
Diorama of a three-masted barque
with smaller sailing vessels in the
foreground. Made by a sailor.
• *length 90cm*
• *height 46cm*
• £1,450
• Langfords Marine

## Model of a Yacht ◄

- *circa 1910*

A shipbuilder's half-block model of a yacht, made of polished pine on a teak backboard.

- *length 95cm*
- £1,850
- Langfords Marine

## Viking Ship Brooch ▼

- *circa 1940*

Silver Scottish shawl brooch showing a Viking ship on a shielded base. Scottish.

- £39          • Ocean Leisure

## Anchor Lamp ▲

- *circa 1940*

Copper and brass anchor lamp. With 'Seahorse' trade mark.

- *height 22cm*
- £180          • Ocean Leisure

## Prismatic Compass ▼

- *circa 1940*

An English brass, hand-held, military compass from the Second World War.

- £99          • Ocean Leisure

## Sextant ▼

- *mid 19th century*

Fine polished and lacquered brass sextant with silver scale. Signed G.E. Hicks, Portsmouth, England.

- *height 23cm*
- £1,195          • Ocean Leisure

## Four-Volume Work ▲

- *circa 1997*

Jean Boudriot's four-volume opus, *The Seventy-Four Gun Ship*, published by Jean Boudriot Publications.

- *height 27.5cm*
- £225          • Motor

## Naval Telescope ➤

- *circa 1870*

Rare, single-draw naval telescope made of silver and brass. Rope bound with 'Turk's head' at both ends of the tunnel. By John Browning, London.

- £549          • Ocean Leisure

### Brass Telescope ◄
- *late 19th century*
Made by W. Ladd, Chancery Lane, London. In original mahogany box.
- **£2,900**
- **Langfords Marine**

### Anchor ▼
- *circa 1880*
Cast-iron ship's anchor.
- *height 1m*
- **£80** • **Curios**

### Taffrail Ship's Log ▲
- *circa 1920*
Polished and lacquered brass Cherub III. Outrigger pattern in original, specially constructed and weatherproofed box. By Thos. Walker and Son.
- **£250** • **Ocean Leisure**

### Ship's Linen ▲
- *circa 1950*
Souvenir linen from the Cunard company's RMS *Mauretania*.
- **£19** • **Ocean Leisure**

### Model of an Anchor ▼
- *circa 1900*
Polished brass model of an anchor, probably a paperweight.
- *height 18cm*
- **£59** • **Ocean Leisure**

### Cunard Ashtray ▲
- *circa 1950*
Cunard R.M.S. *Queen Elizabeth* bone-china ashtray, showing starboard view of ship. With scalloped gilt edge.
- **£35** • **Ocean Leisure**

## Expert Tips

*One of the most celebrated and accomplished manufacturers of telescopes during the 19th century was John Dollond of London. Many attempts were made by rival manufacturers to cash in on his celebrity. The most common to look out for are examples signed 'Dolland' or 'Dolland – Day or Night'.*

### Signalling Telescope ►
- *circa 1920*
A three-draw signalling telescope. Polished and lacquered brass on the outer barrel.
- **£339** • **Ocean Leisure**

## Cunard White Star Jigsaw Puzzle ▼

- *circa 1930*
Jigsaw puzzle of *RMS Queen Elizabeth*. Made in England by Lumar. Excellent condition.
- £59 • Ocean Leisure

## Binnacle ▼

- *circa 1930*
A 'Faithful Freddie' brass binnacle, commonly used on submarines. This one refitted to one of the 'Little Ships' for the evacuation of Dunkirk.
- *height 48cm*
- £1,650 • Langfords Marine

## Wooden Box ▶

- *20th century*
An oval wooden box with shipping scenes painted to the sides and the top showing a running battle between an English and a French man'o' war, both with all sails set and firing cannon on a turbulent sea.
- £75 • Sullivan

## Barograph and Thermometer ▲

- *circa 1910*
Wall barograph with thermometer, in a mahogany box with brass handle. Probably made for a yacht club.
- £1,850 • Langfords Marine

## Oak Helm ▲

- *circa 1910*
A six-spar oak ship's wheel, bound in brass.
- £299 • Ocean Leisure

## Expert Tips

The variation of a compass is different at different places on the earth. The variation of a compass also changes slightly at different times of the year and in different years. Thus, to use a magnetic compass accurately, a person must know the amount of variation at his location and what variation correction must be made in reading the compass. This information appears on all mariners' charts and on many maps.

## Decanter Case ▼

- *circa 1910*
A fine, four-bottled, brass-inlaid box with decanters and glasses, by Thornhill & Co, London.
- *height 27cm*
- £4,000 • Langfords Marine

## Carved Tusk ◄
- **19th century**
A carved whale's tusk showing
Caribbean scene, with compass
mark. The initials 'J.H. J.A.' are
on the reverse.
- *length 32cm*
- **£40** • Briggs

## Book ▼
- **date 1991**
A copy of the book, *Old Figure
Heads & Sterns*, by L.G. Carr
Laughton, one of a limited
edition of 750, published by
Conway Maritime Press.
- **£80** • Motor

## Compass ▲
- **date 1902**
An early Edwardian liquid boat's
compass, of teak with brass
fittings. Made by Dent for the
Royal Navy.
- *height 37cm*
- **£1,850** • Langfords Marine

## Backstaff ▲
- **circa 1779**
A boxwood and lignum backstaff.
The central crossbar is lignum on
one side and boxwood on the
other and the reverse of the scale
is stamped '44'.
- **£6,500** • Trevor Phillips

## Ship's Log ▼
- **circa 1950**
A brass ship's log by Walker &
Sons of Birmingham.
- *length (on mount) 60cm*
- **£550** • Simon Hatchwell

## Expert Tips

*The best scrimshaw – the art of
carving and inking whalebone or
teeth, turtle-shell etc., was
produced by American whalers
in the early 1800s.*

## Ship's Wheel ▲
- **circa 1890**
A late 19th-century ship's wheel,
made of oak, with brass hub and
banding and eight turned spokes.
- *diameter 87cm*
- **£580** • Briggs

## Scrimshaw Box ►
- **circa 1900**
A scrimshaw box with incised
carving showing the central motif
of a two-fluke anchor surrounded
by breaking waves.
- *length 6cm*
- **£60** • Sullivan

## Telescope ➤
- **19th century**
Brass polished and lacquered telescope with oak tunnel. Signed 'George Leone, Liverpool' on the single draw.
- **£349** • **Ocean Leisure**

## Model of a Pond Yacht ▲
- *circa 1900*
Pond-yacht model of an East Coast oyster smack, showing full sail including gaff topsail and staysails to the bowsprit.
- *length 1.1m*
- *height 1.05m*
- **£3,300** • **Langfords Marine**

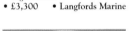

## Brass Sextant ▼
- *circa 1910*
By Lawrence & Mayo, London. With various telescopes, fittings and unusual attachments. In original mahogany box. Last tested by Kelvin & Hughes Ltd in 1953.
- **£1,680** • **Langfords Marine**

## Chinese Bowl ◄
- *circa 1850*
A blue and white oriental dish recovered from a wreck of the *Diana* in the China Seas.
- *diameter 14cm*
- **£240** • **The Deep**

## Pater Compass ▲
- *circa 1800*
Dry card, Pater compass on a two-inch turned wood base. Hand-painted card. By Stockert, Bavaria, for the English market.
- **£429** • **Ocean Leisure**

## Expert Tips

*Scrimshaw was not only decorative. Sailors also produced useful things for their ladies – notably darning needles and corset stays.*

## Anchor Brooch ▼
- **late 19th century**
Silver sweetheart anchor bar brooch.
- **£49** • **Ocean Leisure**

## Ship's Box ◄
- *circa 1870*
Brass studded and domed-topped ship's box.
- *height 19cm*
- **£99** • **Ocean Leisure**

## Compendium  ▼
• *circa 1910*
A ship's compendium housed in a mahogany box and consisting of, inter alia, chess, draughts, backgammon and cribbage.
• *height 20cm*
• **£1,900**    • **Langfords Marine**

## Model Ship  ▼
• *circa 1860*
A model of a four-masted clipper, with long bowsprit, including all rigging, deck fitments and figures. Housed in a glass case.
• *height 42cm*
• **£175**    • **Sullivan**

### Expert Tips

*Marine barometers are always aneroid barometers, which are less precise but less delicate than mercury barometers.*

## Globe  ▲
• *20th century*
A reproduction of a 12-inch diameter, 19th-century globe on a mahogany stand. The original by Nerzbach & Falk, published in 1881.
• *height 43cm*
• **£680**    • **Langfords Marine**

## Barometer  ▲
• *circa 1910*
A rare, Edwardian brass-casede aneroid barometer with scale and weather indications around the circumference of the dial.
• *diameter 24cm*
• **£880**    • **Langfords Marine**

## Telegraph  ▼
• *circa 1880*
A brass model of the engine-room terminal of a ship's telegraph, with bone handle.
• *height 16cm*
• **£90**    • **Sullivan**

## Porthole  ▼
• *circa 1930*
A brass porthole with hinge, but missing locking screw, with six bevelled screw holes.
• *diameter 29cm*
• **£45**    • **Briggs**

## Ship's Wheel  ◄
• *circa 1890*
A small, teak, eight-spoked ship's wheel, with turned spokes and brass hub and banding.
• *diameter 62cm*
• **£590**    • **Langfords Marine**

# Musical Instruments

**Some musical instruments are also beautiful pieces of furniture, some have been played by the famous. Only the musically excellent are worth real money.**

In the field of collecting musical instruments, as in no other, it can be very expensive not to know what you are buying. Violins and cellos by Stradivari fetch astronomical sums of money, as everyone knows; on the other hand, it is quite possible to find an early nineteenth-century violin for no more than a couple of hundred pounds – and then find that it isn't even worth that. Quality of materials, craftsmanship and, crucially, musical quality are all important. There is no way of mass-producing musical instruments, so every one is an individual. Whether they will last depends on the quality of the materials and the manufacture. Stradivari used materials that made his instruments improve with age; many people did not.

Because of their individuality and hand-made quality, even very new instruments are highly collectable. Guitars, for instance, can fetch stratospheric prices. The Gibson flying Vee, listed here, was made in 1958, one of a total of 98 produced, and is worth a staggering £55,000.

Modern musical instruments are subject to the memento trade – famous players signing their instruments for charity sales. Remember, no two instruments are alike, and it is unlikely that they will be giving away their best.

**Avocado Gretsch** ▲
- *circa 1961*
Two-tone, smoked-green, semi-acoustic guitar with original scratch-plate and fittings.
- £2,200   • Vintage Guitar

**Amplifier** ◄
- *circa 1958*
Tweed Fender amp with leather handle. Pre-CBS Fender.
- *height 42cm*
- £795   • Vintage Guitar

**Lighting Ornament** ▼
- *circa 1965*
Drum kit light – 110 volt – with green and red flashing alternately.
- *height 32cm*
- £250   • Vintage Guitar

**Harp Lute** ▲
- *circa 1810*
A light harp lute with a painted black case with gold work and raised detailing to the pillar.
- £2,525   • Robert Morley

## White Falcon ⌄
- *circa 1962*
Cutaway White Falcon, by
Gretsch, serial no. 50120,
designed by Jimmy Webster, with
24-carat gold plating.
  - **£4,950** • Vintage Guitar

## Square Piano ⌃
- *circa 1787*
Thomas Haxby square piano,
made in York, with mahogany
case with inlaid banding and
decorative nameboard.
  - **£5,360** • Clive Morley

## Art Deco Piano ⌄
- *circa 1930*
An Art Deco, mahogany baby
grand piano, by Monnington &
Western, with German
mechanism, resting on square,
tapered legs.
  - *length 1.26m*
  - **£3,400** • Oola Boola

## Grecian Harp ⌄
- *circa 1850*
A typical Grecian harp, with
Etruscan decoration and gilded
and reeded pillar.
  - **£8,000** • Clive Morley

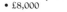

## Flying Vee ⌄
- *circa 1958*
Gibson Flying Vee, serial no.
83161. The 'Holy Grail' of
vintage, solid body guitars.
  - **£55,000** • Vintage Guitar

## Gibson 12-String ⌃
- *circa 1967*
Acoustic guitar in cherry
sunburst, previously owned by
Noel Gallagher, with
authenticating letter.
  - **£1,495** • Vintage Guitar

## Console Piano ⌅
- *circa 1840*
A Pape console piano in
rosewood, with bracket-type legs.
  - *height 99cm*
  - **£2,500** • Riverbank

## Gibson Les Paul ▲
- *date 1959*
With faded flame top, serial no.
91258. The '59, between the
chubbier '58 and the flat '60, was
regarded as the players' favourite.
- £35,000   • Vintage Guitar

## Epiphone Riviera ▲
- *circa 1967*
Riviera, in sunburst, with a
Frequentata tailpiece, mini-
humbuckers and 'f' holes.
Favoured by The Beatles.
- £1,800   • Vintage Guitar

## Silver Sparkle ▼
- *circa 1955*
A Gretsch Duo Jet with Bigsby
tremelo and block inlays. Serial
no. 17177.
- £5,000   • Vintage Guitar

## Grecian Harp ▼
- *circa 1821*
Grecian harp by S. & P. Erard of
Paris, with 43 strings. Painted
black with gold decoration to the
pillar.
- £9,575   • Clive Morley

## Grand Piano ➤
- *circa 1939*
Steinway model M grand piano,
fully rebuilt by Steinway, in high-
polished mahogany.
- *length 1.7m*
- £27,500   • Steinway

## Drum ▲
- *circa 1970*
Native American drum made of
wood and skin and decorated
with bone and feathers, with a
green turtle on the skin.
- *height 65cm*
- £400   • Wilde Ones

## Gothic Harp ▲
- *circa 1850*
Gothic, 46-string harp in maple
and gold, with decorated pillar.
Made in Paris, in the mid-19th-
century, by Erard.
- £15,000   • Clive Morley

### Fender Broadcaster  ▼
• *date 1950*
Completely original Fender
Broadcaster – serial no. 0729 – of
which only 200 were made.
• £15,000    • Vintage Guitar

### Fender Stratocaster  ▼
• *date 1964*
Pre-CBS Fender Stratocaster
serial no. L70376. As-new finish
with no playing wear – 'probably
the cleanest in Europe'.
• £6,000    • Vintage Guitar

### Square Piano  ➤
• *circa 1790*
Richyardus Horfburgh mahogany
square piano, made in Edinburgh.
• *width 1.58m*
• £5,775    • Clive Morley

### Hook Harp  ▲
• *circa 1790*
A Nadarman harp with gilded
scrolled head. Favoured by the
French aristocracy.
• £18,500    • Clive Morley

### Valve Guitar Amp  ▲
• *date October 1956*
Gretsch 'Western Roundup' amp,
with leather belt and brass studs.
• *height 40cm*
• £2,000    • Vintage Guitar

### Fender Stratocaster  ▼
• *date 1960*
A Blue Sparkle Stratocaster,
serial no. 50172. Unique,
commissioned from Fender, with
original brown Tolex case.
• £18,500    • Vintage Guitar

### Steinway Grand Piano  ▼
• *circa 1960*
Mahogany, model B grand piano,
rebuilt by Steinway.
• *length 2.1m*
• £40,000    • Steinway

## Mandolin ◄
- **date 1897**
A signed mandolin by Giovanni
Meglio of Naples. With a vaulted
back of 17 rosewood ribs with
maple stringing.
- **£690** • Hygra

## Single-Action Harp ◄
- **circa 1805**
Harp with ram's-head decoration
to the crown and acanthus-leaf
scrolling, ebonized back and
gilded pedestal.
- **£9,000** • Clive Morley

## Grand Piano ▲
- **circa 1868**
A London grand piano by John
Broadwood and Sons, with
rosewood case.
- **length 2.35m**
- **£4,820** • Robert Morley

## Acoustic Guitar ▼
- **date 1960**
Gibson Country & Western
model, with round shoulders and
parallelogram inlay.
- **£1,995** • Vintage Guitar

## Thunderbird Bass ▲
- **date 1976**
Rare black model with reverse
body styling, bass, treble and
volume knobs.
- **£1,750** • Vintage Guitar

## Gibson Firebird III ▲
- **circa 1968**
Firebird in gold finish, with non-
reverse body, three pick-ups and a
vibrato. All original fittings.
- **£2,650** • Vintage Guitar

## Violin ►
- **circa 1815**
An early 19th-century John
Baptiste Schweitzer violin, made
for Amati Pestini.
- **£550** • Finchley

## Amplifier ➤
- *circa 1965*
A very early Orange Matamp with hand-painted Orange logo, finished in orange vinyl with single black handle.
- £995 • **Vintage Guitar**

## Grecian Harps ▲
- *circa 1850*
Two Grecian harps with gilded pillars and Etruscan decoration. For sale separately.
- £18,500 • **Clive Morley**

## Les Paul Deluxe ▼
- *circa 1972*
Gold top finish with mini-humbuckers, the pick-up surrounds stamped 'Gibson'. A great investment.
- £1,495 • **Vintage Guitar**

## Fender Esquire ▲
- *date 1954*
Butterscotch Blonde, serial no. 4047. In original condition down to slot-headed screws.
- £5,000 • **Vintage Guitar**

## Fender Jazz Bass ▲
- *date 1961*
Sunburst Jazz Bass, serial no. 44210. A fine example of the most sought-after vintage bass.
- £7,250 • **Vintage Guitar**

## Gibson Acoustic ➤
- *date 1952*
Serial no. A 8760, with original case and natural colour finish. One of 89 produced in 1952.
- £7,500 • **Vintage Guitar**

## Concert Mandolin ◄
- *circa 1890*
Double-soundboard concert mandolin by Umberto Ceccherine of Naples.
- £4,500 • **Hygra**

# Silver & Pewter

**Cream jugs, sugar bowls, salt cellars and tea pots are a sensible place to start collecting silver. Utility is always worth its price.**

Smaller and less spectacular items in silver and pewter tend to be valued more highly if they are useful. Large, important pieces by well-known makers are expensive because there is always a demand at the top of the market, but, at the lower end of the market, it is utility that holds sway.

Silver collectors have the advantage over the collectors of other types of antiques, in that most items carry hallmarks, which give information on the date and place of manufacture and the maker. Pewter too carries makers' marks,

known as 'touch marks', which were registered with Pewterers' Hall in London until 1824.

In theory, therefore, a collector equipped with a comprehensive key to all the codes should need to know very little else, but the practice, fortunately, is not so simple. Hallmarks, like most things, can be faked and the serious collector will be more concerned to identify a piece stylistically and by other characteristics – such as weight and general 'feel' – and will only consult the hallmark for confirmation.

---

**Dinner Plates** ◀
- *date 1892*
Set of twelve dinner plates with beaded edge and moulded border and cartouches with crested, rampant lion. Made by James Garrard, London.
- *diameter 25cm*
- **£4,200** • **J. First**

**Beaker** ▲
- *circa 1900*
Persian beaker from Kirmanshah. Profusely decorated and embossed with rural and domestic scenes.
- *height 10cm*
- **£150** • **Namdar**

**Napkin Rings** ▼
- *date 1937*
Boxed set of six, solid silver Art Deco napkin rings with engraved, engine-turned scallop-shell design. Birmingham.
- **£650** • **Stephen Kalms**

**Claret Jug** ▲
- *date 1881*
Claret jug with naturalistically styled silver mounts showing lily pad; double woven handle and glass engraved with fish and aquatic scenes. By E.H. Stockwell, London.
- *height 19cm*
- **£7,500** • **Langfords**

## Expert Tips

*Regular cleaning of antique silver produces a patina quite different from that of new silver, and one which cannot be accelerated or reproduced artificially.*

Salvers ◀

## Salvers
- *circa 1745*
Fine pair of George II armorial
salvers, with gadrooned borders,
by Paul de Lamerie, London.
- *diameter 20cm*
- **£55,000** • **Marks Antiques**

## Chinese Vases ▼
- *date 1920*
Pair of Chinese vases with twin
ring handles engraved with four
panels, showing prunus trees with
cats and storks on reverse.
- *height 28cm*
- **£1,100** • **J. First**

## Cake Basket ▲
- *date 1759*
George II cake basket with
pierced decoration and hinged
handle. Made in London by
Samuel Herbert & Co.
- *length 35cm*
- **£17,950** • **Marks Antiques**

## Aberdeen Teapot ▼
- *date 1735*
A fine and rare provincial teapot
of George II period, made in
Aberdeen by George Cooper,
with relief floral decoration
around the shoulders and lid and
ebonised handle and finial.
- *height 16cm*
- **£8,500** • **Nicholas Shaw**

## Jug ▲
- *date 1573*
Elizabethan silver-gilt tigerware
jug. Maker's mark 'CC'.linked
with shaped punch above a
device. London.
- *height 22cm*
- **£27,500** • **Marks Antiques**

## George III Salver ▲
- *date 1763*
With crested boar's head with
inscription 'Gang forward',by
James Gilsland, Edinburgh.
- *diameter 22cm*
- **£1,150** • **Nicholas Shaw**

## Salt Cellars ▶
- *date 1783*
French Louis XVII salts with
pierced trophy decoration and
finial handle.
- *height 10cm*
- **£550** • **Vivienne Carroll**

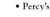

## Claret Jug ▼
- **date 1870**
Claret jug with silver mounts, showing frieze with vine decoration from mask cartouches, with Baccanale spout, laurel decoration to girdle and rampant lion and shield finial.
- *height 28cm*
- **£750**          • **Langfords**

## Cigarette Case ▼
- **date 1928**
Silver, turquoise and black enamel cigarette case with silver gilt interior. European with London import mark.
- *length 8cm*
- **£950**
- **Sue & Alan Thompson**

## Peppermill ▲
- **date 1910**
Ivory peppermill banded with silver.
- *height 7.5cm*
- **£525**          • **John Clay**

## Card Case ▲
- **date 1872**
Victorian silver card case, profusely decorated with maple leaf and scrolled designs. By Frederick Marson, Birmingham.
- *height 10cm*
- **£440**          • **Linden & Co**

## Claret Jug ▼
- **date 1886**
A claret jug with heavy vine and leaf decoration, twig handle and leaf finial thumb-piece. London.
- *height 31cm*
- **£5,250**          • **Percy's**

## Tea Caddies ▼
- **date 1764**
One of pair of George III tea caddies, stamped H.N., with lion's feet.
- *12x9cm*
- **£4,750**          • **Marks Antiques**

## Magnifying Glass ◀
- **date 1813**
Silver magnifying glass with ornate handle and original lens. Birmingham.
- *length 19cm*
- **£68**          • **Vivienne Carroll**

## Dish Cross

• *date 1776*
A George III dish cross plate warmer with burner by Robert Hennel, with adjustable supports and legs.
• £1,500 • J. First

## Coffee Pot

• *date 1734*
George II coffee pot of cylindrical form and plain design. With fruitwood handle. London, by Gabriel Sleath.
• *height 23cm*
• £5,950 • Langfords

## Candlesticks

• *date 1811*
Set of four George III silver-gilt candlesticks, made in London by Paul Storr for William, 1st Earl of Lonsdale, with crest.
• *height 23cm*
• £120,000 • Marks Antiques

## Sweet Box

• *date 1918*
Unusual sweet box shaped as paint tin, by H. Woodward & Co, Birmingham.
• *height 7.5cm*
• £1,270
• Sue & Alan Thompson

## Entrée Dishes

• *date 1807*
Set of four George III silver entrée dishes, from the Rutland Marine Service, made in London by Benjamin Smith. The arms are those of John Henry Manners, 5th Duke of Rutland (1757-1844). Decorated with gadrooning, beading and fluting, with domed cover and highly ornate finial.
• *height 23cm: width 23cm; length 30cm*
• £175,000 • Marks Antiques

## Claret Jug

• *date 1875*
Cut glass, classical form claret jug by Barnards of London.
• *height 28cm*
• £3,650 • Percy's

## Spice Tower

• *date 19th century*
Austrian silver filigree spice tower with pennants.
• *height 20cm*
• £650 • John Clay

## Fruit Bowl ▲

- *date 1911*
Art Nouveau silver fruit bowl
with organic styled panelling on a
fluted pedestal base. Sheffield.
- *diameter 26cm*
- £750 • J. First

## Centaur ▲

- *date 1900*
Silver statue of a centaur drawing
bow and arrow and rearing on
hind legs. Signed on back left leg
R. de Luca. The whole on a
marble plinth.
- *height 29cm*
- £2,400 • Stephen Kalms

## Candlesticks ▲

- *date 1902*
Pair of candlesticks with trophy
and leaf decoration on a
serpentine base. Sheffield.
- *height 17cm*
- £675 • Vivienne Carroll

## Candlesticks ▼

- *date 1768*
Pair of George III cast silver
candlesticks, on square beaded
bases, made in London by
Ebenezer Coker.
- *height 26cm*
- £6,750 • Marks Antiques

## Photograph Frame ▼

- *date 20th century*
Pierced silver photograph frame
with original leather back and
velvet backing to filigree. By L.
Emmanuel, Birmingham.
- *height 19cm*
- £790
- Sue & Alan Thompson

## Straining Spoon ▼

- *date 1611*
James I silver straining spoon made
by Edward Martin of London.
- *length 44cm*
- £27,500 • Marks Antiques

## Napkin Ring ▲

- *date 1890*
Single triangular napkin ring,
with engraved fern decoration
and "Daisy" inscription.
Birmingham.
- £250 • Stephen Kalms

## Pepperpot ▲

- *date 1908*
Rare monkey pepperpot, seated
with one arm tucked under the
other. By H. Heywood.
- *height 7cm*
- £2,300
- Sue & Alan Thompson

### Expert Tips

*When not in use,
silver should be kept away from
contact with the air, ideally in
sealed, airtight bags.*

## Jardinière ➤
- **date 1890**
Solid silver, rococo-style
asymmetrical design jardinière or
planter, on four scrolled legs.
- *length 45cm*
- **£2,500**                    • J. First

## Coasters ▲
- **date 1807**
Set of four George III wine
coasters, with pierced vine and
fruit decoration and beading to
rim and base.
- *diameter 14cm*
- **£9,500**        • Marks Antiques

---

### Expert Tips

*Decorated glass was the norm
with 19th-century claret jugs. If
the glass is not decorated, be
wary – check carefully how it fits
with the mount. It may
be a replacement.*

---

## Tea Caddies ▼
- **date 1719**
Fine pair of George I tea caddies,
made in London by John Farnell.
- *height 10cm*
- **£13,500**      • Marks Antiques

## Tea and Coffee Set ➤
- **date 1835**
William IV tea and coffee set of
four pieces, compressed melon
design, each piece on four feet,
silver gilt lining. Made in London
by J.A. Savory.
- **£4,250**            • Langfords

## Claret Jug ▲
- **date 1888**
Victorian claret jug with silver
mounts and glass engraved with
wheatsheaves and butterflies.
Made in London.
- *height 26cm*
- **£3,450**              • Percy's

## Chamber Candlestick ▼
- **date 1800**
George III chamber stick with
gadrooned border and fluted
capital. By R. Crossley, London.
- *height 9.5cm*
- **£1,250**            • Langfords

## Stamp Dispenser ▼
- **date 1904**
Rare English piece made in
Birmingham by Gray & Co.
- *length 8cm*
- **£1,250**
- Sue & Alan Thompson

## Note Clip ➤
- *date 1900*
Unusual silver and tortoiseshell note clip, in the form of a seesaw. By H.A. Batson, London.
- *length 14cm*
- £2,300
- Sue & Alan Thompson

## French Candlesticks ▲
- *date 1880*
Pair of French candlesticks with assymetric wave forms to the base, made to 950 standard.
- *height 21cm*
- £750                    • J.First

## Photograph Frame ▼
- *date 1903*
Silver and green/grey and red agate photograph frame in the style of two basket-hilt swords and shields. Birmingham.
- *height 8cm*
- £890
- Sue & Alan Thompson

## Candlesticks ▲
- *date 1819*
Set of four George III candlesticks, made by William Elliot of London. Weight 321 Troy ounces.
- *height 36cm*
- £52,000    • Marks Antiques

## Sugar Vase ▼
- *date 1839*
Sugar vase with profuse floral piercing with rose-tinted glass reservoir and acanthus finial. By J. & G. Angel, London.
- *height 26cm*
- £1,575               • Percy's

## Cup and Cover ▲
- *date 1714*
George I Britannia standard silver cup and cover, made in London by Anthony Nelme.
- *height 33cm*
- *width 27cm*
- *diameter 17cm*
- £9,500      • Marks Antiques

### Expert Tips

*Every detachable part of a candelabra (branch, sconce, nozzle) should be marked with the silver standard and maker's mark.*

## Claret Jug ▲
- *date 1873*
Etched glass with silver mounts and pierced thumbpiece.
- *height 27cm*
- £3,000       • Stephen Kalms

## Cream Jug ▼
- *date 1802*
George III cream jug with ornate flower and scallop tooling and a ribbon handle.
- *height 12cm*
- £220 • **Vivienne Carroll**

## Coffee Pot ▼
- *date 1762*
Large George III coffee pot of exceptional weight, with 'C' scroll spout, gadrooned border and armorial cartouche. By Smith & Sharp, London.
- *height 31cm*
- £4,750 • **Percy's**

## Candlesticks ▲
- *date 1713*
Fine pair of Queen Anne candlesticks on octagonal bases. Made by William Twell.
- *height 19cm*
- £22,500 • **Marks Antiques**

## Set of Napkin Rings ▲
- *date 1895*
Originally boxed set of four napkin rings with cartouches and heavy floral decoration and serpentine borders. By George Jackson, London.
- £700 • **Stephen Kalms**

## Baluster Tankard ▼
- *date 1765*
Solid silver tankard marked inside lid and base with 'C' scroll handle. By John and William Bold, London.
- *height 20.5cm*
- £1,800 • **J. First**

## Centrepiece ▼
- *date 1890*
Showing a romantic figure holding aloft a cornucopia and etched glass dish, on heavily engraved base and lion feet.
- *height 50cm*
- £5,750 • **Stephen Kalms**

## Wine Coolers ◀
- *date 1825*
Pair of Sheffield plate wine coolers, camana-shaped. Original condition with original liners, leaf, shell and gadroon decoration with let-in shield.
- *height 23cm*
- £3,650 • **Langfords**

## Butter Tubs ➤
- *date 1806*
An excellent pair of silver-gilt
butter tubs with glass liners, made
by Digby Scott and Benjamin
Smith. The arms are of
Montgomerie, Earl of Eglington.
- *length 19cm; height 15cm*
- **£110,000** • **Marks Antiques**

## Candlesticks ▲
- *date 1920*
A pair of neoclassical
candlesticks, with trumpet-style
stems on circular bases. By L.A.
Crichton of London.
- *height 29cm*
- **£2,650** • **Langfords**

## Tazzas ▲
- *Date 1880*
A pair of silver-gilt tazzas with
engraved glass dishes and
moulded, serpentine bases. Made
by Tiffany.
- *height 15cm*
- **£9,500** • **Marks Antiques**

## Ewer ▼
- *date 1860*
Kashmiri silver ewer with
intricate floral designs with snake
handle terminating in snake's
head thumbpiece on lid.
- *height 29cm*
- **£350** • **Namdar**

## Wine Coaster ◀
- *date 1809*
George III wine coaster with
pierced, fluted and gadrooned
body, with egg and dart border
and wooden base. By Richard
Crossley of London.
- *height 5cm*
- **£1,050** • **Langfords**

## Bachelor Tea Set ▲
- *date 1870*
Boxed bachelor set comprising
three melon-shaped pieces with
gold-washed interior, teapot with
ivory handle. By H. Wilkinson,
London.
- **£1,950** • **Stephen Kalms**

## Epergne ▲
- *date 1908*
Epergne with three flower-form
flutes on a moulded base. By
Martin Hall, Sheffield.
- *height 47cm*
- **£2,950** • **Stephen Kalms**

## Expert Tips

*On most coasters, look for the
hallmark on the lower rim which
overlaps the wooden base.*

## Condiment Set ➤
- *date 1935*

Six-piece condiment set comprising two salt, two pepper and two mustard pots of rectangular form with champfered corners. Art Deco by Mappin & Webb of London.
- £600    • Linden & Co

## Liberty Cup ▲
- *date 1900*

Liberty cup of beaten pewter with traditional tree pattern typical of Art Nouveau period.
- *height 20cm*
- £600    • Victor Arnas

## Fruit Stands ▲
- *date 1795*

Set of three fruit stands with solid silver bases and cut-glass bowls. By William Pitts and William Preedy, London.
- £5,700    • J. First

## Candlesticks ▲
- *date 1770*

Pair of George III cast silver candlesticks on gadrooned bases. By John Carter, London.
- *height 25cm*
- £6,250    • Marks Antiques

## Candelabra ▼
- *date 1901*

An unusual pair of silver candelabra of woven stem and branches with leaf motif. On gadrooned square bases. By Charles Stuart Harris, London.
- *height 42cm*
- £6,750    • Percy's

## Neff ▼
- *date 1902*

A four-wheeled neff in the shape of a schooner, with several figures, cannon, pennants, anchors and all exaggerated detail. By B. Müller.
- *height 41cm*
- £6,000    • Stephen Kalms

## Urn ▲
- *circa 1790*

Silver-plated urn with scallopped rim and lion-mask handles on ball foot pedestal base.
- *height 49cm*
- £1,250    • Langfords

### Expert Tips

*Large and decorative items which are difficult to clean may be professionally lacquered with a fine layer of plastic, which is invisible to the naked eye.*

## Fruit Basket ▼

- *date 1877*
Silver fruit basket with hinged
bocage handle, decorated with
panels of tropical fruit with
crested cartouche. The whole of
oval form on oval pedestal foot.
By Atkin Brothers, Sheffield.
- *length 37cm*
- £1,250                      • J. First

## Mug ▼

- *date 1887*
Embossed with woodland scenes
of children playing by gate. By
Bradbury & Henderson, London.
- *height 9cm*
- £1,200          • Stephen Kalms

## Candelabra ▶

- *circa 1890*
Pair of silver and engraved glass
three-light candelabra of
renaissance pattern. Designed by
Farnham for Tiffany.
- *19x34cm*
- £13,500          • Marks Antiques

## Snuff Box ◀

- *date 1817*
George III silver, reeded snuff box
with an enclosed painting on ivory
of a hunter with dogs. Rubbed
maker's mark, Birmingham.
- *length 8cm*
- £2,100
- **Sue & Alan Thompson**

## German Candlesticks ▲

- *circa 1900*
Pair of solid silver, cannon-
shaped candlesticks, one with the
figure of a 17th-century
musketeer and the other of an
18th-century foot soldier. With
coronet monogram.
- *height 21cm*
- £1,500                      • J. First

## Tea Caddy ▲

- *date 1793*
George III tea caddy of oval form
with lock and key. Bands of
engraving and floral finial. By
John Swift, London.
- *height 12cm*
- £3,500                  • Langfords

## Candelabra ▲

- *date 1773*
Pair of cast silver, George III
candelabra, with 'C' scroll
detachable branches on gadroon
base. By John Carter, London.
- *height 36cm*
- £25,000              • Langfords

## Chinese Box ▲

- *date 1880*
Rectangular, pierced box with
dragon decoration with clouds.
Standing on stylised tiger feet. By
Wang Hinge.
- *height 9cm*
- £650                        • J. First

### Expert Tips

*Almost all candlesticks and
candelabra were produced in
pairs. Singles are worth
considerably less than half a pair.*

### Soup Ladle ➤
- *date 1790*
George III soup ladle, old English pattern. By Hester Bateman.
- *length 32cm*
- £1,050 • Langfords

### Vesta ⋀
- *date 1887*
Very fine silver and enamel vesta with hunting scene of three riders and hounds at water's edge.
- *length 6cm*
- £3,400
- Sue & Alan Thompson

### Goblet ⋁
- *date 1792*
Embossed with floral and leaf decoration, with cartouche (possible later application). Made in London.
- *height 15cm*
- £850 • Stephen Kalms

### Wine Coolers ⋀
- *circa 1850*
A pair of silver-plated wine coolers with heavy vine and fruit decoration and profuse beading to lip and base. By Elkington & Co.
- *height 31cm*
- £7,250 • Percy's

> ## Expert Tips
>
> *Decorations involving a popular sport or recognisable place are popular with collectors.*

### Menorah ⋁
- *date 1925*
Jewish menorah candle holder in solid silver.
- *height 32cm*
- £850 • J. First

### Chinese Silver Tray ➤
- *circa 1860*
Tray with pierced trellis and floral border. Centre of tray with engraved floral spray decoration. Bamboo form handles and four ball feet. By Luen Wo.
- *length 55cm*
- £900 • J. First

### Bonbon Dish ➤
- *19th century*
Continental silver bonbon dish embossed with a central panel showing musicians in a wooded glade, with pierced surround.
- *length 13.5cm*
- £160 • John Clay

## Mug ▼

- *date 1839*

Solid-silver mug with gold wash interior, fluted and waisted body with scrolled handle with thumb piece. Made in London.
- *height 11cm*
- **£400**     • **Stephen Kalms**

## Dutch Spoon ▼

- *circa 1900*

Water-carrier motif on engraved handle. Tavern scenes and pierced floral decoration.
- *length 23cm*
- **£90**     • **Namdar**

## Argyles ▶

**Left:** By Benjamin Cartwright. 1788, Sheffield. **£4,650**
**Centre:** By Aldridge & Green. 1773. **£4,950**
**Right:** by John Laugland, 1779 Sheffield. **£4,650**
- **Percy's**

## Tankard ▲

- *date 1887*

Victorian tankard with fluted decoration and bands of floral engraving. Gold wash interior.
- *height 8cm*
- **£360**     • **Linden & Co**

## Centrepiece on Stand ▲

- *date 1873*

Mirrored stand and matching figural centrepiece by Stephen Smith, London.
- *height 48cm*
- **£4,750**     • **J. First**

## Candelabra ▼

- *date 1885*

Pair of Victorian candelabra, made in London by Edward Barnard & Sons. Scrolled branches and gadrooned base.
- *height 45cm*
- **£9,750**     • **Marks Antiques**

## Mustard Pot ▼

- *date 1910*

Elegant George V drum mustard pot with pierced pattern and blue glass liner.
- *height 9cm*
- **£375**     • **Linden & Co**

### Fabergé Bowl and Ladle ▼
- *circa 1917*
Imperial Russian silver bowl and ladle, made by Fabergé in St Petersburg immediately prior to the revolution.
- **£24,750**   • **Marks Antiques**

### Claret Jug ▼
- *date 1866*
Silver-mounted claret jug with etched glass and scrolled handle. By W. & G. Sissons, Sheffield.
- *height 28cm*
- **£3,850**   • **Percy's**

### Hand Mirror ▲
- *date 1892*
Silver hand mirror with swirl fluted back and twist fluted handle. Made in Birmingham.
- *length 29cm*
- **£350**   • **Linden & Co**

### Centrepiece ▲
- *circa 1843*
A magnificent, solid-silver, finely cast, figural centrepiece of leaf and foliage design, surmounted by original cut-glass dish, the whole on acanthus-scroll feet. By J. & J.F. Hunt, London.
- *height 53cm*
- **£16,750**   • **Percy's**

### Cream Pail and Sugar Basket ▼
- *circa 1770*
Pierced silver with blue glass liners and pierced lattice handles, the pail on a pedestal. London.
- **£1,625** (or separately)• **Percy's**

### Regimental Statuette ▼
- *date 1894*
Barometer and clock set in marching drum of military figure of the Prince of Wales regiment, on silver and slate plinth. Mappin & Webb, London.
- *height 26cm*
- **£6,500**   • **Langfords**

### Dressing Table Set ➤
- *date 1966*
Three-piece enamel and silver set consisting of hairbrush, clothes brush and mirror in white enamel with red rose design. By Barker, Ellis Silver Co, Birmingham.
- **£360**   • **Linden & Co**

## Teapot ➤
- *date 1822*
By royal silversmith Paul Storr, circular half fluted and compressed body with leaf shell and gadrooned borders.
- *height 10cm*
- **£6,500** • **Langfords**

## Christening Cup ▼
- *date 1882*
Christening cup with engraved floral designs and trellis borders. Made in London.
- *height 9cm*
- **£220** • **Vivienne Carroll**

## Toast Rack ▲
- *date 1898*
Victorian silver toast rack with six bays on engraved serpentine base with floral design.
- *height 17cm*
- **£1,100** • **Stephen Kalms**

## Cruet Frame ▲
- *date 1761*
A Warwick cruet frame comprising three casters and two glass bottles all in a vase shape. by John Delmester.
- *height 22cm*
- **£5,500** • **Langfords**

## Brandy Saucepan ▼
- *date 1788*
Splay-lipped brandy saucepan with turned wooden handle. By Samuel Meriton.
- *height 8cm*
- **£1,250** • **Percy's**

## Tankard ▲
- *date 1744*
Baluster form tankard with domed lid and banding, by Humphrey Payne of London.
- *height 18cm*
- **£3,250** • **Percy's**

### Expert Tips

*Teapots made before the reign of George III have a very small capacity, as tea was then an extremely expensive luxury. As tea became more affordable, the pots became larger until the beginning of the 19th century, when they became more usually produced as part of a service.*

## Entrée Dishes ◄
- *date 1825*
Pair of entrée dishes in old Sheffield plate, with acanthus and fluted design and serpentine scrolled borders.
- *height 30cm*
- **£3,250** • **Percy's**

449

## Flatware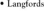
- *date 1876-82*
A full set of cutlery for twelve settings, double-struck bead pattern. Made in England by George Adams.
- **£8,500**          • **Langfords**

## Dinner Service ▲
- *circa 1900*
Russian silver-gilt and enamel plique-à-jour dinner service with twelve settings, comprising plates, sorbet cups, saucers and spoons in varying colours.
- **£200,000**     • **Marks Antiques**

## Assorted Pewter ▲
- *19th century*
Flagon, two chalices and two plates in English pewter. Quart capacity flagon banded with domed lid and moulded base.
- **£425**          • **Castlegate**

## Cruet ▼
- *date 1832*
Cruet comprising seven pieces, with shell and leaf moulding and interlaced floral designs to the handle. By Emes & Barnard.
- *height 26cm*
- **£2,750**          • **Percy's**

## Claret Jugs ◄
- *date 1875*
Pair of French silver claret jugs with cut and engraved glass with leaf designs and pierced lattice panels, the whole on a moulded foot. Made in Paris.
- *height 30cm*
- **£5,750**          • **Percy's**

### Expert Tips

*Never tie knives and forks together with rubber bands. Rubber reacts with silver to produce deep oxydisation which is almost impossible to remove.*

## Candlesticks ▼
- *date 1781*
Set of four George III candlesticks with fluted stems on a fluted, twisted base with beading. John Winter, Sheffield.
- *height 30cm*
- **£11,505**          • **Percy's**

## Sauce Tureens ◄
- *date 1793*
Pair of George III sauce tureens, with fluted lids and half bases, by Cornelius Bland of London.
- *length 24cm*
- **£5,500**          • **Marks Antiques**

## Tankard ▼
- *date 1908*
Silver tankard with scrolled
handle, domed lid and moulded
banding. By H. Atkin, Sheffield.
- *height 17cm*
- £790       • **Stephen Kalms**

## Sovereign Case ▲
- *date 1912*
Heart-shaped silver sovereign
case, engraved with floral designs.
By E.J. Houlston, Birmingham.
- *length 5cm*
- £250       • **Linden & Co**

## Cigarette Case ▼
- *circa 1910*
With enamelled plaque of a
robust Cleopatra with asp at her
breast. European 900 mark.
- *length 9.5cm*
- £1,400
- • **Sue & Alan Thompson**

## Pair of Cockerels ➤
- *circa 1900*
Pair of continental silver
cockerels, finely and
naturalistically detailed, in
fighting stance.
- *height 23cm approx.*
- £1,200       • **Stephen Kalms**

## Stirrup Cups ▲
- *date 1920*
Set of four large German stirrup
cups with 835 standard mark.
The cups rest on fox-head bases.
- *height 13cm*
- £1,500       • **J. First**

## Claret Jugs ◄
- *date 1901*
Pair of highly ornate Edwardian
silver-gilt claret jugs in hand-
etched crystal. Made by Walter
Keith of London.
- *height 41cm*
- £16,750    • **Marks Antiques**

### Expert Tips

*Hinges are almost
impossible to repair on silver
boxes, so check them carefully.
Repairs can only be effected by
heating the metal, which is
generally too malleable
to retain its strength
after retempering.*

## Tudric Dish ◄
- *date 1895*
Art Nouveau by Liberty in
polished pewter with hammered
finish on a splayed pedestal foot,
with organic, pierced handles.
- *diameter 32cm*
- £250       • **Percy's**

## Punch Set ➤
• *date 1894*
Russian silver-gilt punch set
comprising bowl, ladle, tray and
six cups. Made in Moscow by
Fabergé. Scrolled handles to bowl
and cups; tray on balled feet.
• *diameter 30cm*
• £32,000  • **Marks Antiques**

## Sugar Basket ▲
• *date 1790*
George III sugar basket of
octagonal form, bright cut with
gold-wash interior. London.
• *height 16cm*
• £875  • **Percy's**

## Claret Jugs ▲
• *date 1880*
French hand-cut crystal, made in
Paris by G. Keller.
• *height 23cm*
• £5,950  • **Marks Antiques**

## Claret Jug Boxed Set ▲
• *circa 1880*
Fluted glass and silver mounted
claret jug with twelve pierced
silver and etched glass beakers,
the whole in original case.
European silver.
• £9,500  • **Stephen Kalms**

## Cup and Cover ▼
• *circa 1880*
Rock crystal, Viennese silver-gilt
and enamel cup and cover with
finial figure.
• *height 47cm*
• £47,500  • **Marks Antiques**

## Tea and Coffee Service ◄
• *date 1842*
Tea and coffee service comprising
coffee and tea pots, sugar bowl
with tongs and cream/milk jug,
with fine, flat-chased, melon
fluted pattern. By Emes &
Barnard, London.
• £5,750  • **Percy's**

## Salt Cellars ◄
- *date 1732*

Fine pair of salt cellars, made by Peter Archaubo of London. Weight 10.89 ounces.
- *diameter 7cm*
- **£5,500**        • **Nicholas Shaw**

## Sugar Bowl ◄
- *date 1761*

Fine George III sugar bowl, made in Edinburgh by Lothian & Robertson. Engraved with initials 'CM'. Flared, serpentine rim.
- *height 12cm*
- **£800**        • **Nicholas Shaw**

## Inkstand ▲
- *date 1745*

Very fine George III inkstand comprising inkwell, sand or pounce caster and original bell on florally engraved, serpentine tray, all on fourscrolled feet. By John Swift, London.
- *length 27cm*
- **£14,500**        • **Marks Antiques**

## Goblet ▼
- *date 1909*

With beaded base and knop stem; the bowl has fluting. By Walker & Hall, Sheffield.
- *height 20cm*
- **£400**        • **Stephen Kalms**

## Rattles ▲
- *1887-1909*

Group of rattles with bells and whistles, red coral handles. One in form of sea monster. By Hilliard & Thompson.
- **£500-£1,000**        • **Jack Simons**

## Expert Tips

*Bells were the most desirable single items of the inkstand and tended to be separated from the rest and sold separately. Replacement bells can usually be detected because they tend not to be marked. Inkstands with their original bells are much more valuable, because they are now something of a rarity.*

## Tea and Coffee Set ►
- *date 1871*

Four pieces, with engraved floral design, made in Birmingham by Elkington & Co.
- **£5,250**        • **Marks Antiques**

## Sauce Tureens ◄
- *date 1808*
Pair of English Regency sauce tureens. With acorn finial, standing on four ball feet. Made by Henry Nutting and Robert Hennel, London.
- *height 13cm*
- £1,900 • J. First

## Cruet ▼
- *date 1817*
A fine George III Regency silver cruet, with two miniature claret jugs on a base with a heart-shaped handle. Made in London by Paul Storr.
- *height 29cm*
- £9,500 • Marks Antiques

## Punch Bowl ▼
- *date 1911*
Punch bowl with fluted body with inverted beading, pedestal foot and serpentine rim with moulded edge. Made in London.
- *diameter 29cm; height 22cm*
- £2,475 • Langfords

## Cymric Dish ►
- *date 1880*
Liberty-marked cymric dish with two enamelled ears with blue/green organic enamel.
- *diameter 14cm*
- £800 • Kieron

## Fruit Dish ▲
- *date 1910*
A silver pierced Edwardian fruit dish with floral swag decoration on three scrolled feet. London.
- *diameter 23cm*
- £900 • Linden & Co

## Tankard ▲
- *date 1706*
Queen Anne Britannia standard tankard by Robert Timbrell.
- *height 17cm*
- £9,000 • Marks Antiques

## Stirrup Cup ▲
- *date 1974*
Sheffield stirrup cup with excellently formed etched hound base. Heavy quality silver.
- *height 11.5cm*
- £575 • Linden & Co

### Expert Tips

*Every time silver is cleaned, it is diminished. It is not dirt which is removed, but tarnish – effectively the top layer.*

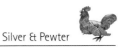

## Beaker ∨

• *circa 1785*
Swedish pewter beaker of fluted
design with splayed foot.
• *height 14cm*
• £85                    • Jane Stewart

## Pair of Candlesticks ∨

• *circa 1800*
A pair of English pewter
candlesticks with baluster knop
and push-up ejectors on circular
bases, gadrooned at the edge.
• *height 19cm*
• £225                   • Jane Stewart

## English Beaker ➤

• *circa 1800*
An English, half-pint pewter
beaker, with owner's initials –
J.H.C. – and banded decoration
to circular foot.
• *height 10cm*
• £50                    • Jane Stewart

## English Charger ∧

• *circa 1726*
A William and Mary-style
'wriggle' work charger, made
during the George I period.
Shows ownership initials – A.K.
Wriggle work, which was effected
by punching with a hammer, is
evident around the rim.
• *diameter 41cm*
• £275                   • Jane Stewart

## Dish Cover ∧

• *circa 1850*
An oval-shaped dish cover in
polished pewter, by James
Dickson of Sheffield, with
beading around the base and base
of handle, which has moulded,
floral decoration.
• *height 20cm*
• £75                    • Jane Stewart

## Expert Tips

*Britannia metal is a refined
form of pewter which was
developed in the late 18th
century from plate pewter. It
was widely used in the 19th
century for factory production
of pieces, which were marked on
the underside with names or
trade marks. Pieces with a mark
including a pattern number are
Britannia metal, not
earlier pewter.*

## Tankard ∧

• *circa 1850*
English straight-sided, handled
tankard of quart capacity, with
banded decoration, the whole in
polished pewter.
• *height 15cm*
• £85                    • Jane Stewart

## Armorial Dish ∧

• *circa 1800*
German armorial pewter dish
with ownership mark – F.A.K.
Central panel engraved with
armorial crest, surrounded by
gadrooned border; floral engraved
decoration to rim; the whole
showing original patina.
• *diameter 33cm*
• £150                   • Jane Stewart

## Sauce Boat ◄

- *circa 1860*
Mid-Victorian sauce boat in Britannia metal (high-grade pewter), with pear-shaped body on three claw feet with scrolled, curved handle and moulded rim.
- *height 10cm*
- £50 • Jane Stewart

## Georgian Charger ◄

- *circa 1750*
English George II charger, with single reeded rim in polished pewter, by Richard King.
- *diameter 42cm*
- £275 • Jane Stewart

## Church Flagon ▶

- *circa 1840*
A Victorian, spouted ecclesiastical wine flagon, in pewter, by Walker & Hall of Sheffield, with scrolled handle and acorn thumb-piece.
- *height 30cm*
- £150 • Jane Stewart

## English Tankard ▲

- *circa 1850*
English, Victorian pewter half-pint tankard, with banded and double-banded decoration around body and curved handle with moulded leaf decoration. By Yates & Birch of Sheffield.
- *height 9cm*
- £45 • Jane Stewart

## Pewter Spoon ▲

- *circa 1750*
Dutch pewter spoon, recovered from the River Thames with 'Nature's Gilding'.
- *length 15.5cm*
- £75 • Jane Stewart

## Stuart Charger ▶

- *circa 1680*
Touchmarked Stuart charger, triple-reeded with ownership initials – P.M.W.
- *diameter 51cm*
- £650 • Jane Stewart

## Teapot ▶

- *circa 1850*
Pewter teapot, by Shaw & Fischer of Sheffield, with fluted spout and acanthus-leaf handle.
- *height 16cm*
- £65 • Jane Stewart

# Sporting Items

**The constantly ascending value of sporting artefacts and memorabilia provides a fascinating study – and an object lesson in not throwing anything away.**

The area of sporting antiques is one in which the urban myth of 'finding a fortune in the attic' may actually come true. Old golf clubs, for instance, and old golf balls have fetched staggering sums of money – but they do have to be significantly old.

The prices of sporting artefacts have been helped by the fact that they are nostalgically attractive. They adorn the walls of many a pub, wine bar and private house.

Some items start off with a built-in advantage, if they are signed, can be proven to have belonged to a well-known sportsman or are of a generally commemorative nature, although these latter do not gain value as fast as the others, in view of the thousands that are produced – and the fact that no-one throws them away.

The most sought after items relate to the most popular pastimes, so golf, football, tennis, cricket, rugby and skiing memorabilia are avidly collected, together with related ceramic and printed ephemera.

The most popular participant sport of them all is fishing and this is a particularly fascinating and rewarding field for the enthusiastic collector.

## General Sporting Items

### Plates and Tea Strainer ▼
- *circa 1885*
Pair of terracotta tennis plates and a silver tea strainer.
- *length 15cm*
- *diameter 15cm*
- £485,£440    • Sean Arnold

### Framed Photograph of Michael Owen ▶
- *date 1998-1999*
Recently photographed single mounted photograph of footballer Michael Owen, one of Britain's rising stars. Matted with Owen's signature. Photograph shows the Liverpool team's yellow strip.
- £50
- Star Signings

### Badminton Rackets ▲
- *circa 1920*
Wooden with presses. Gut strings. Feather shuttle cocks.
- £65 racket, £7 cock
- Sean Arnold

### Golf Putters ▼
- *circa 1905*
Hickory-shafted patent aluminium putters. Made by, from left; Schenectady, Fred Saunders and Mallet putter.
- £460, £840, £480 resp.
- Sean Arnold

### Hickory Golf Clubs ▼
• *circa 1910*
Hickory shafts. Leather grips and makers' names. Persimmon headed wood, hand-forged.
• £75, £45, £55
• Sean Arnold

### European Cup Photograph ▼
• *date 1998 -1999*
Manchester United squad photo taken in the 1998-1999 season at a European Cup match. Photo and signatures include Beckham, Cole and Schmeichel.
• £350                • Star Signings

### Alpine Equipment ▼
• *circa 1930*
Wooden skis, continental ice axe and pair of early wooden skates with leather bindings.
• *210cm, 85cm, 28cm*
• £120, £95, £55
• Sean Arnold

### Cricket Bats ▲
• *circa 1920*
'Autographed' cricket bats – incised with names of famous players. Quality willow, English.
• £85                • Sean Arnold

### Aeroplane Propeller ▲
• *circa 1925*
Aeroplane propeller in laminated mahogany with brass edges. From Cirrus III. Boss stamped.
• £1,400                • Sean Arnold

### Signed Liverpool Team Shirt ▲
• *circa 1999-2000*
Football jersey from the Liverpool team, 2000 season. With all the team signatures including football greats such as Owen, Fowler, Hyppia and Camara.
• £350
• Star Signings

### Wooden-Headed Putters ▼
• *circa 1880*
Hickory shafted wooden-headed putters. From left to right shows a rare longnose by McEwan, a gassiat putter and a socket-head putter.
• £1650, £950, £380 resp.
• Sean Arnold

### One of a Pair of Water Buffalo Horn Oil Lamps ▼
• *circa 1880*
Lamps are brass-mounted and are decorated with a heavy leaf design.
• *height 77cm*
• £950 for pair
• Holland & Holland

## Wicker and Leather Pelota Cradles ▲
• *circa 1910*
Early 20th-century pelota cradles. Made from wicker with leather gloves. Used for high-speed ball game of Spanish origins.
• *length 50cm*
• £110 each
• Sean Arnold

## Football Medals ▲
• *circa 1920*
A collection of football medals. Silver enamelled.
• £80, £120, £120 resp.
• Sean Arnold

## Croquet Mallets ▲
• *circa 1920*
From top, brass-bound croquet mallet by Jacques of London, and square mallet by Slazenger of London. Made from box wood.
• *height 95cm*
• £65, £110     • Sean Arnold

## Lizard Skin Flask ▼
• *circa 1930*
Early 20th-century large silver lizard-skin flask. Flask is hallmarked with inscription 'Death to Filias'. Shows a silver hinged screw to the stopper. Has a glass reservoir inside. Flask is in very good condition.
• £435     • Holland & Holland

## Telescope & Binoculars ▼
• *circa 1900*
Telescope and binoculars made from leather and brass. By F. Davidson.
• £345, £95     • Sean Arnold

## Polished Pewter Figure ▲
• *circa 1920*
Naturalistically styled polished pewter golfing figure. The figure is mounted on a pewter rectangular base. Signed by Zwick.
• *height 34cm*
• £1,075     • Sean Arnold

## Expert Tips

*Be very wary of autographs unless well substantiated. Do you know how W.G. Grace signed his name?*

## Football Caps ▼
• *circa 1898-1930*
Velvet sporting caps. Metallic tassels representing various sports.
• £180-£360     • Sean Arnold

### Long-Nose Driver ▲
- *circa 1850*
A beech head long-nose driver.
Made by McEwan of Scotland.
- £1,850 • Sean Arnold

### Cigar Polo Mallets ▶
- *circa 1925*
Pair of cigar polo mallets with
bamboo shafts, sycamore or ash
heads. Made by Salters.
- *length 130cm*
- £48 • Sean Arnold

### Golf Ball Vesta ▼
- *circa 1907*
Golf ball vesta in the form of a
golf ball. Shows incised patterns.
Made by Henry Williamson Ltd,
Birmingham.
- *length 5cm*
- £745 • S&A Thompson

### Sporting Books ▼
- *circa 1910*
Sporting books on golf, tennis,
fishing, and cricket, including a
Morocco-bound limited edition
book on British Sports and
Sportsmen.
- *from £65 - £280*
- Sean Arnold

### Signed World Cup Football ◀
- *date 1990*
Football signed by the English
team from the Italian World Cup
of 1990. The signatures include
those of Gazza, Lineker and
Platt.
- £850 • Sean Arnold

### A Croquet Set ▲
- *circa 1950*
Boxed croquet set by John
Jacques, London. Pine box.
- *110cm x 25cm x 30cm*
- £225 • Sean Arnold

### Hazell Tennis Racket ▲
- *date 1934*
Hazell streamline tennis racket of
first aerodynamic design. Blue
star, gut strings.
- *length 68cm*
- £425 • Sean Arnold

## Expert Tips

*Golf has always been a sport for
established, usually wealthy
people and its artefacts
popularly collected. It also has
the advantage over other sports
of having club houses in which
to display them. Golf clubs need
to be in good condition, but can
show signs of plenty of use.
Long-nosed woods, which were
all spliced to the shaft, date
before 1910.*

## Team Barcelona Photograph ▼

• *date 1999-2000*
Photograph of the 1999-2000
Barcelona squad. Signed at
Wembley stadium, in the match
against Arsenal. Includes
Rivaldo, Kluivert and Figo.
• £350            • **Star Signings**

## Mounted Car Mascot ▼

• *circa 1950*
A horse-racing figure with an
enamelled rider. On marble.
• *height 16cm*
• £225            • **Sean Arnold**

## Signed Arsenal Shirt ▲

• *date 2000*
Signed Arsenal shirt from the
2000 season. Signatures include
popular football players such as
Bergkamp, Overmars and Kanu.
• £350            • **Star Signings**

## Group of Handstitched Footballs ▲

• *circa 1920*
Group of 20th-century
handstitched leather footballs.
Made with 12 and 18 leather
panels. Best English cowhide.
With laces and bladders.
• £95 each        • **Sean Arnold**

## Marine Navigation Instruments ▼

• *circa 1980*
Rare copy of Marine Navigation
Instruments by Jean Randier.
• £149            • **Ocean Leisure**

## Lawn Tennis Racket ▼

• *circa 1860*
Mid 19th-century lawn tennis
racket. Racket has original thick
gut strings. Shown with
mahogany multipress with brass
butterfly screws and mounts.
Used to maintain racket shape.
• £1,850, £495 resp.
• **Sean Arnold**

### Expert Tips

*Lawn tennis was first
played in the 1850s, using
real tennis rackets. Thereafter,
racket-shape development dates
them very accurately. Names
to look for are Ayers, Bussey,
Lunn, Mullings, Slazenger
and Buchanan.*

## Squash Rackets ◄

• *circa 1910*
Pair of early 19th-century
squash rackets. Shown with
heavy gut stringing. Rackets
bound with leather grips. In
good condition.
• *length 68cm*
• £125 ea         • **Sean Arnold**

## Polo Helmet and Various Polo Mallets ▼

- *circa 1890-1930*
Polo helmet shown with various shaped polo mallets. Largely manufactured in India, where polo was popularised by the army in the 19th century.
- £38-£120
- Sean Arnold

## Lawn Bowls ▲

- *circa 1910*
Set of four lignum vitae lawn bowls. Ivorine inserts with owner's initials and numbers. Pictured with white porcelain jack.
- £38, £26 each
- Sean Arnold

## Victorian Cricket Bat ▲

- *circa 1890*
Late 19th-century Victorian cricket bat. Styled with rounded back and crafted from willow. Shows good patina and bound handle.
- £220 • Sean Arnold

## WWII Flying Headgear ◄

- *date WWII*
World War II leather flying helmet. Includes face mask, head sets and Mark V Series III flying goggles.
- £595 • Sean Arnold

## Bronze Football Figure ◄

- *circa 1910*
Naturalistically styled bronze on oval base showing a footballer in period costume. Art deco period.
- *height 48cm*
- £2,480
- Sean Arnold

## Signed Leather Football ▲

- *date 1950*
Mid 20th-century leather football recently signed by Vialli. The ball is constructed using twelve panels of handstitched leather.
- £120 • Sean Arnold

## Caddie Stand ►

- *circa 1890*
Caddie stand golf-club carrier in wood with canvas bag. First form of club carrier patented 1890 by Bussey. Very good condition.
- *height 95cm*
- £1,450 • Sean Arnold

## Cricket Bats ▲
- *circa 1940*
Two standard cricket bats.
Leather or whipped handles.
- £35 each • **Sean Arnold**

## Signed Manchester United Shirt ▲
- *date 1999-2000*
Manchester United football shirt
from the 2000 season. The shirt is
signed by the team including key
players such as Beckham, Giggs
and Keane.
- £350 • **Star Signings**

## Football Rattle ▲
- *circa 1920*
Early 20th-century football rattle.
Made from wood and used by
football supporters. In good
condition.
- £75 • **Sean Arnold**

## Football Collectables ▲
- *circa 1940*
Leather-covered trinket box in
shape of a football. Marble
ashtray. Football tankard.
- £125, £135, £95
- **Sean Arnold**

## 1999 European Cup Final Programme ▽
- *date 1999*
Programme signed by the
Manchester United squad. Game
between Manchester United and
Bayern Munich.
- £600 • **Star Signings**

## Signed Chelsea Team Photograph ▽
- *date 1999-2000*
Chelsea team photograph
including signatures of the
players. Taken prior to playing
AC Milan in Champions League.
- £350 • **Star Signings**

## Football Items ◄
- *circa 1920*
Football items from early 20th
century. From left of picture:
football boots, shin pads and
hotspur boots. All items are
handmade from leather.
Made in England.
- £165, £65, £225 resp.
- **Sean Arnold**

Dayton Badminton Racket ◀

## Dayton Badminton Racket ◀
- *circa 1920*
Badminton racket made by Dayton, U.S.A. Painted metal frame with strings. Shuttlecock. made from natural feathers.
- **£190 racket, £7 shuttlecock**
- **Sean Arnold**

## Bronze Figure of a Skier ▼
- *date 1930*
A stylized bronze of a downhill skier. Art deco. Signed.
- *height 25cm*
- **£3,250**    • **Sean Arnold**

## Leather Footballs ▶
- *circa 1930*
Handstitched leather footballs. Show various team names with names in gilt lettering. Top is a leather medicine ball.
- *diameter 19cm and 33cm*
- **£65, £95 resp.**  • **Sean Arnold**

## Horseshoe Vesta Case ▼
- *circa 1890*
Vesta case in form of horseshoe. Brass with enamelling.
- *length 5cm*
- **£145**    • **Sean Arnold**

## Spelter Football Figure ▼
- *circa 1930*
A spelter football figure in typical outfit.
- *height 26cm*
- **£380**    • **Sean Arnold**

## Manchester United Football Shirt ▲
- *date 1998-1999*
Signed Manchester United football shirt of treble winners. Showing 21 signatures from the 98-99 season squad. Signatures include Beckham, Sheringham, Schmeichel and Keane.
- **£1,750**    • **Star Signings**

## Selection of Boxing Items including Boots, Gloves and Bag ◀
- *circa 1920*
Group of sporting items showing leather boxing boots, leather boxing gloves and a leather punch bag. Made by various English sporting manufacturers.
- **£165, £60, £125 resp.**
- **Sean Arnold**

## Signed Chelsea Football Shirt ▼

- *date 2000*

Chelsea football shirt from the 2000 season. Shirt is signed by the team, including Zola, Vialli and De Goey.

- £350 • **Star Signings**

## Signed Fiorentina Photograph• ▼

- *date 1999 -2000*

Fiorentina squad photograph, 1999-2000 season. Signed at Wembley stadium at a game against Arsenal.

- £350 • **Star Signings**

## Ping Pong Bats ▲

- *circa 1880*

Pair of 19th-century ping pong bats. Head of bats made from vellum. Handles are tapered and made of mahogany. In good condition.

- *length 40cm*
- £125 • **Sean Arnold**

## Football Tobacco Box ▲

- *date 1905*

Silver tobacco box styled as a rugby ball. Hinged flap. Made in Birmingham.

- *length 8cm*
- £525
- **Sue & Alan Thompson**

## Expert Tips

*Modern signed artefacts are mementos worth a great deal to a limited number of people. It should be remembered that the prices of these have been loaded from the outset.*

## Signed Liverpool Football ▼

- *date 1999-2000*

Liverpool team ball from the 1999-2000 season. Signatures from the team include players such as Owen, Redknapp, Fowler and Berger.

- £150 • **Star Signings**

## Shooting Stick ▼

- *circa 1900*

Early 20th-century shooting stick with bamboo and cane seat. Stick made from mallacca. Brass fittings.

- *height 68cm*
- £215 • **Sean Arnold**

## Tennis Rackets ◄

- *circa 1895-1910*

Tennis rackets with convex and concave wedges. The rackets are made from beech and ash. Gut strings and wooden handles. Stamped with maker's name. In good condition.

- £145 each
- **Sean Arnold**

## Cricket Bat Bookmark ➤
• *date 1907*
Early 20th-century bookmark in
the form of a cricket bat. The
top of the bat shows an ivory ball.
Made by A. & J. Zimmerman of
Birmingham.
• *length 9.5cm*
• £425 • S. & A. Thompson

## English Longbow ▲
• *circa 1900*
Early 20th-century Old English
longbow. The bow is made from
yew and has a leather grip.
Includes the bow string.
• *length 120cm*
• £165 •Sean Arnold

## Silver Sandwich Box
## and Leather Pouch ▼
• *circa 1930*
From left; a leather carrying
pouch with a strap and two belt
loops and a sandwich box made
from silver.
• £500
• Holland & Holland

## Rugby Jersey ➤
• *circa late 19th century*
Original early England rugby
shirt. Thick cotton jersey with
heavy metallic embroidery.
• £1,550 • Sean Arnold

## Pigskin Flask ▲
• *circa 1930*
Early 20th-century tan flask.
Made from pigskin leather.
Shows a silver hinged screw
stopper and also has a glass
reservoir.
• £225 • Holland & Holland

## Signed Leeds Photograph ▼
• *circa 1999-2000*
Signed Leeds football team
photograph from the 1999-2000
season. Includes football greats
such as Kewell, Bridges and
Woodgate.
• £350 • Star Signings

## Tennis Rackets ◄
• *date 1895-1915*
Early fish tail tennis rackets.
Convex and concave.
• £80-£420 • Sean Arnold

## 1920s Tennis Rackets ➤
• *circa 1920*
Tennis rackets with wooden
handles and presses.
• £38 each          • Sean Arnold

## Tennis Jelly Mould ▲
• *circa 1885*
Tennis jelly mould by Copeland.
Crossed tennis rackets appear in
the centre of the mould.
• *length 15cm*
• £380          • Sean Arnold

## Model of Thames Barge ▼
• *circa 1910*
Well constructed 20th-century
model of a River Thames barge.
Gaff rigg, metal keel and rudder.
In good condition.
• *height 105cm, width 80cm*
• £695          • Sean Arnold

## Golfing Figure ▲
• *circa 1930*
Donald Duck plaster figure.
• *height 23cm*
• £850          • Sean Arnold

## Hunting Tankards ▼
• *circa 1940*
A set of 3 pottery tankards with
hunting motifs. Made by Arthur
Wood. Shows a treacle glaze.
• *height 12cm*
• £130 set          • Sean Arnold

## Gianfranco Zola
Photograph ▲
• *date 1998*
Signature with photographs of
Gianfranco Zola scoring the
winning goal in the Cup Winners
Cup Final, Stockholm, 1998.
• £200          • Star Signings

## Golf Club Ballot Box ▲
• *circa 1900*
Authentic golf-club ballot box
from Muirfield Golf Club. Made
of mahogany. Of very fine quality.
• *height 34cm*
• £6,500          • Sean Arnold

# Fishing

### Devon Bait Lure ➤
- *circa 1930*
Artificial bait lure, with four
triple hooks, manufactured by
Devon. With original case.
- £40 • The Reel Thing

### Small Creel ▲
- *circa 1940*
Mid 20th-century small child's
creel. Made from wicker.
- £95 • The Reel Thing

### Hardy 3-inch Reel ▼
- *circa 1903*
A Hardy Perfect 3-inch metal
body with ivory handle.
- £475 • The Reel Thing

### Three Fishing Reels ▲
- *circa 1900-1930*
Selection of fishing reels. The
reels are made, from left to
right, of walnut and brass,
brass and steel.
- £45-£65 • Sean Arnold

### Bamboo Rod Holder ▲
- *circa 1920*
Hardy Brothers bamboo rod
holder. String-bound with leather
carrying handle and cover.
- £145 • The Reel Thing

### Hardy Reel Case ➤
- *circa 1930*
Well-preserved Hardy reel case.
For 4 inch reel. Made from
leather and lined in red velvet.
- £125 • The Reel Thing

### Split-Cane Rods ◄
- *circa 1900-1930*
Assortment of split-cane trout
and salmon rods. Various makers;
cork handles, brass or alloy
fittings. All in excellent
condition.
- £65- £220 • Sean Arnold

## Hardy Telescopic Gaff ▶
• *early 20th century*
Deep-sea telescopic gaff, for big
game fishing. With belt clip.
Brass with rosewood handle
and spring safety clip.
• £250
• **The Reel Thing**

## Hardy 'St George' ▲
• *circa 1932*
Hardy 'St George' 3 ³/₈ inch.
Brass and metal components.
Agate line guard.
• £295       • **The Reel Thing**

## Leather Reel
## Case – 3 ¹/₈ Inch ▼
• *circa 1920s*
Early 20th-century reel case. The
case is made from leather and has
red velvet lining.
• £145       • **The Reel Thing**

## Every Star Salmon Fly ▲
• *circa 19th century*
Particularly bright and alluring
replica of star fly used for
salmon fishing.
• £45       • **The Reel Thing**

## Hardy Neroda Dry
## Fly Box ◀
• *circa 1920*
Hardy Neroda case with nickle
plated fittings, in tortoiseshell
and bakelite. Compartmentalised
into six sections with trout flies.
• £245       • **The Reel Thing**

## Crocodile Fly Wallet ▲
• *circa 1910*
Made by G. Little & Co.,
Haymarket. The wallet contains
various compartments.
• £225       • **The Reel Thing**

### Expert Tips
*Early artificial baits are highly
collectable. They are unique,
hand-made and were often
made of solid silver and other
valuable – and glittery –
materials.*

*Split-cane rods are not
extensively collected, because
almost everyone who owns one
uses it.*

## Fly Rod ◀
• *date 1975*
A Hardy 'Palakona' fly fishing
rod. Split-cane, 7 feet 2 inches
with canvas sleeve.
• £500       • **The Reel Thing**

### Salmon Fly Wallet ◄
- *circa 1900*
Real-leather bound with leather compartments and paper leaves with musical notes on inner flap.
- £145 • The Reel Thing

### Bakelite Powder Case ▼
- *circa 1900*
Dusting powder case made of bakelite.
- *height 8cm*
- £30 • The Reel Thing

### Hardy Creel ▲
- *early 20th century*
With webbing strap and netting.
- £650 • The Reel Thing

### Hardy Neroda Case ▲
- *circa 1925*
Large. Brass fittings. Metal liner with hooks to hang flies. Tortoiseshell and bakelite.
- £195 • The Reel Thing

### Boat Rod ▼
- *circa 1910*
Split-cane boat rod. 7 feet. Two sections.
- £125 • The Reel Thing

### Landing Net ▲
- *circa 1930*
With bamboo handle and metal frame. Net intact.
- £125 • The Reel Thing

### Hardy 2 ¹/₄-Inch Reel ▲
- *circa 1890*
Hardy 2 ¹/₄-inch 'Red' reel. Brass body with ivory handle. Made in Birmingham. Very good example.
- £445 •The Reel Thing

## Landing Net ▼

• *early 20th century*
Poker pattern, bamboo landing
net. Bowed wood hoop and
brass fittings.
• £275　　• **The Reel Thing**

## Fishing Priest ▲

• *circa 1940*
A fishing priest of antler
horn, with leather strap.
• £85　　• **The Reel Thing**

## Hardy Fishing Lure ▼

• *circa 1940*
An unused 'Jock Scott' lure,
manufactured by Hardy for
sea angling.
• £60　　• **The Reel Thing**

## Salmon Fly Box ▲

• *circa 1910*
Japanned box with four
compartments including
various gut-eyed flies.
• £245　　• **The Reel Thing**

## Hardy 3 ⅛ Reel ▲

• *circa 1930*
A perfect 3-inch agate line guard.
Brass and metal components.
• £295　　• **The Reel Thing**

## The Dry Fly Dresser ▼

• *circa 1930*
Used as a line dryer. Made by
Hardy Brothers Ltd.
• £75　　• **The Reel Thing**

### Expert Tips

*Finely made early reels of brass,
ivorene and ebonite are highly
desirable. Names to look out for
are Hardy Bros, Charles
Farlow, Alfred Illingworth and
S. Allcock.*

## Hardy Perfect 4-Inch ▲

• *date 1896*
Late 19th-century 'Perfect 4-inch'
ivory handled brass-faced reel
with brass and steel components.
Very rare and in excellent
condition.
• £595　　• **The Reel Thing**

**Angler's Knife**   ◀
- *mid 20th century*
Unnamed angler's knife with six attachments including scissors in steel and brass. Sideplates marked with imperial scale 1-3 inches.
- £245   • The Reel Thing

**Brass Fly Case**   ▲
- *date 1910*
Circular brass fly case with hinge. Three cloths.
- *diameter 10cm*
- £75   • The Reel Thing

**Farlows Spring Balance**   ▼
- *circa 1920*
Farlows spring balance. Metric and imperial weights up to 100lbs and measuring 9 inches. Made in London.
- £95   • The Reel Thing

**Creel**   ▲
- *circa 1910*
Fine French weave wicker split reed pot-bellied creel with sloping lid and fish slot.
- £145   • Sean Arnold

**Reel and Case**   ▼
- *circa 1920*
Early 20th-century unmarked reel with velvet-lined leather case.
- £345   • The Reel Thing

**Canvas/Leather Fly Wallet**   ▲
- *date 1930*
Canvas and leather fly wallet with fly-making equipment and Alfred Randle's 'Fly Fisher's Entymology'. With various compartments.
- £175   • The Reel Thing

**Hardy Allinono**   ▶
- *date 1925*
An early 20th-century fisherman's companion from Hardy Neroda, containing a brass weighing measure. The item incorporates various pouches.
- £495   • The Reel Thing

**Salmon Fly**   ▲
- *date 1895*
Well kept 'gut-eyed' fly used for salmon fishing.
- £95   • The Reel Thing

# Shooting

## Shooting Bag ▼
- *circa 1950*
Canocs leather and net shooting bag with leather strap.
- £175          • The Reel Thing

## Pair of 12-bore Guns ▼
- *date 1978*
One of a pair of Royal Deluxe guns with acanthus-leaf and game scene engraving. Single trigger, French walnut. 28-inch barrels.
- £54,000
- Holland & Holland

## Leather Gun Case ▼
- *circa 1930*
Single oak and leather gun case, with red base interior and leather straps. Brass mounts with carrying handle. Various compartments.
- £1,250
- Holland & Holland

## Gun Case ▲
- *circa 1930*
Leg of mutton gun case. Brass fittings. Cogswell and Harrison. Six compartments with leather pull straps.
- £375-£425 • The Reel Thing

## .375 Calibre Rifle ▲
- *date 1926*
Original Mauser bolt action, 24-inch barrel. With Q/D mounts and peep sight to bolt head.
- £5,250
- Holland & Holland

## Shooting Stick ▲
- *circa 1910*
Early 20th-century malacca shooting stick with a walnut seat. Excellent condition.
- *height 68cm*
- £195          • Sean Arnold

## 12-bore Self Opener ▶
- *date 1960*
12-bore Royal self opener with 26.5-inch barrel with double trigger. Royal scroll engraved with coin finish to action. Stock and fore. Superb walnut finish.
- £18,000
- Holland & Holland

## Decoy Duck ▲
- *date 1940s-50s*
Mid-20th-century vintage duck decoy. Made from apple wood. With painted highlights and realistic colouring.
- £225          • The Reel Thing

## Hunter's Display Case ▼
- *circa 1923*
Display case showing tusks
and moths of India.
- *32x30cm*
- £420 • Holland & Holland

## Shotgun Belt ▼
- *circa 1930*
Leather shotgun belt. Twenty-five
cartridge compartments and a
brass buckle.
- £55 • The Reel Thing

## .375 (2 ¹/₂ inch) Calibre Rifle ▲
- *date 1901*
.375 calibre Royal rifle. Folding
leaf sights, double trigger; 26-inch
barrels.
- £21,000
- • Holland & Holland

## Paradox Gun ▼
- *date 1890*
10-bore paradox gun. Decorated
with a fading leaf design along
the grip. 27-inch barrels. Gun of
excellent condition.
- *length 65cm*
- £7,500 • Holland & Holland

### Expert Tips

*It is not advisable
to shoot modern smokeless
powder in a damascus barrel.
Apart from giving due
deference to the age of such
barrels and to the method of
their construction, smokeless
powder burns more slowly,
lowering the pressure at
the breech end, but considerably
raising it further down the
barrel to a level such
barrels were rarely designed
to handle.*

## Gun Cases ▼
- *circa 1900*
Two leg of mutton gun cases in
fine condition.
- *length 30cm, top*
- *length 31cm, bottom*
- £445 top, £390 bottom
- • Sean Arnold

## Duck Decoy ▼
- *circa 1890*
Vintage duck decoy. Painted in
natural colourings.
- £295 • The Reel Thing

## Cap Remover ▲
- *circa 1890*
16-bore all brass cap remover
with wooden handle.
- £195 • The Reel Thing

## Leather Gun Case ▶
- *circa 1900*
Early 20th-century gun case.
Made from black leather and
oak. The case has brass mounts to
protect corners and two leather
straps. Inside there are various
compartments.
- £2,200 • Holland & Holland

## 16-bore Guns ◄
- *date 1911*
A composed pair of Royal non-self openers; 28-inch barrels, scroll engraved. Coin finish to action. All French walnut wood. New barrels fitted. Gold inlay.
- **£25,000 for pair**
- **Holland & Holland**

## Dominion .300 Rifle ►
- *date 1935*
Dominion .300 gun, back action double rifle. Rubber pad, shoulder strap fittings and 25-inch barrels.
- **£19,000**
- **Holland & Holland**

## Hunting Items ▲
- *circa 1920*
Canvas game bag, silver-topped flask in leather case, deer-hoof walking stick, and game carrier.
- **£95 game bag, £245 flask**
- **£65 deer stick**
- **£130 carrier**
- **Sean Arnold**

## Expert Tips

*As barrels are drawfiled or buffed for rebluing and as occasional pits are honed out of the bores, steel is gradually removed from the barrels. The barrel walls, already built thin for lightness, become thinner still. At some point they become too thin for safety. It is important to know the barrel-wall thickness of an old, well-used shotgun before shooting it. A rule of thumb states that the minimum barrel wall thickness should be .020" in a 12-bore gun.*

## Magazine Case ▼
- *circa 1930*
Leather magazine case with brass fittings. Cogswell and Harrison. Six compartments with leather pull straps.
- **£750**     • **The Reel Thing**

## Shooting Stick ▲
- *circa 1900*
Gentleman's shooting stick with malacca cane and bamboo seat. Folding seat with handsome brass mounts.
- *height 68cm*
- **£215**     • **Sean Arnold**

## .240 Calibre Rifle ▼
- *date 1927*
.240 calibre gun with a 22.5-inch barrel and mahogany stock and telescopic sight. Of best quality.
- **£5,000**
- **Holland & Holland**

## Ammunition Pouch ▲
- *circa 1920*
Leather ammunition ten-pouch belt with well-preserved and polished leather pouches and straps and brass mounts. In good condition.
- **£75**     • **The Reel Thing**

# Taxidermy

**The demand for taxidermy has fallen off a little since the Victorian period, when no drawing room was complete without the glassy stare of a furry mammal.**

The word 'Taxidermy' is derived from an amalgamation of the Greek words meaning 'arrangement' and 'skin', which may have led to a little confusion around the fleshpots of Athens, but proves that taxidermy is an ancient craft.

Taxidermy is a complex art. It requires a knowledge of anatomy, natural history, drawing, sculpture, mechanics, tanning and dyeing. It is also quite a laborious process, from the careful removal of the skin and its treating with a preservative, through the preliminary drawings of an animal's anatomy, with all its muscles, bones and depressions, to making a model from wood, metal and clay, followed by a hollow casting in plaster, papier-mâché, burlap and wire mesh and the replacement of skin, addition of features, mounting and presentation. It takes time and patience.

Which makes it all the sadder that, as a collecting area, taxidermy is not enjoying a golden age at the moment. Victorian stuffed fish do well, but our furry friends seem to be, well, too furry for today's tastes. Which, given the notorious mood swings of the collecting public, might make it exactly the time to start buying.

## Beaver ▼

- *20th century*
Adult North American or Canadian beaver. Shown on hindlegs with forearms raised.
- *height 55cm*
- **£395**            • Get Stuffed

## Finch ▲

- *20th century*
Goldfinch mounted on twig upon an oval polished wood base.
- *height 17cm*
- **£95**            • Get Stuffed

## Lesser Anteater ➤

- *20th century*
An African lesser anteater posed on a branch.
- *height 56cm*
- **£375**            • Get Stuffed

## Crowned Crane ▼

- *20th century*
African crowned crane shown on an oval base.
- *height 103cm*
- **£295**            • Get Stuffed

### Cased Insects ➤

- *20th century*
Cased selection of three Asian insects showing a black scorpion and two beetles.
- *length 26cm*
- £45 • Get Stuffed

### Wolf ▲

- *20th century*
Adult North American timber wolf, on all fours baring teeth.
- *height 88cm*
- £1,800 • Get Stuffed

### Squirrel ▲

- *20th century*
An adult grey squirrel perched upon a tree-stump set within a wooden base.
- *height 28cm*
- £95 • Get Stuffed

### Lemur ▼

- *20th century*
Madagascan black and white ruffed lemur on natural perch.
- *height 100cm*
- £750 • Get Stuffed

### Tortoise ◄

- *20th century*
An adult leopard tortoise with finely preserved shell.
- *height 16cm*
- £185 • Get Stuffed

## Expert Tips

*The glass domes which protect stuffed animals are extremely expensive and notoriously hard to find. It is unwise to buy an item in the hope of finding a dome to fit.*

### Hedgehog ▼

- *20th century*
Adult hedgehog on all fours, mounted on wooden base.
- *height 15cm*
- £125 • Get Stuffed

### Lizard ◄

- *20th century*
Egyptian monitor lizard modelled in an alert posture.
- *length 1.0m*
- £375 • Get Stuffed

## Red Fox ➤

• *20th century*
Adult European Red Fox
standing naturalistically on all
fours, without a base.
• *height 51cm*
• **£200**          • Get Stuffed

## Butterfly Collection ▲

• *20th century*
A collection of nine South
American butterflies, mounted in
a display case.
• *height 31cm*
• **£65**          • Get Stuffed

## Bird Collection ◀

• *circa 1880*
Victorian oval glass dome with a
display of ten South American
birds, perched on branches.
• *height 53cm*
• **£375**          • Get Stuffed

## Falcon & Partridge ◀

• *20th century*
A well-preserved Saker falcon,
mounted on a branch with an
English partridge clasped in its
talons, the whole on an oval base.
• *height 69cm*
• **£650**          • Get Stuffed

## Pheasant ▲

• *20th century*
A cock pheasant in mating pose,
with erect tail feathers, mounted
on a branch, on a wooden base.
• *height 95cm*
• **£175**          • Get Stuffed

## Mallard Drake ▼

• *20th century*
Mallard drake shown with wings
outstretched, mounted on a base.
• *height 45cm*
• **£195**          • Get Stuffed

### Expert Tips

*Taxidermy is a flourishing
business in the USA, where
there is still a powerful hunting
and gun lobby.*

## Owl ◀

• *20th century*
Eagle owl mounted on a branch set
on a polished wood base.
• *height 60cm*
• **£550**          • Get Stuffed

## Magpie ∨
• *20th century*
Magpie traditionally perched
upon a branch. With base.
• *height 51cm*
• £95  • Get Stuffed

## Dog ∨
• *20th century*
Lhasa Apso Tibetan dog on all
fours, with attentive expression.
• *height 36cm*
• £425  • Get Stuffed

## Rabbit ▶
• *20th century*
White rabbit modelled on the
theme of *Alice in Wonderland*.
• *height 48cm*
• £190  • Get Stuffed

## Jungle Cat ▲
• *20th century*
Asiatic jungle cat shown on a
branch set upon a polished
wooden base.
• *height 105cm*
• £650  • Get Stuffed

## Peacock ∨
• *20th century*
A peacock, shown with tail
closed, set on a square base.
• *height 1.8m*
• £395  • Get Stuffed

## Owl ∨
• *20th century*
Well preserved and mounted barn
owl with wings spread.
• *height 65cm*
• £275  • Get Stuffed

## Display Case ◀
• *20th century*
A South American spider and
insect, mounted in display case.
• *length 40cm*
• £75  • Get Stuffed

# Textiles & Fans

**Often no longer useful for their original purpose, textiles are frequently hung on the wall, a practice which has maintained their value.**

Age and condition are fundamental to the value of collectable textiles. Most old textiles are too inherently fragile to be put to their original purpose, but they are enjoying a revival as wall-hangings. Sewing was, until recently, regarded as an important skill and pastime for a lady, and a great deal of embroidery has resulted. In general, the finer the stitching and the brighter the colours the more desirable. Silk is more valuable than wool, naturally enough, but 19th-century examples of both are quite freely available, with the brightest colours coming from the Middle East, China, Japan and India.

Samplers – needlework pictures incorporating different stitching, in wool or silk and often carrying a religious message, are also very collectable. The earliest example known was made in 1598, but most of those on the market tend to be 19th century.

Fans were much collected in the 19th century, when some great collections were built up. Most of those on the market date from the 18th and 19th centuries, although late 17th-century ones can be found. Some of those from the 1920s, either advertising or made of extravagant ostrich feathers, are highly sought after.

## Embroidered Panel ➤
- *circa 1725*
A canvas-work embroidered panel showing classical vase with flowers on a red ground.
- *height 72cm*
- £4,500    • Marilyn Garrow

## English Cushions ▼
- *circa 1750*
One of a pair of English, 18th-century crewelwork cushions, with stylized floral decoration on a white ground. With generous fringe.
- £350        • Marilyn Garrow

## European Embroideries ▼
- *circa 1690-1720*
A pair of embroideries – European, probably German – in chinoiserie style.
- *height 1.85m*
- £7,000    • Marilyn Garrow

## Biba Jacket ⋀
- *circa 1972*
Woollen Biba jacket, in light brown, with assymetrical pockets.
- *size 10*
- £125        • Sheila Cook

## Mandarin Fan ◄
- *circa 1820*
Ivory and sandlewood fan with silver-gilt, enamel and mother-of-pearl sticks.
- *length 53cm*
- £2,000    • Robert Brandt

## Georgette ▼
- *circa 1935*
A black, floral-patterned, silk Georgette with stitched bust with square collar at the back and matching silk scarf.
- *size 10*
- £295    • Sheila Cook

## Hanging Fragment ▼
- *17th century*
A fragment of a hanging – Portuguese or Italian – with canvas work on silk, showing oversized birds and flowers.
- £4,000    • Marilyn Garrow

## Silk Panel ▼
- *18th century*
A panel of French embroidered silk showing vines, flowers and leaf designs on a gold ground.
- *height 45cm*
- £5,500    • Marilyn Garrow

## Egyptian Stole ▲
- *circa 1925*
An extra-large silk stole with a central camel design.
- *length 2.25m*
- £265    • Sheila Cook

## Straw Hat ▲
- *circa 1935*
Black straw hat by Wooland Brothers, trimmed with two large beige flowers. Crown decorated with top-stitching.
- £48    • Sheila Cook

## Part of Bed Hanging ►
- *circa 1775*
Strong, polychrome silks and gold thread with swirled floral design and frieze.
- *length 1.3m*
- £4,500    • Marilyn Garrow

## Four Panels ➤

- *18th century*
Four panels in blue, pink, green
and yellow silk, rectangular in
shape, with sloping shoulders,
showing geometric maze patterns.
- *height 1.64m*
- **£10,000**   • **Marilyn Garrow**

## Shawl ◄

- *circa 1850*
A woven silk and satin shawl in
peacock blue with woven edging
and border, showing a pattern of
flowers, wheat and serpents.
- *length 2.1m*
- **£550**            • **Tintin**

## Chinese Panels ▼

- *circa 1790*
Four monochrome panels of
painted paper, showing tree
peonies, dogwood and birds.
- *height 2.15m*
- **£4,800**   • **Marilyn Garrow**

## Gold Bolero ▼

- *circa 1900*
A fine, handmade golden-braided
Greek bolero, of circular design,
set on red satin and lined with
cream satin.
- *UK size 12*
- **£145**        • **Sheila Cook**

## Silkwork Picture ▲

- *circa 1785*
A late 18th-century silkwork
picture, worked by ten-year-old
Mary Philcox, showing roses,
bluebells and honeysuckle. Oval
in form and gilt-framed.
- *height 55cm*
- **£1,200**     • **Marilyn Garrow**

## Italian Frontpiece ▼

- *17th century*
Framed Italian tabernacle
frontpiece with religious scenes of
Catholic origin.
- **£900**        • **Marilyn Garrow**

## Ivory Fan ◄

- *circa 1820*
Chinese ivory filigree fan, for
export to Europe, with armorial
crest and pierced decoration.
- *length 41cm*
- **£1,200**        • **Robert Brandt**

## Mandarin Fan ◄
- *circa 1830*
Chinese fan with ivory sticks in natural and red and showing a mandarin in silk robes, with parallel panels of river views.
- *length 50cm*
- £1,000    • Robert Brandt

## Carriage Blanket ▼
- *circa 1900*
A monogrammed tartan carriage blanket, hand-woven from pure wool.
- £95    • Tintin

## Cushion ▲
- *circa 1930*
Cushion with stylized prince and princess, of embroidered canvas on satin.
- £65    • Tintin

## French Cushion ▲
- *18th century*
A French cushion, filled with down and fine feather, with silver and gold thread interlacing among floral designs of pink and blue, with roses.
- £1,200    • Marilyn Garrow

## Expert Tips

*Humidity in the air and direct sunlight are the biggest enemies of antique textiles. The air can hold less water at lower temperatures, so cool is good, but most important of all is stability.*

## Textile Panel ▼
- *circa 1720*
Panel showing chrysanthemums, roses and daffodils in a double-handled vase.
- £3,900    • Marilyn Garrow

## Wool Panel ◄
- *circa 1685*
Dutch panel with Gothic architectural designs with band of horsemen to centre.
- £6,000    • Marilyn Garrow

## Crewelwork Hanging ➤
- *circa 1680*
A pair of 'Tree of Life' wall hangings showing animals, birds and exotic flowers.
- *height 1.75m*
- £10,000    • Marylin Garrow

# Tools

**The only rule in collecting tools is that there are no rules.
This most arcane of all fields baffles the layman.**

Collectable tools are invariably joiner's or cabinet maker's tools, the works of art which were used to construct works of art. Tool collecting is a particularly arcane subject, with, to the layman, not a lot of logic in it. In general terms, the tools which are most collected fall into three categories, smoothing tools, grooving tools and boring tools.
Smoothing tools are basically planes, which vary in value according to the maker, how limited the edition may have been and any unusual features, even if not very efficacious. A joiner would have had about

30 of these, so they are not hard to come by. Planes could also be used as grooving tools, but more collectable are ploughs, which were the most expensive tools in a joiner's kit and which could make several different widths and depths of groove. A joiner would have owned only one of these, and so they are rarer as well as intrinsically more valuable.
The best braces, for boring, were usually made in brass or steel and filled with rosewood, beech, boxwood or ebony but, as with all tools, the most expensively made do not necessarily hold the highest value.

---

### Lawn Edger ▼
- *circa 1950*
Steel and cast-iron lawn edger with aluminium handle and rubber grips. The edger cuts by means of a rotating serrated blade and wheel.
- £55 • S. Brunswick

### Tinsmith's Shears ▶
- *circa 1800*
Cast-iron shears.
- *length 61cm*
- £38 • The Old Tool Chest

---

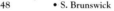

### Pruner ▲
- *date 1920*
Trademarked 'Mighty Cutter' pruner, with patented action for use with lever arms or worked by wire on pole. Made in England for fruit tree pruning.
- £48 • S. Brunswick

---

### Badger Plane ▼
- *circa 1790*
Large wooden 'badger' plane, for planing into corners by John Green, a famous tool-maker of the late 18th/early 19th century.
- *length 33cm*
- £250 • The Old Tool Chest

## Swan-Neck Mortise Chisel ▲
- *circa 1840*
A 19th-century, swan-necked mortise chisel for use in precision cutting of slots or recesses in wood for the receipt of the 'tenon' in a 'mortise and tenon joint'.
- *length 55cm*
- £38    • The Old Tool Chest

## Webb Lawnmower ▲
- *circa 1955*
A Webb's push mower with cross-over handles and rubber grips. With grass box, adjustable cutter bar and cutter base-plate and adjustable height nuts on the front roller.
- £40    • Curios

## Watering Can ▼
- *circa 1940*
Galvanised steel watering can with a large, detachable nozzle rose and handle of a tubular construction. Possibly a converted milk-churn.
- *height 42cm*
- £38    • Myriad

## Brace ▼
- *circa 1780*
Late 18th-century brace, made by John Green, with brass chuck.
- *length 36cm*
- £140    • The Old Tool Chest

## Mandrell Lathe ▼
- *circa 19th century*
Hand-driven, for making pocket-watch parts. Comprising cross slide, T-rest and centre. Of brass, steel and wood construction.
- *height 27cm*
- £1,000
- Aubrey Brocklehurst

## Mortise Chisel ▲
- *circa 1780*
A stonemason's mortise chisel for use in precision recessing.
- *length 33.5cm*
- £40    • The Old Tool Chest

## Garden Sprinkler ▲
- *circa 1900*
Brass and cast-iron sprinkler with two arms with brass nozzles which rotate under the pressure of water emanating from an attached hosepipe. Of very good weight and in full working order.
- £85    • S. Brunswick

## Expert Tips

*There will always be premiums charged for full sets of tools in their original boxes. Condition is important, but evidence of appropriate wear is not a devaluing factor.*

## Cooper's Joiner Plane ➤
- *circa 18th century*
An Austrian construction plane for use in the manufacture of barrels.
- *length 112cm*
- £375  • The Old Tool Chest

## Bulb Planter ▲
- *circa 1900*
A Kentish bulb-planting tool with turned ash handle and cross-piece for exerting foot pressure. For use in planting bulbs in lawns and replacing turf plug.
- £75  • S. Brunswick

## Garden Shears ▼
- *circa 1930*
A pair of tempered steel-bladed garden shears with turned ash handles. In working order.
- £25  • Curios

## Bow Saw ▲
- *circa 19th century*
An English carpenter's bow saw of mahogany construction, with original blade and tension stay.
- *length 63cm*
- £28  • The Old Tool Chest

## Lawn Edger ◄
- *circa 1940*
A well-worn half-moon lawn edger with rustic shaft of hornbeam construction and rusted steel blade. For sale as decorative artefact.
- *height 94cm*
- £15  • Curios

## Wheelwright's Hub Borer ▲
- *circa 18th century*
An English wheelwright's hub tool with turned double handle and tapered, concave blade.
- *height 76cm*
- £350  • The Old Tool Chest

## Expert Tips

*Carpenters' tools by known makers are the most valuable. Many tools were made by the carpenters themselves and may become valuable when the provenance becomes known.*

## French Watering Can ◄
- *circa 1930*
Enamelled French watering can of drum construction and screw-on lid, for indoor use.
- *height 38cm*
- £110  • Myriad

## Shovel ➤
• *circa 1940*
Classic English shovel of steel
and wood construction with
turned shaft and partly turned,
all-wooden handle.
• *height 94cm*
• £15          • Curios

## Garden Sprayer ▲
• *circa 1930*
Pressurised sprayer with copper
and brass components, with
copper cylinder and brass pump
with turned wooden handle.
Webbing carrying straps. All
original materials.
• *height 77cm*
• £140          • S. Brunswick

### Expert Tips

*Classic garden tools were very
often much better made than
their modern equivalent. There
is a growing market for old
cylinder mowers, by Dennis, for
instance, in working order for
use rather than as mere
collectables.*

## Joiner Plane ▲
• *circa 1890*
A French joiner's plane of
exceptional length; all wood with
original cutter bar.
• *length 103cm*
• £475     • The Old Tool Chest

## Boot Scraper ▲
• *circa 1800*
Dual-purpose boot scraper which
can either be used in the hand to
remove mud from boots, or dug
into the ground for scraping soles.
• *length 53cm*
• £75      • The Old Tool Chest

## Brace ▼
• *circa 1830*
An ebony brace with steel chuck
with the bit as a permanent
feature, dating from the early
19th century, for use in the
coopering trade.
• *length 40cm*
• £85     • The Old Tool Chest

## Dividers ▼
• *circa early 18th century*
Set of French cabinet-makers'
dividers used for transferring
measurement from plans to the
workbench.
• *length 37cm*
• £350     • The Old Tool Chest

## Dividers ◄
• *circa 17th century*
Large pair of English dividers for
transferring measurements to
substantial items of furniture.
• *length 62cm*
• £280     • The Old Tool Chest

## Dado Plane ▼

• *circa 1780*
An 18th-century English dado
plane, by the celebrated
manufacturer John Green.
• *length 24cm*
• £24      • The Old Tool Chest

## Austrian Sideaxe ▼

• *circa 1820*
An early 19th-century Austrian
sideaxe, cast in iron with a
beachwood haft, used for forestry
and related occupations.
• *length 65cm*
• £475      • The Old Tool Chest

## Set of Gardening Tools ▼

• *early 20th century*
A set of assorted garden tools, all
with hornbeam wood shafts,
including a 14-tine garden rake
and a three-quarter spit trenching
shovel. Mostly steel
construction.
• £48 each      • Myriad

## Garden Fork ▲

• *circa 1940*
An English classic four-tine
garden fork. Steel with turned
wooden shaft and half-turned,
all wooden handle.
• *height 94cm*
• £15      • Curios

## Cooper's Anvil ▲

• *circa 1680*
A very fine French late 17th-
century anvil, fashioned in cast
iron and used in the manufacture
of hammered iron bandings for
barrels.
• *height 94cm*
• £950     • The Old Tool Chest

## Expert Tips

*With tools as with all antiques
and collectables, condition is
paramount. If you believe an
article may become valuable,
take it out of the shed.*

## Rounding Plane ▲

• *circa 1850*
A rounding plane with original
locking plates. Curved both ways,
for use by a cooper or coach
maker.
• *length 28cm*
• £130      • The Old Tool Chest

## Lawn Aerator ▲

• *circa 1950*
A lawn aerator with a turned,
polished wood shaft and handle.
The mechanism is a rotating
cylinder with flat spikes driven by
the forward motion of the front
rollers. English made in full
working order.
• £65      • S. Brunswick

Tools

## Bedrock Jointer plane ▲
- *circa 1920*
A rare plane by the US company, Stanley, with greatly extended base plate for the precision smoothing of larger wooden surfaces. With mahogany grips and original cutter plate.
- *length 62cm*
- **£175** • **The Old Tool Chest**

## Pair of Garden Tools ▲
- *early 20th century*
Tools for aid in the growing of asparagus. A hoe for the amassing of soil over and round the 'head', and a cutter for harvesting the plant by cutting it off under the soil.
- *height 139cm*
- **£48 each** • **Myriad**

## Mitre Plane ▲
- *circa 1790*
An 18th-century plane, by John Green, used for bevelling wood, after it had been cut to size, into corresponding angles for the creation of a mitred corner.
- *length 31cm*
- **£850** • **The Old Tool Chest**

## Soil Sifter ▲
- *circa 1940*
Made of bentwood, cut and steamed to be moulded into shape, with a steel grill for catching stones when sifting.
- *diameter 45cm*
- **£20** • **Curios**

## Expert Tips

*An upsurge in the prices of second-hand gardening tools – many still in production – has been caused by peoples' desire to 'theme' pubs.*

## Bridle Plane ▼
- *circa 1890*
Scottish plough, by well-known maker, Mathieson of Glasgow. With adjustable fence.
- *length 27cm*
- **£165** • **The Old Tool Chest**

## Topping Tool ▼
- *circa 19th century*
Used for trimming the profiles of watch-wheel teeth. With separate box and cutters. A precision instrument, constructed of brass and steel and standing on a wooden base.
- *height 30cm*
- **£1,000**
- **Aubrey Brocklehurst**

## Watering Cans ▼
- *circa 1920s*
A selection of galvanised watering cans, one with an unusually large spout emanating from the top.
- **from £24** • **S. Brunswick**

# Toys, Games & Dolls

**Toys need to have been depressingly well cared for to appeal to the collector.**

It always appears that the toys which are worth a lot of money have been the ones that were least loved. A toy car which has been properly played with, with chipped paint and three wheels missing, is never going to excite a collector. Whereas a pristine model which has never enjoyed the wind in its headlights prior to smacking into the skirting board can be worth a fortune. If it has got its original box, of course.

Most valuable toys are not strictly antiques, generally having been produced in the half century 1890-1940, when factory production was taking over from

craftsman manufacture. Surprisingly, most collectable toys were produced in factories, rather than studios or workshops, and most often in Germany, where specialist toy manufacturers existed on a large scale. As result of this, many toys included mass-produced factory parts which can be difficult to reproduce, and are thus hard to restore.

Dolls and teddy bears are more individual, made with artistry and by revered manufacturers and are not dependent on packaging – but it is important that they, too, have not been overloved.

### Mussolini Figure ▽
- *circa 1940*
Hand-painted, lead figure of Il Duce in typically aggressive arms akimbo pose.
- *height 25cm*
- £150    • Stephen Naegel

### Robot ▽
- *circa 1970*
A tin robot spaceman, made in Japan, with walking mechanism. Silver painted with yellow and blue design.
- *height 14cm*
- £75    • Dollyland

### Peugeot Fire Engine ◀
- *circa 1930*
Peugeot 601 fire engine in painted bright red tinplate. Made by Charles Rossignol, Paris. Three firemen inside and a swivelling ladder on the top.
- *height 37cm*
- £485    • Pete McAskie

### Rope Swinging Cowboy ▲
- *circa 1950*
Rodeo cowboy made of tinplate and celluloid. Dressed in cotton trousers and printed shirt. Also equipped with felt hat, tin feet, tin arms and tin gloves. Contains clockwork mechanism which swings the lasso and moves his hips. Original box. Japan.
- *height 22cm*
- £165    • Pete McAskie

## Snap ▼
• *date 1920*
Pack of Snap cards, complete and in good condition with original box, depicting characters from the pantomime and nursery rhymes. British.
• **£55** • **Judith Lassalle**

## Britains' Zoo Series ▼
• *date 1950*
Set 908 Indian rhinoceros, grey with cream-coloured horn. With original box and paint.
• *height 5cm*
• **£50** • **Stephen Naegel**

## Trix Twin Train ▼
• *circa 1937*
Train of four coaches, loco and tender. L.M.S '00' gauge. Maroon with dark green roofs. Each coach has four wheels.
• *length 50cm per coach*
• **£110** • **Wheels of Steel**

## Rocking Horse ▲
• *circa 1960*
Pressed steel arm with seat and painted head. With leather ears. Simulated rocking action caused by spring and lever movement.
• *length 52cm*
• **£54** • **After Noah**

## Teddy Bears ▲
• *circa 1993*
A replica of a 1907 Steiff bear, one of the largest made. The materials used are all as the original. The bear is in the sitting position, wearing a red bow.
• *height 70cm*
• **£750** • **Dollyland**

### Expert Tips

*Toy locomotives and rolling stock should not be damaged, rusty or repainted. Track does not sell well, but trackside items, such as water towers, help to boost locomotive prices.*

## Kiddy Computer ▼
• *date late 1970s*
Kiddy computer, with original box, which features addition, subtraction, multiplication and division, but looks as if it does rather more.
• *height 19cm*
• **£18** • **Retro**

## Bébé Jumeau Doll ▼
• *date 1907*
Jumeau doll, with small firing mark to right ear, otherwise perfect china head, with original white lace costume, white shoes and mob cap.
• *height 47cm*
• **£1,250** • **Big Baby Little Baby**

## Thunderbirds Doll  ▲
- *circa 1966*
A 'Brains' doll from the Gerry and
Sylvia Anderson TV programme,
'Thunderbirds', complete with
original clothing, plastic
spectacles, spanner and pliers.
- *height 30cm*
- £200  • Dollyland

## Miss Piggy  ▲
- *date 1979*
The Muppet Show's Miss Piggy
shown in pink sports car in
famous waving pose.
- *length 11cm*
- £10  • Retro

## Dumper Truck  ▼
- *circa 1950*
English, all wood dumper truck.
The moving wheels activate the
tipping action. In original painted
livery of red and green.
- *length 67cm*
- £75  • After Noah

## Mickey Mouse Toy  ▼
- *date 1930s*
Cardboard Mickey Mouse 'rolly'
toy with bakelite round base.
Made from cardboard. Chad
Valley, USA.
- *height 23cm*
- £180  • Pete McAskie

## Dutch Rocking Horse  ▲
- *circa 1900*
Dutch wooden rocking horse
with two semi circular side
panels. All originally painted
with horsehair tail.
- *height 63cm*
- £425  • Rosemary Conquest

## Ford Zodiac Model  ▲
- *circa 1960*
Model of a Ford Zodiac
convertable. Matchbox toy
number 39. Pink bodywork with a
white and green interior and
green towbar. Original box.
- *length 9cm*
- £45  • Pete McAskie

## Expert Tips

*After 1939, the mark 'Walt
Disney Productions' appears on
their toys. Prior to that you will
find 'Walter E. Disney' or 'Walt
Disney Enterprises' on German
or American toys, and 'Walt
Disney Mickey Mouse Ltd.' on
British ones.*

## 11th Hussars Models  ◄
- *date 1949*
Britains lead soldiers set 182,
with huzzars dismounted with
officer and horses. Original Fred
Whisstock hand-painted box.
Immaculate condition.
- *length 60 cm*
- £200  • Stephen Naegel

## Wooden Garage ➤

• *circa 1950*
Wooden Esso garage with forecourt and petrol pumps. Original white paint with blue details. Includes hand-operated lift.
• *height 26cm*
• £85          • After Noah

## Celluloid Doll ▲

• *circa 1930*
A French celluloid doll in a green velvet suit and white blouse – both original. A 'bent limb boy'.
• *height 45cm*
• £145          • Dollyland

## German Squeak Toy ▼

• *circa 1860*
Painted German squeak toy of papier maché in the shape of a dog's head with two faces. Sound produced by leather diaphragm.
• *height 10cm*
• £350          • Judith Laselle

## Light Goods Van ▲

• *date 1948*
Van from Britains' Motor and Road Series set 2024, with driver. All original paintwork with 'Britains Ltd' signwritten on side panels. Original box.
• £350          • Stephen Naegel

## Rubik's Cube ▲

• *date 1980*
Rubik's cube in box shown in complete form with sticker 'Toy of the Year 1980'. From the Ideal Toy Corporation. Made in Hungary.
• *8cm square*
• £20          • Retro

## Ford Sedan ▼

• *date 1950s*
Marusan Ford Sedan toy car. A lovely bright yellow with lithographed seat and crosshatched floor. Chrome bumper, lights and trim.
• *length 25.5cm*
• £250          • Pete McAskie

## Cloth Doll ➤

• *date 1920*
All original and in good condition, with red hair, a red hair ribbon and flirting eyes.
• *height 59cm*
• £298     • Big Baby Little Baby

## Hornby 4-4-4 Train  ▲
- *circa 1920s*

Clockwork Hornby model of L.M.S. 4-4-4 locomotive, with original burgundy and black paint and brass fittings.
- *length 26.5cm*
- £195          • **Wheels of Steel**

## Paper Puppet  ▲
- *date 1870*

A German dancing paper puppet. A man holding a honey pot with tongue intermittantly protruding to lick it during dancing caper. Activated by drawstring.
- £195          • **Judith Lassalle**

## GI Soldier  ▼
- *date 1987*

US soldier in combat uniform with helmet and rifle. Battery-operated sequence where soldier crawls and fires weapon.
- *length 34cm*
- £40          • **Retro**

## Horse Roller  ▼
- *date 1940*

Farm roller with farm hand and horse, from Britains Home Farm series, set of nine. Patriotic wartime toy in original strong cardboard box.
- £80          • **Stephen Naegel**

## Golly & Bear Set  ▼
- *date 1996*

Jolly Golly & Bear set – one of an edition of 1,500. Undressable, jointed golly with red jacket and striped trousers. In original box.
- *height 30cm*
- £295          • **Dollyland**

## Skedoodle  ▼
- *date 1979*

A Skedoodle etching game with stencils made in Brevete, France, by Estanger. Complete with all original attributes.
- £16          • **Retro**

## Dream Baby  ◄
- *date 1920*

Dream Baby doll in excellent condition with open and close eyes, original white apparel and painted features.
- *length 34cm*
- £325    • **Big Baby Little Baby**

## Jousting Knights ➤

• *circa 2000*
Hand-made and painted pewter
15th-century Jousting Knight
(right) and Crusader Knight.
90mm scale.
• *height 17cm*
• £1,000 (Jousting)
• £850        • The Armoury

## Shirley Temple Doll ▲

• *circa 1930s*
Very collectable Shirley Temple
composition doll, with all original
clothes and club badge.
• *height 65cm*
• £450        • Dollyland

## Expert Tips

*Early lead soldiers by Britains
were packed in boxes hand-
painted with scenes by F.
Whisslock, with his name on the
lid. These are immensely
collectable.*

## Model T Ford Model ▲

• *date 1960s*
Dinky toy 109 cabriolet model of
a Model T Ford car. Based on
Gerry Anderson's TV series "The
Secret Service". Black and yellow
in colour. England.
• *length 8.5cm*
• £78        • Pete McAskie

## Dutch Sled and Spikes ▼

• *circa 19th century*
Dutch sled with hand ice spikes
for propulsion. In green with
white highlights. Sled has
metal runners.
• *length 57cm*
• £325        • Rosemary Conquest

## ET Doll ▼

• *date 1982*
Plastic stuffed doll from the
feature film 'ET' by Stephen
Spielberg.
• *height 24cm*
• £18        • Retro

## Model Pandas ▲

• *date 1949*
Set 9011 in Britains Zoo series.
Giant panda standing on all fours
and two baby pandas (one on two
legs and the other on all fours).
With original box.
• £35        • Stephen Naegel

## Hubert the Cottage Youth ▲

• *date 1812*
Hubert the cottage youth by S.&
J. Fuller. Comprises a head, one
hat and six colour pictures
showing Hubert in various scenes
from his life. With original
slip case.
• *height 13cm*
• £400        • Judith Lassalle

## Merrythought Cheeky ▲
- *circa 1994*
One of the largest 'Cheekies', in cream mohair with cream pads, a cream bow and yellow nose.
- *height 60cm*
- £230　　　　　• Dollyland

## Expert Tips

*Many highly collectable toys are not particularly old, so it is worth visiting junk shops, jumble sales and boot fairs looking for bargains.*

## Noah's Ark ▶
- *date 1860*
53 carved wooden pieces, comprising three people and fifty animals, all hand-painted, with a hand-painted wooden ark with a hinged roof.
- *height 20cm*
- £750　　　　　• Judith Lassalle

## Wild West Models ▼
- *date 1960*
A set of Britains' Swoppets Wild West plastic models, hand-painted and all complete with the original box shaped to accommodate the ten scale models.
- £150　　　• Stephen Naegel

## View Master ▼
- *date 1980*
A GAF View Master and one ornathological slide. In working order. Circular slides contain several transparencies which are selected by lever on side of viewer.
- *width 15cm*
- £8　　　　　• Retro

## Master Blaster Station ◀
- *date 1981*
UFO Master Blaster Station battery operated by Bambino, made in Japan.
- *length 21cm*
- £15　　　　　• Retro

## Robot ▼
- *date 1985*
Battery-operated robot named 'Crackpot'. By Tomy, made in Singapore, with animated preset moves, moving arms, head and flashing lights.
- *height 17cm*
- £55　　　　　• Retro

## Bucking Bronco ▼
- *date 1910*
Bucking bronco horse with rider. Made in Germany by Lehmann, serial no. 625. Tinplate clockwork and base. Man is in red shirt and brown trousers.
- *height 19cm*
- £585　　　• Pete McAskie

## Military Band ▲
- *circa 1948*
Imperial Napoleonic Band with escort. Twenty-one piece figure set. Made in Belgium by M.I.M.
- £1,000 • **Stephen Naegel**

## Sommersault Bear ▲
- *circa 1990*
A replica of a 1909 Sommersault bear with clockwork mechanism which makes him lift his arma and do his trick. In old gold mohair. Edition limited to 5,000.
- *height 29cm*
- £375 • **Dollyland**

## Fischer Car ▲
- *circa 1910*
Stylish version of Fischer car cabriolet with driver. Predominantly white with brown canopy. Was featured in 'American Motor Toys' by Lillian Gottschalk.
- *length 19cm*
- £1,780 • **Pete McAskie**

## Walnut Carved Doll ▼
- *date 17th century*
A seventeenth century walnut carved doll wearing a dress. English.
- *length 19cm*
- £500 • **Judith Lassalle**

## El des Colombus ▼
- *circa 1900*
Puzzle game, comprising several pieces which make up different shapes and instructions. Made in Germany.
- *10 x 8cm*
- £80 • **Stephen Long**

## Simon and Halbig Doll ▼
- *date 1910*
Simon and Halbig 1078 doll with perfect bisque head. Contains glass flirty eyes and moveable joints.
- *height 69cm*
- £795 • **Big Baby Little Baby**

## UFO Jigsaw ▼
- *date 1970*
A complete UFO jigsaw puzzle comprising 320 pieces by Anow Games ltd., after a TV series. Shows a scene with 'Shadows' space engineers – one of a series of three designs.
- *18 x 18cm*
- £10 • **Retro**

### Model Train ◀
- *circa 1947*
Lionel GG1 model train. Rare USA train '0' gauge. Black cast metal. 'Pennsylvania' written on the side. This is one of the first models produced by the company.
- *length 36cm*
- £450          • Wheels of Steel

### Battery-Operated Robot ▼
- *late 1970's*
Robot with preset animated programme with moving head and illuminating eyes.
- *height 11cm*
- £18                    • Retro

### Roly Poly ▼
- *circa 1860-1870*
Roly Poly papier maché with weighted balance in the figure of a large boy wearing tunic of blue and red with yellow buttons.
- *height 14cm*
- £350          • Judith Lassalle

### Selection of Marbles ▲
- *late 19th century*
Selection of marbles on solitaire board. Most are onion skins of various colours. The marbles alone are extremely collectable.
- £300          • Judith Lassalle

### Formula 1 Car ▼
- *circa 1950*
Lancia Formula 1 by Mercury of Italy. Unusual with petrol tanks on the side. With original box.
- *length 9cm*
- £78                    • Pete McAskie

### Rock and Roll Flower ▶
- *date 1988*
Sound-activated, dancing 'rock and roll' flower shown with painted face upside-down glasses and yellow trumpet, in white flower pot.
- *height 35cm*
- £18                    • Retro

### Timpo Models ▼
- *date 1970*
Clay County Jail Wagon and horse with seven cowboys in different poses. Still boxed.
- £80                    • Stephen Naegel

## Hornby 'O' Garage ➤

• *date 1950s*
French Hornby 'O' gauge model representing the main station at Bordeaux. White and orange handpainted wood, decorated with small posters of Normandy and a painted clock.
• *length 53cm*
• £125          • Wheels of Steel

## Le Loto Comique ▲

• *circa 1905*
Lotto/Bingo style game. Contains games pieces with numbers, pictures and boards with pictorial montages.
• *43 x 35cm*
• £118          • Stephen Long

## Clockwork Whoopee Car ▼

• *circa 1930*
American clockwork tin plate orange Whoopee car. Grafitti on bonnet, for example 'squeak easy'. Makes crazy erratic movements. Illustrated on Maxime Pinksy volume 2. Made by Louis Marx toys. Clown shown driving.
• *length 19cm*
• £245          • Pete McAskie

### Expert Tips

*'Open-closed', 'pouty', 'water melon' and 'bee-sting' mouths, 'wired', 'fixed', 'flirting', 'intaglio' and 'googli' eyes are technical terms used by serious doll collectors.*

## Acrobat on Trapeze ▲

• *date 1880*
French somersaulting acrobat on trapeze wearing blue conical hat and red tunic with painted face. Made from wood and paper.
• *height 23cm*
• £350          • Judith Lassalle

## Sailorboy and Girl Doll ▲

• *circa 1930*
A Schuco sailor and girl doll, made in Germany, both made of tinplate and celluloid, with clothes in felt. Clockwork mechanism in full working order.
• *height 7cm*
• £250          • Dollyland

## Hornby Pullman Coach ▼

• *circa 1930s*
Hornby series, 'O' gauge Pullman coach with a beige roof and a dark-brown body. Windows with the original cellophane panes. Interior has lamps and curtains. Doors open and have keys.
• *length 33cm*
• £120          • Wheels of Steel

## Motorbike and Sidecar ▲

• *circa 1930*
Composition elastolin model of German army motorbike and sidecar with driver and passenger. Made in Germany.
• *height 10cm*
• £150          • Stephen Naegel

### Model Trojan Van ➤
• *circa 1950*
Dinky toy 455 'Brooke Bond Tea'
model red Trojan van with silver
grill and bumper and company's
name in silver on side panel.
With original box.
• *length 9cm*
• £85 • Pete McAskie

### Pedigree Doll ◄
• *date 1950*
Pedigree doll in original dress.
Walking doll with flirting eyes,
naturalistic hair and red
hair ribbon.
• *height 56cm*
• £110 • Big Baby Little Baby

### Motor Coach ▼
• *date 1971*
A Dinky model of a Vega Major
coach, by Meccano Ltd with
original box. Model has
independently flashing indicators
and 'prestomatic' steering.
• *length 24cm*
• £20 • Retro

### Solitaire ▲
• *late 19th century*
'The Good Old Game of
Solitaire' showing a young
Professor Hoffman, an author on
magic, with full set of solitaire
marbles. Made by Spears.
• £200 • Judith Lassalle

### VW Beetle Model ▼
• *date 1998*
A gold beetle of 1: $1/18$ scale
modelled after 1955 car,
1,000,000 off the production
line. In dye-cast aluminium, with
opening doors, boot and bonnet.
• £20 • Retro

### Rule Britannia Box ◄
• *circa 1910*
A box with 'Britannia Rules the
Waves' comprising many carved
pieces for building men o' war,
cruisers, torpedoes, boats and
forts. All in original box.
• *length 45cm*
• £300 • Judith Lassalle

### Hornby Nord Loco ➤
• *circa 1930*
Hornby Nord Loco and Tender.
Clockwork mechanism. Brown
tin plate and black Hornby front.
• *length 43cm including tender*
• £295 • Wheels of Steel

## Railway Station Platform ◄
- *circa 1950*

Station platform called 'Trent' made by Hornby. Yellow platform with green roof. Made of tinplate material. Original box.
- *length 82.5cm*
- £160 • **Wheels of Steel**

## Expert Tips

*Hollow-cast lead soldiers will have a small hole where the excess molten metal was poured out of the mould when they were manufactured.*

## Yeomen Guard Models ▼
- *date 1950*

Britains set 1257 Yeomen of the Guard from their "Original Historical Series", complete with box displaying the nine figures.
- £140 • **Stephen Naegel**

## Comic Girl ▼
- *date 1830*

The comic girl by Faber, comprising three heads, a rabbit, a chicken and two hats. With stand and jacket complete with original box. German.
- *height 29cm*
- £665 • **Judith Lassalle**

## Tailless Donkey Game ▼
- *circa 1905*

"Pin the tail on the Donkey" game, complete with donkey poster and tails and a curious snake.
- *49 x 27cm*
- £55 • **Stephen Long**

## Spooners Transformation ▲
- *date 1820*

Spooners transformation No. 3. Print of woman and cat transform when lit from behind, eyes open and cat turns tortoiseshell, with eyes open.
- *height 29cm*
- £175 • **Judith Lassalle**

## Replica Bear ►
- *date 1991*

A replica of a Steiff 35PB teddy bear of 1904, with string mechanism and sealing wax nose.
- *height 50cm*
- £450 • **Dollyland**

## Military Field Smithy ►
- *date 1950*

Field smithy drawn by four horses with two outriders on original plinth. Modelled in lead by Lucotte Mignot.
- £250 • **Stephen Naegel**

## Clockwork Sparrow ▲
• *date 1976*
Chinese clockwork sparrow in full working order and complete with original box. Sparrow is vividly painted and pecks the ground when activated.
• *height 8.5cm*
• £13                    • Retro

## Magic Set ▲
• *circa 1860*
French boxed magic set, complete with three cups, two dice, balls, magic wand and other tricks with original instruction book.
• *length 38cm*
• £500                   • Coleman

## Mounted Drummer ▼
• *circa 2000*
Hand-made and painted pewter mounted French drummer, with plumes to rider and mount, on a modelled painted base and a wooden plinth.
• *height 17cm*
• £850            • The Armoury

## Replica Bear ▼
• *date 1990*
A replica of a 1926 Steiff teddy bear called 'Big Happy', with tinted mohair fur, a red bow and big eyes. This bear really does have a happier than average expression.
• *height 61cm*
• £700              • Dollyland

## Pedigree Doll ◄
• *circa 1950*
Early 1950s pedigree doll with stylized hair, moving limbs and open and shut eyes. Figure shown in grass skirt.
• *height 34cm*
• £120   • Big Baby Little Baby

## Railway Signal Box ▲
• *circa 1950s*
Tinplate signal box made by Hornby. Green roof and orange brick work. In good condition and with original box.
• *length 6.5cm*
• £45           • Wheels of Steel

## Magic Set ▲
• *late 19th century*
French magic set with fine lithograph on box, containing complete array of tricks.
• £1,700              • Coleman

## Expert Tips

*Collectors of diecast models, such as Dinky Toys, demand that every mint model is accompanied by its original box, because repainting and faking such items is not too difficult and the presence of the original box helps to re-assure them. Unfortunately, rumours abound that there is now a thriving business in forging boxes! Handling good originals frequently is still the best way of spotting fakes.*

## Papier Maché Doll ▼
• *circa 1850*
German boy doll, attired in
original costume of frock coat,
silk waistcoat, white stock and
brown trousers and shoes, and
equipped with penknife and
fob watch.
• *height 54cm*
• £895   • Big Baby Little Baby

## Model Soldier ▼
• *date 1940*
First Empire Imperial Guard
mounted standard bearer. Made
in Belgium by M.I.M.
• *height 6cm*
• £80   • Stephen Naegel

## Jigsaw ▲
• *date 1853*
Jigsaw of the Spithead Review
1853. Comprises key picture,
taken from a contemporary
painting, the original box
and the complete jigsaw.
• *length 20cm*
• £37   • Judith Lassalle

## Heinrich Doll ▼
• *date 1905*
Pretty doll made by Heinrich.
Hand-worked head with perfect
open and shut eyes. Body in
good condition.
• *height 57cm*
• £450   • Big Baby Little Baby

## Sailor D
• *date 1*
A doll rep
original s
firing cra
otherwise perfect.
• *height 39cm*
• £450   • Big Baby Little Baby

## Troll ◄
• *circa 1990*
One of the celebrated Troll
family, made in Denmark. This
particular effort has long white
hair and is wearing a yellow dress
with white trim.
• *height 26cm*
• £18   • Dollyland

## Replica Bear ▲
• *date 1991*
A black replica of a 1912 Steiff
bear, originally made in mourning
for the victims of the Titanic.
With black eyes and cream pads.
• *height 48cm*
• £425   • Dollyland

## ɔw White ➤

*date 1938*
Snow White and the Seven
Dwarfs, in painted lead. Part
of Britains' Civilian Series.
• *height 4-6.5cm*
• **£225**          • **Stephen Naegel**

### Merrythought Bear ▲

• *circa 1980*
A Merrythought Sloth Bear – one
of a limited edition of 250 – in
black and white, with very long
hair and growler. Fully jointed
and with hand-embroidery.
• *height 60cm*
• **£225**          • **Dollyland**

## Expert Tips

*It is easier to restore pre-1890,
hand-finished tinplate toys than
it is the later, lithographed
versions. Commercially
lithographed tinplate is almost
impossible to reproduce.*

### Magic Set ▲

• *circa 1860*
French magic trick with two
cylindrical painted tins with
hidden compartments, for
performing the illusion of
disappearance.
• *height 13cm*
• **£150**          • **Coleman**

### Bagatelle ▼

• *circa 1860*
German bagatelle board showing
a sylvan scene on half-moon
surface. Complete with original
balls, six holes and in working
order. With floral decoration.
• *height 46cm*
• **£200**          • **Judith Lassalle**

### Tin Beetle ▼

• *circa 1895*
Crawling beetle with green and
gold wings, red eyes, black body
and six legs. A superb example of
an early lithographic tin toy.
Made by Lehmann. No 431.
• *length 11cm*
• **£185**          • **Pete McAskie**

### Doll ▲

• *circa 1920s*
A German character doll from
the 1920s, in original woollen
romper suit with open and shut
eyes and a china head.
• *height 25cm*
• **£265**   • **Big Baby Little Baby**

### Animated Santa Bank ▲

• *circa 1960s*
Deluxe animated Santa piggy
bank with original box. Battery-
and coin-operated. Eyes flash,
head moves, and bell rings. Santa
has a vinyl face and sits on a
tinplate house, holding presents
and a bell. Japan.
• *height 30cm*
• **£285**          • **Pete McAskie**

# Treen

**Treen means 'made from trees'; anything wooden qualifies. Artefacts vary from the highly decorated to the basically carved, and all have their own charm.**

Treen has become valuable in recent years partly by default. Previous generations discarded it as valueless; as a result, the scarcity of early treen today can lead to extremely high prices. It is peasant, provincial art – household items and ornaments fashioned from wood. You would have to be very lucky to find sixteenth-century treen outside a museum – usually items such as standing cups and platters. Objects from the seventeenth century occasionally turn up, the more workaday in hardwoods such as sycamore and holly, the more important fashioned

from lignum vitae, which had to be imported. Most treen consists of domestic and practical items of which interesting and pleasing collections can be made for a relatively small investment – but quite a large expenditure in time spent tracking them down.

Among the most expensive is Scandinavian treen. Long nights and an abundance of wood led the Scandinavians to carve and decorate their handiwork to an extent seldom found elsewhere. Many treen artefacts were originally carved as love tokens, and these are among the most charming.

## Powder Flask ▼
- *17th century*
German powder flask with iron mounts and turned decoration.
- *diameter 17cm*
- **£850**          • **A. & E. Foster**

## Tea Caddy ◄
- *circa 1790*
George III fruitwood single tea caddy, comprising six sections of stained and natural woods.
- *height 14cm*
- **£4,950**          • **J. & T. Stone**

## Virgin and Child ▲
- *circa 1500*
German/Flemish group with extensive original polychrome.
- *height 39cm*
- **£2,200**          • **A. & E. Foster**

## Cornucopia ▲
- *circa 1680*
A pair of carved oak 17th-century, Flemish cornucopia.
- *height 55cm*
- **£2,600**          • **A. & E. Foster**

### Expert Tips

*The rules of wooden furniture apply to treen. Direct sunlight, proximate radiators and damp atmosphere should be avoided.*

## Carved Panel ➤
- *circa 1500*

English carved oak panel, with very early representations of an elephant and a leopard, perforce carved from hearsay.
- *length 39cm*
- £850 • A. & E. Foster

## Cribbage Board ▼
- *circa 1780*

A chip-carved maple board from Friesland, with additional carving to front forming a cribbage board.
- *length 83cm*
- £490 • A. & E. Foster

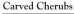

## Tea Caddy ▼
- *circa 1790*

Late 18th-century fruitwood tea caddy, fashioned in the shape of a pear, with stalk finial and keyplate to the front.
- *height 15cm*
- £4,950 • J. & T. Stone

## Carved Cherubs ▼
- *19th century*

A pair of carved walnut figures of adolescent cherubic girls; one holds an apple, the other a flower, while their other hands preserve modesty by holding together a sheet.
- *height 45cm*
- £395 • Castlegate

## Toolbox ▼
- *circa 1780*

Wooden, possibly elm, toolbox with locking mechanism to front.
- *length 56cm*
- £150 • Curios

## Carved Panel ▲
- *circa 1600*

A very fine English carved oak caryatid of exceptionally large size, probably from a bedhead.
- *height 120cm*
- £2,800 • A. & E. Foster

## Scottish Ladle ◄
- *circa 1720*

A Scottish ladle with chip carving to handle and fish carved on the bowl.
- *length 31cm*
- £395 • A. & E. Foster

## Pipe Tamper ➤
- *18th century*
A silver mounted pipe tamper, carved in the shape of a head, inscribed to Francis Stone.
- *length 10cm*
- £695 • A. & E. Foster

## Tea Caddy ▲
- *circa 1790*
Fine 18th-century fruitwood apple tea caddy with traces of original colour.
- *height 14cm*
- £4,950 • J. & T. Stone

## Oak Panel ▼
- *circa 1620*
Carved Dutch panel depicting the conversion of St Paul, retaining original polychrome.
- *height 62cm*
- £2,200 • A. & E. Foster

## Toad ▼
- *19th century*
Japanese carving of a toad, with inlaid eyes, naturalistically carved and polished. Signed Ryukei.
- *length 6cm*
- £5,800 • Gregg Baker

## Towel Rack ▼
- *circa 1900*
French faux bamboo towel rack with turned decoration.
- *length 50cm*
- £78 • Myriad

## Pew Ends ▲
- *19th century*
Pair of scrolled leaf pew ends with lion mask decoration.
- *length 41cm*
- £220 • Red Lion

## Nutcracker ◀
- *circa 1720*
A good boxwood nutcracker with the carving of a bearded man with teeth. English.
- *length 16cm*
- £1,650 • A. & E. Foster

## American Handclapper ▼
- *circa 1940*
All wood American football rattle. 'Giants' painted on one side. Solid wooden handle.
- *height 30cm*
- £34 • After Noah

## Oak Roundel ▼
- *circa 1680*
A significant Christian finely carved oak roundel, late 17th-century Flemish, depicting a bust of St James.
- *diameter 72cm*
- £2,200 • A. & E. Foster

## Corinthian Capitals ▶
- *19th century*
Large carvings, one of a large Corinthian capital, the other in a swirling, organic form. Both carved from walnut.
- £165 & £100 respectively
- Castlegate

## Religious Carvings ▲
- *17th century*
Italian walnut carvings of St Theresa and St Fillipo, on architectural plinths, bought in Florence in 1877, by J D Irven.
- *height 51cm*
- £650 • Castlegate

## Coffer Frontpiece ◀
- *circa 1600*
English oak coffer frontpiece with carved double spiral and oak leaf spandrels.
- *length 112cm*
- £3,200 • A. & E. Foster

## Pipe Tamper ▲
- *18th century*
A boxwood pipe tamper with handle in the shape of a greyhound devouring its prey.
- *height 10cm*
- £695 • A. & E. Foster

## Expert Tips
*Care is a long-term process with no short cuts. Wax polish should be used for regular polishing – never aerosols.*

## Paintbox ◀
- *circa 1890*
An English mahogany paintbox with colours, porcelain mixing dishes with glass water pot.
- *length 19cm*
- £150 • Judith Lasalle

# Tribal Art

**The proliferation of fakes from Africa and the Far East makes Tribal Art a perilous, but nonetheless rewarding, area for the collector.**

Tribal art is characterized by strong images and shapes and has become increasingly popular in recent years. The problem concomitant with this popularity is that the fakes market has proliferated and that these fakes are very difficult for the amateur to identify. It is important, therefore, to buy from a reputable source who can guarantee authenticity.

African masks are a particularly popular collecting area, especially desirable if they have been used in some form of ritual and carry some spiritual significance. Like all wooden items, they tend to be adversely affected by the extremes of climate and examples predating the twentieth century are rare. Because of this natural deterioration, a worn patina on wooden objects tends rather to add to the value than detract from it.

Tribal art usually finds its best market in countries with which it has an association. Thus, Native American and Hawaiian artefacts fetch high prices in the USA and Indonesian artefacts are very popular in Holland, which has a colonial history in the East Indies. The most popular areas in the UK are, generally, Africa and the Pacific Islands.

### Round Box ▲
- *circa 1880*
A cylindrical wooden box with carved lid and elaborately carved finial, the body with three individually carved figures, attached with rafiawork. From Sarawak, North Borneo.
- *height 16cm*
- £120   • Gordon Reece

### Mahogany Stool ▼
- *circa 1970*
A red mahogany stool, carved from one piece of wood, showing an elephant. From the Shona or Matabele tribe of Zimbabwe.
- *height 51cm*
- £230   • Something Different

### Chieftain's Stool ◄
- *circa 1890*
Ashanti Abzma Owa chieftain's stool, carved from one piece of wood and into interlocking, semicircular symmetrical design. Once used by Queen Elizabeth, the Queen Mother.
- *height 31cm*
- £480   • Gordon Reece

### Currency ▼
- *late 19th century*
An excavated, wrought-iron stick-man figure, used as currency on the Chad/Cameroon border. Mounted on a wooden plinth.
- *height 50cm*
- £380   • Gordon Reece

## Embroidered Panel ➤
- *circa 1935*
A Shoowa tribe velvet knotted and embroidered panel, with geometric, repeated diamond patterns. From Zaire, formerly the Belgian Congo.
- *1.3cm square*
- £330 • Gordon Reece

## Painted Drum ⌄
- *circa 1980*
A wooden painted drum with calfskin drumskin, pegged for tension, the body decorated with masks and geometric patterns.
- *height 58cm*
- £48 • Something Different

## Bambara Mask ⌄
- *circa 1900*
A fine example of a mask of the Bambara tribe of Mali, stylized with hair standing on end. From a continental collector.
- *height 35cm*
- £3,200 • Gordon Reece

## Mask ⌃
- *circa 1900*
A fine example of a mask from the Punli of Gabon Society, originally in a Paris collection and with excellent provenance.
- *height 28cm*
- £3,800 • Gordon Reece

## Table ⌄
- *circa 1990*
An ebony table, with interlocking carved support and top carved with rhino pattern and elephant pattern on reverse.
- *height 42cm*
- £30 • Something Different

## Weapon ⌄
- *circa 1910*
Ngombe Doko-Mbudja double-edged cutting weapon from Zaire, formerly the Belgian Congo.
- *height 40cm*
- £220 • Gordon Reece

## Tree of Life Carving ⌃
- *circa 1990*
A carved ebony statue showing a small tree of life with ancestral characters about a central figure.
- *height 31cm*
- £48 • Something Different

### Himalayan Storage Chest ◄
- *18th century*
Storage chest in Himalayan hardwood with deep, chip-carved decoration with images of the sun. Figure of horseman carved at a later date.
- *height 93cm*
- £1,100 • Gordon Reece

### Bookends ▼
- *circa 2000*
A pair of large, water-buffalo bookends made from kiaat wood. From Zimbabwe.
- *height 41cm*
- £150 • Something Different

### Ebony Chair ▼
- *circa 2000*
Ebony chair made of two pieces of wood, with pierced, carved back showing two suns.
- *height 81cm*
- £48 • Something Different

### Kulu Mask ▲
- *circa 1800*
A mask of the Himalayan Indian Gaddei tribe of the Kulu Valley. Flat and simple in form with two bars representing teeth.
- *height 25cm*
- £770 • Gordon Reece

### Mythical Guardians ▲
- *circa 1880*
A pair of statues from Orissa, Eastern India, repesenting male human forms with bovine heads, in carved and painted wood.
- *height 83cm*
- £1,750 • Gordon Reece

### Chieftain's Stool ▲
- *circa 1915*
An excellent chieftain's stool carved from one piece of wood. From Tanzania, East Africa.
- *height 35cm*
- £790 • Gordon Reece

### Anchor Currency ▲
- *circa 1880*
A heavily patinated, excavated anchor-shaped piece of currency, from the Congo.
- *height 51cm*
- £210 • Gordon Reece

## Mask ▾
• *circa 1910*
A fine Borneo mask, complete
with original paintwork and
applied skin and fibre.
• *height 34cm*
• **£3,200**    • **Gordon Reece**

## Weapon ▾
• *circa 1900*
A Manjbetu, Mambele tribe or
Trumbafit cleaver weapon, with
wooden handle. From Zaire,
formerly the Belgian Congo.
• *length 40cm*
• **£220**    • **Gordon Reece**

## Himalayan Chest ➤
• *20th century*
A chest in Himalayan pine, with
three panels to the front showing
profuse chip carving and curved
apron, the whole on straight legs.
• *height 83cm*
• **£770**    • **Gordon Reece**

## Burmese Statue ▲
• *circa 1900*
Statue of the squatting figure of a
man, in a relaxed, fluid style.
From the Burmese Naga tribe.
• *height 54cm*
• **£1,750**    • **Gordon Reece**

## Ceremonial Shawl ▾
• *circa 1920*
A Ghanaian ceremonial shawl,
woven in narrow strips on a back-
strap loom.
• *height 2.1m*
• **£890**    • **Gordon Reece**

## Elephant Stool ◄
• *circa 1930*
A small, hardwood stool, carved
from one piece of hardwood,
showing an African bull elephant
on pedestal as support.
• *height 28cm*
• **£15**    • **Something Different**

## Armenian Kilim ➤

• *circa 1940*
An Armenian, plain-weave kilim with naturally dyed stripes.
• *height 2m*
• £750          • **Gordon Reece**

## Ebony Mask ▲

• *circa 1999*
Zimbabwean mask of woman, in ebony, with carved ceremonial head-dress and characteristic forehead growth.
• *height 98cm*
• £135     • **Something Different**

## Mask ▼

• *circa 1900*
A Dan-Khan mask showing some Guere influence.
• *height 25cm*
• £3,600          • **Gordon Reece**

## Mask with Birds ▼

• *circa 1820*
A fine early Ivory Coast mask with the crest of two birds and facial fringe. In intact condition. From a London collection.
• *height 42cm*
• £1,250          • **Gordon Reece**

## Kiaat Wood Chair ▲

• *circa 2000*
A chair in kiaat hardwood, made in two interlocking pieces, with heavily carved back relief showing a rhinoceros and a giraffe. From Zimbabwe.
• *height 57cm*
• £32     • **Something Different**

## Pair of Doors ▲

• *19th century*
A pair of antique, tribal doors from Bastar, Middle India, with primitive carving.
• *height 1.58m*
• £1,800          • **Gordon Reece**

## Currency ▲

• *ancient*
Large, wrought-iron mahonia leaf-form currency. Excavation piece from the Cameroon.
• *height 62cm*
• £200          • **Gordon Reece**

## Maori Canoe ➤

• *circa 1992*
A model of a Maori war canoe,
with space for four oarsmen, with
traditional Maori carvings to
sides and heavily carved prow.
• *length 50cm*
• **£80**          • **Pacifico**

## Ebony Pot ▼

• *circa 2000*
An ebony pot and stand, carved
from one piece of wood, with
zoomorphic and figurative
designs. From Zimbabwe.
• *height 22cm*
• **£20**     • **Something Different**

## Ceremonial Sword ▲

• *circa 1915*
An Ngombe Doko Poto sword
from Central Africa.
• *length 61cm*
• **£285**          • **Gordon Reece**

## Hat and Pipe Man ▲

• *circa 2000*
A traditional Southern African
hat and pipe man, carved into a
piece of verdit granite.
• *height 37cm*
• **£38**     • **Something Different**

## Story Board ▼

• *circa 1992*
Traditional story board from
Papua New Guinea, showing
half-man, half-crocodile central
figure. From the Sepik river.
• *width 1.03m*
• **£200**          • **Pacifico**

## Tree of Life ◄

• *circa 2000*
A large tree of life totem with
pierced central decoration
showing the graduation of age
and wisdom from bottom to top.
• *height 1.52m*
• **£180**     • **Something Different**

## Dance Sceptre ▲

• *ancient*
A rare ceremonial dance sceptre,
excavated in Chad and thought
to belong to Dogon tribe of Mali.
• *height 61cm*
• **£1,200**          • **Gordon Reece**

# Twentieth-Century Design

**The twentieth century was rich in innovatory design and revolutionary manufacture. What were 'the antiques of tomorrow' are rapidly becoming the antiques of today.**

Each succeeding century is more artistically innovative and revolutionary than its predecessor, due to improved methods, new materials, better communication and, we hope, an increase in wisdom. Currently, the twentieth century is the standard-bearer of this tradition, with not only those advances, but a series of the bloodiest wars in history to enhance the imagination.

As recently as the 1960s, Victoriana was mercilessly lampooned by antique dealers and critics alike, before gaining respectability and massive price increases. Any criticism levelled at Victoriana was as

nothing compared with the critics' merciless reaction to the Art Nouveau style which emerged at the start of the twentieth century. Now that style has a fantastic following, combining, at its best, quality, originality and, if you're lucky, affordability. Antiques from the Art Deco period, evocative of the giddy 1920s and '30s, with their high quality craftsmanship and inventive shapes, is also greatly in demand.

It is not only nostalgia that fuels the collector's demand for twentieth-century artefacts, it is appreciation of genuine craftsmanship and imagination. Get collecting.

## Ceramics

### Floral Poole Vase  ▼
- *circa 1929-34*
Poole pottery vase with floral decoration consisting of tulips and crocuses, depicting spring. Slight hairline damage to rim. Design painted at a later date.
- *height 26cm*
- £550 • R. Dennis

### Sears Plate  ▲
- *date 1999*
An octagonal plate showing an Eastern scene with an elephant. The plate is hand made and painted with a tree in the foreground. It is signed by Deborah Sears.
- *diameter 33cm*
- £88 • R. Dennis

### Unusual Teapot  ▼
- *date 1998*
David Burnham Smith teapot is of unusual shape with a fish-like quality. Intricately painted with architectural scrolling pattern. It is signed and dated.
- *height 10cm*
- £700 • R. Dennis

### Dennis Bowl  ◄
- *date 1998*
Dennis Chinaworks bowl of oriental shape with blue and pink glaze. Two dragonflies are imprinted on the inside of the dish. Bowl rests on a small base.
- *diameter 18cm*
- £100 • R. Dennis

## Moorcroft Vase ▲

- *date 1995*

Lisa Moorcroft urn-shaped vase or planter with a raised design of mushrooms in red on a tobacco backround.
- *height 60cm*
- £175 • R. Dennis

## Floral Poole Vase ▲

- *circa 1929-34*

Poole pottery vase with stamp mark decorated with crocuses and daffodils with a leaf design and interlacing floral pattern.
- *height 25cm*
- £600 • R. Dennis

## Moorland Vase ▼

- *date 1999*

Moorland conical vase with a repeated pyramid pattern in white, black and grey. Metalic banding running around neck.
- *height 19cm*
- £40 • R. Dennis

## Baxter Plate ▼

- *date 1999*

Glen Baxter plate created for the Poole pottery showing cartoon printed on the face, wording around the edge of the rim and Glen Baxter's signature.
- *diameter 22cm*
- £18 • R. Dennis

## Gouda Deep Dish ➤

- *date 1928*

Early 20th-century. Zuid-Holland factory. Gouda deep dish on stand. Dish designed by Rembrandt Pottery.
- £600 • P. Oosthuizen

## Dennis Pot ▲

- *date 1999*

Dennis Chinaworks pot and cover decorated in a cobweb pattern in black and brown glaze with cobweb and leaf indentation. A spider is painted on the inside of the lid.
- *height 10cm*
- £180 • R. Dennis

## Pantomime Vase ▲

- *date 1997*

Vase decorated with pantomime buttons and the ugly sisters. Showing three faces with different expressions, detailed painting inside and out with enamelling. By David Burnham Smith.
- *height 10cm*
- £950 • R. Dennis

## Roger Low Vase ▼
- *20th century*
In association with Durtington pottery. High-fired deep red and purple glaze with iguana appliqué.
- *height 24cm*
- £120  • R. Dennis

## Baluster Vase ▼
- *date 1929*
Zuid-Holland factory. Gouda vase. Design 'Unique' by G.P. Van der Akker..
- *height 67.5cm*
- £2,250  • P. Oosthuizen

## Boch & Freres Vase ▶
- *date 1925*
Early 20th-century Keramis baluster vase by Charles Catteau.
- *height 31cm*
- £500  • P. Oosthuizen

## Porcelain Cup and Saucer ▲
- *date 1903*
Rozenburg. The Hague eggshell porcelain cup and saucer, with orchid and parrot decoration. By Rudolph Sterken.
- *height 8cm*
- £1,100  • P. Oosthuizen

## Dennis Plate ▲
- *date 1999*
A Dennis Chinaworks plate showing a cockerel with head turned and tail feathers on display. Brightly painted on a beige base, with a green glaze to the reverse.
- *diameter 36cm*
- £423  • R. Dennis

## Stamped Poole Vase ▼
- *circa 1980s*
A bulbous vase with short neck stamped with the Poole pottery mark. The detailing shows a bracelet pattern of bands running around the base, middle and neck. Banding also around base and rim.
- *height 20cm*
- £500  • R. Dennis

## Moorland Vase ▼
- *date 1999*
A Moorland thistle vase. Cast and turned on a lathe with hand-painted metallic glaze. Signed and dated.
- *height 26cm*
- £95  • R. Dennis

## Gouda Wall Plate  ▾

- *date 1928*
Zuid-Holland factory. Gouda wall
plate. 'Corona' design by W.P.
Hartsring.
- *height 31.5cm*
- £380          • P. Oosthuizen

## Poole Studio Vase  ▾

- *date 1997*
Signed and dated. The design
shows peacocks and floral
decorations on a blue background
with a painted green rim.
- *height 21cm*
- £100          • R. Dennis

## Poole Planter  ▸

- *circa 1960s*
A Poole pottery planter printed
with the Poole mark of a dolphin.
The pot is thrown and then
incised with a scratched pattern
and glazed with burnt orange,
yellow and blue.
- *height 22cm*
- £200          • R. Dennis

## Large Gouda Vase  ▴

- *date 1910*
Zuid-Holland factory. Gouda
two-handled large vase.
- *height 43cm*
- £2,050          • P. Oosthuizen

## D. Bernam Smith Pot  ▴

- *date 1998*
A small pot and cover decorated
with an architectural repeated
pattern on a blue ground. The lid
is also similarly decorated and
signed by David Burnham Smith.
- *height 11cm*
- £150          • R. Dennis

## Two-Handled Vase  ▾

- *date April 1920*
Large two-handled baluster
vase by Zuid-Holland factory.
Gouda design 'Crocus'.
- *height 44cm*
- £1,100          • P. Oosthuizen

## Ceramic Model of a Tower  ▾

- *date 1998*
A tower, inspired by scenes from
the Bayeux tapestry, by David
Burnham Smith. Demonstrates
highly dedicated and intricate
technique in painting and craft.
The painting is internal as well as
external.
- *height 30cm*
- £1,100          • R. Dennis

## Eggshell Porcelain Pot ▼
- *date 1902*

Mocca pot with lid by H.G.A. Huyvenaar, from Rozenburg of the Hague, in the finest eggshell porcelain. Painted with purple floral decoration and in perfect condition.
- *height 25.5cm*
- **£10,000**   • P. Oosthuizen

## Swedish Sculpture ▲
- *date 1953*

Swedish abstract sculpture in avante garde style, of interwoven, architectural designs forming an assymetrical whole and painted in black and white. The shape and the colour combine to create a complex play on light and form.
- *height 25.5cm*
- **£1,500**   • Kieran

## Terracotta Poole Vase ▲
- *circa 1929-34*

A well-proportioned Poole pottery vase. The vase is in terracotta with white glaze overpainted with greens, blues and purples, depicting summer scenes of swallows, passion flowers and buddleia.
- *height 18cm*
- **£350**   • R. Dennis

## Poole Studio Plate ▼
- *date 1999*

Showing a scene of a sunset with seagull, predominantly in black, orange and blue glaze. By Tony Morris, with Poole dolphin mark.
- *diameter 40cm*
- **£450**   • R. Dennis

## Poole Vase ▲
- *date 1950*

Poole vase with printed Poole mark. The vase is of a conical shape with a hand-painted basket pattern in purple and yellow.
- *height 19cm*
- **£400**   • R. Dennis

## Bernam Smith Owl ▲
- *date 1999*

A David Bernam Smith owl, laboriously hand-painted in intricate detail with a matt glaze. Highly collectable. The owl is signed and dated D.B.S.
- *height 19cm*
- **£600**   • R. Dennis

## Expert Tips

*Highland Stoneware produces a limited quantity of freehand painted tableware. The shapes are repeated but no two pieces are identical – thus very collectable.*

## Highland Dish ➤
- *date 1999*

A Highland Stoneware painted salmon dish. The dish has a representation of a Salmon in blue and purple glazes with a yellow underbelly.
- *height 42cm*
- **£52.50**   • R. Dennis

519

## Royal Worcester Bird ▼

- *date 1936*
American bluebird of a
limited edition perched on
apple blossom branch. Shown
to life size depicting a spring
scene, the whole standing on
a wooden plinth.
- *height 30cm*
- £900            • R.A. Barnes

## Moorcroft Vase ▼

- *date 1994*
Lisa Moorcroft vase of oriental
shape, with poppy flower and
leaf design in red and green, on
a green base.
- *height 14cm*
- £105            • R. Dennis

## Gagnier Vase ▲

- *circa 1998*
Double cone form with spherical
centre around which are four
nodules. Olivier Gagnier, Italy.
- *height 49cm*
- £250   • Themes & Variations

## Lotus Pattern Poole Plate ▲

- *date 1999*
A contemporary and highly
collectable Poole studio plate,
printed with dolphin mark and
signed N. Massarella. Painted
with a lotus pattern with orange
glaze. Black glaze on the reverse.
- *diameter 40cm*
- £300            • R. Dennis

## Eagle and Pine Tree Vase ▼

- *date 1924*
Unusually large Royal
Copenhagen vase, signed and
dated. Baluster form vase with
eagle and pine tree decoration.
- *height 49cm*
- £7,500        • Cameo Gallery

## Bird on Pine Cone ▼

- *circa 1950*
Poole pottery. Bluetit on a pine
cone. Heavily modelled
naturalistic representation,
with pine-cone design reflected
in the plumage.
- *height 12.5cm*
- £70            • P. Oosthuizen

## Bowl ◄

- *date 1999*
A bowl showing a hare positioned
among woods and hills with the
crescent moon and two stars.
Corn and bean decoration and
blue rim.
- *diameter 18cm*
- £36            • R. Dennis

## Expert Tips

*The flamboyant colours and
often comic or satirical subjects
of late 20th century pottery
have held their prices very well.*

## Poole Vase  ▼

- *circa 1950s*
Organic shape with blue, grey and green abstract vertical banners, interlacing circles. Stamped with dolphin mark.
- *height 20cm*
- £450 • R. Dennis

## Gouda Night Light  ➤

- *date 1915*
Zuid-Holland factory. Design 'A Jour'. Made for La Marquise de Sevigne Rouzand'.
- *height 17.5cm*
- £300 • P. Oosthuizen

## Gouda Tile  ▲

- *date 1923-1930*
Zuid-Holland factory. Gouda tile, with stork motif, designed by Jan Schonk.
- *11x19cm*
- £350 • P. Oosthuizen

## Paysage Vase  ▲

- *circa 1930*
Zuid-Holland factory. Gouda 'Paysage' vase. Realistically painted farmer with horse ploughing, with sunset sky in background.
- *height 47cm*
- £950 • P. Oosthuizen

## Picasso Plate  ▼

- *date 1930s*
Ovate form, raised decoration of face. Hand-painted and glazed. Foundry stamped and numbered 22/100.
- *height 31cm*
- £6,000 • Cameo Gallery

## Doulton Flambé Vase  ▼

- *date 1920s*
Royal Doulton flambé vase of tapered circular form, showing shepherd in landscape. Vermillion with a lustre finish.
- *height 19cm*
- £600 • Cameo Gallery

## Albino Rabbit  ◄

- *circa 1930*
Japanese model of a comical, albino rabbit, with pink highlights, painted red eyes, disproportionately small feet and large, caricatured ears.
- *height 22cm*
- £780 • G. Baker

## Two Bluetits ◄
• *date 1961*
A pair of Royal Worcester bluetits, male and female, made by Dorothy Doughty. Made to lifesize, showing a spring scene with pussy willow, each mounted on a wooden plinth.
• £750          • R. A. Barnes

## Rozenburg Jug ▼
• *date 1898*
Unusual square form jug with ovoid decorative panels of sunflower and leaf, on a square base. The Hague.
• *height 30.5cm*
• £1,000          • P. Oosthuizen

## Lion's Head Vase ▲
• *date 1999*
Dennis Chinaworks vase of bulbous form, showing three resplendant lion heads on an interlacing background of burnt orange and yellow glaze.
• *height 21cm*
• £300          • R. Dennis

## Painted Poole Vase ▲
• *circa 1950s*
Poole pottery vase showing the printed dolphin mark. Paint has been applied directly to the pot, unlike the ealier pre-war models which were terracotta with a tin glaze. Decoration shows an assymetrical serpentine pattern with yellow and black detailing.
• *height 29cm*
• £500          • R. Dennis

## White Throats ▲
• *date 1959*
A pair of lifesize White Throat birds, male and female. Shown perched on eglantine. Limited edition of 500. Mounted on wooden plinths.
• £750          • R. A. Barnes

## Tea Service ▼
• *circa 1920s*
Belleek Irish porcelain tea service with shamrock pattern and a basketweave design with twig handle. Stamped with black mark. Made in Fermanagh.
• £1,500          • R.A. Barnes

## Polar Bears ▲
• *circa 1920s*
Royal Copenhagen model of two adult polar bears fighting. The whole design is circular in form, giving it momentum. Signed.
• *height 15.5cm*
• £475          • Cameo Gallery

### Solitary Polar Bear ▲
- *date 1920s*
Royal Copenhagen solitary polar bear walking on all fours, all feet on the ground. Dated and signed.
- *height 10.5cm*
- £280       • Cameo Gallery

### Vienna Baluster Vase ▲
- *circa 1925*
Ernst Wahliss 'Pergamon' Vienna baluster vase. Abstract floral pattern with lustre finish.
- *height 32cm*
- £300       • P. Oosthuizen

### Royal Bonn Vase ▼
- *date 1916*
'Old Dutch' design vase of bulbous form, with disproportionately narrow, baluster-shaped neck. By Frank Anton Mehlem.
- *height 21cm*
- £350       • P. Oosthuizen

### Zuid-Holland Candlesticks ▼
- *date 1923*
Gouda pair of candlesticks in the 'Rio' design, with extra-large, moulded drip-pans and globular bases tapering upwards.
- *height 30cm*
- £360 (pair)   • P. Oosthuizen

### Gouda Baluster Vase ◄
- *date 1920*
From Regina factory, Zuid-Holland. A baluster vase in the 'D'Arla' design, with repeated design of stylised bird, swirls and floral decoration, with matt gilding, rich blues and black.
- *height 43cm*
- £300       • P. Oosthuizen

### Floral Poole Vase ▲
- *circa 1929-34*
Smaller Poole Pottery vase shown with a highly coloured floral decoration. There is a chain-link pattern to the neck of the vase and a floral frieze about the waist.
- *height 17cm*
- £220       • R. Dennis

### Arnhem Factory Vase ▲
- *date 1916*
'Lindus' design two-handled vase from the Arnhem factory. Vase is bottle-shaped.
- *height 27cm*
- £325       • P. Oosthuizen

## Expert Tips

*Always remove the lid before inspecting the underside of items of pottery or porcelain.*

### Amsterdam Tiles ➤
- *date 1900*

Panel of six 'Distel' Amsterdam tiles, mounted in the original wooden frame with gilded inset. The whole shows a rural winter landscape, after Mauve.
- *62x47cm*
- £700
- P. Oosthuizen

### Belgian Budgerigars ▲
- *circa 1900*

A pair of white budgerigars in biscuit porcelain, the characteristic unglazed modelling allowing for excellent detail in the plumage, which is modelled in flowing lines. Each bird mirrors the other's image, set on square plinths incorporating the tail feathers. Possibly bookends.
- *height 15cm*
- £250
- P. Oosthuizen

### Elephant Bookends ➤
- *circa 1920s*

Pair of pink French elephant bookends in working pose, on octagonal plinths.
- *height 15cm*
- £150
- P. Ooosthuizen

### Cockram Ewer ∨
- *date 1998*

Roger Cockram water ewer with metallic glaze over green and rust ground. Naturalistically formed fish handle and fish decoration on the body of the ewer. Flamboyantly signed by Roger Cockram.
- *height 23cm*
- £90
- R. Dennis

### Baxter Mug ▲
- *date 1999*

A Glen Baxter mug created for Poole pottery with a cartoon representation. Signature and motif is on reverse.
- *height 9cm*
- £8
- R. Dennis

### Glazed Inkwell ◄
- *date 1915*

Zuid-Holland factory. Gouda. Glazed inkwell with two lids. By A.M. Rijp.
- *length 22cm*
- £250
- P. Oosthuizen

## Union Jack Poole Plate ▲
- *date 1999*

A Poole pottery plate showing the Union Jack pattern in red, white and blue glaze. Yellow glaze on the reverse with dolphin mark and date and signed by Nicky Massarella.
- *diameter 40cm*
- £400 • R. Dennis

## Dessert Plates ▲
- *date 1935*

Part of set of Royal Worcester plates in silver form with beaded gilt edge. Fruit Worcester design of apples, peaches and grapes painted by Smith.
- *diameter 24cm*
- £200 each • R. A. Barnes

## Deep Dish on Stand ▽
- *date 1928*

Made at the Rembrandt factory in Gouda and decorated at the Zuid-Holland factory. Tulip border with water lily in centre.
- *diameter 36cm*
- £600 • P. Oosthuizen

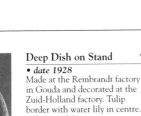

## Dennis Vase ▽
- *date 1999*

Dennis Chinaworks vase in Indian shape. The vase shows a tiger on a tiger-print ground. Charcoal glaze on inside with red bands.
- height 46cm
- £750 • R. Dennis

## Spiral Poole Plate ▲
- *date 1999*

A Poole pottery plate showing a spiral pattern in red glaze with blue overglaze and black overglaze on the reverse. Signed by Janice Tchelenko.
- diameter 40cm
- £375 • R. Dennis

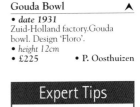

## Gouda Bowl ▲
- *date 1931*

Zuid-Holland factory.Gouda bowl. Design 'Floro'.
- *height 12cm*
- £225 • P. Oosthuizen

### Expert Tips

*'Made in England' indicates 20th-century manufacture. Any mark giving the country of origin is usually post-1891.*

## Dessert Service ◄
- *circa 1920*

Wedgwood porcelain dessert service, set of twelve, with typical 18th-century design. Borders of vines and grapes edged with gold. Decorated with centre medallion of Putti taking part in various activities. Made by Holland and Hedgekiss.
- £1,500 • R. A. Barnes

## Durtington Plate ▲
- *date 1999*

A Durtington plate ovate in shape with flower decorations and high-fired reduction glaze.
- *length 43cm*
- £65      • R. Dennis

## Gouda Vase ▲
- *date 1926*

Zuid-Holland, Gouda vase, of baluster form with flamboyant repeated organic pattern in blue, white and gold on a green ground. Made by C.A. Prins.
- *height 21.5cm*
- £225      • P. Oosthuizen

## Leopard Vase ▼
- *date 1999*

Dennis Chinaworks vase showing leopards on a leopard pattern background in shades of brown and black glazes.
- *height 24cm*
- £330      • R. Dennis

## Poole Pottery Vase ▼
- *circa 1950*

A hand-painted and hand-decorated Poole pottery vase, decorated in blue and yellow with a vertical alternating pattern.
- *height 18cm*
- £250      • R. Dennis

## Poole Plate ◄
- *circa 1999*

A Poole pottery plate showing a traditional shipping scene with artistic representation of the sun and wind. The reverse is signed and dated. The ship was drawn by Arthur Broadby and painted by Eileen Hunt.
- *height 41cm*
- £1,000      • R. Dennis

## Jersey Cow ▲
- *circa 1950*

A Royal Worcester Jersey cow, standing on a wooden plinth. Part of a limited edition, all modelled on champion stock by Doris Lindner.
- *height 19cm*
- £490      • R. A. Barnes

## Monkey With Baby ▲
- *date 1920s*

Royal Copenhagen model of a monkey with baby. Signed and dated. Matt stone finish with grey and blue glaze.
- *height 17cm*
- £750      • Cameo Gallery

## Expert Tips

*The most important firm operating from the Poole Pottery at the beginning of the 20th century was Carter, Stabler and Adams. The bases of their pieces are imprinted with their name or initials. If the base is unmarked, then it is not Poole.*

## Furniture

### Art Deco Armchairs ▲
• *circa 1925*
Pair of French armchairs with
inlays of exotic woods, covered in
artificial tiger fabric.
• *height 80cm*
• **£5,900**          • **Cavendish**

### Orange Chair ▲
• *circa 1970*
Thermoplastic, injection-
moulded chair by Verner Panton
from his 'series 2' series.
• *height 78cm*
• **£450**          • **Whitford**

### Umbrella Stand ▼
• *date 1968*
An Italian 'Pluvium' umbrella
stand, designed by Giancarle
Piretti.
• *height 1.05m*
• **£350**          • **Whitford**

### Factory Stool ▼
• *circa 1940*
Factory worker's stool. Originally
painted mild steel, adjustable elm
seat on three legs. English made.
• *height 56cm*
• **£145**          • **After Noah**

### 'Red Object' ◄
• *date 1961*
'Red Object' by Michael Kidner,
sculpture in perspex.
• *height 1.1m*
• **£1,750**          • **Whitford**

### Arrow Armchair ▲
• *20th century*
An armchair of neoclassical
design with arrow-design back
and a white bamboo frame.
• *height 80cm*
• **£995**     • **Butchoff Interiors**

### Pub Table ▲
• *circa 1920*
Mahogany and copper pub table,
on square legs with turned feet
and crossed stretchers.
• *height 71cm*
• **£225**          • **Old Cinema**

## Expert Tips

*The colours of plastic will fade
in direct sunlight. Some plastic
will go out of shape.*

### Commode Serpentine ◄
• *circa 1920*
Italian Venetian painted and
gilded commode serpentine on
cabriole legs with scrolled feet.
• *length 2.06m*
• £2,200 • French Room

### Art Nouveau Sideboard ▼
• *early 20th century*
Oak sideboard with organic
designs and copper handles.
• *height 1.87m*
• £1,250 • Old Cinema

### English Table ▲
• *circa 1930*
Tubular aluminium base, on three
legs with cast bakelite top.
• *height 52cm*
• £250 • After Noah

### Expert Tips

*Collectable office furniture must
be of high quality and of a
functional, usually simple
design.*

### White Table ▼
• *circa 1965*
Small, Italian white 'Tulip'
occasional table.
• *height 1.25m*
• £300 • Whitford

### Diner Stools ▲
• *circa 1940*
A set of four round American
diner stools with chromed steel
base and red leather-covered
seats. Very typical of the Art
Deco, American café style.
• *height 51cm*
• £350 • After Noah

### Shelving Unit ▲
• *circa 1930*
An Art Deco shelving unit, in
bent ply, walnut-veneered,
designed by Finnish architect
Alvar Aalto.
• *height 55cm*
• £4,000 • Libra Design

### Arts and Crafts Chairs ▼
• *circa 1900*
Set of six chairs, four side and
two carvers. With heart motif.
• *height 1.15m*
• £2,500 • After Noah

## Plastic Sideboard ➤
• *circa 1970*
Cream-coloured moulded plastic
sideboard designed by Anow,
France. With two sliding doors.
• *length 1.47m*
• £295        • Planet Bazaar

## Red Onyx Desk ▼
• *date 1973*
Moulded compartments with
adjustable chrome metal lamp.
• *width 1.02m*
• £1,350        • Whitford

## Wicker Chair ▲
• *circa 1960*
An Eero Aarnio wicker chair of
circular form.
• *height 65cm*
• £675        • Libra Design

## Club Chair ▲
• *20th century*
Leather and rattan club chair,
made by Maitland-Smith, with
metal, lion's paw feet.
• *height 80cm*
• £1,850    • Butchoff Interiors

## Wall Cabinet ➤
• *circa 1920*
A French figured beechwood wall
cabinet with ebonized mouldings,
featuring two large panelled doors
above two smaller ones.
• *height 84cm*
• £1,550      • North West 8

## End Table ▲
• *20th century*
A mahogany end table with
carved swan heads. Made by
Maitland-Smith.
• *height 68cm*
• £1,750  • Butchoff Interiors

### Expert Tips
*Art Deco furniture
incorporating glass has not
survived in quantity.*

## 'Safari' Seating Booth ◄
• *circa 1975*
Glass-fibre reinforced-polyester
frame with leather upholstery,
designed by Poltronoua for
Archiroom Associati.
• £18,000        • Whitford

## Octagonal Tables ▲
- *circa 1900*
Pair of Islamic-Egyptian
octagonal tables, with bone and
abalone inlay.
- *height 51cm*
- £680          • North West 8

## The 'Joe' Sofa ▲
- *circa 1970*
Inspired by the American
baseball legend, 'Joltin' Joe
DiMaggio. Designed by J.de Pas,
D. D'Urbino and P. Lomazzi and
produced Poltronova, Italy. the
design is that of a surreal, giant
baseball glove in brown leather.
- *width 1.05m*
- £2,750          • Whitford

## German Fan ▼
- *circa 1940*
German bakelite fan designed by
Dieter Rams.
- *height 27cm*
- £400          • Decodence

## School Desk ▼
- *circa 1940*
English elm school desk with
child-size chair. Good patination.
- *height 84cm*
- £175          • After Noah

## Armchair ▲
- *date 1932*
An Alvar Aalto cantilever
armchair. Model no. 31
- *height 77cm*
- £2,000          • Libra Design

## Arts and Crafts Chairs ▲
- *circa 1910*
Set of six oak chairs with rexine
seats.
- *height 92cm*
- £1,800 (six)          • Riverbank

## Expert Tips

*French Art Deco was picked up
quickly in America. American
Art Deco is characterised by
strong geometrical designs.*

## Danish Bench Seat ◄
- *circa 1950*
Special commission for a bank
with button-cushion leather.
- *height 87cm*
- £1,650
- • Themes & Variations

## Corner Suite ➤
- *circa 1980*
An upholstered corner seating
suite, covered in vermillion cloth,
with all-moveable components.
- *height 1.2m*
- £650            • Spencer

## Art Nouveau Table ▲
- *circa 1918*
Art nouveau table with organic
inlay designs on four pierced legs.
- *height 81cm*
- £420            • Castlegate

## Ganesh ▲
- *circa 1990*
A Southern Indian ganesh with
polychrome decoration.
- *height 1.25cm*
- £1,800          • Fulton

## Auditorium Chair ▲
- *circa 1950*
Italian, by Carlo Mollino, for the
Auditorium in Turin. Rust-
coloured velvet upholstery with
brass fittings and flip-up seat.
- *height 85cm*
- £2,500
- **Themes & Variations**

## Café Table ▲
- *circa 1930*
French café table in the Art Deco
style with stepped tripod base and
fluted triangular columns.
- *height 70cm*
- £465            • After Noah

## Italian Cabinets ▼
- *circa 1930*
Pair of Italian cabinets in French
walnut and burr walnut with steel
fittings and satinwood interior.
- *height 1.6m*
- £15,000
- **Themes & Variations**

## Oak Hall Seat ▼
- *circa 1910*
Unusual carved oak hall seat with
side table and umbrella stand.
- *height 79cm*
- £995            • Old Cinema

## Art Deco Desk ▼
- *early 20th century*
Art deco burr walnut kneehole desk with deep drawers.
- *height 78cm*
- £995 • Old Cinema

## Set of Four Chairs ▼
- *circa 1965*
One of a set of four single chairs with detachable squab seats. Designed by Harry Bertoia.
- *height 31.5cm*
- £865 (four) • Country Seat

## Gout Stool ▼
- *circa 1920*
An adjustable stool for the gout-sufferer, made of oak and metal, on roller castors.
- *height 33cm*
- £150 • North West 8

## Mission Chair ▲
- *circa 1900*
An American oak rocking chair with slatted back and sides and tanned leather seat, possibly by Stickley Bros.
- *height 85cm*
- £950 • After Noah

## Cone Chair ▲
- *circa 1970*
A Danish Verner Panton cone chair, with wool upholstery and cushioned seat and backrest.
- *height 84.5cm*
- £1,200
- Themes & Variations

### Expert Tips

*Tubular steel-framed furniture gained mass popularity after World War II, because of its utilitarian and designer qualities. This popularity was driven by the modernist schools, led by such luminaries as Mies van der Rohe.*

## Figure-Backed Chair ▼
- *circa 1980*
Fornasetti, Italian design. With a printed and lacquered figure in red dress above a black seat.
- *height 96cm*
- £1,600
- Themes & Variations

## Indian Throne ▼
- *circa 1990*
An elaborately carved chair with carved canopy of mother-of-pearl and bone inlay. The carved chair back with floral inlays, flanked with carved lions. The whole resting on four carved elephants.
- *height 3m*
- £10,000 • Fulton

## 'Amphys' Red Sofa ◄
- **date 1968**
Designed by Pierre Paulin for
Mobilier International.
- *length 2.14m*
- £2,800 • Whitford

*'Utility' furniture, from the
post-World War II period,
which the reluctant first owners
loathed, is now collected.*

## Nursing Chair ▼
- *circa 1950*
A mid-20th century nursing chair
with a metal frame and wooden
slatted seat.
- *height 58cm*
- £30 • Curios

## Dining Set ▲
- *circa 1930*
Sixteen-sided rosewood and
mahogany dining table, with six
chairs covered in raw silk.
- £20,000 • Bizarre

## French Chairs ▼
- **20th century**
Set of four provincial chairs in
fruitwood, with asymetric backs
and rush matted seats.
- *height 89cm*
- £680 • Myriad

## Cocktail Cabinet ▲
- *circa 1930*
A modernist, Art Deco British
cocktail cabinet.
- *height 80cm*
- £2,900 • Libra Design

## Lounge Chair ▼
- *circa 1950*
Aluminium and bent rosewood
ply lounge chair, covered in
natural leather.
- *height 1.05m*
- £3,950 • Country Seat

## Hairdresser's Basin ➤
- *circa 1920*
A hairdresser's basin.
- *height 95cm*
- £2,200 • North West 8

## Pair of Armchairs ▲
- *circa 1925*
One of a pair of French-made armchairs in their original salmon pink fabric with carved gilt wood.
- *height 86cm*
- £3,200      • **Bizarre**

## Bathroom Cabinet ▲
- *circa 1930*
An Art Deco tin bathroom cabinet with mirrored door and one shelf.
- *height 36cm*
- £55      • **metro retro**

## Swan Chairs ▼
- *circa 1950*
Arne Jacobsen Danish swan chairs with all-leather upholstery.
- *height 74cm*
- £2,200
- **Themes & Variations**

## Egyptian Chairs ▼
- *circa 1920*
A pair of elbow chairs with Egyptian-design tapestry covers.
- *height 94cm*
- £3,950      • **M. Wakelin**

## 'Up' Chair ▲
- *date 1969*
From the 'Up' series designed in 1969. Beige and red striped stretch fabric over moulded polyurethane foam.
- *height 65cm*
- £4,500      • **Whitford**

## Red Chairs ▲
- *20th century*
Pair of red 'Champagne' chairs, in plastic, on central metal column and circular base.
- *height 77cm*
- £2,500      • **Whitford**

### Expert Tips

*Classic designs of the 1960s are organic to the point of eroticism, with 'lip' sofas, 'egg' chairs and 'mushroom' stools – in hot colours – all now avidly sought.*

## Steel Desk ◄
- *circa 1950*
Twin pedestal with black rubber top, central locking mechanism and seven chrome handles.
- *height 76cm*
- £475      • **metro retro**

## Kitchen Dresser ▼

- *circa 1920*
Oak kitchen dresser with original
jars and various compartments.
- *height 1.88m*
- **£850**          • **Old Cinema**

## Toleware Vase ▼

- *circa 1935*
A Toleware vase with
tortoiseshell finish.
- *height 43cm*
- **£295**     • **Butchoff Interiors**

## 'Wave' Sofa ➤

- *circa 1968*
A sofa designed by the French
designer Pierre Paulin and
entitled 'The Wave'.
- *length 1.67m*
- **£2,750**          • **Whitford**

## Wall Panels ▲

- *circa 1970*
Four decorative Verner Panton
wall panels, in red perspex plastic,
of bulbous design.
- *height 1.2m*
- **£480**          • **Planet Bazaar**

## Art Deco Armchairs ▲

- *circa 1930*
A pair of English-made Art Deco
armchairs, upholstered in leather
with walnut sides.
- *height 84cm*
- **£1,200**          • **Libra Design**

## Ministry Locker ▼

- *circa 1950*
A steel Air Ministry locker with
four doors, vents and label
holders. In government grey.
- *height 1.65m*
- **£175**          • **metro retro**

## Expert Tips

*Laminated wood was first
employed in the Art Deco
period. The wood tends to chip,
flake and bubble and,
consequently, furniture has not
survived in great quantities.*

## Silk Covered Chair ▼

- *20th century*

With striped silk upholstery and
silver arm ends.
- *height 78cm*
- **£1,800** • **Butchoff Interiors**

## Steel Medical Cabinet ▼

- *circa 1930*

Copper and brass fittings, two
glass shelves glazed on the front
and sides. With a hinged door.
- *height 45.5cm*
- **£140** • **metro retro**

## Coffee Table ▲

- *circa 1970*

A unique chrome and glass
crossbar coffee table. Of
rectangular form.
- *height 32cm*
- **£265** • **Planet Bazaar**

## 'Airborn' Armchairs ▲

- *20th century*

A pair of 'Airborn' armchairs, in
black leather. Exact period
unknown, but of Art Deco style.
- *height 70cm*
- **£1,500** • **Libra Design**

## 'Spring' Lamp ▼

- *circa 1970*

French chrome 'spring' lamp with
coiled innovative design and
spherical, light bulb holder.
- *height 36cm*
- **£145** • **Planet Bazaar**

## Coffee Table ▼

- *circa 1970*

Chrome and ceramic tile-topped
coffee table by Belanti, Italy.
Glazed in avant-garde style.
- *height 38cm*
- **£345** • **Planet Bazaar**

## Cocktail Cabinet ◄

- *circa 1938*

A French cocktail cabinet by
Michel Duffet in rosewood and
sycamore with two drawers and
adjustable shelves.
- *height 1.4m*
- **£6,000** • **Bizarre**

## Glass

### Loetz Bowl ▼
- *circa 1905*
A Loetz bowl with blue Papillon oxide finish. The bowl rests on three lemon iridescent feet.
- *height 10.5cm*
- £950 • French Glasshouse

### Italian Glass Vase ▼
- *circa 1950*
A glass vase by Archimede Seguso, decorated with a spiralling pattern in white, dark purple and mauve.
- *height 29cm*
- £1,500
- Themes & Variations

### Rostrato ▲
- *circa 1939*
A Rostrato vase, by Ferro, Barovier and Toso, in Murano glass.
- *height 16cm*
- £3,500
- Themes & Variations

### Daum Vase ▲
- *circa 1900*
A larger than average, double-handled Daum vase with pastoral setting and hand work to foreground toadstools.
- *height 15.5cm*
- £8,500 • French Glasshouse

### Cylindrical Vase ▼
- *circa 1975*
A cylindrical vase by Anthony Stern, with textured glass.
- *height 17.5cm*
- £58 • Circa

### Blue Cylindrical Vase ▼
- *circa 1960*
A blue, cylindrical Holmegaard vase, by Per Lütken, with intrinsic purple streak.
- *height 17cm*
- £75 • Circa

### Whitefriars Kingfisher Blue Set ◄
- *date 1960-1970*
Ashtray and vase set in bark-textured kingfisher-blue glass.
- £20, £34 resp • Circa

**Group of Three Items** ◄
• *circa 1950*
Ashtray, vesta and other
recepticle, of globular design with
gold and bronze inclusion, by
Barovier, Italy.
• £570     • Anna Sambataro

**Loetz Glass Bowl** ▼
• *circa 1910*
A Loetz bowl of ovoid form, with
pinched lip, in rose amber with
gold-lustre finish.
• *height 13cm*
• £1,900     • Kieron

**Lalique Bowl** ▲
• *circa 1920*
Lalique bowl with frosted finish
and four lillies terminating in fan
legs. With acid-etched signature.
• *height 12.5cm*
• £950     • Kieron

**Gallé Vase** ▼
• *circa 1900*
A Gallé vase of tapered form,
acid-etched with wisteria flower
and leaf decoration.
• *height 12cm*
• £2,600     • French Glasshouse

**Glass Sculpture** ▲
• *date 1999*
Glass sculpture by Sir Terry Frost
(b. 1915), entitled Millennium
Disc and made from Murano glass
with spiralled motif.
• £3,800     • Whitford Fine Art

**Bubbled Vase** ▲
• *circa 1970*
An English, lobed vase of tapered
form, by Whitefriars, in blue
bubbled glass.
• *height 23cm*
• £60     • Circa

**Gallé Vase** ▲
• *circa 1870*
Applied and twisted-handled
vase, with enamel floral
decoration, by Emile Gallé.
• *height 20cm*
• £3,800     • Cameo Gallery

## Stained Glass Panel ▼
• *circa 1910*
Decorative panel showing tulip-shaped floral image of nineteen, geometric leaded sections.
• *height 58cm*
• **£45**　　　　　• **Curios**

## Pair of Glass Candlesticks ▼
• *circa 1950*
A pair of glass-pedestalled candlesticks with metal liners.
• *height 21cm*
• **£480**　　　　　• **Kieron**

## Daum Bluebell Vase ▲
• *circa 1900*
A Daum vase with a cut and pulled lip, showing Cross of Lorraine with background of blue sky and a green grass ground.
• *height 12cm*
• **£6,400**　• **French Glasshouse**

## Green Glass ▲
• *circa 1939*
Green glass, by Barovier & Toso, in fluted design with pinched double handles, lustre finish and gold inclusions.
• *height 30cm*
• **£600**　• **Vincenzo Caffarella**

## Perfume Bottle ▼
• *circa 1955*
A Cenedese perfume bottle with an oversized stopper and yellow and amber centres.
• *height 44cm*
• **£800**　• **Vincenzo Caffarella**

## Daum Rain Vase ▼
• *circa 1900*
Vase showing acid-etched rain on the surface, with wind-blown trees in winter landscape of watermelon colour.
• *height 8cm*
• **£3,400**　• **French Glasshouse**

## Vistosi Glass Fist ◄
• *circa 1960*
Made from polychromatic glass, with red soda predominant.
• *height 46cm*
• **£4,000**
• **Themes & Variations**

### Loetz Vase ▼

• *circa 1910*
A Loetz vase with silver overlay
with organic patterns applied to
the surface. Iridescent oxides.
• *height 19cm*
• **£5,500**   • **French Glasshouse**

### Murano Glass Vase ▲

• *circa 1950*
A Murano Flavio Pozzi glass vase,
showing eliptical design and
colour graduation.
• *height 25cm*
• **£650**   • **Vincenzo Caffarella**

### Small Square Daum Vase ▼

• *circa 1900*
A Daum vase showing winter
scene of trees and snow ground
against a pink-tinged sky.
• *height 9cm*
• **£1,500**   • **French Glasshouse**

### Mila Schön Dish ➤

• *circa 1970*
An oval-shape dish with
spiralling design, by Mila Schön
for Arte Vetro Murano.
• *length 59cm*
• **£600**   • **Vincenzo Caffarella**

### Gallé Vase ▲

• *circa 1900*
A Gallé vase showing scenes of
mountain, lake and forest in a
desirable purple-blue colour,
fading to yellow.
• *height 20cm*
• **£2,000**   • **French Glasshouse**

### Antonio Da Ross Dish ▼

• *circa 1958*
Cenedese dish of oval form with
amber and cream design.
• *diameter 26cm*
• **£850**   • **Vincenzo Caffarella**

## Expert Tips

*Vases and other glass pieces are
sometimes cut down in order to
disguise damage. The most
obvious signs of this are irregular
rims and sharp edges. Such
pieces and those with polished
appearances should be avoided.*

### Aubergine Vase ▼

• *circa 1972*
A textured, Whitefriars vase in
aubergine colour, designed by
Geoffrey Baxter.
• *height 14cm*
• **£48**   • **Circa**

## Three Whitefriars Vases ◀

- *circa 1960-70*
A selection of Geoffrey Baxter-designed, Whitefriars kingfisher blue vases in textured glass.
- £33, £48 & £45 • Circa

## Iceberg Vase ▼

- *circa 1950*
A Finnish vase by Tapio Wirkkala. Signed.
- *height 21cm*
- £1,200
- Themes & Variations

## Textured Vase ▲

- *circa 1960-70*
A vase in bark-textured, ruby-coloured glass.
- *height 13cm*
- £22 • Circa

## Two Red 'Gul' Vases ▲

- *circa 1960*
Two 'Gul' vases, designed by Otto Braver for Holmegaard, in cased red over white glaze.
- *height 26cm (left)*
- *height 30cm (right)*
- £50, £70 resp. • Circa

## Whitefriars Glass Bowl ▼

- *circa 1940*
An English glass bowl, by Whitefriars, of circular form with ribbon-trailed decoration.
- *height 24cm*
- £180 • Circa

## Murano Beakers ▲

- *circa 1960*
A pair of Aureliano Toso Murano glass beakers.
- *height 14cm*
- £120 • Vincenzo Caffarella

## Impressionist Daum Vase ▲

- *circa 1900*
A small, beaker-shaped vase with coloured glass overlay showing trees and grass.
- *height 9cm*
- £2,900 • French Glasshouse

## Poppy Vase ▲
- *circa 1920*
Argy-Rousseau pâté de verre vase, of coloured glass with repetitive poppy design.
- *height 7.5cm*
- **£4,200** • **French Glasshouse**

## Glass Sculpture ▲
- *circa 1960*
A glass object, on a square wooden base, with ice relief and smooth back.
- *height 59cm*
- **£300** • **Vincenzo Caffarella**

## Swedish Vase ▼
- *circa 1950*
A Skruf Talaha Swedish vase, with engraved base.
- *height 20cm*
- **£3,800**
- **Themes & Variations**

## Cenedese Glass Vase ▼
- *circa 1950*
A Cenedese glass vase with orange centre fading to many bubbles within ovoid form.
- *height 24cm*
- **£1,350** • **Vincenzo Caffarella**

## Timo Sarranera Vase ➤
- *circa 1950*
A vase, designed by Timo Sarranera for Iittala.
- *height 22cm*
- **£50** • **Circa**

## Expert Tips

*Gallé pieces damaged in the cooling process were, at his insistence, not disposed of, but inscribed 'Études Gallé'. These are very rare and much sought after, particularly when technically innovative.*

## Gallé Ovoid Vase ▲
- *circa 1900*
An Emile Gallé vase of ovoid form, with foliate decoration in purple, blue and yellow.
- *height 12cm*
- **£1,800** • **French Glasshouse**

## Cenedese Deep Bowl ▲
- *circa 1950*
A deep, Cenedese bowl with aquatic scenes of fish, jellyfish and organic forms.
- *height 25cm*
- **£850** • **Vincenzo Caffarella**

## Art Nouveau Inkwell ▼

- *circa 1920*
A German glass inkwell, by
Loetz, with brass top. Stamped
with design registration mark.
- *height 6cm*
- £265                    • Barham

## Whitefriars Bowl ▼

- *circa 1960*
An English, Whitefriars bowl, of
Geoffrey Baxter design.
- *height 18cm*
- £125                    • Circa

## Expert Tips

*Signatures have frequently been
forged and it is sensible and
acceptable to ask for
documentary support for the
provenance of a piece.*

## Tube-Shaped Vase ➤

- *circa 1900*
An Emile Gallé, tube-shaped vase
with popular design of red roses
on red overlay.
- *height 43cm*
- £2,800    • French Glasshouse

## Biomorphic Bowl ▲

- *circa 1962*
A Holmegaard glass bowl by Per
Lütken, with organic lines and a
doubled, pinched lip.
- *height 35cm*
- £90                    • Circa

## Decanter ▼

- *circa 1950*
An amber tinted circular-form
decanter with pinched lip and
splayed base. Signed by Venini.
- *height 23.5cm*
- £180                    • Circa

## Coffin Vase ▼

- *circa 1960-70*
Clear-cased coffin-shaped vase,
bark-textured finish in ruby.
- *height 13cm*
- £22                    • Circa

## Pair of Whitefriars
## Candle Holders ◄

- *circa 1960-70*
A pair of ruby-coloured, bark-
textured candle-holders.
- *height 6cm*
- £22                    • Circa

## Dessert Set  ➤

• *circa 1950*
A Scottish dessert set by Vasart, of five pieces, colour-blown with blue graduating to white.
• £395                    • Circa

## Gallé Glass Box  ▲

• *circa 1900*
A Japanese-inspired box and cover of circular shape in purple, blue and yellow colourings with blue flowerheads.
• *height 9.5cm*
• £2,700   • French Glasshouse

## Whitefriars Powell Vase  ▼

• *circa 1930*
An English vase of baluster form in cloudy French blue colour.
• *height 25cm*
• £345                    • Circa

## Hadeland Vase  ▼

• *circa 1970*
A bulbous, bottle-shaped Hadeland smoked grey vase by Willie Johansson, with globular inner receptacle.
• *height 16cm*
• £85                     • Circa

## Daum Conical Vase  ◄

• *circa 1900*
A Daum vase with splayed foot, showing orchid and spider web. Acid etched decoration.
• *height 25cm*
• £2,700   • French Glasshouse

## Three Ruby Vases  ▲

• *circa 1948*
Collection of three ruby wave-rubbed vases by Whitefriars.
• *height 30cm (left)*
• *height 15cm (middle)*
• *height 21cm (right)*
• £130, £34, £44 resp   • Circa

## Daum Tumbler-Shaped Vase  ▲

• *circa 1900*
A Daum vase showing floral and leaf decoration.
• *height 12.5cm*
• £1,400   • French Glasshouse

## Veart Glass ▼

- *circa 1970*
Italian object of teardrop form
with inverted organic centre and
amber tints.
- *height 72cm*
- £550   • Vincenzo Caffarella

## Oriental-Style Vase ▼

- *circa 1980*
A blue and white vase, by
Michael Bang for Holmegaard,
from his Atlantis series.
- *height 16cm*
- £72   • Circa

## Hadeland Vases ➤

- *circa 1956*
Two engraved vases of ovoid
shape with longship decoration.
- *height 24cm*
- £150 each   • Circa

## Daum Conical Vase ▲

- *circa 1900*
A conical Daum vase showing
deep winter village scene with
windmill, snow within the glass
and acid-etched trees to the
outside.
- *height 30cm*
- £7,500   • French Glasshouse

## Cenedese Vase ▼

- *circa 1950*
Of ovoid form with small
reservoir and red and blue spiral
with tears.
- *height 26cm*
- £1,350   • Vincenzo Caffarella

## Blue Conical Vase ▼

- *circa 1960*
A blue vase of conical form, by
Per Lütken for Holmegaard.
- *height 18cm*
- £55   • Circa

## Monart Bowl ◄

- *circa 1930*
A Scottish, aqua-green bowl, by
Monart, with single-folded rim.
- *height 8cm*
- £90   • Circa

## Loetz Vase ⌄

- *circa 1905*
A Loetz vase, decorated with orange free-form pattern. Gold iridescent medallion splashes.
- *height 27cm*
- **£5,500** • **French Glasshouse**

## Blue Bowl ⌄

- *circa 1960*
A blue bowl with white enamelled rim, probably from Scandinavia.
- *height 12cm*
- **£75** • **Circa**

## Two Vases ⌄

- *circa 1988*
Two, teardrop-shaped vases by Peter Layton, with blue swirled patterns within the predominantly white glass.
- *height 32cm (left)*
- *height 35cm (right)*
- **£250 each** • **Circa**

## Dragonfly Box and Cover ⌃

- *circa 1900*
A Daum box and cover, with applied dragonfly over water lilies, in shades of green.
- *9 x 15cm*
- **£8,000** • **French Glasshouse**

## Expert Tips

*When buying glass lamps, avoid pieces where the base has been drilled to take a wire. The stems of these lamps should be hollow and there should be a recess for the wire.*

## Daum Lampstand and Shade ▶

- *circa 1900-1910*
A toadstool-shaped lampstand and shade with purple overlay showing an evening scene with a lake setting and trees.
- *height 32cm*
- **£4,000** • **French Glasshouse**

## Bubbled Vase ⌄

- *circa 1980*
A bubbled vase by Arvid Bakkene, made for Hadeland.
- *height 17cm*
- **£75** • **Circa**

## Daum Vase ◀

- *circa 1900*
A mauve Daum vase, with overlay of bats in an evening sky.
- *height 23cm*
- **£4,800** • **French Glasshouse**

# Lighting

## American Batman Lamp ▼
- *circa 1940*
Polished steel adjustable lamp on a steel stand. Probably originally for medical use with heat-bulb. By Westinghouse.
- *height 106cm*
- £275 • **After Noah**

## Table Lamp ▼
- *circa 1918*
A cast-brass table lamp fitted with a flakestone glass shade decorated with leaf motifs.
- *height 46cm*
- £450 • **Turn On**

## Italian Table Lamp ▲
- *circa 1950*
Moulded plastic lamp, incorporating base and shade, designed by Flio Martinelli.
- *height 37cm*
- £750 • **A. Sambataro**

## Cast-Iron Lamp ▲
- *circa 1940*
An American industrial, adjustable lamp (ex-factory) with cast aluminium fittings, standing on a cast-steel base.
- *height 58cm*
- £250 • **After Noah**

## Italian Chandelier ▼
- *circa 1930*
An Italian chandelier with six branches and beaded frame with crystal teardrops.
- *height 85cm*
- £850 • **Rainbow**

## Venetian Lamp Base ▼
- *circa 1950*
Cenedese Murano glass with three fish on dark green.
- *height 36cm*
- £500 • **Vincenzo Caffarella**

## Italian Glass Lamp ◄
- *circa 1960*
By Mazzega in Murano glass with yellow and grey swirls.
- *height 57cm*
- £850 • **A. Sambataro**

## Table Lamp ▲
- *circa 1900*
Silver-plated brass table lamp on
a tripod base and fitted with a
cut-crystal glass shade.
- *height 44cm*
- £995 • Turn On

## Hospital Lamp ▲
- *circa 1930*
With ball joint for lateral
adjustment and telescopic shaft.
- *height 1.78m*
- £350 • After Noah

## Laboratory Lamp ▼
- *circa 1930*
By Chas Hearson & Co Ltd,
London. Brass stand on wooden
base with maker's plaque.
- *height 45cm*
- £145 • After Noah

## Edwardian Table Lamp ▼
- *circa 1905*
Chrome and porcelain lamp with
globe, both decorated with Greek
key pattern.
- *height 58cm*
- £895 • Turn On

## Table Lamp ➤
- *circa 1920*
Cast-brass lamp fitted with a
flakestone glass shade, and
decorated with Roman motifs.
- *height 51cm*
- £575 • Turn On

## Coloured Shade Lamp ▲
- *circa 1950*
With three shades of different
colours, on a circular base. By
Gino Sarfatti Arteluce.
- *height 60cm*
- £550 • Vincenzo Caffarella

## Italian Lanterns ▲
- *circa 1930*
A pair of brass Italian lanterns
holding four lights.
- *height 70cm*
- £650 • Rainbow

## Oil Lamp Shade ▲
• *circa 1910*
Light blue opaque with waved,
crimped edging. English, possibly
Stourbridge.
• *height 21cm*
• £150 • Barham

## Chrome Lamp ▲
• *circa 1970*
Of conical form with a chrome
metal finish, in three sections.
• *height 50cm*
• £300 • Vincenzo Caffarella

## Selenova Lamps ▼
• *circa 1970*
A pair of Selenova lamps, with
glass enclosing four coloured
lights, on a circular splayed
chrome base.
• *height 52cm*
• £1,400 • Vincenzo Caffarella

## Bronze Chandelier ▼
• *circa 1900*
Italian Flemish-style bronze
chandelier with eight branches.
• *height 90cm*
• £1,300 • Rainbow

## Italian Wall Light ◄
• *circa 1920*
A pair of Italian wall lights with
hanging crystals.
• *height 45cm*
• £480 • Rainbow

### Expert Tips

*Electrically converted candle-
holders can be reconverted with
brass insert plates.*

## Wedgewood Desk Lamp ▲
• *circa 1920*
Porcelain and chrome adjustable
desk lamp. Signed Wedgewood.
• *height 56cm*
• £1,300 • Turn On

## Anglepoise Lamp ▲
• *circa 1930*
Polished aluminium and chrome,
designed by Cawardine, based on
the constant tensioning
principles of the human arm, and
made by Terry & Sons.
• *height 92cm*
• £175 • After Noah

## 'Comare' by Vistosi  ▾

- *circa 1965*

A typical creation of Vistosi, the most important workshop for this style of artistic lamp.

- *height 43cm*
- **£500**  • **Vincenzo Caffarella**

## Bovolone Chandelier  ▾

- *circa 1930*

Bovolone-style Italian chandelier with six branches and a beaded frame, with turquoise teardrops.

- *height 90cm*
- **£975**  • **Rainbow**

## Vistosi Glass Lamp  ▲

- *circa 1970*

Italian, with pale amber glass, bulbous shape and pinched panel.

- *height 59cm*
- **£950**  • **Themes & Variations**

## Table Lamp  ▲

- *circa 1930*

Chrome and plastic table lamp with a glass shade.

- *height 41cm*
- **£98**  • **H. Hay**

## Chrome Desk Lamp  ▾

- *circa 1930*

A chrome anglepoise desk reading lamp with heavy, stepped, square base.

- *height 90cm*
- **£125**  • **H. Hay**

## Brass Lantern  ▾

- *circa 1900*

An Arts and Crafts brass lantern, of square form, with textured glass and organic decoration to the frame.

- *height 36cm*
- **£750**  • **Turn On**

---

## Expert Tips

*Early purpose-built electrical lights, sometimes known as 'electroliers', tend to be of the Art Nouveau period. These must be updated with care.*

---

## Italian Wall Light  ➤

- *circa 1920*

A single Italian gilt-metal wall light with cut-glass crystals hanging from three branches and central wall-plate.

- *height 70cm*
- **£450**  • **Rainbow**

## Table Lamp ▲
• *circa 1930*
Chrome and plastic table light
with glass shade.
• *height 46cm*
• £150                    • H. Hay

## Art Deco Lamp ▲
• *circa 1930*
Acrylic base fitted with enclosed
frosted and clear glass shade.
• *height 38cm*
• £450              • Turn On

## American Desk Lamp ▼
• *circa 1910*
An Edwardian American desk
lamp in brass with a bell-shaped
shade and circular plinth.
• *height 43cm*
• £875              • Turn On

## Table Lamp ▼
• *circa 1960*
A very rare lamp with chromed
metal, various shaped glass
spheres and a 'U' section support.
• *height 31cm*
• £1,250 • Vincenzo Caffarella

## Italian Metal Chandelier ▼
• *circa 1930*
An Italian metal chandelier with
six lights and brightly coloured
floral motifs.
• *height 70cm*
• £525              • Rainbow

## Venetian Wall Lights ▲
• *circa 1920*
A pair of Venetian gilt and glass
wall lights with a mirror and five
hanging crystals.
• *height 30cm*
• £250              • Rainbow

## Prism Light ▲
• *circa 1960*
A red plastic triangular prism
light with vertical cuts. Designed
by Magistratti and produced
by Francesconi.
• *height 1.37m*
• £950  • Themes & Variations

### 'The Samurai' ▲
- **20th century**
By German designer Ingo Maurer
for the Ma-Mo-Nouchies
collection. Made in Japanese
pleated paper, stainless steel,
silicone and glass.
- *height 80cm*
- £620  • **Themes & Variations**

### Art Deco Uplighter ▲
- *circa 1920*
An Art Deco chromium-plated
table lamp.
- *height 70cm*
- £450  • **Turn On**

### Expert Tips

*Large chandeliers usually come
apart for ease of transportation.
This does not, unfortunately,
make them any easier to sell.*

### Table Lamp ▼
- *circa 1910*
A silver-plated brass table lamp
decorated with a floral transfer
printed glass shade.
- *height 37cm*
- £600  • **Turn On**

### Table Lamp ▼
- *circa 1985*
A table lamp by Skipper with a
variegated marble base.
- *height 32cm*
- £850  • **Vincenzo Caffarella**

### Crystal Chandelier ▶
- *circa 1900*
An Italian copperleaf chandelier
with six branches and faceted,
drop crystals.
- *height 80cm*
- £850  • **Rainbow**

### Brass Library Lamp ▲
- *circa 1900*
A brass library lamp with two
branches, green glass shades,
a finial top and base.
- *height 45cm*
- £350  • **Castlegate**

### Iron Wall Lights ▲
- *circa 1930*
A pair of Italian painted iron
wall lights with floral motifs.
- *height 36cm*
- £100  • **Rainbow**

## Cube Table Lamp ▼
- *circa 1960*
A glass cube table lamp with amber-coloured swirls on an aluminium base.
- *height 47cm*
- **£1,000** • **Vincenzo Caffarella**

## Tulip Lamp ▼
- *circa 1960*
Gio Ponti tulip, chrome, triple lamp from the workshop of Arredo Luce.
- *height 60cm-120cm*
- **£600** • **Vincenzo Caffarella**

## Italian Chandelier ▲
- *circa 1920*
Chandelier with floral motifs, coloured crystal and bronze.
- *height 60cm*
- **£750** • **Rainbow**

## Steel Desk Lamp ▲
- *circa 1930*
A steel desk lamp fitted with a spun-metal shade.
- *height 38cm*
- **£450** • **Turn On**

## Wooden Chandelier ▼
- *circa 1920*
An ornate Italian, gilded, wooden, sixteen-branch chandelier with filigree.
- *height 110cm*
- **£750** • **Rainbow**

## Hand-Painted Table Lamp ▼
- *circa 1920*
A copper-oxidised table lamp with handpainted shade showing an Egyptian landscape.
- *height 44cm*
- **£450** • **Turn On**

## French Table Lamps ◄
- *circa 1920*
A pair of French, two-branch, gilded metal table lamps with oval amethyst and crystal glass pendants, all on a circular base.
- *height 22cm*
- **£350** • **Rainbow**

# Metalware

## Ashtray ▲
• *circa 1970*
A chrome ashtray promoting
Bridges' Tools, featuring a die-cast
drill to centre.
• *height 8cm*
• **£25**                • **metro retro**

## Expert Tips

*Metalwork during the Art Deco
period adopted the stylistic
symbols used in other areas of
decorative arts. Artists to look
out for include Puiforcart, Edgar
Brandt and Georg Jensen.*

## Chrome Bath-Rack ➤
• *circa 1930*
An early compartmentalised
chromium bath-rack with
adjustable shaving mirror.
• *height 23cm*
• **£98**                • **H. Hay**

## Mexican Horse ▼
• *20th century*
A naively-modelled tin horse,
with saddle and four straight legs,
the whole on a square, tin base.
• *height 100cm*
• *width 120cm*
• **£200**                • **Curios**

## Signed Dinanderie Plate ▼
• *date 1930*
By Claudius Linassier, Lyon.
Martelee base with inlaid silver.
• *diameter 13cm*
• **£850**                • **Bizarre**

## Lorenzl Bronze ◄
• *circa 1920*
A gold enamelled figure of a girl
in pyjamas holding a parrot.
Figure standing on a marble and
onyx plinth.
• *height 30cm*
• **£2,300**                • **Kieron**

## Pair of Brass Candlesticks ▲
• *circa 1930*
A pair of candlesticks of barley-
twist form on round bases.
• *height 31cm*
• **£88**                • **H. Hay**

## Chrome & Bakelite Candlestick ▲
• *circa 1926*
An Art Deco candlestick
featuring a two-dimensional
woman, arms outstretched,
holding a candle in each hand.
• *height 21cm*
• **£65**                • **Beverley**

### Pair of Candlesticks ◄
- *circa 1930*
A pair of Art Deco chrome and decorative green plastic candlesticks with clear holders and conical sconces.
- *height 9cm*
- £42 • H. Hay

### Iron Figure ▼
- *20th Century*
Naive figure of Don Quixote standing holding a sword and lance in out-stretched arms, on an ebonised wooden base.
- *height 1.8m*
- £1,200 • Westland & Co

### Oyster Centrepiece ▲
- *20th Century*
Silvered-coral centrepiece with oyster-shell dishes.
- £795 • Butchoff

### Pair of Candlesticks ▲
- *circa 1930*
A pair of chrome, two-branch candlesticks on a circular base, holding a sconce in each hand.
- *height 21cm*
- £78 • H. Hay

### Pair of Ball Candlesticks ▼
- *circa 1930*
A pair of hollowed, decorative chromium-plated balls on a square base. American.
- *height 6.5cm*
- £120 • Bizarre

### Glass Hurricane Lamp ▲
- *20th Century*
A brass-based hurricane lamp with glass shade.
- *height 38cm*
- £295 • Butchoff

### Silver-Plate Vase ▲
- *circa 1930*
A conical, stepped, silver-plated vase on a stepped, circular base.
- *height 31cm*
- £200 • Beverley

## Expert Tips

*Electroplating is susceptible to wear and the nickel or alloy base on which the layer of silver has been put may show through. Replating gives an unnaturally bright appearance.*

## Copper Charger ▼
- *circa 1910*
Gilded, hand-crafted circular charger, exquisitely worked in a continuous band of flowerheads on a punched background.
- *height 30cm*
- £475          • David Pickup

## Tall Bronze Bottle ▼
- *circa 1950*
A Japanese Tsuro flower vessel of Kubi form. Vessel is signed by Roku IV.
- *height 40cm*
- £1,600          • Gregg Baker

## Polychrome Figure ▲
- *circa 1930*
Etched steel model of a Greek Kouros princess. French.
- *height 190cm*
- *width 60cm*
- £3,500          • Westland & Co.

## Radiator/Convector Heater ▲
- *circa 1950*
Made of sheet metal with chrome legs, bakelite switches and knobs. By Soforo.
- £250          • Zoom

## Metal Paper Knife ❯
- *circa 1960*
A paper knife with patterned handle in original box. By Viners from the Berlin Collection.
- *length 25cm*
- £18          • metro retro

## Standing Ashtray ▼
- *circa 1960*
Chrome floor ashtray with tiered trays, engraved pattern and rubber-coated stand.
- *height 65cm*
- £60          • metro retro

## Tin Coca-Cola Sign ▼
- *circa 1960*
Square promotional sign in red. Slightly distressed.
- *36cm x 36cm*
- £38          • metro retro

## Five-Piece Tea Service ◄
- *circa 1930*
Tea service in EPNS, consisting
of teapot, coffeepot, milk jug,
sugar bowl and tray, with bakelite
handles. By Art Krupp.
- *length 43cm (tray)*
- £750                    • Bizarre

## Chase Candlestick ◄
- *circa 1930*
J-shaped, two-branched
candlestick with circular chrome
base. Made by Chase
- *height 24cm*
- £180                    • Bizarre

## Aluminium Vase ▲
- *date 1999*
Modern vase made from a
compressed gas cylinder.
- *height 27cm*
- £20                 • metro retro

## Bronze Candlestick ▼
- *20th century*
A bronze candle-holder on tripod
base with three pad feet.
- *height 14.5cm*
- £650                    • Butchoff

## Bronze Flower Vessel ▲
- *20th century*
Japanese vessel with carp in low
relief from the Taisho period.
- *height 34cm*
- £5,000              • Gregg Baker

### Expert Tips

*Metal is not a material which
wears out very quickly. Most
metal objects will stay in
reasonable condition, so rarity
may not be a criterion for
collecting. Rely on your taste.*

## Chrome and Bakelite Candlesticks ▲
- *circa 1930*
German candlesticks by WMF.
Asymetric stylised form with
large sconces.
- *height 32cm*
- £750                    • Kieron

## Silverplate Bowl ►
- *circa 1935*
Bowl with green bakelite base.
- *diameter 22.5cm*
- £175                    • Beverley

### Vegetable Dishes ➤
- *circa 1930*
A pair of silver-plated vegetable
dishes with octagonal lids with
wooden finials.
- *diameter 22cm*
- £360 • Bizarre

### Metal Bookends ▲
- *20th century*
A pair of bookends in the form of
a bear's head in repose, set on a
wooden stand.
- £585 • Butchoff

### Metal Milk Churn ➤
- *circa 1920*
A large domestic milk churn.
- *height 51cm*
- £45 • Lacquer Chest

### Bronze Prawn ▲
- *20th century*
A large, model of a prawn in
mother-of-pearl with verdigris
bronze, in naturalistic pose.
- *length 27.5cm*
- £170 • Butchoff

### Floor Standing Light ▲
- *20th century*
A decorative floor-standing light
with wind-proof glass bowl.
- *height 116cm*
- £425 • Butchoff

### 'Ziglical' Column ▼
- *date 1966*
Stainless steel with stove
enamelling. By Joe Tilson.
- *height 81cm*
- £4,500 • Whitford Fine Art

### Pair of Brass Planters ◄
- *circa 1900*
Embossed with oranges and
blossoms. Standing on ball feet
with original zinc liners.
- *height 21cm*
- £1,100 • David Pickup

# Wine-Related items

**From corkscrews to taste vins, labels to wine coolers, coasters to trolleys, funnels to claret jugs, wine antiques are not just a good investment, but great to use.**

Increasing affluence leads to the spread of enthusiasm for fine wines, which, in turn, builds the market for wine-related artefacts and curios. It is much nicer to open your bottle with an antique corkscrew and to fill your guest's glass from a silver-mounted claret jug than to unscrew the bottle top and tip it out!

Greater interest in wine over a wider public has re-engendered an interest not just in these familiar items, but in more arcane and, seemingly, dated objects such as wine funnels, decanting cradles, champagne taps, toddy ladles and wine labels or 'bottle tickets'.

Increasing interest in all things vinous comes from America, where not only the above, but even more obscure and less intrinsically valuable items, such as pottery bin labels and seventeenth- and eighteenth-century sealed glass bottles find a ready market. The most conventionally attractive pieces are generally the most valuable and, if you are going to use them as you should, buying the items that most appeal to you is always the best way to go – Victorian novelty animal claret jugs are highly collected, but do you really want to use them for your prized Haut Medoc?

## Wine Funnel ▼
- *date 1780*
A silver wine funnel with filter insert and beaded borders, made by John Carmen of London.
- *height 13cm*
- **£1,050**      • **Langfords**

## Mahogany Wine Cooler ▲
- *19th century*
An uncommonly tall, octagonal brass-bound body with eight, octagonal tapered legs, with zinc liner, for use in cooling Jereboams.
- *height 82cm*
- **£2,200**      • **Riverbank**

## Handcup Decanter ▼
- *circa 1880*
A cylindrical Victorian lead crystal diamond-cut decanter.
- *height 32cm*
- **£95**          • **Barham**

## Corkscrew ➤
- *circa 1880*
A 19th-century crossbar corkscrew, with the handle fashioned from a stag's horn. Probably from Scotland.
- **£55**          • **Jasmin Cameron**

### Expert Tips

*Decanters engraved with scenes of social, political or patriotic significance are probably Irish – and very rare.*

## Picnic Flasks ➤

• *circa 1900*
Unusual green glass flask with silver and enamel top. Original travelling leather case. English.
• *height 26cm*
• £1,250 • S. & A. Thompson

## Oak Travelling Case ▲

• *circa 1810*
Travelling case fitted with six spirit decanters, two smaller decanters, all with stoppers, three trumpet glasses and four flutes.
• *height 30cm*
• £2,850 • Ranby Hall

## Wine Cooler ▲

• *circa 1840*
A 19th-century mahogany wine cooler with beaded top edge.
• *height 50cm*
• £2,450 • Chambers

## French Corkscrew ▲

• *circa 1890*
A French L'Excelsior patent corkscrew with ivory handle.
• *height 18cm*
• £250 • Emerson

## Decanter Label ▼

• *date 1809*
Thread design silver label with pierced letters 'Sherry'. By Phipps & Robinson, London.
• £140 • Linden & Co

## Travelling Corkscrew ▼

• *circa 1873*
Roundlet travelling corkscrew in heavy white metal. Shank retreats into one half of casing.
• £130 • Jasmin Cameron

## Corkscrews ◄

• *circa 1880*
A selection of three 19th-century corkscrews made of steel and wood with brushes made from pig's hair bristle.
• £40-60 • Henry Gregory

### Corkscrews ➤
• *circa 1880*
Three steel corkscrews, with varying double-action mechanisms and variously shaped handles in wood and steel.
• £18-22          • Henry Gregory

### English Kingscrew ⋀
• *circa 1850*
A classic English kingscrew, with a bronze barrel, steel sidewinder and bone handle.
• *height 18.5cm*
• £400          • Emerson

### Bottle Stopper ⋀
• *early 20th century*
A silver-plated bottle stopper, probably continental.
• £33          • Lesley Bragge

### Games Tantalus ⋁
• *circa 1880*
A late Victorian boxed games tantalus with three lead crystal cut decanters, the tantalus with silver-plated pierced mounts in the Scottish baronial style.
• *height 33cm*
• £690          • Barham

### Wine Labels ⋁
• *circa 1900*
A late-Victorian set of six wine labels, enamelled by Thomas Goode & Co, South Audley Street, London, and in their original velvet-lined case with leather exterior.
• £385          • Lesley Bragge

### Toddy Ladle ⋀
• *date 1745*
An English George II toddy ladle with a silver, lobed bowl and lip and twisted, whalebone handle with a silver finial.
• *length 45cm*
• £690          • Jasmin Cameron

### Expert Tips
*Hand-made decanters always have a number scratched into the stopper, with a corresponding number scratched into the rim. This was to ensure that perfect pairings did not become separated.*

### Wine Taster ⋀
• *circa 1660*
A silver wine taster made in Norwich by Arthur Haselwood, of shallow oval form, pinched and embossed with bead decoration.
• *length 9cm*
• £6,500          • Nicholas Shaw

### Lady's Legs Corkscrew ➤
- *circa 1894*
A German, folding corkscrew
with enamelled lady's legs which
open to form the crossbar.
- *height 6.5cm*
- £310      • Emerson

### Corkscrew ▲
- *circa 1850*
Lignum vitae corkscrew by R.
Burrow. With bristle brush to
remove residue from bottle rim.
- £145      • Jasmin Cameron

## Expert Tips

*'Bottle Tickets' were first
introduced in the 1740s, the
earliest being of simple
cartouche shape, usually bearing
the maker's mark only. Later
tickets became more and more
fanciful and some were fully
hallmarked, although the
government of the day forgot to
list them when introducing duty
on silver and many maker's took
advantage of this fact. The most
collectable tickets, therefore, are
the untaxed ones without the
monarch's head duty stamp on
the hallmark.*

### Bohemian Decanter ▲
- *circa 1900*
Bohemian diamond-cut, tapered
decanter with applied, green
overlay to body and lip.
- *height 41cm*
- £195      • Barham

### Wine Cooler ▼
- *circa 1935*
An oak, lead-lined wine cooler
with fruit, leaf and lion-mask
carved decoration.
- *height 57cm*
- £1,250      • Lesley Bragge

### Wine Cooler ▼
- *circa 1790*
Octagonal mahogany cooler with
original brass binding and lion-
mask handles, on tapered legs.
- *height 58cm*
- £4,450      • Chambers

### Oak Tantalus ◀
- *circa 1900*
An oak tantalus with three
original decanters, shown with
secret drawer open.
- *height 34cm*
- £695      • Finchley

## Champagne Bucket ▼

- *circa 1910*
A silver-plated Edwardian
champagne bucket on open
tripod stand. Made by Mappin &
Webb, Sheffield.
- *height 61cm*
- £350 • Barham

## English Decanter ▲

- *circa 1920*
A lead crystal handcut decanter
of unusual shape.
- *height 32cm*
- £85 • Barham

## Double Lever Corkscrew ▼

- *circa 1888*
An English Heeley double lever
corkscrew. Patent number 6606.
- *height 19.5cm*
- £90 • Emerson

## Barrel Tap ▼

- *circa 1890*
A steel barrel tap by Farrow &
Jackson, with oval, open tap and
square striking head.
- *height 16cm*
- £50 • Emerson

## Silver-Plated Fruit Press ▲

- *19th century*
A fruit press by Kirby & Beard &
Co. With beaten organic-shaped
stem and maker's name plaque.
- *height 32cm*
- £440 • Lesley Bragge

## Steel Corkscrews ▶

- *circa 1880*
Three steel corkscrews, two
identical with folding handles
and one with handgrip doubling
as bottle opener.
- £18-22 each • Henry Gregory

### Wooden Barman ▼
- *circa 1930*
An American syrocco wood barman with cocktail shaker.
- *height 20cm*
- £140　　　　• Emerson

### Clamp Wine Opener ▼
- *circa 1890*
Gaskell & Chambers clamp wine opener with extensive moulding.
- *height 24cm*
- £200　　　• Henry Gregory

### Silver Ladle ➤
- *19th century*
A good Danish silver ladle with a turned bone handle.
- *length 45cm*
- £680　　　• A. & E. Foster

### Italian Corkscrew ▲
- *circa 1880*
Italian boxwood corkscrew with an Archemedian worm.
- *height 19.5cm*
- £340　　　　• Emerson

### English Corkscrew ▲
- *circa 1900*
An English bar corkscrew with steel clamp in polished brass with an ebonised handle.
- *height 33cm*
- £320　　　　• Emerson

### Liqueur Funnel ▼
- *circa 1820*
An early 19th-century fluted glass liqueur funnel of twisted shape.
- *height 13cm*
- £55　　　• Jasmin Cameron

### Brandy Flagon ▼
- *circa 1895*
Miniature silver brandy flagon by H. Thornhill, London, with handle and screw top.
- *height 13cm*
- £590　　• S. & A. Thompson

# Works of Art & Sculpture

**Collecting ancient sculptures and works of art presents the most compelling insight into early civilisations, but is not without its difficulties.**

This most fascinating area is fraught with problems for the collector. The most immediate and obvious of these being that there is no way of knowing exactly what quantities of artefacts were made and have been preserved. The Chinese were the great wanderers of the Orient, and tombs are constantly being found revealing more, better and earlier treasures than had hitherto been suspected.

Faking is thus a problem. Although it is possible to have a piece thermo-luminescence tested to establish its age to within 300 years or so, the process is not really designed to prevent fraud and is not impossible for the determined criminal to circumvent. Then there is exportation and importation and the documentation required for both. All antiques and works of art can be imported into the UK, as long as the correct paperwork is completed, but it is not necessarily as easy to export from a country of origin.

Of course, all these problems become exacerbated in direct ratio to the value of the artefact purchased, and great pleasure can be derived with little red-tape and risk if your requirements are fairly modest.

## Asian/Oriental

### Hill Jar ▼
- **200BC-200AD**
In dark green glaze showing creatures from Chinese mythology.
- *height 28cm*
- **£850**          • **J.A.N. Fine Art**

### Bronze Food Vessel ➤
- **1100-771BC**
A western Chinese bronze Giu from the Zhou dynasty..
- *height 20cm*
- **£12,000**  • **Malcolm Rushton**

### Glazed Horse ▲
- **386-535AD**
One of a pair of rare amber and brown glazed horses from the Wei dynasty of northern China. Both have Oxford TL cents.
- *height 31cm*
- **£38,000**  • **Malcolm Rushton**

### Chinese Bronze Bottle ▼
- **206BC-220AD**
A Chinese bronze Han dynasty bottle in original patination with a garlic neck.
- *height 37cm*
- **£1,000**     • **Nicholas Pitcher**

## Bronze Incense Burner ∨
- **476-221BC**
A Chinese bronze incense burner
from the Warring States period.
Double handled, with three legs.
- *height 28cm*
- **£2,500** • **Nicholas Pitcher**

## Cambodian Bronze Figure ∨
- *12th century AD*
Ankor-wat Cambodian bronze
kymen sculpture from Badishatva.
Shows figure wearing dhoti and
holding religious objects.
- *height 18cm*
- **£850** • **David Baker**

## Pottery Rooster ➤
- **206BC-220AD**
A Chinese Han-dynasty tomb
figure of a rooster, with traces of
green, lead glaze.
- *height 12cm*
- **£350** • **David Baker**

## Terracotta Head ∧
- **200-300AD**
Head of a secular youth with an
elaborate curled hairstyle. From
Gandhara and showing a blend of
Greek and eastern styles.
- *height 23cm*
- **£4,500** • **Malcolm Rushton**

## Boar ∧
- **206BC-220AD**
A Han-dynasty burial object of a
well-modelled boar, with head
down and standing on all fours.
From the Sichuan province.
- *height 24.5cm*
- **£1,800** • **Nicholas Pitcher**

## Ear Cup ∨
- **200BC-200AD**
A Han-dynasty ear cup of ovate
shape and double handles with a
green glaze. A tomb find.
- *height 11cm*
- **£280** • **J.A.N. Fine Art**

## Funeral Jar ∨
- **265-317 AD**
An intricately modelled pottery
Daoist funeral jar showing a
pagoda-roofed celestial city,
presided over by six Daoist
immortals. Of the Jin dynasty,
from western China.
- *height 31cm*
- **£3,200** • **Malcolm Rushton**

### Expert Tips

*For the purposes of this book,
generally, everything west of
Babylon is considered to be an
'antiquity', whereas artefacts
from countries to the East fall
into the category of Asian and
Oriental Works of Art.*

## South Indian Sandstone ◄
- *10th-11th century AD*
Part of a frieze, showing three
elephants and two women.
- *height 34cm*
- £6,000 • Shahdad

### Cups and Tray ▲
- *618-907AD*
Tang San-Sai glazed cups and tray
in green, brown and yellow glaze.
- *diameter 24cm*
- £1,250 • J.A.N. Fine Art

### Jade Bi Disc ▼
- *206BC-220AD*
Jade disc with raised spirals,
dating from the Han dynasty.
- *diameter 19cm*
- £3,000 • Malcolm Rushton

### Pottery Camel ▲
- *618-907AD*
A Chinese unglazed pottery
model of a Bactrian camel. The
tomb-figure still has traces of
paint on the surface. From the
Tang dynasty.
- *height 30cm*
- £1,400 • David Baker

### Green Glazed Horse ▲
- *206BC-220AD*
A Chinese green-glazed pottery
horse from the Han dynasty.
- *height 110cm*
- £12,000 • Malcolm Rushton

### Bronze Heads ▼
- *1600-1100BC*
Two bronze halberd heads 'ge'
showing a tiger and owl with gout
patination.
- *height 20cm*
- £1,100 • Malcolm Rushton

## Expert Tips

*The insured value of a piece
should include the cost of
packing and shipping.*

### Cambodian Figure ►
- *9th-10th century*
Ankor-wat Cambodian bronze
multi-armed deity, from
Avlokitesvara.
- *height 16.5cm*
- £900 • David Baker

# European

## European Glass Panel ∨
- *circa 1788*
Central European stained and
leaded glass, probably Swiss.
Depicting armorial devices.
- *length 58.5cm*
- £4,250          • Shahdad

## Carved Wood Figure ∨
- *early 18th century*
Bohemian fine carved wood and
polychrome figure of St John
Nepomuk.
- *height 1.63m*
- £8,500          • Westland & Co

## Cruet Set ∧
- *circa 1870*
A fine Viennese cruet set carved
from rock crystal, with silver gilt
and enamelling.
- *height 25cm*
- £10,000          • Bazaart

## Stained-Glass Windows ∧
- *circa 1860*
Set of twelve windows. The arch
centred by a cross with a heart.
- *height 2.72m*
- £12,000          • Westland & Co

## Expert Tips

*Authentic stained glass is
coloured during the glassmaking
process, the colours produced by
adding certain metal oxides.
Colourless glass may be painted
or chemically treated to look like
stained glass. It is important to
tell the difference.*

## Three Graces ∨
- *circa 1880*
Signed French marble clock with
movement in black enamel,
marble signed 'Falconet'.
- *height 67cm*
- £18,500          • Emanouel

## Earthenware Vase ∨
- *circa 1880*
Massive earthenware vase with gilt
decoration and pastoral scenes.
- *height 1.1m*
- £25,000          • Emanouel

## Statue of Boy ▲

- *circa 1880*

Statue of Boy with Windmill, by Butti of Milan. Finely carved in white marble on a four-foot, green marble rotating base.

- *height 1m*
- **£11,750**  • **Drummonds**

## Stained-Glass Window ▲

- *circa 1890*

English Victorian Gothic-arched stained-glass window showing Jesus preaching. In arts and crafts style and colouring.

- *height 1.5m*
- **£1,500**  • **Westland & Co**

## Marble Figure ▼

- *circa 1890*

An Italian marble figure of virtue after Tino di Camaino. Possibly work of Alceo Dossena.

- *height 1.05m*
- **£4,500**  • **Westland & Co**

## Sèvres Vases ▼

- *circa 1880*

Pair of large gilt metal mounted vases with covers. Painted with figures in 18th-century costume, with birds to reverse.

- *height 32cm*
- **£13,000**  • **Emanouel**

## Stone Lion ▲

- *19th century*

Carved statuary stone lion, in Portland stone, on stone base.

- *height 1m*
- **£11,750**  • **Drummonds**

## Expert Tips

*Paintings and statues of religious subjects tend to command lower prices than similar, secular pieces.*

## Statue ▲

- *circa 1825*

An original statue of Sir Walter Raleigh from the Palace of Westminster.

- *height 3.3m*
- **£28,000**  • **Drummonds**

**Torso** ▼
- *circa 1920*
Modernist Jiri Strada torso of a woman cropped at top of head and thighs.
- *height 1.5m*
- £5,300 • Drummonds

**Chimneypiece** ▲
- *circa 1890*
Catalonian Art Nouveau modernista chimneypiece, decorated with mosaics.
- *height 3.48m*
- £150,000 • Westland & Co

**French Statue** ▲
- *circa 1890*
French statuary marble and alabaster statue of Le Poete de la Danse. Belle epoque.
- *height 57cm*
- £2,500 • Westland & Co

**Terracotta Model** ▼
- *late 19th century*
French model of a river god. The god crowned with a bullrush and wearing drapery around waist.
- *height 59cm*
- £3,500 • Westland & Co

**Marble Bust** ▲
- *circa 1840*
Carved statuary bust of a lady with head turned slightly to dexter and wearing a full wig.
- *height 58.5cm*
- £3,850 • Westland & Co

**Carved Figure** ▲
- *circa 1860*
Finely carved pine figure of a Medieval knight. In the Gothic revival manner.
- *height 1.93m*
- £4,500 • Westland & Co

## Wolf and Lamb ➤
- *circa 1880*
Val d' Orse wolf and lamb on oval
stone base.
- *height 1.5m*
- £28,700 • Drummonds

## Neoclassical Statue ▲
- *circa 1840*
French terracotta neoclassical
statue of a muse.
- *height 1.45m*
- £8,500 • Westland & Co

## Overdoor ▼
- *circa 1820*
French carved oak beaux art
overdoor. With central cartouche
and cherub and floral swags.
- *height 59cm*
- £7,500 • Westland & Co

## Torso of a General ▼
- *circa 1890*
Torso of a French general.
- *height 60cm*
- £1,000 • Drummonds

## Glass Panel ▲
- *15th century*
Fragmentary stained and leaded
glass panel. Probably English.
- *length 86cm*
- £3,000 • Shahdad

## Stone Ionic Columns ▲
- *circa 1840*
Pair of columns in the form of
male figures with arms raised
above head supporting the
capital. On a moulded base.
- *height 2.06m*
- £24,000 • Westland & Co

# Middle Eastern

### Early-Christian Limestone ▼
- *5th century*
Limestone carved relief with
dedicatory inscription from
Byzantine Egypt.
- *31cm x 20cm*
- £3,000 • Axia

### Turkish Standard ▼
- *16th-17th century*
Turkish standard, from Tumbak,
with brass base and steel spike
with gold inscriptions.
- *length 64cm*
- £1,000 • Samiramis

### Persian Terracotta Jug ▲
- *13th century*
From Kaschan with kufic
inscriptions, turquoise glaze, stops
to base and iridescence.
- *height 18cm*
- £1,200 • Samiramis

### Persian Ewer ▲
- *13th century*
Bulbous-form ewer from Kashan,
with turquoise glaze, strap handle,
stops to base and small spout.
- *height 22cm*
- £2,500 • Samiramis

### Persian Brass Dish ▲
- *circa 1910*
A Persian oval dish with
engraved floral designs to centre.
- *width 40cm*
- £130 • Sharif

### Cleopatra Stands ▼
- *circa 1920*
A pair of cast-iron stands showing
Cleopatra as a caryatid supporting
a table above her head.
- *height 119cm*
- £1,800 • Sharif

### Persian Tile ▼
- *circa 1850*
A Kajar dynasty round tile in
polychrome showing a musical
setting with a woman and two
men within a floral border.
- *diameter 41cm*
- £160 • Sharif

## Glass Bottle Vase ▲
- *13th century*
Iranian vase, from Kaschan, with globular body, long neck and splayed lip. The vase shows geometric designs around the body, yellow colouration and good iridescence.
- *height 32cm*
- **£3,200**      • Samiramis

## Turkish Vase ▲
- *circa 1930*
Twentieth-century Turkish, bottle-shaped vase with turquoise enamelling to body and neck and orange banding.
- *height 26cm*
- **£90**      • Sharif

## Kashan Tile ▼
- *13th century*
One of a pair of tiles with inscriptions from the Koran among birds and floral meanderings. With a blue and turquoise glaze.
- *height 31cm*
- **£2,300**      • Samiramis

## Bronze Oil Lamp ▼
- *13th century*
A bronze oil lamp on a splayed base with a large arm, ornate thumbpiece with bird decoration and decorated lid.
- *height 17cm*
- **£1,400**      • Samiramis

## Green Stone Oil Lamp ▼
- *13th century*
Stone oil lamp with four triangular burners on a circular base and floral designs to the top.
- *height 6cm*
- **£500**      • Samiramis

## Egyptian Damascus Table ▲
- *circa 1900*
Mother-of-pearl and bone inlay hexagonal table with pierced masharabi panels, on turned feet.
- *height 67cm*
- **£1,000**      • Sharif

### Expert Tips

*Few Islamic artists are known by name, since they would seldom have worked alone, but in religious workshops.*

## Patinated Bronze Ewer ▲
- *13th century*
From Saljuk, northwest Iran. With bulbous body, fluted neck and strap handle with thumbpiece. The whole on a circular base.
- *height 19cm*
- **£2,000**      • Samiramis

## Saljuk Stem Cup ▼
• *13th century*
A bronze cup with engraved
designs of birds, trees and floral
cartouches, with birds and fish to
the centre, all on a splayed base.
• *height 13cm*
• £1,500          • Samiramis

## Teak Octagonal Table ▼
• *circa 1880*
Table with bone and ivory inlay
in geometric patterns and Islamic,
architecturally carved legs.
• *height 62cm*
• £450          • Sharif

## Expert Tips

*Prior to the 7th century, artists
in Assyria, Mesopotamia, and
Persia – the ancient civilizations
of West and Central Asia –
produced monumental figurative
sculpture. After the Muslim
conquests of the AD 600s,
however, figurative sculpture
almost ceased in these areas
because Islam disapproves of
making images of living things.*

## Persian Silver Crown ▲
• *circa 1900*
Three point open work element
composed of floral and scrolling
foliate designs and mounted on a
later suede backing.
• *height 21cm*
• £700          • Samiramis

## Stone Cat ▲
• *10th century*
Stone carving of a cat with
turquoise glaze eyes. From
Samanid, Iran.
• *height 16cm*
• £1,500          • Samiramis

## Oil Lamp ▼
• *12th century*
An oil lamp in brass with copper
inlay, with ovoid body on a high
foot and showing an arabesque
cartouche. From Afghanistan.
• *height 24cm*
• £1,500          • Samiramis

## Bronze Vase and Stand ▼
• *circa 12th-13th century*
A bronze vase with pierced
decoration to splayed lip and
plinth base, on a tripod stand.
• *height 95cm*
• £5,000          • Hadji Baba

## Cut-Glass Bottle ◄
• *circa 500-600*
Sassanian Persian cut-glass bottle
with circular relief decoration.
• *height 10cm*
• £4,000          • Hadji Baba

# Russian

## Silver Bowl ▲
- *mid 19th century*
Silver-marked Russian silver bowl
from Georgia, showing seven
panels of beasts and forestry
scenes, with central roundel.
- *diameter 20cm*
- £1,200        • Shahdad

## Virgin of Vladimir ▲
- *19th century*
Orthodox iconic depiction of the
Virgin of Vladimir, showing
Virgin Mary with Child.
- *34.5 x 30cm*
- £860          • Temple

## Paperweight ▼
- *circa 1940*
Obsidian and onyx paperweight
with intaglio of Lenin in profile,
looking to sinister.
- *height 15cm*
- £490          • Zaheim

## Commemorative Vase ▼
- *circa 1940*
Baluster-shaped vase, showing
Lenin, in red glaze with gilded
lettering and floral decoration.
- *height 37cm*
- £750          • Zaheim

## Archangel Michael ◄
- *19th century*
Archangel Michael Voyevada in
iconic form, shown on wood
panel and depicted on horseback.
- *34.8 x 30.4cm*
- £1,650         • Temple

## Virgin of Kazan ▲
- *19th century*
Icon of the Virgin of Kazan,
capital of Tartarstan.
- *37.7 x 31.5cm*
- £650          • Temple

## Presentation Vase ▲
- *circa 1950*
Made for the anniversary of the
birth of Lenin. Cut and applied
decoration of social realism.
- *height 59cm*
- £6,500         • Zaheim

### Expert Tips

*The biggest market for artefacts
from the old Soviet Union is
reported to be among rock stars
and bankers!*

## Saint Basil ▼
- *late 18th century*
An iconic depiction of Saint
Basil the Great, the leader of the
Christian Church in the East and
promoter of monasticism.
- *31.5 x 26.6cm*
- **£1,500**  • **Temple**

## Commemorative Plaque ▲
- *circa 1971*
Gilt bronze with red glass inserts,
and central enamelled plaque
showing a nuclear power station
within a wreath.
- *diameter 30cm*
- **£750**  • **Zaheim**

## Bronze High-Jumper ▲
- *circa 1960*
Cast bronze high-jumper
naturalistically styled in the act of
landing on a stone landing mat.
- *height 94cm*
- **£4,500**  • **Zaheim**

## Mould of Lenin ▼
- *circa 1950*
A Plaster mould of Lenin made
for the production of bronze casts.
- *height 71cm*
- **£400**  • **Zaheim**

## Saint Nicholas ▲
- *16th century*
Icon of Saint Nicholas the
Wonderworker, from the Pskov
school. Tempera and gold on a
gesso and wood panel.
- *76 x 55.3cm*
- **£68,000**  • **Temple**

## 'The Partisan' ▲
- *circa 1979*
Painting entitled 'The Partisan'
by M. S. Prokopyuk, in charcoal
and watercolour.
- *86 x 61cm*
- **£850**  • **Zaheim**

## Annunciation ▶
- *19th century*
Good example of the revival of
late 15th-century style. Depicting
various saints.
- *35.6 x 31.1cm*
- **£3,500**  • **Temple**

## Cast Bronze Figure ▼
- *circa 1940*
Cast bronze of Russian Hero.
Copy of a famous, full-size bronze.
- *height 35cm*
- £350  • Zaheim

## 'Dormition' ▲
- *early 19th century*
Traditional image from the
Palekh school, in gesso on wood
panel, with gold. Based on the
Katyed Cami, from Istanbul.
- *37.4 x 10.5cm*
- £2,500  • Temple

## Saint John ▼
- *circa 1450*
Saint John in the Wilderness.
Painted in Constantinople by an
artist of the circle of Angelos.
- *33.5 x 25cm*
- £120,000  • Temple

## Archangel Michael ▼
- *19th century*
Iconic representation of
Archangel Michael of Voyevoda.
- *33.5 x 28.8cm*
- £1,450  • Temple

## Ceramic Platter ▲
- *circa 1920*
Commemorative ceramic platter,
only one other recorded. Showing
Lenin in centre with various faces
of revolutionary Russia in red and
grey charcoal glaze.
- *diameter 42cm*
- £5,500  • Zaheim

## Weightlifter ▼
- *circa 1950*
Alloy model of a weightlifter in
black enamel. In the act of final
lift. On an oval base.
- *height 52cm*
- £890  • Zaheim

## Three Saints ▼
- *17th century*
Carved decoration with Three
Saints (only two shown). Balkan.
- *23.6 x 56.2cm*
- £5,500  • Temple

## Prophet Elijah ◄
- *19th century*
Iconic representation of the
Prophet Elijah. The prophet is in
his cave in the wilderness, with
crow. God is depicted in a chariot
carried by a red cloud.
- *31.5 x 26cm*
- £1,500  • Temple

# Writing Equipment

**Pens, pencils, portable desks and all the paraphernalia of hand-written communication are the most personal of collectables.**

In terms of the categories within this book, fountain pens and propelling pencils fall somewhere between Collectables and Scientific Instruments, but they and other artefacts connected with writing are so avidly collected these days that they deserve a slot of their own. When seeking to buy a pen, perfect condition is of the utmost importance, with no scratches or marks, no fading to the colour and with original fittings.

Originally, pens were made of hardened rubber.

Although manufacture was very expensive, it was not until the 1920s that manufacturers turned to plastic – despite the fact that plastic in a useable form had been available for nearly a century.

Individual pen-makers gave different names, such as Vulcanite and Raclite to the hardened rubber composition. These are worth looking out for.

In general, it is better to spend a lot of money on a pen, with a reputable dealer, and ensure that you have a good one then risk buying one that may have been adapted.

---

### Parker Duofold Set    ∨
- *circa 1928*
A pristine Parker Duofold set with button-filler pen with 18-carat gold nib and propelling pencil.
- £225                    • Sugar

### Waterman Gothic    ➤
- *date 1924*
A Waterman 452 gothic design in sterling silver with American lever fill and 12-carat gold nib.
- *length 15cm*
- £1,000      • Jasmin Cameron

### Writing Box    ∧
- *circa 1870*
A leather-faced writing box, by Halstaff and Hannaford, with ivory rulers, letter-opener, pen and drop-forward letter rack with original key.
- *height 33cm*
- £1,600              • Mathias

### Ink Reservoir    ∨
- *late 19th century*
Silver bronzed cat and mouse with gilt highlights which opens to ink reservoir.
- *height 7cm*
- £1,170    • Elizabeth Bradwin

---

## Expert Tips

*The personalising of precious objects is always a problem for the inheritors. Pens have often been bought from jewellers and the temptation to have initials engraved on them is easy to succumb to. This will lessen the value, unfortunately, unless the provenance is impressive.*

## Parker 51

- *circa 1950*

A Parker 51 Special classic, commemorating 51 years in the business, with burgundy body, rolled gold cap and pearlescent hooded nib.
- *length 15cm*
- £250          • Jasmin Cameron

## Ivory Writing Slope   ∨

- *19th century*

Anglo-Indian ivory writing slope with sadeli mosaic and opening to reveal writing surface.
- *length 29cm*
- £1,200          • Hygra

## Waterman 512V Set   ∧

- *circa 1930*

Pen and propelling pencil in laminated plastic jet and mother-of-pearl.
- *length 14cm*
- £275          • Jasmin Cameron

## Triple Writing Box   ∨

- *circa 1810*

In traditional campaign style of solid mahogany with brass strap corners and countersunk handles.
- *length 50cm*
- £1,400          • Hygra

## Expert Tips

*Makes of pens to look out for are Parker, Waterman, Conway Stewart and Mont Blanc, with a few lesser-known names such as Burnham.*

## Inkwell   ∧

- *circa 1920*

Decorative inkwell with metal eagle figure on marble base.
- *length 30cm*
- £85          • M. Sullivan

## Draftsman's Pen   ∧

- *late 19th century*

Brass draftsman's pen.
- *length 16cm*
- £18          • M. Sullivan

## Silver Inkwell   ➤

- *circa 1931*

Capstan silver inkwell with glass reservoir and large spayed base. Made in Birmingham.
- *diameter 20cm*
- £500          • Stephen Kalms

## Parker 51 ➤

- *date 1950*
Aeromatic filling system with
teal-blue body and solid gold cap
and medium nib.
- *length 16cm*
- £180    • Jasmin Cameron

## Slope/Lap Writing Desk ▲

- *circa 1790*
Rosewood and penwork writing
slope/lap desk with original baize
writing surface.
- *length 24cm*
- £750    • Hygra

## Expert Tips

*Writing boxes, or lap desks,
are really a portable version of
the Davenport and are very
saleable. Factors to look for
are brass or mother-of-pearl
inlay, exotic wood and a
complete interior.*

## Waterman Ideal 0552 ¹/₂ ▼

- *date 1920*
Ladies' pen with lever-fill action
and gold-plated nib.
- *length 14cm*
- £750    • Jasmin Cameron

## Silver Capstan ▼

- *date 1912*
Inkwell made in Birmingham
with porcelain bowl.
- *height 7cm*
- £285    • Jasmin Cameron

## Waterman Ideal 0552 ¹/₂ ▼

- *date 1924*
Ladies' pen with gold-plated
gothic pattern and lever fill.
- *length 14cm*
- £450    • Jasmin Cameron

## Writing Box ◄

- *circa 1820*
An Anglo-Indian writing box
inlaid with ivory, opening down
to reveal a writing surface and
space for writing implements.
- £24    • Hygra

## Bronze Stay ▲

- *mid 19th century*
Lifting cup on a black marble
base. Pens rest on antlers.
- *height 11cm*
- £690    • Elizabeth Bradwin

## Silver Swan ▲
• *circa 1910*
Silver swan gravity-fed, eye-dropper pen with 14-carat gold nib.
• *length 15cm*
• £130 • Sugar

## Expert Tips

*Tunbridge ware was a particularly popular medium for the decoration of writing slopes and stationery boxes, and Kent a good place to find it.*

## Swan Quills ▼
• *19th century*
French swan quills originally from Hudson Bay.
• *length 20cm*
• £30 each • Jasmin Cameron

## Writing Box ➤
• *late 18th century*
Indo-Portuguese writing box with gold-backed tortoiseshell, inlaid with ivory.
• *length 30cm*
• £1,200 • Shahdad

## Inkwell ▼
• *19th century*
A bronzed seated cat with concealed inkwell. Its head lifts to reveal an ink reservoir.
• *height 7cm*
• £950 • Elizabeth Bradwin

## Painted Writing Slope ▼
• *circa 1720*
An English writing slope decorated with oriental figures within floral borders.
• *height 28cm*
• £1,850 • O. F. Wilson

## Glass Ink Pot ▲
• *circa 1930*
Multi-sided glass amethyst colour American inkpot with sliding glass lid.
• *height 5.5cm*
• £260 • Jasmin Cameron

## Stationery Case ▲
• *circa 1930*
Green crocodile case with various compartments and lined with green satin.
• £435 • Holland & Holland

## Parker Duofold ▼
- *circa 1940*
A Parker Duofold pen, made in the U.S.A., with button filler, gold band and clip.
- *length 15cm*
- £100                    • Sugar

## Artist's Paintbox ▲
- *circa 1890*
Victorian rosewood box with various paints and liftout tray.
- *length 31cm*
- £2,950            • J. & T. Stone

## Letter Opener ▲
- *date 1896*
Silver and ivory letter opener by Sheppard and Saunders.
- *length 20cm*
- £1,600          • Sandra Cronan

## Waterman Ideal 452 ¹/₂ ➤
- *circa 1925*
Ladies' pen with basketweave design in sterling silver and American lever fill.
- *length 14cm*
- £750          • Jasmin Cameron

## Inkwell ◄
- *late 19th century*
Bronzed alligator with concealed inkwell. The back opens to reveal two reservoirs.
- *length 25cm*
- £735          • Elizabeth Bradwin

## Letter/Pen Rack ▲
- *circa 1820*
Unusual letter/pen rack.
- *height 28cm*
- £980              • P. L. James

## Bone-Handle Pen ▲
- *circa 1910*
A souvenir, bone handle with steel nib inscribed 'A Present from Skegness'.
- *length 18cm*
- £28              • M. Sullivan

### Expert Tips

*Commemorative pens, pencils, paper knives and biros proliferate. They need to be very special.*

## Parker 51 Set ◄
- *circa 1950*

Grey clutch pencil set with lustraloy cap. Aerometric and hooded nib, not in original box.
- *length 15cm*
- **£180** • **Jasmin Cameron**

## Penwork Box ▼
- *circa 1810*

Sarcophagus box with floral decoration to sides with top panel depicting Chinaman.
- *length 31cm*
- **£850** • **John Clay**

## Regency Writing Slope ▲
- *circa 1820*

Rosewood desk inlaid with cut-brass decoration, fitted with lock.
- *length 50cm*
- **£850** • **J. Collins & Son**

## Parker 51 ▲
- *date 1950*

A Parker 51 aeromatic with maroon body and solid-gold cap. It has a hooded nib and pearlescent jewel cap.
- *length 16cm*
- **£150** • **Jasmin Cameron**

## Brazilian Writing Box ▼
- *circa 1830*

A rosewood writing box with shellac finish, featuring countersunk brass handles in the military manner, a side document drawer, secret drawers, rounded brass edgings, nameplate and escutcheon.
- *length 47cm*
- **£850** • **Hygra**

### Expert Tips

*Leather on writing surfaces obviously wears out, and replacement leather is not detrimental to the value, as long as it is in the style of the piece.*

## Writing Desk ▲
- *circa 1760*

Mahogany writing desk with original brass swan-neck handles.
- *height 1.22m*
- **£10,400** • **Chambers**

## Stationery Cabinet ➤
- *circa 1860*

A burr-walnut stationery cabinet with satinwood interior. Interior has writing slate, calendar, pen tilt and crown top inkwells.
- *height 33cm*
- **£900** • **Mathias**

### Dinkie 540J ➤
- *circa 1920*
Conway Stuart Dinkie 540J. Rare ladies' pen with 14-carat gold nib and multicoloured body.
- *length 15cm*
- £220 • **Jasmin Cameron**

### De La Rue Pen ▲
- *circa 1900*
De la Rue of London 'Onoto' pen, piston filled with 18-carat gold nib.
- *length 15cm*
- £100 • **Sugar**

### Ladies' Parker Pen ▲
- *date 1928*
Canadian Duofold Ladies' pen with lapis permanite body. Pump filled with three gold-plated bands on cap.
- *length 14cm*
- £300 • **Jasmin Cameron**

### Rosewood Slope/Lap Desk ▼
- *circa 1835*
Writing desk inlaid with mother of pearl. It opens to reveal writing surface and compartments.
- *length 35cm*
- £700 • **Hygra**

### Ladies' Writing Slope ◄
- *date 1865*
Royal French kindwood writing slope with engraved hinges and lock plate. Signed Tahan of Paris.
- *length 25cm*
- £1,995 • **J. & T. Stone**

### Coromandel Writing Box ▲
- *circa 1870*
A coromandel writing box with domed lid and gilt and chased fittings, crown-topped inkwells and original velvet lining.
- *height 18cm*
- £1,475 • **Mathias**

## Expert Tips

*John H. Loud, an American inventor, patented a ballpoint pen in 1888. However, they received little notice until World War II, when pilots found them invaluable for writing at altitude. Good and early ballpoint pens are definitely among the antiques of the future.*

### English Writing Desk Set ◄
- *circa 1940*
20th-century English Phendic desk set with blotter sponge holder, double inkwell, and paper holder.
- £250 • **Decodence**

## Silver Pencil ◄
• *circa 1930*
Silver-plated propelling pencil of
the Art Deco period.
• *length 15cm*
• £15                    • M. Sullivan

## Bridge Pencil ▼
• *circa 1930*
Silver-plated bridge pencil,
originally one of a set of four,
with propelling action.
• *length 15cm*
• £22                    • M. Sullivan

## Expert Tips

*Writing boxes and slopes were
made for the traveller, who was
generally either an army officer
or a civil servant with the East
India Company. Thus they
were often made to match
military chests.*

## Ram-Horn Writing Set ▼
• *late 19th century*
Oak-based writing set with silver
mounts and ram-horn centre
piece.
• *height 21cm*
• £1,700   • Holland & Holland

## Writing Box/Lap Desk ▲
• *circa 1800*
Brass-bound mahogany box in
military style with brass drop
handles, a side document drawer,
and brass corners, nameplate and
escutcheon. Opens to reveal
sloping, velvet writing surface
and space for writing implements.
• *length 50cm*
• £440                    • Hygra

## Fruitwood Pen Tray ▲
• *18th century*
Pen tray with inkstand and
turned carrying handle and
drawer. It has twin screw-closed
inkwells and a pounce shaker.
• *length 30cm*
• £650                    • Hygra

## Papier Mâché Slope ▼
• *circa 1820*
Writing slope with chinoiserie
decoration opening to reveal a
surface for writing.
• *length 29cm*
• £850                    • Hygra

## Writing Box ➤
• *circa 1875*
Victorian papier mâché ladies'
writing slope with extensive gilded
mother-of-pearl decoration and
original silver-topped inkwell.
• *length 40cm*
• £1,575           • J.& T. Stone

## Main Chinese Periods

| | |
|---|---|
| SHANG DYNASTY | C. 1523 – 1027 BC |
| CHOW DYNASTY | 1027 – 221 BC |
| WARRING STATES PERIOD | 481 – 221 BC |
| CH'IN DYNASTY | 221 – 206 BC |
| HAN DYNASTY | 206 BC – 220 AD |
| THREE KINGDOMS | 220 – 280 |
| SIX DYNASTIES | 280 – 589 |
| NORTHERN WEI | 385 – 535 |
| EASTERN WEI | 535 – 550 |
| WESTERN WEI | 535 – 557 |
| NORTHERN CH'I | 550 – 577 |
| NORTHERN CHOW | 557 – 581 |
| LIU SUNG (SOUTH) | 420 – 478 |
| SOUTHERN CH'I | 479 – 501 |
| LIANG | 502 – 557 |
| CH'EN | 557 – 588 |
| SUI DYNASTY | 589 – 618 |
| T'ANG | 618 – 906 |
| FIVE DYNASTIES | 907 – 959 |
| SUNG DYNASTIES | 960 – 1280 |
| YUAN DYNASTIES | 1280 – 1368 |
| MING DYNASTIES | 1368 – 1643 |
| CH'ING DYNASTIES | 1644 – 1912 |

## Ming Period

| HUNG WY | 1368 – 1398 |
|---|---|
| CHIEN WIEN | 1399 – 1402 |
| YUNG LO | 1403 – 1424 |
| HUNG HSI | 1425 – 1425 |
| HSUAN TE | 1426 – 1435 |
| CHENG T'UNG | 1436 – 1449 |
| CHING T'AI | 1450 – 1457 |
| T'IEN SHUN | 1457 – 1464 |
| CH'ENG HUA | 1465 – 1487 |
| HUNG-CHIH | 1488 – 1505 |
| CHENG TE | 1506 – 1521 |
| CHIA CHING | 1522 – 1566 |
| LUNG CH'ING | 1567 – 1572 |
| WAN LI | 1573 – 1619 |

## Ch'ing Period

| SHUNG CHIH | 1644 – 1661 |
|---|---|
| K'ANG HSI | 1662 – 1722 |
| YUNG CHENG | 1723 – 1735 |
| CH'IENG LUNG | 1736 – 1795 |
| CHIA CH'ING | 1796 – 1820 |
| TAO KUANG | 1821 – 1850 |
| HSIEN FENG | 1851 – 1861 |
| T'UNG CHIH | 1862 – 1873 |
| KUANG HSU | 1874 – 1908 |
| HSUAN T'UNG | 1909 – 1912 |

## Korean Periods

| LO LANG | 106 BC – 313 AD |
|---|---|
| PAEKCHE | 18 BC – 663 AD |
| KOGURYO | 37 BC – 668 AD |
| SILLA | 57 BC – 668 AD |
| GREAT SILLA | 668 – 936 |
| KORYO | 918 – 1392 |
| YI | 1392 – 1910 |

## Japanese Periods

| JOMON PERIOD | 1000 BC – 200 BC |
|---|---|
| YAYOI PERIOD | 200 BC – 500 AD |
| TUMULUS PERIOD | 300 – 700 |
| ASUKA PERIOD | 552 – 645 |
| EARLY NARA PERIOD | 645 – 710 |
| NARA PERIOD | 710 – 794 |
| EARLY HEIAN PERIOD | 794 – 897 |
| HEIAN OR FUJIWARA PERIOD | 897 – 1185 |
| KAMAKURA PERIOD | 1185 – 1392 |
| ASHIKAGA PERIOD | 1392 – 1573 |
| MOMOYAMA PERIOD | 1573 – 1615 |
| TOKUGAWA PERIOD | 1615 – 1868 |

# French General Periods

| FRANÇOIS-PREMIER | 1515 – 1547 | Reign of Francis I |
|---|---|---|
| HENRI-DEUX | 1547 – 1559 | Reign of Henri II |
| | 1559 – 1560 | Reign of Francis II |
| | 1560 – 1574 | Reign of Charles IX |
| | 1574 – 1589 | Reign of Henri III |
| HENRI-QUATRE | 1589 – 1610 | Reign of Henri IV |
| LOUIS-TREIZE | 1610 – 1643 | Reign of Louis XIII |
| LOUIS-QUATORZE | 1643 – 1715 | Reign of Louis XIV |
| LOUIS-QUINZE | 1715 – 1774 | Reign of Louis XV |
| LOUIS-SEIZE | 1774 – 1793 | Reign of Louis XVI |
| EMPIRE | 1799 – 1814 | Reign of Napoleon |

# English General Periods

| TUDOR | 1485 – 1558 | Reigns of Henry VII Henry VIII Edward VI Mary |
|---|---|---|
| ELIZABETHAN | 1558 – 1603 | Reign of Elizabeth I |
| JACOBEAN | 1603 – 1649 | Reigns of James I Charles I |
| COMMONWEALTH | 1649 – 1660 | Protectorship of Cromwell |
| CAROLEAN / LATE STUART | 1660 – 1689 | Reigns of Charles II James II |
| WILLIAM AND MARY | 1689 – 1702 | Reign of William and Mary |
| QUEEN ANNE | 1702 – 1727 | Reigns of Anne George I |
| GEORGIAN | 1727 – 1820 | Reigns of George II George III |
| REGENCY | 1800 – 1830 | Reigns of George III George IV |
| WILLIAM IV | 1830 – 1837 | Reign of William IV |
| VICTORIAN | 1837 – 1901 | Reign of Victoria |
| EDWARDIAN | 1901 – 1910 | Reign of Edward VII |

# English Monarchs since 1066

| | |
|---|---|
| WILLIAM I | 1066 – 1087 |
| WILLIAM II | 1087 – 1100 |
| HENRY I | 1100 – 1135 |
| STEPHEN | 1135 – 1154 |
| HENRY II | 1154 – 1189 |
| RICHARD I | 1189 – 1199 |
| JOHN | 1199 – 1216 |
| HENRY III | 1216 – 1272 |
| EDWARD I | 1272 – 1307 |
| EDWARD II | 1307 – 1327 |
| EDWARD III | 1327 – 1377 |
| RICHARD II | 1377 – 1399 |
| HENRY IV | 1399 – 1413 |
| HENRY V | 1413 – 1422 |
| HENRY VI | 1422 – 1461 |
| EDWARD IV | 1461 – 1470 |
| HENRY VI | 1470 – 1471 |
| EDWARD I | 1471 – 1483 |
| EDWARD | 1483 – 1483 |
| RICHARD III | 1484 – 1485 |
| HENRY VI | 1485 – 1509 |
| HENRY VIII | 1509 – 1547 |
| EDWARD VI | 1547 – 1553 |
| MARY | 1553 – 1558 |
| ELIZABETH | 1558 – 1603 |
| JAMES I | 1603 – 1625 |
| CHARLES I | 1625 – 1649 |
| COMMONWEALTH | 1649 – 1660 |
| CHARLES II | 1660 – 1685 |
| JAMES II | 1685 – 1688 |
| WILLIAM AND MARY | 1688 – 1694 |
| WILLIAM III | 1694 – 1702 |
| ANNE | 1702 – 1714 |
| GEORGE I | 1714 – 1727 |
| GEORGE II | 1727 – 1760 |
| GEORGE III | 1760 – 1820 |
| GEORGE IV | 1820 – 1830 |
| WILLIAM IV | 1830 – 1837 |
| VICTORIA | 1837 – 1901 |
| EDWARD VII | 1901 – 1910 |
| GEORGE V | 1910 – 1936 |
| EDWARD VIII | 1936 – 1936 |
| GEORGE VI | 1936 – 1952 |
| ELIZABETH II | 1952 – |

**Not all of the terms that follow appear in this volume, but they may all prove useful in the future.**

**abadeh** Highly-coloured Persian rug.

**acacia** Dull yellow hardwood with darker markings used for inlay and bandings towards the end of the eighteenth century.

**acanthus** A leaf motif used in carved and inlaid decoration.

**Act of Parliament clock** Eighteenth-century English clock, wall mounted and driven by weights, with a large, unglazed dial and a trunk for weights. These clocks often hung in taverns and public places and were relied on by the populace after the Act of Parliament of 1797, which introduced taxation on timepieces.

**air-beaded** Glass with air bubbles resembling beads.

**air-twist** Spiral pattern enclosed in a glass stem with air bubbles.

**albarello** Waisted ceramic drug jar.

**alder** Wood used for country-style furniture in the eighteenth century.

**ale glass** Eighteenth-century glass drinking vessel with long stem and tall, thin bowl.

**amboyna** West Indian wood used for veneers, marquetry and inlays. Light brown with speckled grain.

**anchor escapement** Late seventeenth-century English invented clock movement, named after the anchor shape of the linkage which moves the escape wheel.

**angle barometer** Also known as signpost barometers. Barometers where the movement of mercury is shown almost on the horizontal.

**andiron** Iron support for burning logs.

**annulated** Ringed (of glass).

**apostle spoon** Spoon with the figure of an apostle as the finial.

**applied** Attached or added, rather than modelled or carved as part of the body.

**apron** The decorative panel of wood between the front legs of a chair or cabinet.

**arbor** The axle on which the wheel of a clock's mechanism is mounted.

**arch** (clockmaking) The arch above the dial of a post-1700 longcase clock.

**argyle** Double-skinned metal pouring jugs and tea and coffee pots.

**armoire** French wardrobe, linen press or large cupboard.

**ash** Hardwood used for making country furniture and for its white veneer.

**astragal** Small semi-circular moulding, particularly used as glazing bar in furniture.

**automaton clock** A clock where the strike is performed by mechanically operated figures.

**backboard** The unseen back of wall furniture.

**backplate** The rear plate supporting the movement of a clock, often the repository of engraved information relating to its manufacture.

**baff** Knot in rug-making.

**balance** Device counteracting the force of the mainspring in a clock's movement.

**balloon-back chair** Popular, rounded-backed Victorian dining or salon chair.

**baluster** (adj.) Having a dominant convex swell at the base, culminating in a smaller, concave one at the neck. (noun) One of a set of upright posts supporting a balustrade.

**banjo barometer** Wheel barometer dating from circa 1775-1900, with shape resembling a banjo.

**barley-sugar twist** Spiral-turned legs and rails popular in the seventeenth century. Colloquial.

**bat printed** Transfer printed (of ceramics).

**beech** Hardwood used in the manufacture of country furniture and, when stained, as a substitute for mahogany.

**bellarmine** Stoneware flagon made in Germany from the sixteenth century.

**bergère** French for an armchair, used in English to describe a chair with caned back and sides.

**bevel** Decorative, shaved edge of glass, particularly mirror.

**bezel** The metal rim of a glass cover or jewel.

**bird-cage** Support mechanism at the top of the pedestal of some eighteenth-century tilt-top tables.

**birch** Hardwood used principally for carcassing; occasionally for low-quality veneer.

**bird's eye maple** Wood of the sugar maple with distinctive figure caused by aborted buds. Used in veneering.

**biscuit (bisque)** Ceramics fired but unglazed, originating in France in the eighteenth century.

**blind fretwork** Fretwork carving on a solid background.

**block front** Front shaped from thick boards allowing for a recessed centre section.

**blue-dash** Blue dabs around the rim of a delftware plate.

**bob** The weight at the bottom of a pendulum.

**bobbin** Turned furniture element, resembling a row of connected spheres.

**bocage** Foliage, bushes and shrubs supporting, surrounding or standing behind porcelain or pottery figures.

**bombé** Having an outswelling front.

**bone china** Clay with bone ash in the formula, almost entirely porcellanous. First produced at the end of the eighteenth century.

**bonheur du jour** Small, lady's writing desk with a cabinet and drawers above. Originally French, from the mid eighteenth century.

**bottle glass** Low quality coloured glass for bottles, jars etc.

**boulle** An eighteenth-century marquetry style employing brass and tortoiseshell.

**boxlock** Flintlock gun with the mechanism enclosed in the breach.

**boxwood** Pale yellow, close-grained hardwood used for carving and turning and for inlay and pattern veneers.

**bow front** Convex curve on the front of chests of drawers.

**bracket clock** Domestic clock so called because of the necessity of standing it on a bracket to allow its weights to hang down, the term later applied to domestic clocks of the eighteenth and nineteenth centuries regardless of their motive force.

**bracket foot** Plain foot carved into the rail or stretcher to form an ornamental bracket.

**brandy saucepan** Miniature, bulbous or baluster shaped saucepan with long handle at right angles to the spout.

**breakfront** Describing a piece of furniture with a central section which projects forward.

**breech** Rear end of the barrel of a gun.

**breech-loading** Gun loaded through an opening in the breech.

**bright cut** Late eighteenth-century silver engraving technique, making the design brilliant in relief.

**Bristol glass** Eighteenth century coloured (often blue) glass produced in Bristol.

**Britannia metal** Form of refined pewter used as a silver substitute in the early nineteenth century.

**British plate** Silver substitute from the nineteenth century, immediately preceding the introduction of EPNS.

**broken arch** Arch above the dial of a long-case clock which is less than a semi-circle, indicating an early Georgian date.

**broken pediment** Pediment with a symmetrical break in the centre, often accommodating an urn or some such motif.

**bun foot** Flattened spherical foot often found on later seventeenth-century furniture.

**bureau** Desk with a fall front enclosing a fitted interior, with drawers below.

**bureau bookcase** Bureau with glazed bookcase above.

**burr** Veneer used in furniture making, with a decorative pattern caused by some abnormality of growth or knotting in the tree. Usually taken from the base of the tree.

**cabriole leg** Leg of a piece of furniture that curves out at the foot and in at the top.

Introduced in the seventeenth century.

**caddy** Tea caddy.

**caddy spoon** Short-handled, large bowled spoon for extracting tea from the caddy.

**calendar / date aperture** Window in the dial of a clock displaying day, month or date.

**canted corner** Decoratively angled corner.

**canterbury** An eighteenth-century container for sheet music.

**carcase/carcass** The inner frame of a piece of furniture, usually made of inferior wood for veneering.

**card case** Case for visiting cards, usually silver, nineteenth century.

**carriage clock** Portable timepiece, invented in nineteenth-century France, with handle above.

**cartel clock** Eighteenth-century French wall clock with profusely decorated case.

**case furniture** Furniture intended as a receptical, e.g. chest of drawers.

**caster / castor** 1. Sprinkling vessel for e.g. sugar. 2. Pivoted wheel attached to foot.

**Castleford ware** Shiny white stoneware made in Castleford and elsewhere from circa 1790.

**caudle cup** Covered cup, often in silver.

**cellaret** A wine cooler or container, usually eighteenth century.

**centrepiece** Ornament designed to sit in the centre of a dining table. Often in silver.

**chafing dish** Serving dish, often in silver, with stand incorporating a spirit lamp to retain heat.

**chain fusée** The fusée of a clock from which a chain unwinds on to the barrel of the mainspring.

**chamfer** A flattened angle; a corner that has been bevelled or planed.

**chapter ring** The ring on a clock dial on which the numbers of the hours are inscribed.

**Chesterfield** Deep-buttoned, upholstered settee from the nineteenth century.

**chest on chest** Tallboy having two chests fitting together, the lower with bracket feet, the upper with pediment. From the seventeenth and eighteenth centuries.

**chest on stand** Known as a tallboy or highboy, a chest of drawers on a stand.

**cheval mirror** Tall mirror supported by two uprights on swivels.

**chiffonnier** Side cupboard, originally, in the eighteenth century, with solid doors, but latterly with latticed or glazed doors.

**chinoiserie** Oriental-style decoration on lacquered furniture or artefacts.

**chronometer** Precision timepiece, often for navigation.

**circular movement** Clock movement of circular plates.

**cistern** Chamber containing mercury at the base of the tube of a barometer.

**claw-and-ball foot** Foot modelled as a ball clutched in a claw, frequently used to terminate a cabriole leg.

**clock garniture** Mantelpiece ornamentation with a clock as centrepiece.

**close helmet** Helmet covering the whole head and neck.

**coaster** Small, circular tray, often in silver, for holding a bottle.

**cockbeading** Bead moulding applied to the edges of drawers.

**cock bracket** Bracket supporting a watch mainspring.

**coin glass** Early eighteenth-century English drinking glass with a coin moulded into the knop of the stem.

**commode** High quality, highly decorated chest of drawers or cabinet, with applied mounts.

**compensated pendulum** Pendulum with mercury reservoir, the mercury rising and falling to compensate for the effects on the pendulum of changes of temperature.

**composition** Putty-like substance for moulding and applying to e.g. mirror frames, for gilding.

**console table** Often semi-circular table intended to stand against a wall on the pier between two windows (hence also pier table). Usually with matching mirror above.

**cordial glass** Glass originating in the seventeenth century, with a small bowl for strong drinks.

**corner chair** Chair with back splats on two sides and a bowed top rail, designed to fit into a corner.

**cornice** Horizontal top part of a piece of furniture; a decorative band of metal or wood used to conceal curtain fixtures

**coromandel** Wood from India's Coromandel coast, used for banding and inlay.

**counter-well** The small oval wooden dishes inset into early Georgian card tables for holding chips or cash, hence also guinea-well.

**country furniture** Functional furniture made outside the principal cities. Also provincial furniture.

**countwheel strike** Clock mechanism determining the number of strikes per hour.

**cow creamer** Silver or china cream jug modelled as a cow.

**crazing** Fine cracks in glaze.

**creamware** Earthenware glazed in a cream colour giving a porcelain effect, in a widely used technique originally devised by Wedgwood in the 1760s.

**credence table** Late seventeenth-century oak or walnut table with folding top.

**credenza** Long Victorian side cabinet with glazed or solid doors.

**crenellated** Crinkly, wavy.

**crested china** Ware decorated with heraldic crests; originally by Goss, but subsequently by many Staffordshire and German potteries.

**crinoline stretcher** Crescent-shaped stretcher supporting the legs of some Windsor chairs.

**cross-banding** Decorative edging with cross-grained veneer.

**cruet** Frame for holding condiment containers.

**crutch** The arm connecting a clock's pendulum to the pallet arbor.

**cuirass** Breastplate (of armour).

**cup and cover** Round turning with a distinctly separate top, common on legs until circa 1650.

**damascene** Inlay of precious metal onto a body of other metal for decorative purposes.

**davenport** Small English desk, reputedly originally produced by Gillow for a Captain Davenport in 1834. A day-bed or sofa in the USA.

**deadbeat escapement** Version of the anchor escapement that eliminates recoil and improves accuracy.

**deal** Sawn pine wood.

**delftware** Seventeenth- and eighteenth-century tin-glazed earthenware, often decorated in the style of Chinese blue and white porcelain or after Dutch seventeenth-century painting, after the style pioneered by the Delft pottery.

**Delft ware** Items of delftware which actually emanate from Delft.

**dentil** Small, block-shaped moulding found under a furniture cornice.

**dialplate** Frontplate of a clock.

**diamond cut** (of glass) Cut in diamond shape.

**dinanderie** Fifteenth-century brass artefact from the factories of Dinant, Belgium.

**dished table top** Hollowed-out, solid top, particularly of a pie-crust, tripod table.

**distressed** Artificially aged.

**dovetails** Interlocking joints used in drawers.

**double-action** A gun which may be cocked or self-cocking.

**douter** Scissor-like implement for extinguishing a candle.

**dowel** Peg holding together wooden joint.

**dram glass** Small, short-stemmed glass with rounded bowl.

**drop-in seat** Framed, upholstered seat which sits in the framework of a chair.

**drop handle** Pear-shaped brass furniture handle of the late seventeenth and early eighteenth centuries.

**drop-leaf table** Table with a fixed central section and hinged flaps.

**drum table** Circular writing table on a central pedestal with frieze drawers.

**dry-edge** With unglazed edges.

**dummy drawer** False drawer with handle.

**Dutch strike** Clock chime which strikes the next hour on the half hour.

**ebonize** To stain a wood to the dark colour of ebony.

**ebony** Much imitated exotic black hardwood, used as veneer in Europe from the seventeenth century, generally for very high quality pieces.

**écuelle** Two-handled French soup bowl with cover and stand, often Sèvres.

**electroplate** The technique of covering one metal with the thin layer of another.

**elm** Hardwood used in the manufacture of chair seats, country furniture and coffins.

**embossing** Relief decoration.

**enamel** Second, coloured glaze fired over first glaze.

**endstone** In a clock mechanism, jewel on which an arbor pivots.

**English dial** Nineteenth-century English wall clock with large painted dial, previously a fixture in railway stations.

**Engshalskrüge** Large German tin-glaze jug with cylindrical neck.

**épergne** Centrepiece of one central bowl surrounded by smaller ones.

**escritoire** Cabinet with a fall-front which forms a writing surface. With a fitted interior.

**escutcheon** Brass plate surrounding the edges of a keyhole.

**étuis** Small, metal oddments box.

**everted** Outward turned, flaring (e.g. of a lip).

**facet-cut** (of glass) Cut criss-cross into straight-edged planes.

**faience** Tin-glazed earthenware.

**fairings** Porcelain figures, especially German, made in the nineteenth and twentieth centuries in the mould. Usually comical and carrying descriptive captions.

**fall front** Flap of a bureau or secretaire that pulls out to provide a writing surface.

**famille rose** Predominantly pink-coloured Oriental porcelain.

**famille verte** Predominantly green-coloured Oriental porcelain.

**fauteuil** Open-sided, upholstered armchair with padded elbows.

**feather banding** Two bands of veneer laid at opposite diagonals.

**field** Area of a carpet within its decorated borders.

**fielded panel** Raised panel with chamfered edge fitting into a framework.

**figure** Natural pattern created by the grain through the wood.

**finial** Decorative, turned knob.

**flamed veneer** Veneer cut at an angle to enhance the figuring.

**flatware** Plates, knives and forks.

**flintlock** Gun mechanism whereby the priming in the pan is ignited by a spark created by a flint.

**flute glass** Glass with tall, slender bowl.

**fluting** Decorative parallel grooving.

**foliate carving** Carved flower and leaf motifs.

**foliot** Primitive form of balance for clock mechanisms.

**fretwork** Fine pierced decoration.

**frieze** Long ornamental strip.

**frit** The flux from which glass is made. An ingredient of soft-paste porcelain.

**frizzen** The metal which a flint strikes to create a spark in a flintlock mechanism.

**fruitwood** Generally the wood of apple, cherry and pear trees, used for ebonising and gilding, commonly in picture frames.

**fusee** The conical, grooved spool from which a line or chain unwinds as it is pulled by the mainspring of a clock movement.

**gadroon** Carved edge or moulded decoration consisting of a series of grooves, ending in a curved lip, with ridges between them.

**Gainsborough chair** Deep, upholstered armchair with padded, open arms and carved decoration.

**galleried** Having a wood or metal border around the top edge.

**garniture** Set of ornamental pieces of porcelain.

**gateleg** Leg that pivots to support a drop leaf.

**gesso** Plaster-like substance applied to carved furniture before gilding or moulded and applied as a substitute for carving.

**gilt-tooled decoration** Gold leaf impressed into the edges of leather on desk-tops.

**gimbal** Mounting which keeps a ship's barometer level at all times.

**girandole** Wall-mounted candle holder with a mirrored back.

**gorget** Item of armour for protecting the throat.

**Goss china** Range of porcelain, particularly heraldic, produced in Stoke-on-Trent from 1858.

**greave** Armour protecting lower leg.

**Greek key** Ancient key-shaped decoration often repeated in fretwork on furniture.

**gridiron pendulum** Clock pendulum consisting of rods of a mix of metals positioned in such a way that the dynamics of their behaviour when subjected to heat or cold keep the pendulum swing uniform.

**halberd** Double-headed axe weapon with projecting spike.

**half hunter** Watch with an opening front cover with glass to the centre and a chapter ring, giving protection to the glass over the dial.

**hallmark** The mark by which silver can be identified by standard, place of assay and date.

**hard-paste porcelain** Porcelain made with kaolin and petuntse in the Chinese fashion, pioneered in Europe at Meissen in the early eighteenth century.

**hunter** Watch with a hinged, opening front cover in solid metal.

**husk** Formalised leaf motif.

**ice glass** Glass with uneven, rippling surface.

**Imari** Japanese porcelain made in and around Arita from the early eighteenth century and shipped to Europe from the port of Imari. Blue, red and gold coloured.

**improved** A pejorative term implying that a piece has been altered in order dishonestly to enhance its value.

**inlay** The decorative setting of one material into a contrasting one.

**intaglio** Incised design.

**ironstone** Stoneware patented by Mason in 1813, in which slag from iron furnaces was mixed with the clay to toughen the ware.

**istoriato** Of some Italian majolica, meaning 'with a story on it'.

**japanned** Painted and varnished in imitation of Oriental style lacquer work.

**jardinière** An ornamental pot or vase for plants.

**jasper ware** Variety of coloured stoneware developed by the Wedgwood factory.

**joined** Manufactured with the use of mortice and tenon joints and dowels, but without glue.

**kabuto** Japanese Samurai helmet.

**kingwood** Exotic, purplish hardwood used in veneer.

**kneehole desk** Desk with a recessed cupboard beneath the frieze drawer.

**knop** Rounded projection or bulge in the stem of a glass.

**lacquer** Resinous substance which, when coloured, provides a ground for chinoiserie and gilding.

**ladder-back** Chair with a series of horizontal back rails.

**lantern clock** Clocks made in England from the sixteenth century, driven entirely by weights and marking only the hours. Similar in appearance to a lantern.

**lappit** Carved flap at the top of a leg with a pad foot.

**latten** Archaic term for brass.

**lead crystal** Particularly clear, brilliant glass including lead in the process.

**lead-glazed** the earliest glaze for Western pottery, derived from glass making.

**lever escapement** Modification of the anchor escapement for carriage clocks and, particularly, watches.

**lion's paw foot** Foot carved as a lion's paw. Commonly eighteenth century and Regency.

**lock** Firing mechanism of a gun.

**lockplate** Base holding firing mechanism on a gun barrel.

**loo table** Large Victorian card or games table.

**longcase clock** The 'grandfather' clock, housed in a tall wooden case containing the weights and pendulum.

**loper** Pull-out arm that supports the hinged fall of a bureau.

**lowboy** Small side table with cabriole legs, from the seventeenth century.

**lustre ware** Ceramic ware decorated with a metallic coating which changes colour when fired.

**mahogany** The hardwood most used in the production of furniture in England in the eighteenth and nineteenth centuries. Used as a solid wood until the nineteenth century, when its rarity led to its being used for veneer.

**majolica** Originally tin-glazed earthenware produced in Renaissance Italy, subsequently all nineteenth century wares using the same technique.

**mantel clock** Clock with feet designed to stand on a mantelpiece.

**maple** North American hardwood used for its variety of veneers.

**marine chronometer** Precision clock for use in navigation at sea.

**marquetry** The use of wooden and other inlays to form decorative patterns.

**married** Pejorative term applied to a piece of furniture which is made up of more than one piece of the same period.

**matchlock** Firing mechanism of a gun achieved by lowering a slow match into the priming pan.

**mazarine** Metal strainer fitting over a dish.

**mercury twist** Air-twist in glass of a silver colour.

**millefiori** Multi-coloured or mosaic glass.

**moonwork** Clock mechanism which computes and displays the phases of the moon.

**moquette** Heavy imitation velvet used for upholstery.

**morion** Helmet with upturned front peak.

**mortice** Slot element of a mortice and tenon joint.

**moulding** decorative, shaped band around an object or a panel.

**mount** Invariably metal mounting fitted to a piece of furniture.

**mule chest** Coffer with a single row of drawers to the base.

**musical clock** Clock with a cylinder which strikes bells to play a tune.

**Nailsea** Late eighteenth-century, boldly coloured, opaque glass from Nailsea, near Bristol.

**nest of tables** Set of three or four occasional tables which slot into each other when not in use.

**oak** Hardwood which darkens with age, predominant in English furniture manufacture until the middle of the seventeenth century.

**obverse** The front side of a coin or medal.

**ogee** An S-shaped curve.

**ogee arch** Two S-shaped curves coming together to form an arch.

**oignon** Onion-shaped French watch of the eighteenth century.

**ormolu** From French *dorure d'or moulu*: 'gilding with gold paste', gold-coloured alloy of copper, zinc, and sometimes tin, in various proportions but usually containing at least 50% copper. Ormolu is used in mounts (ornaments on borders, edges, and as angle guards) for furniture, especially eighteenth-century furniture.

**orrery** Astronomical clock which shows the position of heavenly bodies. Named after Charles Boyle, fourth Earl of Orrery.

**overglaze** See enamel.

**overmantel mirror** Mirror designed to hang over a mantelpiece.

**ovolo** A rounded, convex moulding, making an outward curve across a right angle.

**oyster veneer** Veneer resembling an open oyster shell, an effect achieved by slanting the cut across the grain of a branch.

**pad foot** Rounded foot on a circular base, used as termination for cabriole legs.

**pair-case** A double case for a watch, the inner for protection of the movement, the outer for decoration.

**pallet** Lever that engages in a clock's escapement wheel in orderb to arrest it.

**papier mâché** Moulded and lacquered pulped paper used to make small items of furniture and other artefacts.

**parian** Typically uncoloured, biscuit-style porcelain developed in the nineteenth century by Copeland and named after Parian white marble.

**parquetry** Veneered pattern using small pieces of veneer, often from different woods, in a geometrical design.

**patera** Circular ornament made of wood, metal or composition.

**patina** The layers of polish, dirt, grease and general handling marks that build up on a wooden piece of furniture over the years and give it its individual signs of age, varying from wood to wood.

**pearlware** White, shiny earthenware, often print decorated.

**pedestal desk** A flat desk with a leathered top standing on two banks of drawers.

**pediment** Architectural, triangular gable crowning a piece of furniture or a classical building.

**pegged furniture** Early furniture constructed with the use of mortice and tenon joints and pegged together with dowels.

**pembroke table** Small, two-flapped table standing on four legs or a pedestal.

**pepperette** Vessel, often in silver, for sprinkling pepper.

**petuntse** Chinese name for the feldspathic rock, an essential element of porcelain, which produces a glaze.

**pewter** Alloy of tin, lead and often various other metals.

**pie-crust** Expression used to describe the decorative edge of a dished-top tripod table.

**pier glass** Tall mirror for hanging on a pier between windows.

**pietra dura** Composition of semi-precious stones applied to panels of – usually Italian – furniture.

**pillar** (watchmaking) A rod connecting the dial-plate and backplate of a movement.

**pillar rug** Chinese rug made to be arranged around a pillar.

**pine** Softwood used for carcassing furniture.

**platform base** Flat base supporting a central pedestal and table-top above and standing on three or four scrolled or paw feet.

**plinth base** Solid base not raised on feet.

**pole screen** Adjustable fire screen.

**pommel** Knob at the end of the handle of a dagger.

**pontil mark** Mark made by the pontil, or blowpipe, on the base of hand-blown glass.

**porcellanous** Having most of the ingredients or characteristics of porcelain.

**porringer** Large, two-handled cup with cover.

**potboard** Bottom shelf of a dresser, often just above the floor.

**pounce box** A sprinkler for pounce, a powder for drying ink.

**Prattware** Staffordshire earthenware of the late eighteenth and early nineteenth centuries, decorated in distinctive colours on a buff ground.

**print decoration** Mass-produced decoration. Not hand painting.

**provincial furniture** See country furniture.

**punch bowl** Large bowl for the retention and dispensation of punch.

**quartered top** Flat surface covered with four pieces of matching veneer.

**quartetto tables** Nest of four occasional tables.

**quillon** Cross-piece of a sword.

**rail** A horizontal member running between the outer uprights of a piece of furniture.

**rating nut** Nut under the bob of a clock's pendulum by which the rate of swing may be adjusted.

**redware** Primitive eighteenth-century American ware made from a clay which turns red when fired.

**reeding** Parallel strips of convex fluting.

**re-entrant corner** Shaped indentation at each corner of a table.

**register plate** Plate on a barometer with inscriptions to be read against the level of mercury.

**regulator** Precision timepiece of the eighteenth century.

**relief** Proud of the surface.

**repeating work** Mechanism by which the pull of a cord or the press of a button operates the striking mechanism of a clock or watch to the last hour.

**repoussé** An embossed design which has been refined by chasing.

**rosewood** Named after its smell when newly cut, rather than its flower or colour, a dark-brown hardwood with an attractive stripe or ripple, used for veneering.

**rule joint** Hinge on furniture which fits so well that, when open, no join can be detected between two hinged parts.

**runners** Strips of wood, fitted to furniture, on which drawers slide.

**sabre leg** Chair leg in the shape of a sabre, typical of the Regency period.

**saltglaze** Stoneware in which salt is added to the recipe creating a porcellanous, glassy surface. Dates back to the early eighteenth century.

**salver** A large metal dish or tray for transporting smaller dishes.

**satinwood** A light golden-coloured, close-grained hardwood used for veneer, panelling and turning from the mid-eighteenth century onwards.

**scagiola** Composite material resembling marble.

**scalloped** Having a series of circular edges in the shape of a scallop shell.

**scalloped leaf** Serpentine flap on some pembroke tables.

**sconce** 1. Cup-shaped candle holder. 2. Metal plate fixed to the wall, supporting candle holder or light.

**scratch blue** Eighteenth-century saltglaze decoration where the body is incised and the incisions painted blue.

**scroll, scrolling** Carving or moulding of a curled design.

**seat rail** Horizontal framework below the chair seat uniting the legs.

**secretaire** Writing desk with false drawer front which lets down to reveal a writing surface and fitted interior.

**secretaire bookcase** Secretaire with bookcase fitted above.

**serpent** The arm holding the match or flint by which the priming of a gun was ignited.

**serpentine** Of undulating shape.

**settee** Upholstered settle.

**settle** Hard bench seat with back. The earliest form of seating for two or more people.

**Sheffield plate** Rolled sheet silver placed either side of a layer of copper and fused. Recognised by the Sheffield assay office in 1784, but made elsewhere, notably Birmingham, as well.

**shoe piece** Projection on the back rail of a chair into which the splat fits.

**side chair** Chair without arms designed to stand against the wall.

**side table** Any table designed to stand against the wall.

**skeleton clock** Clock with the workings exposed.

**slipware** Earthenware to which mixed clay and water has been added as decoration.

**sofa** Well-upholstered chair providing seating for two or more people.

**sofa table** Rectangular table with hinged flaps designed to stand behind a sofa.

**soft-paste porcelain** Porcelain using frit or soapstone instead of the petuntse of hard-paste porcelain. English, from the eighteenth century.

**spade foot** Square, tapered foot.

**spandrel** Pierced, decorative corner bracket found at the tops of legs.

**sparrow-beak jug** Jug with a triangular spout.

**spill vase** Container for lighting-tapers.

**spindle** Thoroughly turned piece of wood. The upright bars of a spindle-back chair.

**splat** The central upright of a chair back.

**sprig** Applied or relief ornamentation of any kind on a ceramic artefact.

**squab** Detachable cushion or upholstered seat of a chair or bench.

**standish** Inkstand, often in silver.

**stick barometer** Barometer with a straight, vertical register plate running alongside the mercury tube.

**stiles** Archaic term for the vertical parts of the framework of a piece of furniture.

**stoneware** Earthenware that is not porous after firing.

**stretcher** Rail joining the legs of a table or chair.

**strike / silent ring** Dial to disengage or re-engage the striking of a clock.

**stringing** Fine inlaid lines around a piece of furniture.

**stirrup cup** Cup used for alcoholic refreshment prior to hunting, usually shaped in the head of a fox or, less usually, a hound.

**stuff-over seat** Chair that is upholstered over the seat rail.

**subsidiary dial** Small dial, usually showing seconds, within the main dial of a clock or watch. Hence **subsidiary seconds**.

**swagged** With applied strips formed in a mould (of metal).

**swan-neck pediment** Pediment with two broken curves.

**swan-neck handle** Curved handle typical of the eighteenth century.

**sycamore** Hardwood of the maple family, light yellow in colour, used for veneering.

**tang** The end of the blade of a sword, covered by the hilt.

**tankard** Large beer-mug with a hinged lid and thumb-piece.

**tazza** Italian plate, cup, basin or wide-bowled glass.

**teapoy** Small piece of furniture designed for holding tea leaves. Usually Anglo-Indian.

**tenons** The tongues in mortice and tenon joints.

**thumb moulding** Decorative concave moulding.

**thumb-piece** Projection attached to a hinged lid which will open the lid when pressure is applied by the thumb.

**tine** Prong of a fork.

**tin-glazed** Lead-glazed earthenware to which tin is added, e.g. majolica.

**toilet mirror** Small dressing mirror with a box base and drawers.

**touch mark** Individual mark of the maker of a piece of early English pewter.

**transfer** Ceramic print decoration using colours held in oil.

**trefid spoon** A seventeenth-century spoon with the handle terminating in the shape of a bud, usually cleft or grooved into two lobes.

**trefoil** Having three lobes.

**trembleuse** Cup-stand with feet.

**tripod table** Small, round-topped table on three-legged base.

**tulipwood** Pinkish, naturally patterned hardwood used in veneer.

**turnery** Any wood turned on a lathe.

**tureen** Large bowl in porcelain or metal, usually with a lid and two handles.

**turret clock** Clock of any size driven by a weight suspended by a rope wrapped round a drum.

**underglaze** Colour or design painted below the glaze of a ceramic artefact.

**uniface** Medal or coin with modelling on one side only.

**urn table** Eighteenth-century table designed to hold an urn.

**veneer** A thin sheet of wood laid across a cheaper carcase or used as inlay decoration.

**verge escapement** Mechanism for regulating a clock movement before the anchor escapement.

**Vesta case** Match box for Vesta matches, often in silver, from circa 1850.

**vinaigrette** Small, eighteenth-century box, often silver, to hold a sponge soaked in vinegar to ward off germs and the unpleasant odours of the day.

**wainscot chair** Joined chair with open arms and a panelled back.

**walnut** The hardwood used in England for the manufacture of furniture from the Restoration, originally in solid form but mostly as veneer, particularly burr walnut, after the beginning of the eighteenth century.

**well** Interior of a plate or bowl.

**Wemyss ware** Late nineteenth-century lead-glazed earthenware originally from Fife, Scotland.

**whatnot** Mobile stand with open shelves.

**wheel-back chair** Originally late eighteenth-century chair with circular back with radiating spokes.

**windsor chair** Wooden chair with spindle back.

**yew** Tough, close-grained hardwood used for turning, particularly in chair legs, and in veneer.

There follows a list of antique dealers, many of whom have provided items in the main body of the book and all of whom will be happy to assist within their areas of expertise.

**51 Antiques**
**(ref: Bazaart)**
51 Ledbury Rd, London W11 2AA
Tel: 020 72296153  Fax: 020 72296153
Justin.bazaart@virgin.net
*Italian ceramics and glass, 15th-20th century.*

**75 Portobello Rd**
**(ref: Elizabeth Bradwin)**
75 Portobello Rd, London W11 2QB
Tel: 020 7221 1121  Fax: 020 8947 2629
Mobile: 0378 731826
*19th- and early 20th-century animal subjects.*

**No.1 Castlegate Antiques**
**(ref: Castlegate)**
1-3 Castlegate, Newark, Notts NG24 1AZ
Tel: 01636 701877
*18th and 19th-century furniture and decorative objects.*

**Norman Adams**
8-10 Hans Rd, London SW3 1RX
Tel: 020 7589 5266  Fax: 020 7589 1968
antiques@normanadams.com
www.normanadams.com
*Fine 18th-century furniture and works of art.*

**B. & T. Antiques**
79/81 Ledbury Road, London W11 2AG
Tel: 020 7229 7001  Fax: 020 7229 2033
*Furniture, silver, objets d'art, paintings, 18th-century to Art Deco.*

**Aaron Gallery**
**(ref: Aaron)**
34 Bruton St, London W1X 7DD
Tel: 020 7499 9434  Fax: 020 7499 0072
www.AaronGallery.com
*Islamic art and antiquities.*

**Emmy Abé**
Stand 33, Bond St Antique Centre, 124 New Bond St, London W1X 9AE
Tel: 020 7629 1826  Fax: 020 7491 9400
*Exclusively selected antique and modern jewellery.*

**Aberg Antiques**
**(ref: Aberg)**
42 The Little Boltons, London SW10 9LN
Tel: 020 7370 7253  Fax: same
Mobile: 0385 958828
*Furniture.*

**Arthur Ackermann & Peter Johnson Ltd**
27 Lowndes Street, London SW1X 9HY
Tel: 020 7235 6464  Fax: 020 7823 1057
*Paintings, drawings and watercolours.*

**A.D.C. Heritage Ltd**
95A Charlwood Street, London SW1V 4PB
Tel: 020 7976 5271  *Fax: 020 7976 5898*
*Silver and old Sheffield plate; valuations.*

**Aesthetics**
Stand V2, Antiquarius,
131-141 King's Road, London SW3 4PW
Tel: 020 7352 0395  Fax: 020 7376 4057
*Silver; ceramics and decorative art; particularly the Aesthetic and Arts and Crafts movements; antiquarian books.*

**After Noah**
121 Upper Street, London N1 1QP
Tel: 020 7359 4281  Fax: 020 7359 4281
*and*
261 King's Rd, London SW3 5EL
Tel: 020 7351 2610  Fax: same
*Specializes in oak and similar furniture, iron and brass beds, decorative items, candlesticks, mirrors, lighting, kitchenalia and jewellery. Furnishment and furbishment.*

**W. Agnew & Company Ltd**
58 Englefield Road, London N1 4HA
Tel: 020 7254 7429  Fax: 020 7254 7429
Mobile: 0973 188272
*Sculpture; works of art; majolica and pottery.*

**Agnew's**
43 Old Bond Street, London W1X 4BA
Tel: 020 7629 6176  Fax: 020 7629 4359
*Old Master paintings and drawings; English paintings and watercolours; prints, sculpture and works of art; valuations.*

**Adrian Alan**
66/67 South Audley Street, London W1Y 5FE
Tel: 020 7495 2324  Fax: 020 7495 0204
*and*
219 Kensington Church St, London W8 7LX
Tel: 020 7727 4783  Fax: 020 7727 7353
*18th- and 19th-century continental furniture; clocks and barometers; European ceramics; decorations.*

**Albany Antiques**
**(ref: Albany)**
8-10 London Road, Hindhead,
Surrey GU26 6AF
Tel: 01428 605528  Fax: 01428 605528
*Georgian furniture, glass, china and works of art.*

**AM-PM**
V35 Antiquarius Antiques Market,
135 King's Rd, London SW3
Tel: 020 7351 5654
*Antique and modern watches.*

**Philip Andrade**
White Oxen Manor, Rattery, South Brent,
Devon TQ10 9JX
Tel: 01364 72454  Fax: 01364 73061
*17th-,18th- and early 19th-century furniture,
porcelain and pottery, interesting objects.*

**Paul Andrews Antiques**
The Furniture Cave,
533 King's Road, London SW10 0TZ
Tel: 020 7352 4584  Fax: 020 7351 7815
www.paulandrews.co.uk
mail@paulandrews.co.uk
*Roman period sculpture, old masters, tapestries,
works of art & 17th- to 20th-century furniture.*

**Angel Antiques
(ref: Angel)**
Church Street, Petworth, West Sussex GU28 0AD
Tel: 01798 343 306  Fax: 01798 342 665
swan189@aol.com
*Country furniture.*

**Antiques Pavilion**
175 Bermondsey Street, London SE1 3UW
Tel: 020 7403 2021
*Furniture, Georgian to 1930s.*

**Antique Warehouse**
9-14 Dentford Broadway, London SE8 4PA
Tel: 020 8691 3062  Fax: 020 8469 0295
martyn@antiquewarehouse.co.uk
www.antiquewarehouse.co.uk
*Decorative antiques.*

**Architectural Emporium, The**
55 St. John's Road, Tunbridge Wells,
Kent TN4 9TP
Tel: 01892 540368
*Antique fireplaces, period lighting and garden
statuary furniture.*

**Argyll Etkin Limited**
1-9 Hills Place, Oxford Circus, London W1R 1AG
Tel: 020 7437 7800  Fax: 020 7434 1060
*Postal history.*

**Armoury of St. James's Military
Antiquarians, The
(ref: The Armoury)**
17 Piccadilly Arcade, London SW 1Y 6NH
Tel: 020 7493 5082  Fax: 020 7499 4422
welcome@armoury.co.uk
www.armoury.co.uk/home
*British and foreign orders, decorations and medals,
18th century to date, militaria, toy and hand-painted
collector's model soldiers.*

**Armstrong**
10 & 11 Montpellier Parade, Harrogate,
North Yorkshire HG1 2TJ
Tel: 01423 506843
www.harrogateantiques.com
*18th- and early 19th-century English furniture and
works of art; valuations.*

**Sean Arnold Sporting Antiques
(ref: Sean Arnold)**
1 Pembridge Villas, London W2 4XE
Tel: 020 7221 2267  Fax: 020 7221 5464
*Sporting antiques.*

**Art Nouveau Originals c.1900**
11 Camden Passage, London N1
Tel: 020 7359 4127  Mobile: 0374 718096
anoc1900@compuserve.com
*Eclectic mix from Art Nouveau period.*

**Victor Arwas Gallery-Editions Graphiques Ltd
(ref: Arwas)**
3 Clifford Street, London W1X 1RA
Tel: 020 7734 3944  Fax: 020 7437 1859
www.victorarwas.com
art@victorarwas.com
*Art Nouveau and Art Deco, glass, ceramics, bronzes,
sculpture, furniture, jewellery, silver, pewter, books
and posters 1880-1940, paintings, watercolours and
drawings, 1880 to date, original graphics, lithographs,
etchings, woodcuts 1890 to date.*

**Ash Rare Books
(ref: Ash Books)**
153 Fenchurch St, London EC3M 6BB
Tel: 020 7626 2665  Fax: same
www.ashrare.com
*Books, maps and prints*

**Garry Atkins**
107 Kensington Church St, London W8 7LN
Tel: 020 7727 8737  Fax: 020 7792 9010
*English and continental pottery to 18th century,
small furniture to 19th century.*

**Atlantic Bay Gallery**
5 Sedley Place, London W1R 1HH
Tel: 020 7355 3301  Fax: 020 7355 3760
*Antique Oriental and European carpets and textiles.*

**Axia Art Consultants Ltd
(ref: Axia)**
21 Ledbury Rd, London W11 2AQ
Tel: 020 7727 9724  Fax: 020 7229 1272
*Islamic and Byzantine works of art, textiles,
metalwork, woodwork, ceramics and icons.*

**Baggott Church Street Ltd**
Church Street, Stow-on-the-Wold,
Gloucestershire GL54 1BB
Tel: 01451 830370  Fax: 01451 832174
*17th- to 19th-century English furniture; portrait
paintings; metalwork; treen.*

**David Baker**
Grays Mews Antique Market,
1-7 Davies Mews, London W1Y 2LP
Tel: 020 8346 1387  Fax: same
davidbaker@asianartlondon.com

**Gregg Baker Oriental Art**
**(ref: Gregg Baker)**
132 Kensington Church St, London W8 4BH
Tel: 020 7221 3533    Fax: 020 7221 4410
www.greggbaker.com
gbakerart@aol.com
*Japanese and Chinese works of art and Japanese
paper screens, mainly 18th- and 19th-century.*

**Christopher Bangs**
PO Box 6077, London SW6 7XS
Tel: 020 7381 3532    Fax: 020 7381 2192
Mobile: 0836 333 532
*Works of art; domestic metalwork and metalware;
valuations.*

**Eddy Bardawil Antiques**
106 Kensington Church St, London W8 4BH
Tel: 020 7221 3967    Fax: 020 7221 5124
*18th- and early 19th-century English furniture; glass
pictures; metalwork; paintings, drawings and prints.*

**Barham Antiques**
**(ref: Barham)**
83 Portobello Road, London W11 2QB
Tel: 020 7727 3845    Fax: 020 7727 3845
*Victorian walnut and inlaid continental furniture,
writing boxes, tea caddies, inkwells and inkstands,
glass epergnes, silver plate, clocks, paintings.*

**R.A. Barnes Antiques**
**(ref: R.A. Barnes)**
26 Lower Richmond Rd, London SW15
Tel: 020 8789 3371
*Porcelain, Wedgwood, ironstone, china, brass,
copper, glass, Regency and Victorian furniture.*

**Barnet Antiques**
79 Kensington Church St, London W8 4BG
Tel: 020 7376 2817
*English furniture, 18th- and early 19th-century.*

**Nigel Bartlett**
67 St Thomas Street, London SE1 3QX
Tel: 020 7378 7895    Fax: 020 7378 0388
*Architectural antiques, mainly English chimneypieces.*

**Baskeville Antiques**
Saddlers House, Saddlers Row, Petworth,
West Sussex GU28 0AN
Tel: 01798 342067    Fax: 01798 343956
*Antique clocks and barometers.*

**H. C. Baxter & Sons**
40 Drewstead Road, London SW16 1AB
Tel: 020 8769 5869/5969    Fax: 020 8769 0898
*Eighteenth century furniture; valuations.*

**Don Bayney**
Grays Mews Antiques Market, 1-7 Davies Mews,
London W1Y 2LP
Tel: 020 7629 3644    Fax: 020 8578 4701
*Japanese works of art.*

**J. & A. Beare Ltd**
7 Broadwick Street, London W1V 1FJ
Tel: 020 7437 1449    Fax: 020 7439 4520
*Musical instruments of the violin family; valuations.*

**Frederick Beck Ltd**
**(ref: F. Beck)**
22/26 Camden Passage, Islington, London N1 8ED
Tel: 020 7226 3403    Fax: 020 7288 1305
banks_roy@hotmail.com
*General antiques.*

**Linda Bee**
Grays in the Mews Antiques Market, 1-7 Davies
Mews, London W1Y 1AR
Tel: 020 7629 5921    Fax: 020 7629 5921
Mobile: 0956 276384
*Vintage costume jewellery and fashion accessories.*

**Julia Bennett**
Tel: 01279 850279
Mobile: 0831 198 550    Mobile: 0831 614009
*Period furniture and decorative antiques.*

**bent ply**
Unit 58 downstairs at Alfie's,
13 Church St, London NW8
Tel: 020 8346 1387    Fax: 020 8346 1387
Mobile: 07711 940931
bruna@bentply.com
*20th-century avant garde furniture and design,
mainly '30s and '50s.*

**Berwald Oriental Art**
101 Kensington Church St, London W8 7LN
Tel: 020 7229 0800    Fax: 020 7229 1101
www.berwald-oriental.com
*Chinese pottery, porcelain; works of art; valuations.*

**Beverley**
30 Church Street, London NW8 8EP
Tel: 020 7262 1576    Fax: 020 7262 1576
*Art Nouveau, Art Deco, decorative objects.*

**Big Baby & Little Baby Antiques**
**(ref: Big Baby Little Baby)**
Grays Antiques Market, Davies Mews, London W1
Tel: 020 8367 2441    Fax: 020 8366 5811
*Dolls, teddies, prams and related collectables.*

**Bike Park**
63 New King's Rd, London SW6 4SE
Tel: 020 7565 0777
info@bikepark.co.uk
www.bikepark.co.uk
*Bikes, rentals, repairs and clothing.*

**Bizarre**
24 Church Street, London NW8 8EP
Tel: 020 7724 1305    Fax: 020 7724 1316
www.antiques-uk/bizarre
*Decorative art 1900-1950, Art Deco.*

**David Black Oriental Carpets**
96 Portland Road, Holland Park,
London W11 4LN
Tel: 020 7727 2566   Fax: 020 7229 4599
*Carpets and rugs; tapestry, needlework and fabrics.*

**Laurence Black Ltd**
60 Thistle Street, Edinburgh EH2 1EN
Tel: 0131-220 3387
*Scottish furniture; pottery; glass; treen; paintings.*

**Oonagh Black Antiques**
**(ref: Oonagh Black)**
Lower Farm House, Coln Rogers
Gloucestershire GL543LA
Tel: 01285 720717   Fax: 01285 720910
Mobile: 0468 568966
victorblack@compuserve.com
*French and English country furniture, decorative
accessories and French Saience and textiles.*

**H. Blairman & Sons Ltd**
119 Mount Street, London W1Y 5HB
Tel: 020 7493 0444   Fax: 020 7495 0766
*Furniture; later 19th- and early 20th-century
western applied arts; glass pictures.*

**A. & B. Bloomstein Ltd**
Bond Street Galleries,
111/112 New Bond Street, London W1Y 0BQ
Tel: 020 7493 6180   Fax: 020 7495 3493
*Silver and old Sheffield plate.*

**Bluthners Pianos Centre**
**(ref: Bluthners)**
8 Berkeley Square, London W1 5HF
Tel: 020 7753 0533   Fax: 020 7753 0535
whelpdle@globalnet.co.uk
*Highly decorated pianos.*

**John Bly**
27 Bury Street, St. James's, London SW1Y 6AL
Tel: 020 7930 1292   Fax: 020 7839 4775
*English furniture, silver, glass, porcelain and fine
paintings, 18th- and 19th-century.*

**Bobinet Ltd**
PO Box 2730, London NW8 9PL
Tel: 020 7266 0783   Fax: 020 7289 5119
*Clocks and watches; scientific instruments;
valuations.*

**Book & Comic Exchange**
14 Pembridge Road, London W11
Tel: 020 7229 8420
www.buy-sell-trade.co.uk
*Also pop memorabilia.*

**Malcolm Bord Gold Coin Exchange**
**(ref: Malcolm Bord)**
16 Charing Cross Road, London WC2H 0HR
Tel: 020 7836 0631 / 240 0479   Fax: 020 7240 1920
*Dealing in all types of coins, medals and bank notes.*

**Julia Boston**
2 Michael Road, London SW6 2AD
Tel: 020 7610 6783   Fax: 020 7610 6784
Mobile: 0468 254 662
juliaboston@jbostonantiques.demon.co.uk
www.juliaboston.co.uk
*Tapestry cartoons, engravings, 18th- and 19th-
century decorative antiques.*

**M.J. Bowdery**
12 London Road, Hindhead, Surrey
Tel: 01428 606 376   Mobile: 0374 821444
*18th- and 19th-century continental and English
furniture.*

**Robert Bowman**
PO Box 13393, London SW3 4RP
Tel: 020 7730 8057   Fax: 020 7259 9195
www.icollector.com
*19th- and early 20th-century sculpture in bronze
and marble.*

**Elizabeth Bradwin**
75 Portobello Road, London W11 2QB
Tel: 020 7221 1121   Fax: 020 8947 2629
Mobile: 0378 731 826
*Animal subjects.*

**Lesley Bragge**
**(ref: Bragge)**
Fairfield House, High Street,
Petworth, West Sussex
Tel: 01798 342324
*Wine-related items.*

**Brand Inglis**
4th Floor, 5 Vigo Street, London W1X 1AH
Tel: 020 7439 6604   Fax: 020 7439 6605
*Silver.*

**Brandt Oriental Art**
**(ref: Brandt)**
First Floor, 29 New Bond Street,
London W1Y 9HD
Tel: 020 7499 8835   Fax: 020 7409 1882
Mobile: 0374 989661
*Chinese and Japanese works of art.*

**Arthur Brett & Sons Ltd**
42 St Giles Street, Norwich, Norfolk NR2 1LW
Tel: 01603 628171   Fax: 01603 630245
*Furniture; European sculpture and works of art;
metalwork.*

**Simon Brett**
Creswyke House, High Street, Moreton-in-
Marsh, Gloucestershire GL56 0LH
Tel: 01608 650751   Fax: 01608 651791
*Fishing-related items; portrait miniatures.*

**Bridge Bikes**
137 Putney Bridge Rd, London SW15 2PA
Tel: 020 8870 3934
*Bikes.*

**Christine Bridge Antiques**
78 Castelnau, London SW13 9EX
Tel: 020 8741 5501   Fax 020 8755 0172
*Open by appointment only. Fine 18th-century
collector's glass and 19th-century coloured glass.*

**F. E. A. Briggs Ltd**
77 Ledbury Road, London W11 2AG
Tel: 020 7727 0909
*Marine items.*

**Aubrey Brocklehurst**
**(ref: A. Brocklehurst)**
124 Cromwell Rd, London SW7 4ET
Tel: 020 7373 0319   Fax: 020 7373 7612
*English clocks and barometers.*

**David Brower Antiques**
**(ref: David Brower)**
113 Kensington Church St, London W8 7LN
Tel: 020 7221 4155   Fax: 0207 221 6211
www.davidbrower-antiques.com
david@davidbrower.com
*Oriental and continental decorative porcelain,
French and Oriental furniture, bronzes and clocks.*

**I. & J.L. Brown Ltd**
**(ref: I. & J.L. Brown)**
636-632 King's Road,
London, SW6 2DU
Tel: 020 7736 4141
www.brownantiques.com
enquiries@brownantiques.com
*Furniture.*

**Brown's Antique Furniture**
**(ref: Browns)**
1st Floor, The Furniture Cave, 533 King's Rd,
London SW10 0TZ
Tel: 020 7352 2046   Fax: 020 7352 3654
mail@firstfloor.co.uk
*Library and dining furniture and decorative objects,
from early 18th century.*

**S. Brunswick**
13 Church Street, London NW8 8DT
Tel: 020 7724 9097   Fax: 020 8902 5656
*House, garden and conservatory.*

**Peter Bunting Antiques**
Harthill Hall, Alport, Bakewell,
Derbyshire DE45 1LH
Tel: 01629 636 203   Fax: 01629 636 190
Mobile: 0860 540 870
peter@peterbunting.com
*Early oak and country furniture, portraits
and tapestries.*

**W.G.T. Burne**
**(Antique Glass) Ltd**
PO Box 9465, London SW20 9ZD
Fax: 0208 543 6319   Mobile: 0374 725834
*English and Irish glass; chandeliers; valuations.*

**Burns & Graham**
27 St Thomas Street, Winchester,
Hampshire SO23 9HJ
Tel: 01962 853779
*Furniture up to 1850 and related objects.*

**Butchoff Antiques**
**(ref: Butchoff)**
220 Westbourne Grove, London W11 2RH
Tel: 020 7221 8174   Fax: 020 7792 8923
www.butchoff.co.uk ian@butchoff.co.uk
*18th- and 19th-century English and continental
furniture.*

**Butchoff Interiors**
**(ref: Butchoff Interiors)**
229 Westbourne Grove, London W11 2SE
Tel: 020 7221 8163   Fax: 020 7792 8923
www.butchoff.co.uk
adam@butchoff.co.uk
*Furniture, lighting.*

**C.A.R.S of Brighton**
**(ref: C.A.R.S)**
4-4a Chapel Terrace Mews, Kemp Town,
Brighton BN2 1HU
Tel: 01273 622 722   Tel/Fax: 01273 601 960
cars@kemptown-brighton.freeserve.co.uk
www.carsofbrighton.co.uk
*Classic automobilia & regalia specialists, children's
pedal cars.*

**Vincenzo Caffarella**
Alfie's Antique Market, 13-25 Church Street,
London NW8 8DT
Tel: 020 7723 1513   Fax: 020 8731 8615
monicag@clara.net
www.vinca.co.uk
*20th-century decorative arts and antiques.*

**Cameo Gallery**
151 Sydney St, London SW3 6NT
Tel: 020 73520909   Fax: 020 73520066
www.cameogallery.com
*Art Nouveau and Art Deco.*

**Jasmin Cameron**
Antiquarius Antiques Market,
135 King's Rd, London SW3 4PW
Tel: 020 7351 4154   Fax: 020 7351 4154
Mobile: 0374 871257
*Specialising in drinking glasses and decanters 1750-
1910, vintage fountain pens, writing materials and
Rene Lalique glass/Art Deco.*

**Malcolm Cameron**
The Antique Galleries, Watling Street,
Paulerspury, nr. Towcester, Northamptonshire
NN12 6LQ
Tel: 01327 811238
*17th-, 18th- and early 19th-century English
furniture and barometers.*

**Gerard Campbell**
Maple House, Market Place, Lechlade-on-
Thames, Gloucestershire GL7 3AB
Tel: 01367 252267
*Clocks; speciality: early Viennese Biedermeier
period regulators.*

**Canonbury Antiques**
**(ref: Canonbury)**
174 Westbourne Grove, London W11 2RW
Tel: 020 7727 4628   Fax: 020 7229 5840
*Dutch, English and French furniture and some
porcelain.*

**Patric Capon**
350 Upper Street, Islington, London N1 0PD
Tel: 020 7354 0487 or 020 8467 5722 anytime
Fax: 0181-295 1475
*Clocks, marine chronometers, barometers;
valuations.*

**Carlton Hobbs Ltd**
46a Pimlico Road, London SW1W 8LP
Tel: 020 7730 3640 / 3517   Fax: 020 7730 6080
*18th-century and early 19th-century English and
continental furniture and works of art.*

**John Carlton-Smith**
17 Ryder Street, London SW1Y 6PY
Tel: 020 7930 6622   Fax: 020 7930 9719
*Clocks and barometers; valuations.*

**Vivienne Carroll**
Antiquarius, Stand N1,
135 King's Road, London SW3 4PW
Tel: 020 7352 8882   Fax: 020 7352 8734
*Silver, jewellery, porcelain and ivory.*

**Cartoon Gallery, The**
**(ref: Cartoon Gallery)**
39 Great Russell Street, London WC1 3PH
Tel: 020 7636 1011   Fax: 020 7436 5053
www.cartoongallery.co.uk
gosh-com@easynet.co.uk
*Comics.*

**Mia Cartwright Antiques**
**(re: Mia Cartwright)**
20th C. Theatre Arcade,
291 Westbourne Grove, London W11
Tel: 01273 579700   Mobile: 0956 440260
*Saturdays only.*

**Manuel Castilho Antiques**
53 Ledbury Road, London W11 2AA
Tel: 020 7221 4928

**R. G. Cave & Sons Ltd**
Walcote House, 17 Broad Street, Ludlow,
Shropshire SY8 1NG
Tel: 01584 873568   Fax: 01584 875050
*Furniture; clocks; metalware; bijouterie; paintings
and drawings; valuations.*

**Rupert Cavendish Antiques**
**(ref: R. Cavendish)**
610 King's Road, London SW6 2DX
Tel: 020 7731 7041   Fax: 020 7731 8302
www.rupertcavendish.co.uk
RCavendish@aol.com
*Empire, Biedermeier and Art Deco furniture; 20th-
century oil paintings, Swedish Gustavian, Louis
XVI, Empire.*

**Ronald G. Chambers Fine Antiques**
**(ref: Ronald G. Chambers)**
The Market Square, Petworth, West Sussex
Tel: 01798 342305   Fax: 01798 342724
Mobile: 07932 161 968
www.ronaldchambers.com
Jackie@ronaldchambers.com

**Paul Champkins**
41 Dover Street, London W1X 3RB
Tel: 020 7495 4600   Fax 01235 751658
*Oriental art, specialising in Chinese, Korean
and Japanese.*

**Antoine Cheneviere Fine Arts Ltd**
27 Bruton Street, London W1X 7DB
Tel: 020 7491 1007   Fax: 020 7495 6173
*18th- and 19th-century Russian, Austrian, German,
and Italian furniture and objets d'art.*

**Circa**
L43, Grays Mews Antiques Market,
1- 7 Davies Mews, London W1Y 2LP
Tel: 01279 466260   Fax: 01279 466260
Mobile: 07887 778499
*Decorative and collectable glass.*

**Classic Library**
1st Floor, The Furniture Cave, 533 King's Road,
London SW10 0TZ
Tel: 020 7376 7653   Fax: 020 7259 0323
*Antiquarian books and period library furniture.*

**John Clay Antiques**
**(ref: John Clay)**
263 New King's Road, London SW6 4RB
Tel: 020 77315677
claycorps@yahoo.com
*Furniture, objets d'art, silver and clocks, 18th- and
19th-century.*

**Teresa Clayton (TRIO)**
**(ref: Trio)**
L24, Grays Mews Antiques Market,
1-7 Davies Mews, London W1Y 2LP
Tel: 020 7493 2736   Fax: 020 7493 9344
*Perfume bottles and Bohemian glass.*

**Clock Workshop, The**
**(ref: Clock Workshop)**
17 Prospect St, Caversham, Reading RG4 8JB
Tel: 0118 947 0741
*Fine clocks for decoration.*

**Close Antiques**
Alresford, Hampshire
Tel: 01962 732189
*17th- and 18th-century country furniture;*
*metalwork; English delftware; pottery;*
*samplers and needlework pictures.*

**Cobwebs**
78 Northam Road, Southampton SO14 0PB
Tel: 01703 227 458   Fax: 01703 227 458
www.cobwebs.co.uk
*Ocean liner memorabilia.*

**Cohen & Cohen**
101B Kensington Church St, London W8 7LN
Tel: 020 7727 7677   Fax: 020 7229 9653
www.artnet.com/cohen&cohen
michaelcohen@excite.com
*Chinese export porcelain and works of art.*

**Garrick D. Coleman**
**(ref: G.D. Coleman)**
75 Portobello Rd, London W11 2QB
Tel: 020 7937 5524   Fax: 020 7937 5530
coleman_antiques_london@compuserve.com
*Antiques, fine chess sets and glass paperweights.*

**Collectiques**
44 Arundel Close, New Milton,
Hampshire BH25 5UH
Tel: 014256 20794   Fax: 07989 775891
www.antiquebottles.com
robkayrobkay@globalnet.co.uk
*Antique collectable bottles.*

**J. Collins & Son**
**(ref: J. Collins)**
The Studio, 28 High St, Bideford,
Devon EX39 2AN
Tel: 01237 473103   Fax: 01237 475658
*Antiques, uniques, period furniture and*
*fine paintings.*

**Colnaghi**
15 Old Bond Street, London W1X 4JL
Tel: 020 7491 7408   Fax: 020 7491 8851
www.art-on-line.com/colnaghi/colnaghi/
*Old Master paintings and drawings from the*
*14th to the 19th century; English paintings.*

**Marc Constantini Antiques**
**(ref: M. Constantini)**
313 Lillie Road, London SW6 7LL
*English.*

**Rosemary Conquest**
4 Charlton Place, London N1 8AJ
Tel: 020 7359 0616
*French, Dutch and English lighting, furniture and*
*decorative objects.*

**Hilary Conqy**
K6, Antiquarius Antiques Market, 135 King's Rd,
London SW3 4PW
Tel: 020 7352 2099
*Jewellery.*

**Sheila Cook Textiles**
**(ref: Sheila Cook)**
184 Westbourne Grove, London W11 2RH
Tel: 020 7792 8001   Fax: 020 7229 3855
www.sheilacook.co.uk
*Textiles, costume and accessories – mid 18th-century*
*to 1970.*

**Jonathan Cooper**
Park Walk Gallery, 20 Park Walk,
London SW10 0AQ
Tel: 020 7351 0410   Fax: 020 7351 0410
*19th- and 20th-century British and continental*
*paintings.*

**Thomas Coulborn & Sons**
Vesey Manor, 64 Birmingham Road,
Sutton Coldfield, West Midlands B72 1QP
Tel: 0121 354 3974   Fax: 0121 354 4614
*18th-century furniture and works of art; valuations.*

**Country Antiques (Wales)**
Castle Mill, Kidwelly,
Carmarthenshire SA17 4UU
Tel: 01554 890534
*17th- to 19th-century furniture; pottery, treen*
*and folk art with emphasis on items of Welsh*
*interest; valuations.*

**Country Seat, The**
**(ref: Country Seat)**
Huntercombe Manor Barn,
Henley-on-Thames, Oxfordshire RG9 5RY
Tel: 01491 641349   Fax: 01491 641533
www.thecountryseat.com
ferry&clegg@thecountryseat.com
*17th- to 20th-century English furniture allied art.*

**County Antiques**
Burlton Hall, Burlton, Shrewsbury SY4 5SX
Tel: 01939 270819
*17th- and 18th-century oak and walnut country*
*house furniture - contact Mr & Mrs Michael Bailey.*

**Polly de Courcy-Ireland**
PO Box 29, Alresford, Hampshire SO24 9WP
Tel: 01962 733131
*17th- to early 19th-century treen and unusual*
*objects.*

**Richard Courtney Ltd**
112-114 Fulham Road,
South Kensington, London SW3 6HU
Tel: 020 7370 4020   Fax: 020 7370 4020
*18th-century English furniture.*

**Crawley and Asquith Ltd**
20 Upper Phillimore Gardens, London W8 7HA
Tel: 020 7937 9523   Fax: 020 7937 2159
*17th-, 18th- and 19th-century oils and watercolours;
original engravings and lithographs (topographical,
architectural and natural history); rare books.*

**Peter A. Crofts**
Briar Patch, 117 High Road, Elm, Wisbech,
Cambridgeshire PE14 0DN
Tel: 01945 584614
*18th-century furniture; jewellery, bijouterie and
snuff boxes; porcelain, pottery and enamels; silver
and old Sheffield plate; valuations.*

**Sandra Cronan Ltd**
18 Burlington Arcade, London W1V 9AB
Tel: 020 7491 4851   Fax: 020 7493 2758
Sandracronanltd@btinternet.com
*Art Deco jewellery.*

**Curios Gardens & Interiors**
**(ref: Curios)**
130c Junction Road, Archway, London N19
Tel: 020 7272 5603
*Decorative objects especially unusual items; general
antiques, pictures and garden furniture.*

**Andrew Dando**
4 Wood Street, Queen Square, Bath,
Somerset BA1 2JQ
Tel: 01225 422702   Fax: 01225 310717
www.andrewdando.co.uk
andrew@andrewdando.co.uk
*Open Monday-Friday 9.30-1, 2.15-5.30;
Saturday 10-1.
Specialist in English, continental and Oriental
pottery and porcelain 1650 to 1870; small stock
of furniture.*

**Michael Davidson**
54 Ledbury Road, London W11 2AJ
Tel: 020 7229 6088
*Regency and period furniture, objets d'art.*

**Barry Davies Oriental Art**
1 Davies Street, London W1Y 1LL
Tel: 0171-408 0207   Fax: 0171-493 3422
*Japanese works of art.*

**Reginald Davis (Oxford) Ltd**
34 High Street, Oxford, Oxfordshire OX1 4AN
Tel: 01865 248347   Fax: 01865 200915
*Jewellery; silver and old Sheffield plate; valuations.*

**Decodence**
21 The Mall, Camden Passage, 359 Upper St,
London N1 0PD
Tel: 020 7354 4473   Fax: 020 7689 0680
gad@decodence.demon.co.uk
*Classic plastics and vintage radios.*

**Deep, The**
**(ref: The Deep)**
The Plaza, 535 King's Rd, London SW10 0SZ
Tel: 020 7351 4881   Fax: 020 7352 0763
*Recovered shipwrecked items.*

**Richard Dennis**
**(ref: R. Dennis)**
144 Kensington Church St, London W8 4BN
Tel: 020 7727 2061   Fax: 020 7221 1283
*Contemporary and antique British ceramics.*

**Dodo**
Stand Fo73, Alfie's Antiques Market,
13-25 Church Street, London NW8 8DT
Tel: 020 7706 1545   Fax: 0207 724 0999
*Posters, tins and advertising signs 1890-1940.*

**Dolly Land**
864 Green Lanes, Winchmore Hill,
London N21 2RS
Tel: 020 8360 1053   Fax: 020 8364 1370
www.dollyland.com
*Dolls, teddies, trains, die-cast limited editions.*

**Anno Domini Antiques**
66 Pimlico Road, London SW1W 8LS
Tel: 020 7730 5496
or 020 7352 3084 when closed
*Furniture (17th-, 18th- and early 19th-century).*

**Donohoe**
Elliott House (3rd Floor),
28a Devonshire Street, London W1N 1RF
Tel: 020 8455 5507   Fax: 0181-455 6941
Mobile: 0973 174904
*Jewellery, bijouterie and snuff boxes; silver and old
Sheffield plate; valuations.*

**Gavin Douglas**
75 Portobello Rd, London W11 2QB
Tel: 01825 723 441   Tel: 020 7221 1121
Tel: 01825 724 418   Mobile: 0860 680521
www.antique-clocks.co.uk
*Clocks, bronzes, sculpture, porcelain.*

**Drummonds Architectural Antiques Ltd**
**(ref: Drummonds)**
Kirkpatrick Buildings, 25 London Road (A3),
Hindhead, Surrey GU26 6AB
Tel: 01428 609444   Fax: 01428 609445
www.drummonds/arch.co.uk
*Period bathrooms, period flooring, brassware,
furniture, garden statuary and period gates.*

**Charles Edwards**
582 King's Road, London SW6 2DY
Tel: 020 7736 8490   Fax: 020 7371 5436
*Antique lighting; furniture; pictures; garden objects;*
*late 19th- and early 20th-century western applied arts.*

**Emanouel Corporation U.K. Ltd.**
**(ref: Emanouel)**
64 South Audley Street, London W1Y 5FD
Tel: 020 7493 4350   Fax: 020 7499 0996
Fax: 020 7629 3125
emanouel@emanouel.
demon.co.uk
*19th-century European fine art and works of art.*

**Emerson Antiques**
**(ref: Emerson)**
Shop 2, Bourbon & Hanby Antiques Centre
Shop, 151 Sydney St, London SW3 6NT
Tel: 020 7351 1807   Fax: 020 7351 1807
iemerson @aol.com
*Corkscrews and collectables.*

**Ermitage Ltd**
23 Stanhope Gardens, London SW7 5QX
Tel: 020 7731 1810   Fax 020 7731 1810
*Fabergé, continental silver and Russian works of art.*

**Eskenazi Ltd**
10 Clifford St, London W1X 1RB
Tel: 020 7493 5464   Fax: 020 74993136
EskArt@aol.com
*Early Chinese ceramics, bronzes, sculpture, works*
*of art.*

**John Eskenazi Ltd**
**(ref: Eskenazi)**
15 Old Bond St, London W1X 4JL
Tel: 020 7409 3001   Fax: 020 7629 2146
www.john-eskenazi.com
john.eskenazi@john-eskenazi.com
*Oriental art, antique rugs and textiles; Indian,*
*Himalayan and south-east Asian art.*

**Eyre & Greig Ltd**
2 Rosenau Crescent, London SW11 4RZ
Tel: 020 7738 0652   Fax: 020 7738 0652
Mobile: 0468 410764
*18th-century English furniture; paintings related*
*to India.*

**Peter Farlow**
The Coach House, 189 Westbourne Grove,
London W11 2SB
Tel: 020 7229 8306   Fax: 020 7229 4297
*Gothic revival, Aesthetic period, Arts and Crafts and*
*period decoration; late 19th- and early 20th-century*
*western applied arts.*

**Penny Fawcitt at Tilings**
**(ref: Penny Fawcitt)**
High Street, Brasted, Kent TN16 1JA
Tel: 01959 564 735   Fax: 01959 565 795
penny.fawcitt@objects.co.uk

**Antony Fell**
The Old Shoes, Church Road, Bessingham,
Norwich NR11 7JW
Tel: 01263 577372   Fax: 01263 577372
Mobile: 0850 004731
*Antiques and works of art.*

**Brian Fielden**
3 New Cavendish Street, London W1M 7RP
Tel: 020 7935 6912
*English 18th- and early 19th-century furniture.*

**Hector Finch Lighting**
**(ref: Hector Finch)**
88-90 Wandsworth Bridge Rd, London SW6 2TF
Tel: 020 7731 8886   Fax: 020 7731 7408
hector@hectorfinch.com
www.hectorfinch.com
*Specialist period lighting.*

**Finchley Fine Art Gallery**
**(ref: Finchley)**
983 High Road, North Finchley, London N12 8QR
Tel: 020 8446 4848
finchleyfineart@ukonline.uk
*Watercolours and paintings, fine 18th- and 19th-*
*century furniture, pottery, porcelain and smalls.*

**Jack First**
**(ref: J. First)**
Grays Mews Antiques Market, 1-7 Davies Mews,
London W1Y 2LP
Tel: 020 7409 2722
*Silver and pewter.*

**David Ford**
2 Queenstown Road, Battersea, London SW8
Tel: 020 7622 7547
forddesign@compuserve.com
*An eclectic range of furniture, furnishings and*
*accessories.*

**Ford Design**
2 Queenstown Road, Battersea, London SW8
Tel: 020 7622 7547

**A.& E. Foster**
Little Heysham, Forge Rd,
Naphill, Bucks HP14 4SU
Tel: 01494 562024   Fax: 01494 562024
*Early treen, European works of art.Strictly by*
*appointment only.*

**Nicholas Fowle Antiques**
Websdales Court, Bedford Street, Norwich,
Norfolk NR2 1AR
Tel: 01603 219964   Fax: 01603 219964
*17th-, 18th- and 19th-century furniture; works of*
*art; valuations.*

**Judy Fox Antiques**
**(ref: J. Fox)**
81 Portobello Rd & 176 Westbourne Grove,
London W11
Tel: 020 7229 8130 or 020 7229 8488
Fax: 020 7229 6998   Mobile: 0836 234575
jackfox@compuserve.com
*Furniture.*

**Lynda Franklin Antiques**
**(ref: L. Franklin)**
25 Charnham Street, Hungerford, Berkshire
RG17 0EJ
Tel: 01488 682404   Fax: 01488 686089
Mobile: 0831 200834
*Antiques and interior design, French furniture -*
*17th- and 18th-century.*

**N. & I. Franklin**
11 Bury Street, St James's, London SW1Y 6AB
Tel: 020 7839 3131   Fax: 020 7839 3132
*Silver and works of art.*

**Victor Franses Gallery**
57 Jermyn Street, St James's, London SW1Y 6LX
Tel: 020 7493 6284   and 020 7629 1144
Fax: 020 7495 3668
*19th-century animalier sculpture; rare carpets and*
*rugs; valuations.*

**Apter Fredericks Ltd**
265-267 Fulham Road, London SW3 6HY
Tel: 020 7352 2188   Fax: 020 7376 5619
*18th- and early 19th-century English furniture,*
*specialising in dining-room furniture and bookcases.*

**Vincent Freeman Antiques**
**(ref: V. Freeman)**
1 Camden Passage, Islington, London N1 8EA
Tel: 020 7226 6178   Fax: 020 7226 7231
Mobile: 07889 966880
*19th-century music boxes.*

**Freeman & Lloyd**
44 Sandgate High Street, Sandgate, Folkestone,
Kent CT20 3AP
Tel: 01303 248986   Mobile: 0860 100073
*18th- and early 19th-century furniture and works of*
*art; valuations.*

**French Country Living**
**(ref: French Country)**
Rue des Remparts, Mougins, France
Tel: (33) 4 93 75 53 03   Fax: (33) 4 93 75 63 03
Mobile: 0370 520 371
*Antiquities and decoration.*

**French Glasshouse, The**
**(ref: French Glasshouse)**
P14/P16 Antiquarius Antiques Market,
135 King's Rd, London SW3 4PW
Tel: 020 7376 5394   Fax: 020 7376 5394
Mobile: 07768 720329
*Gallé, Daum and Japanese works of art.*

**French Room, The**
**(ref: French Room)**
5, The High Street, Petworth, West Sussex
Mobile: 01798 344454
*French furniture.*

**Charles Frodsham & Co Ltd**
**(ref: C. Frodsham)**
32 Bury Street, London SW1Y 6AU
Tel: 020 7839 1234   Fax: 020 7839 2000
www.frodsham.com
info@frodsham.com
*Clocks, watches, marine chronometers and other*
*horological items.*

**Frost & Reed**
2-4 King Street, St James's, London SW1Y 6QP
Tel: 020 7839 4645   Fax: 020 7839 1166
*British and continental 19th- and 20th-century*
*paintings; fine Impressionist and Post-Impressionist*
*drawings and watercolours; contemporary*
*British artists.*

**Fulham Antiques**
**(ref: Fulham)**
318-320 Munster Road, London SW6 6BH
Tel: 020 7610 3644   Fax: 020 7610 3644
aeantique@tesco.net
*Furniture, restoration of lacquer, gilding and*
*French polish.*

**Furniture Vault, The**
**(ref: Furniture Vault)**
50 Camden Passage, Islington, London N1 8AE
Tel: 020 7354 1047
*Selection of 18th- to late 19th-century furniture.*

**G Whizz**
17 Jerdan Place, London SW6 1BE
Tel: 020 7386 5020   Fax: 020 8741 0062
www.metrocycle.co.uk
gordon@metrocycle.co.uk
*Bikes.*

**Gallery Yacou**
**(ref: Yacou)**
127 Fulham Road, London SW3 6RT
Tel: 020 7584 2929   Fax: 020 7584 3535
*Antique and decorative, Oriental & European,*
*carpets/textiles.*

**Marilyn Garrow**
The Farmhouse, Letheringham,
Woodbridge, Suffolk IP13 7RA
Tel: 01728 746215   Fax: 01728 746215
Mobile: 07774 842 074
marogarrow@aol.com
*Fine and rare textiles.*

**Rupert Gentle**
The Manor House,
Milton Lilbourne, Pewsey, Wiltshire SN9 5LQ
Tel: 01672 563344  Fax: 01672 564136
*Specialist in English and continental domestic
metalwork; treen and bygones; needlework, pictures
and decorative objects.*

**Michael German Antiques**
**(ref: Michael German)**
38b Kensington Church St, London W8 4BX
Tel: 020 7937 2771 or 020 7937 1776
Fax: 020 7937 8566
info@antiquecanes.com
info@antiqueweapons.com
www.antiquecanes.com
www.antiqueweapons.com
*Antique walking canes and quality European and
Oriental arms and armour.*

**Get Stuffed**
105 Essex Rd, London N1 2SL
Tel: 020 7226 1364  Fax: 020 7359 8253
Mobile: 0831 260062
www.thegetstuffed.co.uk
*Taxidermy and natural history artefacts.*

**Nicholas Gifford-Mead**
68 Pimlico Road, London SW1W 8LS
Tel: 020 7730 6233
*Antique fireplaces.*

**Gabrielle de Giles**
The Barn at Bilsington, Swanton Lane,
Bilsington, Ashford, Kent TN25 7JR
Tel: 01233 720 917  Fax: 01233 720 156
*Antique and country furniture, home interiors,
designer for curtains, screens, etc.*

**Godson & Coles**
310 King's Road, London SW3 5UH
Tel: 020 7352 8509  Fax: 020 7351 9947
*18th- and early 19th-century furniture and
decorative works of art.*

**Michael Goedhuis**
116 Mount Street, London W1Y 5HD
Tel: 020 7629 2228  Fax: 020 7409 3338

**Gordon's Medals Ltd**
**(ref: Gordon's Medals)**
Grays Mews Antique Market,
1-7 Davies Mews, London W1Y 2LP
Tel: 020 7495 0900
*Medals.*

**Gosh**
39 Great Russell Street, London, WC1B 3PH
Tel: 020 7436 5053  Fax: 020 7436 5053
*Comics.*

**Gillian Gould Antiques**
18a Belsize Park Gardens, London NW3 4LH
Tel: 020 7419 0500  Fax: 020 7419 0400
Mobile: 0831 150060
Gillgould@dealwith.com
*Scientific instruments and collectables.*

**Graham & Green**
4, 7 &10 Elgin Crescent, London W11 2JA
Tel: 020 7243 3695  Fax: 020 7243 3695
smackworth-praed@grahamandgreen.co.uk

**Granville Antiques**
The High Street, Petworth,
West Sussex GU28 0AU
Tel: 01798 343250  Fax: 01798 343250
*Furniture, pre-1840; valuations.*

**Solveig Gray, Anita Gray**
**(ref: Anita Gray)**
Grays Mews Antiques Market, 1-7 Davies Street,
London W1Y 2LP
Tel: 020 74081638  Fax: 020 74950707
info@chinese-porcelain.com
*Antique Oriental works of art.*

**Abbey Green Antiques**
**(ref: Abbey Green)**
Mariaplaats 45, 3511 LL Utrecht,
The Netherlands
Tel: 030 232 8065

**Anthony Green Antiques**
**(ref: Anthony Green)**
Unit 39, Bond Street Antique Centre,
124 New Bond Street, London W1Y 9AE
Tel: 020 7409 2854  Fax: 020 7409 7032
vintagewatches@hotmail.com
www.anthonygreen.com
*Vintage wristwatches and antique pocket watches.*

**Richard Green**
147 New Bond Street, London W1Y 9FE
Tel: 020 7493 3939  Fax: 020 7629 2609
paintings@richard-green.com
www.richard-green.com
*British, sporting and marine paintings; French
Impressionist and modern British paintings.*

**Richard Green**
33 New Bond Street, London, W1Y 9HD
Tel: 020 7499 5553  Fax: 020 7499 8509
paintings@richard-green.com
www.richard-green.com
*Fine Old Master paintings.*

**Richard Green**
39 Dover Street, London, W1X 3RB
Tel: 020 7499 4738  Fax: 020 7499 3318
paintings@richard-green.com
www.richard-green.com
*Victorian and Dutch romantic paintings.*

**Henry Gregory**
82 Portobello Rd, London W11 2QD
Tel: 020 7792 9221
*Antique jewellery, silver and objects.*

**Nicholas Grindley**
13 Old Burlington Street, London W1X 1LA
Tel: 020 7437 5449   Fax: 020 7494 2446
*Chinese furniture and works of art.*

**Grosvenor Antiques Ltd**
27 Holland Street, London W8 4NA
Tel: 020 7937 8649   Fax: 020 7937 7179
*Porcelain, enamels, works of art and 18th- and 19th-century bronzes.*

**Guest & Gray**
Grays Mews Antiques Market, 1-7 Davies Mews,
London W1Y 2LP
Tel: 020 74081252   Fax: 020 7499 1445
anthony@guest-gray.demon.co.uk
www.guest-gray.demon.co.uk
*Oriental and European ceramics and works of art; reference books.*

**Gurr and Sprake Antiques**
**(ref: Gurr & Sprake)**
283 Lillie Road, London SW6 7LL
Tel: 020 7381 3209   Fax: 020 7381 9502
Mobile: 0410 922225
*18th- and 19th-century English/French furniture, lighting, unusual architectural pieces.*

**Gütlin Clocks and Antiques**
**(ref: Gütlin Clocks)**
616 King's Rd, London SW6
Tel: 020 7384 2439   Fax: 020 7384 2439
www.gutlin.com
mark@gutlin.com
*Longcase clocks, mantel clocks, furniture and lighting, all 18th- and 19th-century.*

**J. de Haan & Son**
**(ref: J. de Haan)**
PO Box 95, Newmarket, Suffolk CB8 8ZG
Tel: 01440 821388   Fax: 01440 820410
*Old English furniture, barometers, gilt mirrors and fine tea caddies.*

**Hadji Baba Ancient Art**
**(ref: Hadji Baba)**
34a Davies Street, London, W1Y 1LG
Tel: 020 7499 9363
*Ancient art.*

**Robert Hales Antiques**
**(ref: Robert Hales)**
131 Kensington Church St, London W8 7LP
Tel: 020 7229 3887   Fax: 020 7229 3887
*Fine Oriental arms and armour, tribal art.*

**Ross Hamilton Ltd Antiques**
95 Pimlico Road, London SW1W 8PH
Tel: 020 7730 3015   Fax: 020 7730 3015

**Hancocks & Co (Jewellers) Ltd**
52-53 Burlington Arcade, London W1X 2HP
Tel: 020 7493 8904   Fax: 020 7493 8905
Antique.Collectors-on-line.com/dealers/hancocks
*Antique jewellery; antique silver; objects; valuations.*

**Jim Hanson & Argyll Etkin Ltd**
18 Claremont Field, Ottery St Mary,
Devon EX11 1NP
Tel: 01404 815010   Fax: 01404 815224
*Philatelist and postal historian.*

**Keith Harding's World of Mechanical Music**
**(ref: Keith Harding)**
The Oak House, High Street, Northleach,
Gloucestershire GL54 3ET
Tel: 01451 860181   Fax: 01451 861133
www.mechanicalmusic.co.uk
Keith@mechanicalmusic.co.uk

**Robert Harman Antiques**
The Red House, Church Street, Ampthill,
Bedfordshire MK45 2EH
Tel: 01525 402322   Fax: 01525 756177
*Furniture; works of art; valuations.*

**Adrian Harrington**
64A Kensington Church St, London W8 4DB
Tel: 020 79371465   Fax: 020 73680912
www.harringtonbooks.co.uk
rarerare@harringtonbooks.co.uk

**Jonathan Harris**
9 Lower Addison Gardens, London W14 8BG
Tel: 020 7602 6255   Fax: 020 7602 0488
*English, continental and Oriental furniture and works of art; later 19th- and early 20th-century western applied arts; valuations.*

**Nicholas Harris Gallery**
PO Box 14430, London SW6 2WG
Tel: 020 7371 9711   Fax: 020 7371 9537
*English and American 19th- and 20th-century silver and art silversmiths; metalwork.*

**Harvey & Gore**
41 Duke Street, St James's, London SW1Y 6DF
Tel: 020 7839 4033   Fax 020 7839 3313
*Jewellery, bijouterie and snuff boxes; silver and old Sheffield plate; miniatures; valuations.*

**Kenneth Harvey Antiques**
**(ref: Kenneth Harvey)**
The Furniture Cave, 533 King's Road,
London SW10 0TZ
Tel: 020 7352 3775   Fax: 020 7352 3759
mail@kennethharvey.com
*Continental/English decorative furniture.*

**Victoria Harvey at Deuxième**
**(ref: V. Harvey)**
44 Church Street, London NW8 8EP
Tel/Fax: 020 7724 0738   Mobile: 07702 308 495
*General decorative antiques.*

**W. R. Harvey & Co (Antiques) Ltd**
86 Corn Street, Witney, Oxfordshire OX8 7BU
Tel: 01993 706 501   Fax: 01993 706 601
www.wrharvey.co.uk
*English furniture; clocks, barometers, mirrors and
works of art, 1650-1830; valuations.*

**W. R. Harvey & Co (Antiques) Ltd**
70 Chalk Farm Road, London NW1 8AN
Tel: 01993 706501   Fax: 01993 706601
antiques@wrharvey.co.uk
www.wrharvey.co.uk
*Open by appointment only. English furniture;
clocks, barometers, mirrors and works of art,
1650-1830; valuations.*

**Hatchwell Antiques**
**(ref: Hatchwell)**
Furniture Cave, 533 King's Road,
London SW10 0TZ
Tel: 020 7351 2344   Fax: 020 7351 3520
hatchwell@callnetuk.com
*English and continental furniture - late 18th- to
early 20th-century.*

**Gerard Hawthorn Ltd**
104 Mount Street, London W1Y 5HE
Tel: 020 7409 2888   Fax: 020 7409 2777
*Oriental art.*

**Henry Hay**
**(ref: H. Hay)**
Unit 5054, 2nd Floor, Alfie's Market,
13/25 Church Street, London NW8
Tel: 020 7723 2548
*Art Deco, chrome and brass lamps, bakelite
telephones, 20th-century.*

**Jeanette Hayhurst Fine Glass**
32a Kensington Church St, London W8 4HA
Tel: 020 7938 1539
*British glass from 17th- to 20th-centuries.*

**Hempson**
c/o 20 Rutland Gate, London SW7 1BD
Tel: 020 7584 8058
*Continental furniture and works of art.*

**M. Heskia**
c/o CFASS Ltd, 42 Ponton Road,
London SW8 5BA
Tel: 020 7373 4489
*Mainly 19th-century Oriental carpets and rugs;
European tapestries; valuations.*

**Highgate Antiques**
PO Box 10060, London N6 5JH
Tel: 020 8340 9872   Tel: 020 8348 3016
Fax: 020 8340 1621
*18th- and early 19th-century English and Welsh
porcelain and glass.*

**W. E. Hill**
PO Box 4, Aylesbury,
Buckinghamshire HP17 9UB
Tel: 01844 274 584   Fax: 01844 274 585
*Open by appointment only. Musical instruments of
the violin family, valuations.*

**Robert E. Hirschhorn**
83 Camberwell Grove, London SE5 8JE
Tel: 020 7703 7443   Mobile: 0831 405937
*English and continental furniture, particularly oak,
elm, walnut and fruitwood, and works of art, 18th-
century and earlier; European ceramics; textiles;
metalwork.*

**Milton J. Holgate**
36 Gracious Street, Knaresborough,
North Yorkshire HG5 8DS
Tel: 01423 865219
*Pre-1830 English furniture and accessories.*

**Holland & Holland**
31-33 Bruton St, London W1X 8JS
Tel: 020 7499 4411   Fax: 020 7409 3283
*Guns.*

**Holmes (Jewellers) Ltd**
24 Burlington Arcade, London W1V 9AD
Tel: 020 7629 8380
*Silver and jewellery; old Sheffield plate; valuations.*

**Hope & Glory**
131a Kensington Church St, London W8 7LP
Tel: 020 7727 8424
*Commemorative china.*

**Paul Hopwell Antiques Ltd**
30 High Street, West Haddon,
Northamptonshire NN6 7AP
Tel: 01788 510636   Fax: 01788 510044
*17th- and 18th-century oak and walnut furniture;
metalwork; valuations.*

**Jonathan Horne**
**(ref: J. Horne)**
66b & 66c Kensington Church St,
London W8 4BY
Tel: 020 7221 5658   Fax: 020 7792 3090
*Early English pottery, needlework and works of art.*

**Hotspur Ltd**
14 Lowndes Street, London SW1X 9EX
Tel: 020 7235 1918   Fax: 020 7235 4371
hotspurltd@msn.com
*18th-century English furniture and works of art.*

**Howard & L. Hamilton**
**(ref: Howard & Hamilton)**
151 Sydney Street, London SW3 6NT
Tel: 020 7352 0909   Fax: 020 7352 0066
*Scientific instruments.*

**Christopher Howe Antiques**
**(ref: Howe)**
93 Pimlico Road, London SW1W 8PH
Tel: 020 7730 7987   Fax: 020 7730 0157
c.howe@easynet.co.uk
*Furniture and lighting from the 17th- to 20th-century.*

**Huxtable's Old Advertising**
**(ref: Huxtable's)**
Alfie's Market, 13-25 Church Street,
London NW8 8DT
Tel: 020 7724 2200   Mobile: 01727 833445
*Advertising, collectables, tins, signs, bottles,
commemoratives, old packaging from late Victorian.*

**Hygra, Sign of the**
**(ref: Hygra)**
2 Middleton Road, London E8 4BL
Tel: 020 7254 7074   Fax: 0870 125 669
www.hygra.com
boxes@hygra.com

**Iconastas**
5 Piccadilly Arcade, London SW1
Tel: 020 7629 1433   Fax: 020 7408 2015
*Russian fine art.*

**Iona Antiques**
PO Box 285, London W8 6HZ
Tel: 020 7602 1193   Fax: 020 7371 2843
www.art-on-line.com/iona
*Paintings – speciality: 19th-century English paintings
of animals.*

**J.A.N. Fine Art**
134 Kensington Church St, London W8 4BH
Tel: 020 7792 0736   Fax: 020 7221 1380
*Specialising in Oriental porcelain, painting and works
of art.*

**Jonathan James**
52/53 Camden Passage, Islington, London
Tel: 020 7704 8266
*Antique furniture and decorative objects.*

**P.L. James**
590 Fulham Road, London SW6 5NT
Tel: 020 7736 0183
*Gilded mirrors, English and Oriental lacquer, period
objects and furniture.*

**Tobias Jellinek Antiques**
20 Park Road, East Twickenham,
Middlesex TW1 2PX
Tel: 020 8892 6892   Fax: 020 8744 9298
toby@jellinek.com
www.jellinek.com/oak
*Early English furniture; European ceramics;
European sculpture and works of art; early
metalwork; treen and bygones; valuations.*

**Jessop Classic Photographica**
67 Great Russell Street, London WC1
Tel: 020 7831 3640   Fax: 020 7831 3956
classic@jessops.co.uk
*Classic photographic equipment, cameras and
optical toys.*

**C. John (Rare Rugs) Ltd**
70 South Audley Street, London W1Y 5FE
Tel: 020 7493 5288   Fax: 020 7409 7030
*Carpets and rugs; tapestry, needlework and fabrics.*

**Lucy Johnson**
2 Chester Street, London SW1X 7BB
Tel: 020 7235 2088   Fax: 020 7235 2088
*Fine English furniture; Delftware and period
interiors.*

**Johnson, Walker & Tolhurst Ltd**
64 Burlington Arcade, London W1V 9AF
Tel: 020 7629 2615/6   Fax: 020 7409 0709
*Jewellery and bijouterie; valuations.*

**Alexander Juran & Co**
74 New Bond Street, London W1Y 9DD
Tel: 020 7629 2550   Tel: 020 7493 4484
Fax: 020 7493 4484
*Carpets and rugs; tapestry, needlework and textiles;
valuations.*

**K6**
Antiquarius Antiques Market, 135 King's Rd,
London SW3 4PW
Tel: 020 7352 2099
*1880-1960 antiques.*

**Stephen Kalms**
Chancery House, 53-64 Chancery Lane,
London WC2 1QS
Tel: 020 7430 1254   Fax: 020 7405 6206
Mobile: 0831 604001
stephen@skalms.freeserve.co.uk
*Fine silver specialist.*

**Kenworthy's Ltd**
226 Stamford Street, Ashton-under-Lyne,
Manchester OL6 7LW
Tel: 0161-330 3043
*Jewellery, bijouterie and snuff boxes; silver and old
Sheffield plate; valuations.*

**Keshishian**
73 Pimlico Road, London SW1W 8NE
Tel: 020 7730 8810   Fax: 020 7730 8803
*Antique carpets, tapestries and Aubussons; Arts &*
*Crafts and Art Deco carpet specialists.*

**John Keil Ltd**
154 Brompton Road, London SW3 1HX
Tel: 020 7589 6454   Fax: 020 7823 8235
*17th-18th and early 19th-century English furniture*
*and works of art.*

**Roger Keverne**
120 Mount Street, London W1Y 5HB
Tel: 020 7355 1711   Fax: 020 7409 7717
*Chinese, Japanese and Oriental works of art.*

**Kieron**
K6, Antiquarius Antiques Market
135 King's Rd, London SW3 4PW
Tel: 020 7352 2099
*Decorative arts.*

**John King**
Raynalds Mansion, High Street,
Much Wenlock, Shropshire TF13 6AE
Tel: 01952 727456
john.king21@virgin.net
*Fine and unusual antiques.*

**John King**
74 Pimlico Road, London SW1W 8LS
Tel: 020 7730 0427   Fax: 020 7730 2515
john.king21@virigin.net
*Fine and unusual antiques.*

**Robert Kleiner & Co Ltd**
30 Old Bond Street, London W1X 4HN
Tel: 020 7629 1814   Tel: 020 7622 5462
Fax: 020 7629 1239
*Chinese works of art, jades, porcelains and*
*snuff bottles.*

**L. & E. Kreckovic**
559 King's Road, London SW6 2EB
Tel: 020 7736 0753   Fax: 020 7731 5904
*Antiques, decorative objects, restoration.*

**La Bohéme**
c21 Grays Mews,
1-7 Davies Mews, London W1Y 2LP
Tel: 020 7493 0675
*Glass.*

**Lacquer Chest, The**
**(ref: Lacquer Chest)**
75 Kensington Church St, London W8 4BG
Tel: 020 7937 1306   Tel: 020 7938 2070
Fax: 020 7376 0223
*Country antiques.*

**Lamberty**
The Furniture Cave, 533 King's Road,
London SW10 0TZ
Tel: 020 7352 3775   Fax: 020 7352 3759
mail@lamberty.co.uk
www.lamberty.co.uk

**Langfords**
**(ref: Langfords)**
Vault 8/10, London Silver Vaults,
Chancery Lane, London WC2A 1QS
Tel: 020 7242 5506   Fax: 020 7405 0431
vault@langfords.com
www.langfords.com
*Antique and modern silver and silver plate.*

**Langfords Marine Antiques**
**(ref: Langfords Marine)**
The Plaza, 535 King's Rd, London SW10 0SZ
Tel: 020 7351 4881   Fax: 020 7352 0763
*Marine antiques – ship models and nautical items.*

**Judith Lassalle**
7 Pierrepont Arcade, Camden Passage,
London N1 8EF
Tel: 020 7607 7121
*Optical toys, books and games.*

**LASSCO**
St. Michael's, Mark St, London EC2A 4ER
Tel: 020 7739 0448   Fax: 020 7729 6853
www.lassco.co.uk
*Architectural antiques including panelled rooms,*
*garden ornaments, stained glass and stonework.*

**D.S. Lavender Antiques Ltd**
26 Conduit Street, London W1R 9TA
Tel: 020 7629 1782   Fax: 020 7629 3106
*Miniatures, jewellery and objets d'art; valuations.*

**Michael Lewis**
6/7 Peabody Yard, Greenman Street,
London N1 8SB
Tel: 020 7359 7733   Fax: same
*Pine and country furniture, British and Irish 18th-*
*and 19th-century.*

**Lewis & Lloyd**
65 Kensington Church St, London W8 4BA
Tel: 020 7938 3323   Fax: 020 7361 0086
*18th- and 19th-century English furniture.*

**Libra Designs**
34 Church Street, London NW8 8EP
Tel: 020 7723 0542   Fax: 020 7286 8518
libradeco@aol.com
www.libradeco.com

**Lida Lavender**
39-51 Highgate Road, London NW5 1RS
Tel: 020 7424 0600   Fax: 020 7424 0404
lida@lavenders.co.uk
*Antique carpets and textiles for design and*
*decoration.*

**Linden & Co (Antiques) Ltd**
Vault 7, London Silver Vaults,
Chancery Lane, London WC2A 1QS
Tel: 020 7242 4863   Fax:020 7405 9946
*Silver, plate, works of art.*

**Lindfield Galleries**
62 High Street, Lindfield,
West Sussex RH16 2HL
Tel: 01444 483817   Fax: 01444 484682
*Carpets and rugs; valuations.*

**Andrew Lineham Fine Glass**
The Mall, Camden Passage, London N1 8ED
Tel: 020 7704 0195 or 01243 576241
*Rare and unusual 19th- and 20th-century coloured
glass and European porcelain.*

**Peter Lipitch Ltd
(ref: P. Lipitch)**
120 and 124 Fulham Road, London SW3 6HU
Tel: 020 7373 3328   Fax: 020 7373 8888
*General antiques.*

**London Antique Gallery**
66e Kensington Church St, London W8 4BY
Tel: 020 7229 2934   Fax: 020 7229 2934
pomolondon@hotmail.com
*Porcelain including Dresden, Meissen, English and
Sevres; French and German bisque dolls.*

**Stephen Long Antiques**
348 Fulham Road, London SW10 9UH
Tel: 020 7352 8226
*English Pottery, 18th- and 19th-century, English
painted furniture, toys and games, household and
kitchen items, chintz, materials and patchwork.*

**Clive Loveless**
54 St Quintin Avenue, London W10 6PA
Tel: 020 8969 5831   Fax: 020 8969 5292
*18th- and 19th-century Oriental tribal rugs; 17th to
19th-century Ottoman, central Asian, African and
Pre-Columbian textiles; valuations.*

**Michael Luther
(ref: M. Luther)**
590 King's Road, London SW6 2DX
Tel: 020 7371 8492   Fax: 020 7371 8492
luthermichael416@aol.com
*18th- and 19th-century furniture and lighting.*

**Mac's Cameras**
262 King Street, Hammersmith, London W6 0SJ
Tel: 020 8846 9853
*Antique camera equipment.*

**Mac Humble Antiques**
7-9 Woolley Street, Bradford-on-Avon,
Wiltshire BA15 1AD
Tel: 01225 866329   Fax: 01225 866329
*Open Monday-Saturday 9-6; other times by
appointment. 18th- and 19th-century English
furniture; metalwork; needlework; treen and bygones.*

**William MacAdam**
86 Pilrig Street, Edinburgh EH6 5AS
Tel: 0131 553 1364
*Specialist in 18th-century collectors' drinking glasses,
also later glass; valuations.*

**Pete McAskie Toys
(ref: Pete McAskie)**
A12/13, Grays Mews Antiques Market,
1-7 Davies St, London W1Y 2LP
Tel: 020 7629 2813   Fax: 020 7493 9344
*Tin toys – 1880-1980.*

**Fiona McDonald**
57 Galveston Road, London SW15 2RZ
Tel: 020 8870 5559   Mobile: 07788 746 778
fiona.l.mcdonald@btinternet.com
*Mirrors, decorative furniture and lighting.*

**Maggs Bros Ltd**
50 Berkeley Square, London W1X 6EL
Tel: 020 7493 7160   Fax: 020 7499 2007
*Rare books, autographs, manuscripts and miniatures.*

**Magpies**
152 Wandsworth Bridge Rd, London SW6 2UH
Tel: 020 7736 3738
*Antique collectables and lighting, door furniture and
kitchenalia.*

**Magus Antiques**
4 Church Street, London NW8 8ED
Tel: 020 7724 1278   Fax: 020 7724 1278
Mobile: 0374 271214
*Antique rugs, furniture, lighting and mirrors.*

**Mallett & Son
(Antiques) Ltd**
141 New Bond Street, London W1Y 0BS
Tel: 020 7499 7411   Fax: 020 7495 3179
*18th-century English furniture; works of art; glass;
paintings and watercolours.*

**Mallett Gallery, The**
141 New Bond Street, London W1Y 0BS
Tel: 020 7499 7411   Fax: 020 7495 3179
*Fine paintings, watercolours, drawings; sculpture
and works of art; valuations.*

**D.M. & P. Manheim (Peter Manheim) Ltd**
PO Box 1259, London N6 4TR
Tel: 020 8340 9211
*18th- and early 19th-century English porcelain,
pottery and enamels.*

**E. & H. Manners**
66a Kensington Church St, London W8 4BY
Tel: 020 7229 5516   Fax: 020 7229 5516
www.europeanporcelain.com
manners@europeanporcelain.com
*European ceramics – pre 19th century.*

**Map House, The**
**(ref: Map House)**
54 Beauchamp Place, London SW3 1NY
Tel: 020 7589 4325   Tel: 020 7584 8559
Fax: 020 7589 1041
maps@themaphouse.com
www.themaphouse.com
*Antique and rare maps, atlases, engravings
and globes.*

**Marks Antiques**
49 Curzon Street, London W1Y 7RE
Tel: 020 7499 1788   Tel: 020 7409 3183
Marks@marksantiques.com
www.Marksantiques.com
*Decorative and functional silver.*

**G.E. Marsh (Antique Clocks) Ltd**
**(ref: G.E. Marsh)**
32a The Square, Winchester,
Hampshire SO23 9EX
Tel: 01962 844443
*Clocks, watches and barometers; valuations.*

**G.E. Marsh (Antique Clocks) Ltd**
Jericho House, North Aston,
nr Bicester, Oxfordshire OX6 4HX
Tel: 01869 340087   Fax: 01869 340087
*Open by appointment only. Clocks, watches and
barometers; valuations.*

**David Martin-Taylor Antiques**
**(ref: D. Martin-Taylor)**
558 King's Road, London SW6 2DZ
Tel: 020 7731 4135   Fax: 020 7371 0029
dmt@davidmartintaylor.com
*18th- and 19th-century decorative antiques.*

**Paul Mason Gallery**
149e Sloane Street, London SW1X 9BZ
Tel: 020 7730 3683 / 7359   Fax: 020 7581 9084
www.art-on-line.com/pmason
*18th- and 19th-century marine, sporting and
decorative paintings and prints; ship models; portfolio
stands and picture easels; glass pictures; valuations.*

**Megan Mathers Antiques**
**(ref: M. Mathers)**
571 King's Road, London SW6 2 EB
Tel: 020 7371 7837   Fax: 020 7371 7895
*Furniture.*

**A. P. Mathews**
283 Westbourne Grove, London W11
Tel: 01622 812590
*Antique luggage.*

**David Messum**
8 Cork Street, London W1X 1PB
Tel: 020 7437 5545   Fax: 020 7734 7018
*British Impressionism and contemporary art.*

**metro retro**
1 White Conduit Street, London N1 9EL
Tel: 020 7278 4884
Warehouse: 01245 442047
www.metroretro.co.uk
saxon@metroretro.demon.co.uk
*20th-century. furniture – 1960- 70s' industrial
design.*

**Mora & Upham Antiques**
**(ref: Mora & Upham)**
584 King's Road, London SW6 2DX
Tel: 020 7731 4444   Fax: 020 7736 0440
*Furniture.*

**More Than Music Collectables**
**(ref: More Than Music)**
C24/25, Grays Mews Antiques Market,
1-7 Davies Mews, London W1Y 2LP
Tel: 020 7629 7703   Fax: 01519 565 510
www.mtmglobal.com
morethnmus@aol.com
*Rock and pop music memorabilia, specialising in
The Beatles.*

**Clive Morley Harps Ltd**
**(ref: Clive Morley)**
No.8 Berkeley Square, London W1 5HF
Tel: 020 7495 4495   Tel: 01367 860 493
Fax: 020 7495 4898   Fax: 01367 860 659
www.morleyharps.com
morley@harps.demon.co.uk
*Harps.*

**Robert Morley and Company Ltd**
**(ref: Robert Morley)**
34 Engate Street, Lewisham, London SE13 7HA
Tel: 020 8318 5838   Fax: 020 8297 0720
jvm@morley-ru-net.com
*Pianoforte and harpsichord workshop.*

**Maureen Morris**
Folly Cottage, Littlebury, Saffron Walden,
Essex CB11 4TA
Tel: 01799 521338   Fax 01799 522802
*Quality samplers; early needlework; late 18th-
century and early 19th-century quilts; small
country furniture.*

**Terence Morse & Son Ltd**
**(ref: Terence Morse,**
**T. Morse & Son)**
237 Westbourne Grove, London W11 2SE
Tel: 020 7229 4059   Fax: 020 7792 3284
*Antique and fine furniture.*

**Sydney L. Moss Ltd**
51 Brook Street, London W1Y 1AU
Tel: 020 7629 4670 and 020 7493 7374
Fax: 020 7491 9278
*Chinese and Japanese works of art.*

**Motor Books**
**(ref: Motor)**
33 St Martin's Court, London, WC2N 4AN
Tel: 020 7836 3800   Fax: 020 7497 2539
*Motoring books.*

**Mousa Antiques**
**(ref: Mousa)**
B20, Grays Mews Antiques Market,
1-7 Davies Mews, London W1Y 1AR
Tel: 020 7499 8273   Fax: 020 7629 2526
*Bohemian glass specialists.*

**Murray Cards International Ltd**
**(ref: Murray Cards)**
51 Watford Way, Hendon Central,
London NW4 3JH
Tel: 020 8202 5688   Fax: 020 8203 7878
murraycards@ukbusiness.com
*Ephemera.*

**Music & Video Exchange**
**(ref: Music & Video)**
38 Notting Hill Gate, London W11 3HX
Tel: 020 7243 8574
www.mveshops.co.uk
*CDs, tapes, vinyl – deletions and rarities.*

**Myriad Antiques**
**(ref: Myriad)**
131 Portland Rd, London W11 4LW
Tel: 020 7229 1709
*Decorative objects and furniture for the house and garden.*

**Stephen Naegel**
Grays Mews Antiques Market, 1/7 Davies Mews,
London W1Y 2LP
Tel: 020 7491 3066   Fax: 01737 845147
www.btinternet.com/~naegel
*Toys.*

**Namdar Antiques**
**(ref: Namdar)**
B22, Grays Mews Antiques Market,
1-7 Davies Mews, London W1Y 2LP
Tel: 020 7629 1183   Fax: 020 7493 9344
*Metalware, Oriental and Islamic ceramics, glassware and silver.*

**Colin Narbeth & Son Ltd**
**(ref: C. Narbeth)**
20 Cecil Court, London WC2N 4HE
Tel: 020 7379 6975   Mobile: 01727 811244
Colin.Narbeth@btinternet.com
www.colin-narbeth.com
*Scripophily.*

**Gillian Neale Antiques**
PO Box 247, Aylesbury,
Buckinghamshire HP20 1JZ
Tel: 01296 23754   Mobile: 0860 638700
Fax: 01296 23754
*English blue and white transfer printed pottery 1780-1850.*

**New King's Road Vintage Guitar Emporium**
**(ref: Vintage Guitar)**
65a New King's Road, London SW6 4SG
Tel: 020 7371 0100   Fax: 020 7371 0460
and
1st floor, 25 Denmark St, London WC2
Tel: 020 7836 8008
guitars@new-kings-rd.u-net.com
www.newkingsroadguitars.co.uk
*Vintage guitars.*

**Chris Newland Antiques**
**(ref: C. Newland)**
30/31 Islington Green, Lower Level,
Georgian Village, London N1 8DU
Tel: 020 7359 9805   Fax: 020 7359 9805
*Furniture.*

**North West Eight**
**(ref: NW8/North West 8)**
36 Church Street, London NW8 8EP
Tel: 020 7723 9337
*Decorative antiques.*

**Edward Nowell & Sons**
12 Market Place, Wells, Somerset BA5 2RB
Tel: 01749 672415   Tel: 01749 678738
Fax: 01749 673519
*Mid 18th-century English furniture; Chinese blue and white porcelain; silver and jewellery; valuations.*

**Oasis**
E14, Grays Mews Antiques Market,
1-7 Davies Mews, London W1 1AR
Tel: 020 7493 1202   Fax: 020 8551 4487
*Ancient and Islamic art.*

**Ocean Leisure**
11-14 Northumberland Avenue,
London WC2N 5AQ
Tel: 020 7930 5050   Fax: 020 7930 3032
www.oceanleisure.co.uk
info@oceanleisure.co.uk

**Glenda O'Connor**
Grays Antique Market,
Davies Mews, London W1
Tel: 020 8367 2441   Fax: 020 8366 5811
*Dolls, teddies, prams and related collectables.*

**Richard Ogden Ltd**
28-29 Burlington Arcade, London W1V 0NX
Tel: 020 7493 9136 / 7   Fax: 020 7355 1508
*Jewellery, specialising in rings.*

**Old Cinema Antiques Warehouse, The**
**(ref: Old Cinema)**
157 Tower Bridge Road, London SE1 3LW
Tel: 020 7407 5371   Fax: 020 7403 0359
theoldcinema@antiques-uk.co.uk
www.antiques-uk.co.uk
*Period antiques and quality reproductions.*

## Old Cinema Antiques Warehouse, The
**(ref: Old Cinema)**
160 Chiswick High Road  London W4 1PR
Tel: 020 8995 4166   Fax: 020 8995 4167
theoldcinemachiswick@antiques-uk.co.uk
www.antiques-uk.co.uk
*Period antiques and quality reproductions.*

## Old Father Time Clock Centre
1st floor, 101 Portobello Rd, London W11 2QB
Tel: 020 8546 6299   Fax: 020 8546 6299
Mobile: 0836 712088
www.oldfathertime.netclocks@oldfathertime.net
*Unusual and quirky clocks.*

## Old Telephone Co, The
**(ref: Old Telephone Co)**
The Battlesbridge Antiques Centre,
The Old Granary, Battlesbridge,
Essex SS11 7RE
Tel: 01245 400 601
www.theoldtelephone.co.uk
*Antique and collectable telephones.*

## Old Tool Chest, The
**(ref: Old Tool Chest)**
41 Cross Street, Islington, London N1 2BB
Tel: 020 7359 9313
*Tools for all trades – ancient and modern.*

## Old World Trading Co
565 King's Road, London SW6
Tel: 020 7731 4708
*Large range including handeliers, fireplaces, mirrors.*

## Oliver-Sutton Antiques
34c Kensington Church St, London W8 4HA
Tel: 020 7937 0633
*Staffordshire pottery figures.*

## Oola Boola Antiques
**(ref: Oola Boola)**
166 Tower Bridge Road, London SE1 3LS
Tel: 020 7403 0794 or 020 8693 5050
Fax: 020 7403 8405
*Furniture: mahogany, oak, some walnut, Victorian
Arts & Crafts, Art Nouveau, Edwardian and
shipping.*

## Jacqueline Oosthuizen
23 Cale St, Chelsea Green, London SW3 3QR
Tel: 020 7352 6071   Mobile: 0385 258 806
*Staffordshire figures, jewellery, decorative ceramics.*

## Pieter Oosthuizen
**(ref: P. Oosthuizen)**
Unit 4, Bourbon Hanby Antiques Centre,
151 Sydney St, London SW3
Tel: 020 7460 3078   Fax: 020 7376 3852
*Dutch and European art nouveau pottery and Boer
War memorabilia.*

## Oriental Bronzes Ltd
96 Mount Street, London W1Y 5HF
Tel: 020 7493 0309   Fax: 020 7629 2665
*Chinese archaeology.*

## Oriental Rug Gallery
**(ref: Oriental)**
230 Upper High Street,
Guildford, Surrey GU1 3JD
Tel: 01753 623000   Fax: same
www.orientalruggallery.com
rugs@orientalruggallery.com
*Russian, Afghan, Turkish and Persian carpets,
rugs and kelims; Oriental objets d'art.*

## Paul Orssich
2 St Stephen's Terrace, London SW8 1DH
Tel: 020 7787 0030   Tel: 020 7735 9612
paulo@orssich.com
www.orssich.com
*Old books and maps.*

## Anthony Outred (Antiques) Ltd
533 King's Road, London SW10 0TZ
Tel: 020 7352 8840   Fax: 020 7376 3627
*18th- and 19th-century English and continental
furniture.*

## Pacifica
Block 7, 479 Park West Place,
Edgware Road, London W2
Tel: 020 7402 6717
*Tribal art.*

## Parker Gallery
28 Pimlico Road, London SW1W 8LJ
Tel: 020 7730 6768   Fax: 020 7259 9180
www.art-on-line.com/parker
*Prints, paintings, watercolours; maps; ship models.*

## Pars Antiques
**(ref: Pars)**
A14/15, Grays Mews Antique Market,
1-7 Davies Mews, London W1Y 1AR
Tel: 020 7491 9889   Fax: 020 7493 9344
Mobile: 0410 492552
*Antiquities.*

## Payne & Son (Goldsmiths) Ltd
131 High Street, Oxford, Oxfordshire OX1 4DH
Tel: 01865 243787   Fax: 01865 793241
*Jewellery, bijouterie and snuff boxes; silver.*

## John A. Pearson
Horton Lodge, Horton Road,
Horton, nr. Slough, Berkshire SL3 9NU
Tel: 01753 682136
*Antiquities and works of art; furniture; porcelain,
pottery and enamels; valuations.*

**Pelham Galleries Ltd**
24 & 25 Mount Street, London W1Y 5RB
Tel: 020 7629 0905  Fax: 020 7495 4511
*Furniture; antiques and works of art; clocks and
barometers; musical instruments; tapestries,
needlework and fabrics; Oriental works of art.*

**Pendulum of Mayfair Ltd
(ref: Pendulum of Mayfair)**
King House, 51 Maddox Street, London W1
Tel: 020 7629 6606  Fax: 020 7629 6616
*Clock specialists.*

**Percy's Silver Ltd
(ref: Percy's)**
Vault 16, The London Silver Vaults,
Chancery Lane, London WC2A 1QA
Tel: 020 7242 3618  Fax: 020 7831 6541
www.percys-silver.com
sales@percys-silver.com
*Antique silver.*

**David Pettifer Ltd**
73 Glebe Place, London SW3 4JB
Tel: 020 7352 3088  Fax: 020 7352 4088
*Furniture; works of art; glass pictures; bygones.*

**Phelp**
59 Ledbury Road, London W11 2AA
Tel: 020 7727 7915
*Old master drawings – 16th- and 17th-century
European figures and busts.*

**Trevor Philip & Sons Ltd
(ref: T. Phillips & Son, T. Phillips)**
75a Jermyn Street, St. James's,
London SW1Y 6NP
Tel: 020 7930 2954
Fax: 020 7321 0212
www.trevorphilip.comglobe@trevorphilip.com

**Ronald Phillips Ltd**
26 Bruton Street, London W1X 8LH
Tel: 020 7493 2341  Fax: 020 7495 0843
*18th- and early 19th-century English furniture;
clocks and barometers; works of art.*

**Photographer's Gallery, The
(ref: Photographer's Gallery)**
5 Great Newport Street, London WC2H 7HY
Tel: 020 7831 1772  Fax: 020 7836 9704
info@photonet.org.uk
www.photonet.org.uk

**David Pickup Antiques
(ref: David Pickup)**
115 High Street, Burford,
Oxfordshire OX18 4RG
Tel: 01993 822555  Mobile: 0860 469959
*Fine English furniture and works of art.*

**Pieces of Time**
Units 17-19, 1-7 Davies Mews,
London W1Y 2LP
info@antique-watch.com
*Antique and precision pocket watches; Judaica.*

**Pillows of Bond Street
(ref: Pillows)**
London W11
Mobile: 0468 947 265
*By appointment only. Pillows.*

**W. A. Pinn & Sons**
124 Swan Street,
Sible, Hedingham, Essex CO9 3HP
Tel: 01787 461127
*Furniture, clocks and barometers, antique lighting.*

**Nicholas Pitcher**
1st Floor, 29 New Bond St, London W1Y 9HD
Tel: 020 7499 6621  Mobile: 0831 391574
*Oriental ceramics and works of art.*

**Planet Bazaar**
151 Drummond Street, London NW1 2PB
Tel: 020 7387 8326  Fax: same
Mobile: 07956 326301
www.planetbazaar.co.uk
maureen@planetbazaar.demon.co.uk
*50s' to 80s' designer furniture, art, glass,lighting,
ceramics, books and eccentricities.*

**Jonathan Potter Ltd**
1st Floor, 125 New Bond St, London W1Y 9AF
Tel: 020 7491 3520  Fax: 020 7491 9754;
jpmaps@ibm.net
*Maps and atlases; books and manuscripts;
valuations.*

**Christopher Preston Ltd
(ref: C. Preston)**
The Furniture Cave, 533 King's Rd,
London SW10 0TZ
Tel: 020 7352 4229
*Antique furniture and decorative objects.*

**Pritchard Antiques at Christopher Preston Ltd.**
Furniture Cave, 533 King's Road,
London SW10 0TZ
Tel: 020 7352 8587  Fax: 020 7376 3627
*18th- and 19th-century furniture.*

**Annette Puttnam**
Norton House, nr. Lewes, Iford, Sussex BN7 3EJ
Tel: 01273 483366  Fax: 0273 483366
Mobile: 0973 421070

**Bernard Quaritch Ltd**
5-8 Lower John Street, Golden Square,
London W1R 4AU
Tel: 020 7734 2983  Fax: 020 7437 0967
rarebooks@quaritch.com; www.quaritch.com
*Rare books and manuscripts.*

**Radio Days**
87 Lower Marsh, London SE1 7AB
Tel: 020 7928 0800   Fax: 020 7928 0800
*1930s-70s' lighting, telephones, radio, clothing
and magazines.*

**Raffety Walwyn
(ref: Raffety, Raffety Clocks)**
79 Kensington Church St, London W8 4BG
Tel: 020 7938 1100   Fax: 020 7938 2519
www.raffetyantiqueclocks.com
raffety@globalnet.co.uk
*Fine antique clocks.*

**Rainbow Antiques
(ref: Rainbow)**
329 Lillie Road, London SW6 7NR
Tel: 020 7385 1323   Mobile: 0870 0521693
Mobile: 07775 848494
fabio@rainbow-antiques.demon.co.uk

**Ranby Hall Antiques
(ref: Ranby Hall)**
Barnby Moor, Retford, Nottingham DN22 8JQ
Tel: 01777 860696   Fax: 01777 701317
www.ranbyhall.antiques-gb.com
paul.wyatt4@virgin.net
*Antiques, decorative items and contemporary
objects.*

**Mark Ransom Ltd
(ref: Mark Ransom)**
62&105 Pimlico Road, London SW1W 8LS
Tel: 020 7259 0220   Fax: 020 7259 0323
contact@markransom.co.uk
*Decorative Empire/French furniture.*

**Derek and Tina Rayment Antiques**
Orchard House, Barton Road, Barton, nr.
Farndon, Cheshire SY14 7HT
Tel: 01829 270429
*Open by appointment. Specialists in 18th- and 19th-
century English and continental barometers;
valuation.*

**Red Lion Antiques
(ref: Red Lion)**
New Street, Petworth, West Sussex GU28 0AS
Tel: 01798 344 485   Fax: 01798 342 367
Fax: 01932 343 536
www.co.uk/tangent/redlion
redlion@tangent.demon.co.uk
*Antiques for the country home, oak walnut and pine
furniture.*

**William Redford**
PO Box 17770, London W8 5ZB
Tel: 020 7376 1825   Fax: 020 7376 1825
*Continental furniture; works of art.*

**Gordon Reece Gallery
(ref: Gordon Reece)**
16 Clifford Street, London, W1X 1RG
Tel: 020 7439 0007   Fax: 020 7437 5715
and
24 Finkle Street, Knaresborough,
North Yorks HG5 8AA
Tel: 01423 866219   Fax: 01423 868165
www.gordonreecegalleries.com
*Flat woven rugs and nomadic carpets, tribal
sculpture, jewellery, furniture, decorative and
non-European folk art, especially ethnic and
Oriental ceramics.*

**Reel Poster Gallery, The
(ref: Reel Poster Gallery)**
72 Westbourne Grove, London W2 5SH
Tel: 020 7727 4488   Fax: 020 7727 7799
www.reelposter.comellen@reelposter.com
*Posters.*

**Reel Thing, The
(ref: Reel Thing)**
17 Royal Opera Arcade,
Pal Mall, London SW1Y 4UY
Tel: 020 7976 1830   Fax: 020 7976 1850
www.reelthing.co.uk
reelthinginfo@reelthing.co.uk
*Purveyors of vintage sporting memorabilia.*

**Paul Reeves**
32b Kensington Church St, London W8 4HA
Tel: 020 7937 1594   Fax: 020 7938 2163
*Furniture and artefacts 1860-1960.*

**Resners'**
124 New Bond Street, London W1Y 9AE
Tel: 020 7629 1413   Fax: 020 7629 1413
*Jewellery, bijouterie and snuff boxes; valuations.*

**Retro Exchange
(ref: Retro)**
20 Pembridge Road, London W11
Tel: 020 7221 2055   Fax: 020 7727 4185
www.i/fel.trade.co.uk
*Space age style furniture, 50s' kitsch.*

**Retro Home**
20 Pembridge Rd, London W11
Tel: 020 7221 2055   Fax: 020 7727 4185
www.i/fel.trade.co.uk
*Bric-a-brac, antique furniture, objects of desire.*

**Riverbank**
The High Street, Petworth,
West Sussex GU28 0AU
Tel: 01798 344401   Fax: 01798 343135
antiques@riverbank-antiques.com
*Antiques and the picturesque.*

**Robyn Robb**
43 Napier Avenue, London SW6 3PS
Tel: 020 7731 2878   Fax: 020 7731 2878
*18th-century English porcelain.*

**Derek Roberts Antiques**
25 Shipbourne Road,
Tonbridge, Kent TN10 3DN
Tel: 01732 358986   Fax: 01732 771842
*Clocks and barometers; music boxes; some furniture.*

**J. Roger (Antiques) Ltd**
London W14 0RR
Tel: 020 7381 2884   Tel: 020 7603 7627
*18th- and early 19th-century furniture,*
*especially small elegant pieces; prints; porcelain;*
*decorative items.*

**Brian Rolleston**
**(Antiques) Ltd**
104a Kensington Church St, London W8 4BU
Tel: 020 7229 5892   Fax: same
*18th-century English furniture.*

**Ronan Daly Antiques**
**(ref: Ronan Daly)**
Alfie's Antique Market, 13-25 Church Street,
London NW8
Tel: 020 7723 0429   Mobile: 07957 295462

**Michele Rowan**
**(ref: Rowan & Rowan)**
V36, Antiquarius Antiques Market,
135 King's Rd, London SW3 4PW
Tel: 020 7352 8744   Fax: 020 7352 8744
rowan&rowan@aol.com
*Antique jewellery.*

**Malcolm Rushton Early Oriental Art Ltd**
Studio 3, 13 Belsize Grove, London NW3 4UX
Tel: 020 7722 1989
*Early Oriental art.*

**Russell Rare Books, T.A.**
**Cherrington Rare Books Ltd**
**(ref: Russell Rare Books)**
81 Grosvenor St, London W1X 9DE
Tel: 020 7629 0532 or 020 7493 1343
Fax: 020 7499 2983
folios.co.uk
*Rare books.*

**Georgina Ryder & Piers Pisani**
The Music House, The Green, Sherborne,
Dorset DT9 3HX
Tel: 01935 815209   Fax: 01935 815209
Mobile: 07785 391710
antiques@pierspisani@sarghost.co.uk
*Country house antiques from England and France.*

**Frank T. Sabin Ltd**
13 The Royal Arcade, Old Bond Street,
London W1X 3HB
Tel: 020 7493 3288   Fax: 020 7499 3593
*18th- and 19th-century English sporting and*
*decorative engravings.*

**Samiramis Ltd**
**(ref: Samiramis)**
M14-16, Grays Mews Antiques Market,
Davies Mews, London W1Y 2DY
Tel: 020 7629 1161   Fax: 020 7493 5106
*Fine Islamic art.*

**Alistair Sampson**
**Antiques Ltd**
120 Mount Street,  London W1Y 5HB
Tel: 020 7409 1799   Fax: 020 7409 7717
*17th- and 18th-century English furniture; metalwork*
*and English brass; primitive paintings; 17th- and*
*18th-century English pottery and Delftware; Chinese*
*porcelain and works of art; needlework*

**Patrick Sandberg Antiques**
140-142 and 150-152 Kensington Church Street,
London W8 4BN
Tel: 020 7229 0373   Fax: 020 7792 3467
*18th- and early 19th-century English furniture*

**A. V. Santos**
1 Camden Street, London W8 7EP
Tel: 020 7727 4872   Fax: 020 7229 4801
*Chinese export porcelain*

**Seago**
22 Pimlico Road, London SW1W 8LJ
Tel: 020 7730 7502   Fax: 020 7730 9179
*17th-, 18th- and 19th-century garden ornament and*
*sculpture; works of art; valuations.*

**C.F. Seidler**
Unit 4, Bourbon Hanby Antiques Centre,
151 Sydney Street, London SW3
Tel: 020 7460 3078
*Dutch and European Art Nouveau pottery and Boer*
*War memorabilia.*

**M. & D. Seligmann**
37 Kensington Church Street, London W8 4LL
Tel: 020 7937 0400   Fax: 020 7722 4315
*English country furniture; works of art and unusual*
*items; early English pottery.*

**Jean Sewell (Antiques) Ltd**
3 & 4 Campden Street, London W8 7EP
Tel: 020 7727 3122   Fax: 020 7229 1053
*English, Continental and Oriental porcelain, pottery*
*and enamels.*

**Shahdad Antiques**
**(ref: Shadad/Shahdad)**
A16/17, Grays Mews Antiques Market,
1-7 Davies Mews, London W1Y 2LP
Tel: 020 7499 0572   Fax: 020 7629 2176
amir@arts1.freeserve.co.uk
*Islamic and ancient works of art.*

**Mark Shanks**
The Royal Oak, High Street, Watlington,
Oxfordshire OX9 5QB
Tel: 01491 613 317  Fax: 01491 613 318
*Open Monday-Saturday 10-5; at other times by
appointment. 17th-, 18th- and 19th-century
furniture and barometers.*

**Bernard Shapero**
2 Saint George St, London W1R 0EA
Tel: 020 7493 0876  Fax: 020 7229 7860
rarebooks@shapero.com
www.shapero.com
*Rare books.*

**Sharif**
27 Chepstow Corner, London W2 4XE
Tel: 020 7792 1861  Fax: 020 7792 1861
*Oriental rugs, kilims, textiles and furniture.*

**Nicholas Shaw Antiques
(ref: Nicholas Shaw)**
Great Grooms Antique Centre, Parbrook,
Billingshurst, West Sussex RH14 9EU
Tel: 01403 785731  Fax: 01403 786656
Mobile: 0585 643000
www.nicholas-shaw.com
silver@nicholas-shaw.com
*Fine antique silver, especially Scottish and Irish,
and small collectors' items.*

**Shiraz Antiques
(ref: Shiraz)**
H 10/11, Grays Mews Antiques Market,
1-7 Davies Mews, London W1Y 2LP
Tel: 020 7495 0635
*Islamic and ancient works of art.*

**S. J. Shrubsole Ltd**
43 Museum Street, London WC1A 1LY
Tel: 020 7405 2712
*Antique silver of the Georgian and early periods; also
a large collection of interesting old Sheffield plate.*

**Sieff**
49 Long Street, Tetbury,
Gloucestershire GL8 8AA
Tel: 01666 504477  Fax: 01666 504478
sieff@sieff.co.uk
*French and English provincial country furniture
1780-1900.*

**Sign of the Hygra, Antique Boxes at
(ref: Hygra)**
2 Middleton Road, London E8 4BL
Tel: 020 7254 7074  Fax: 0870 125 669
www.hygra.com
boxes@hygra.com

**B. Silverman**
London Silver Vaults,
63 Chancery Lane, London WC2A 1QS
Tel: 020 7242 3269  Fax: 020 7430 1949
www.silverman-london.com
silverman@cocoon.co.uk
*Silver and silver flatware.*

**Jack Simons (Antiques) Ltd**
The London Silver Vaults, Chancery House,
53-65 Chancery Lane, London WC2
Tel: 020 7242 3221
*Antique silver.*

**Oswald Simpson**
Hall Street, Long Melford, Suffolk CO10 9JL
Tel: 01787 377523
*17th to 19th-century oak and country furniture;
samplers; Staffordshire pottery; metalwork.*

**Sinai Antiques
(ref: Sinai)**
219-21 Kensington Church St, London W8 7LX
Tel: 020 7229 6190  Fax: 020 7221 0543
*Antiques and works of art.*

**Sladmore Sculpture Gallery Ltd**
32 Bruton Place, Berkeley Square,
London W1X 7AA
Tel: 020 7499 0365  Fax: 020 7409 1381
*Fine 19th- and 20th-century sporting and animal
bronze sculpture.*

**Sleeping Beauty**
579-581 King's Road, London SW6 2DY
Tel: 020 7471 4711  Fax: 020 7471 4795
www.antiquebeds.com
*Antique beds.*

**Something Different**
254 Holloway Road, London N7 6NE
Tel: 020 7697 8538  Fax: 020 7697 8538
*African wood and stone carvings and objets d'art.*

**Somlo Antiques
(ref: Somlo)**
No.7 Piccadilly Arcade, London SW1Y 6NH
Tel: 020 7499 6526  Fax: 020 7499 0603
mail@somlo.com
www.somloantiques.com
*Specialists in fine vintage and antique wrist and
pocket watches.*

**David L.H. Southwick**
Beacon Lodge, Beacon Lane,
Kingswear, Devon TQ6 0BU
Tel: 01803 752533  Fax: 01803 752535
*Oriental ceramics and works of art.*

**A. & J. Speelman Ltd Oriental Art**
129 Mount Street, London W1Y 5HA
Tel: 020 7499 5126   Fax: 020 7355 3391
*Oriental ceramics and works of art; valuations.*

**Ian Spencer**
**(ref: Ian Spencer, Spencer)**
17 Godfrey Street, London SW3 3TA
Mobile: 0973 375940
*Large desks, sets of chairs and dining tables.*

**Spink**
21 King Street, St James's, London SW1Y 6QY
Tel: 020 7930 5500   Fax 020 7930 5501
lengtan@spinkandson.com
*Indian, Himalayan, south-east Asian and Islamic art; textiles; valuations.*

**Spink & Son Ltd**
69 Southampton Row,
Bloomsbury, London WC1B 4ET
Tel: 020 7563 4000   Fax: 020 7563 4066
info@spinkandson.com
www.spink-online.com
*Coins and banknotes; stamps; orders, decorations, campaign medals and militaria; numismatic; war medals and related books; valuations.*

**Stair & Company Ltd**
14 Mount Street, London W1Y 5RA
Tel: 020 7499 1784   Fax: 020 7629 1050
*18th-century English furniture and works of art.*

**Louis Stanton**
299-301 Westbourne Grove, London W11 2QA
Tel: 020 7727 9336   Fax: 020 7727 5424
*16th- to 19th-century furniture, specialising in early oak; medieval sculpture and works of art; curiosities and unusual items; metalwork and pewter; valuations.*

**Star Signings**
Unit A18/A19, Grays Mews Antiques Market,
1-7 Davies Mews, London W1Y 2LP
Tel: 020 7491 1010   Fax: 020 7491 1070
starsignings@hotmail.com
*Sporting autographs and memorabilia.*

**Steinway & Sons**
**(ref: Steinway)**
44 Marylebone Lane, London W1M 6EN
Tel: 020 7487 3391   Fax: 020 7935 0466
pianosales@steinway.co.uk
*New and refurbished pianos.*

**Steppes Hill Farm Antiques**
Steppes Hill Farm, Stockbury, Sittingbourne,
Kent ME9 7RB
Tel: 01795 842205
*Porcelain, pottery and enamels; silver and old Sheffield plate; valuations.*

**Jane Stewart**
C 26/27, Grays Mews Antiques Market,
Davies Mews, London W1Y 2LP
Tel: 020 7355 333
*Pewter early 17th- to 19th-century, oak, writing slopes.*

**Constance Stobo**
31 Holland St, London W8 4NA
Tel: 020 79376282
*English lustreware, Staffordshire animals, Wemyss, 18th- and 19th-century pottery.*

**Colin Stock**
8 Mossborough Road, Rainford, St Helens,
Merseyside WA11 8QN
Tel: 0174 488 2246
*18th- and early 19th-century furniture.*

**Stockspring Antiques**
114 Kensington Church St, London W8 4BH
Tel: 020 7727 7995
*18th- and early 19th-century English porcelain and pottery.*

**Jacob Stodel**
Brook Street Mansion,
Flat 4, 41 Davies Street, London W1Y 1FJ
Tel: 020 7491 7717   Fax: 020 7491 9813
*18th-century English and continental furniture; Oriental and European ceramics and works of art.*

**June & Tony Stone**
**(ref: J. & T. Stone)**
75 Portobello Rd, London W11 2QB
Tel: 020 7221 1121   Tel: 01273 500024
Mobile: 07768 382424
info@boxes.co.uk
*Fine antique boxes.*

**Strike One (Islington) Ltd**
48A Highbury Hill, London N5 1AP
Tel: 020 7354 2790   Fax: 020 7354 2790
*Clocks and barometers; music boxes; valuations.*

**Studio 2000**
4 Pierrepont Row Arcade, Camden Passage
London N1 8EF
Tel: 020 7359 4127 or 01733 244717
*Pottery.*

**Mark Sullivan**
**(ref: M. Sullivan)**
14 Cecil Court, London WC2N 4EZ
Tel: 020 7836 7056   Tel: 020 8741 7360
Fax: 020 8287 8492
*Antiques and decoratives.*

**Sugar Antiques**
**(ref: Sugar)**
8-9, Pierrepont Arcade, Camden Passage,
London N1 8EF
Tel: 020 7354 9896   Fax: 020 8931 5642
Mobile: 0973 179 980
elayne@sugar-antiques.demon.co.uk
www.sugar-antiques.demon.co.uk
*Jewellery and costume jewellery, antique watches,*
*classic fountain pens.*

**Summers Davis Antiques Ltd**
Calleva House, 6 High Street, Wallingford,
Oxfordshire OX10 0BP
Tel: 01491 836284   Fax: 01491 833443
*English and continental furniture of the 17th- to*
*19th-centuries.*

**Sweerts de Landas**
Dunsborough Park, Ripley, Surrey GU23 6AL
Tel: 01483 225366   Fax: 01483 224525
Antique.Collectors-on-line.com/dealers/sweerts
*Antique garden ornament.*

**Tadema Gallery**
10 Charlton Place, Camden Passage,
London N1 8AJ
Tel: 020 7359 1055   Fax: 020 7359 1055
*Jewellery: Art Nouveau, Arts & Crafts and*
*Art Deco.*

**Stuart Talbot FRAS**
**(ref: Talbot)**
65 Portobello Road, London W11 2QB
Tel: 020 8969 7011
*Fine scientific instruments.*

**Talking Machine**
**(ref: Talk Mach)**
30 Watford Way, Hendon, London NW4 3AL
Tel: 020 8202 3473   Fax: 020 8202 3473
www.gramophones.ndirect.co.uk
*Mechanical music, gramophones phonographs,*
*vintage records.*

**Taurus Antiques Ltd**
**(ref: Taurus)**
The Forge, rear of 39 Chancery Lane,
Beckenham, Kent BR3 2NR
Tel: 020 8650 9179   Mobile: 04689 48421
*Furniture.*

**Telephone Lines Ltd**
304 High Street, Cheltenham, Glos GL50 3JF
Tel: 01242 583699   Fax: 01242 690033
*Telephones.*

**Temple Gallery**
**(ref: Temple)**
6 Clarendon Cross, Holland Park,
London W11 4AP
Tel: 020 7727 3809   Fax: 020 7727 1546
templegallery@cs.com
www.templegallery.com
*Icons, Russian and Greek, 12th- to 16th-century.*

**Tessiers Ltd**
26 New Bond Street, London W1Y 0JY
Tel: 020 7629 0458   Fax: 020 7629 1857
*Jewellery, silver and boxes; valuations.*

**Themes and Variations**
231 Westbourne Grove, London W11 2SE
Tel: 020 7727 5531   Fax: 020 7221 6378
go@themesandvariations.co.uk
*Post-war design.*

**Thompson Antiques**
Tel: 01306 711970   Fax: same
Mobile: 07770 882746
*By appointment only. Tortoiseshell, ivory, silver,*
*enamels and papier maché.*

**Sue & Alan Thompson**
**(ref: S. & A. Thompson, Thompson)**
Highland Cottage, Broomne Hall Road,
Cold Harbour RH5 6HH
Tel: 01306 711970   Fax: 01306 711970
Mobile: 0370 882746
*Objects of vertu, antique tortoiseshell items, period*
*furniture and unusual collectors items.*

**Through the Looking Glass Ltd**
**(ref: Through the Looking Glass)**
563 King's Road, London SW6 2EB
Tel: 020 7736 7799   Fax: 020 7602 3678
*18th- and 19th-century mirrors.*

**William Tillman Ltd**
30 St James's Street, London SW1A 1HB
Tel: 020 7839 2500   Fax: 020 7930 8106
*18th- and early 19th-century English furniture and*
*works of art.*

**S. & S. Timms Antiques Ltd**
2/4 High Street, Shefford, Beds SG17 5DG
Tel: 01462 851051   Fax: 01462 817047
Mobile: 07860 482995
Sstimms@tesco.net
*Antique furniture.*

**Tin Tin Collectables**
**(ref: Tin Tin)**
Unit G38-42, Alfie's Market,
13-25 Church Street, London NW8 8DT
Tel: 020 7258 1305   Fax: 020 7258 1305
tin.tin@teleregion.co.uk
www.tintincollectables.com
*Period costumes and accessories.*

**Jacqueline Toffler Pruskin**
32 Ledbury Road, London W11 2AB
Tel: 020 7221 2306  Fax: 020 7221 2306
Mobile: 07971818776
*Decorative arts of the 19th and 20th centuries.*

**Tower Bridge Antiques**
**(ref: Tower Bridge)**
159/161 Tower Bridge Road, London SE1 3LW
Tel: 020 7403 3660   Fax: 020 7403 6058

**Town & Country Antiques**
**(ref: Town & Country)**
88 Fulham Road, London SW3 1HR
Tel: 020 7589 0660   Fax: 020 7823 7618
www.anthony-james.com
*English furniture.*

**Travers Antiques**
**(ref: Travers)**
71 Bell Street, Marylebone, London NW1 6SX
Tel: 020 7723 4376
*and*
F080-82, Alfie's Antiques Market, London NW8
Tel: 020 7258 0662  Fax: 020 7724 0999
*Antique furniture and restoration.*

**Tredantiques**
77 Hill Barton Road, Whipton, Exeter EX1 3PW
Tel: 01392 447082  Fax: 01392 462200
Mobile: 07967 447082
*Furniture.*

**trio**
**(ref: Trio)**
Grays Mews Antiques Market, 1-7 Davies Mews,
London W1Y 2LP
Tel: 020 7493 2736  Fax: 020 7493 9344
*Perfume bottles and Bohemian glass.*

**Trio Antiques**
Antiquarius, 131-141 King's Road,
London SW3 4PW
Tel: 020 7352 8734
*Country style antiques.*

**Turn On Lighting**
**(ref: Turn On)**
116-118 Islington High St,
Camden Passage, London N1 8EG
Tel: 020 7359 7616  Fax: 020 7359 7616
*Antique lighting specialists.*

**Jan Van Beers**
34 Davies Street, London W1Y 1LG
Tel: 020 7408 0434  Fax: 020 7355 1397
*Oriental ceramics and works of art; porcelain,*
*pottery and enamels; valuations.*

**Earle D. Vandekar of Knightsbridge**
305 East 61st Street, New York, NY 10021, USA
Tel: 001 212 308 2022  Fax: 001 212 308 2105
*Fine 18th- and 19th-century ceramics; furniture;*
*portrait miniatures and works of art.*

**Vintage Wireless Shop**
**(ref: Vintage Wireless)**
The Hewarths, Sadiacre,
Nottingham NG10 5NQ
Tel: 0115 939 3139
*Radios.*

**M. Wakelin & H. Linfield**
PO Box 48, Billingshurst,
West Sussex RH14 0YZ
Tel: 01403 700004  Fax: 01403 700004
*Furniture, early bronze, brass and iron.*

**Alan Walker**
Halfway Manor, Halfway, Newbury,
Berkshire, RG20 8NR
Tel: 01488 657 670   Fax: 01488 657 670
Mobile: 0370 728 397
*Fine antique barometers.*

**Walker Galleries Ltd**
6 Montpellier Gardens, Harrogate,
North Yorkshire HG1 2TF
Tel: 01423 567933  Fax: 01423 536664
www.harrogateantiques.com
*English and continental oil paintings, watercolours*
*and drawings; valuations.*

**Graham Walpole Antiques**
**(ref: G. Walpole)**
The Coach House, 189 Westbourne Grove,
London W11 2SB
Tel: 020 7229 8311   Fax: 020 7727 7584
*19th-century antiques.*

**Graham Walpole**
**(ref: G. Walpole)**
187 Westbourne Grove, London, W11 2RS
Tel: 020 7229 0267
*Metalware, furniture and collectables.*

**William Walter Antiques Ltd**
London Silver Vaults, Chancery Lane,
London WC2A 1QS
Tel: 020 7242 3248  Fax: 020 7404 1280
*Antique silver and old Sheffield plate; valuations.*

**Wartski Ltd**
14 Grafton Street, London W1X 4DE
Tel: 020 7493 1141  Fax: 020 7409 7448
*18th- and 19th-century jewellery; Russian works of*
*art; 18th-century gold boxes; silver.*

**S. J. Webster-Speakman**
52 Halesworth Road, Reydon, Southwold,
Suffolk IP18 6NR
Tel: 01502 722252
*18th- and early 19th-century English furniture;*
*clocks and barometers; valuations.*

**A.W. Welling**
Broadway Barn, High Street,
Ripley, Surrey GU23 6AQ
Tel: 01483 225384
*17th- and 18th-century oak and country furniture.*

**Mark J. West**
Cobb Antiques Ltd, 39B High Street,
Wimbledon Village, London SW19 5BY
Tel: 020 8946 2811   Fax: 020 8946 2811
Antique.Collectors-on-line.com/dealers/mjwest
*18th- and 19th-century English and continental glass.*

**Westland & Company
(ref: Westland & Co)**
St. Michael's Church,
Leonard St, London EC2A 4ER
Tel: 020 7739 8094   Fax: 020 7729 3620
westland@westland.co.uk
*Period fireplaces, architectural elements and
panelling.*

**Wheels of Steel**
B 10/11, Grays Mews Antiques Market,
1-7 Davies Mews, London W1Y 2LP
Tel: 020 8505 0450   Fax: 020 7629 2813
*Trains, toys.*

**Whitford Fine Art
(ref: Whitford)**
6 Duke Street, St. James's, London SW1Y 6BN
Tel: 020 7930 9332   Fax: 020 7930 5577
*Oil paintings and sculpture, late 19th-century to
20th-century; post-war abstract and pop art.*

**Wilde Ones**
283 King's Road, London SW3 5EW
Tel: 020 7352 9531   Fax: 020 7349 0828
shop@wildeones.com
*Jewellery.*

**Willow Gallery**
75 Queens Road, Weybridge, Surrey KT13 9UQ
Tel: 01932 846095
*British and European Victorian oil paintings.*

**O.F. Wilson Ltd
(ref: O.F. Wilson)**
Queen's Elm Parade,
Old Church St, London SW3 6EJ
Tel: 020 7352 9554   Fax: 020 7351 0765
Mobile: 0973 384133
ofw@email.msn.com
*Antique furniture, works of art and decoration.*

**Witney Antiques**
96-100 Corn Street, Witney,
Oxfordshire OX8 7BU
Tel: 01993 703902   Fax: 01993 779852
*17th- and 18th-century English furniture; clocks;
works of art; textiles; pewter.*

**Christopher Wood**
20 Georgian House, 10 Bury Street, St James's,
London SW1Y 6AA
Tel: 020 7839 3963   Fax: 020 7839 3963
*Victorian, Pre-Raphaelite and European
19th-century paintings, watercolours and drawings;
Gothic furniture and Arts and Crafts movement;
valuations.*

**Clifford Wright Antiques Ltd**
104-106 Fulham Road, London SW3 6HS
Tel: 020 7589 0986   Fax: 020 7589 3565
*18th- and early 19th-century English furniture and
giltwood looking glasses; glass pictures; prints.*

**Yacobs Gallery**
Grays Mews Antiques Market, 1-7 Davies Mews,
London W1Y 2LP
Tel: 020 7629 7034   Fax: 020 7493 9344
*Islamic art.*

**D.A. & V.A. Yates**
Hewarths, Sandiacre, Nottingham NG10 5NQ
Tel: 0115 939 3139   Fax: 0115 949 0180
Mobile: 0973 958039

**Youlls Antiques
(ref: Youlls)**
28 Charnham Street, Berks,
Hungerford RG17 0EJ
Tel: 01488 682046   Fax: 01488 684335
www.youll.combruce.
youll@talk21.com
*French and English furniture and decorative items.*

**Robert Young Antiques**
68 Battersea Bridge Road, London SW11 3AG
Tel: 020 7228 7847
*Early country furniture, folk art, naïve paintings
and treen.*

**Zaheim**
52 Ledbury Road, Westbourne Grove,
London W11
Tel: 020 7629 1433   Mobile: 0585 930 630
*Russian works of art.*

**Nina Zborowska**
Damsels Mill, Paradise, Painswick,
Gloucestershire GL6 6UD
Tel: 01452 812460   Fax: 01452 812912
nina@zborowska.co.uk
*Late 19th- and early 20th-century British paintings
and drawings, including the St Ives and
Bloomsbury Group.*

**Rainer Zietz Ltd**
1a Prairie Street, London SW8 3PX
Tel: 020 7498 2355   Home: 020 7352 0848
Fax: 020 7720 7745
*European works of art and sculpture.*

**Zoom**
Arch 65, Cambridge Grove, Hammersmith,
London W6 OLD
Tel: 07000 966 620   Tel/Fax: 020 8846 9779
Mobile: 0958 372975
www.retrozoom.com
eddiesandham@hotmail.com
*1950s-1970s' furniture, lighting and unusual
retro objects.*

There follows our selection of the best antiques centres and markets in the country. These present the best of both worlds, with several dealers showing their particular specialities at the fair prices we expect from the reputable retailer.

## BEDFORDSHIRE, BUCKINGHAMSHIRE, HERTFORDSHIRE

**Antiques at Wendover Antiques Centre**
The Old Post Office, 25 High Street,
Wendover HP22 6DU
Tel: 01296 625335
*Dealers: 30*

**Barkham Antiques Centre**
Barkham Street, Barkham RG40 4PJ
Tel: 0118 9761 355   Fax: 0118 9764 355

**Buck House Antiques Centre**
47 Wycombe End, Old Town,
Beaconsfield HP9 1LZ
Tel: 01494 670714

**Luton Antiques Centre**
Auction House, Crescent Road,
Luton LU1 2NA
Tel: 01582 405281   Fax: 01582 454080

**Woburn Abbey Antiques Centre**
Woburn Abbey, Bedfordshire MK17 9WA
Tel: 01525 290350   Fax: 01525 290271
*Dealers: 50*

## BRISTOL, BATH, SOMERSET

**Bartlett Street Antiques Centre**
5-10 Bartlett Street, Bath BA1 2QZ
Tel: 01225 466689   Fax: 01225 444146
*Dealers: 50+*

**Bath Saturday Antiques Market**
Walcot Street, Bath BA1 5BD
Tel: 01225 448263   Fax: 01225.317154
Mobile: 083653 4893
*Dealers: 70+*

## CAMBRIDGESHIRE

**Fitzwilliam Antique Centre**
Fitzwilliam Street, Peterborough PE1 2RX
Tel: 01733 565415

**Hive Antiques Market, The**
Unit 3, Dales Brewery, Gwydir St,
Cambridge CB1 2LG
Tel: 01223 300269

**Gwydir Street Antiques Centre**
Untis 1&2 Dales Brewery, Gwydir St,
Cambridge CB1 2LJ
Tel: 01223 356391

**Old Bishop's, The Palace Antique Centre**
Tower Road, Little Downham, Nr Ely
Cambridgeshire CB6 2TD
Tel: 01353 699177

## CHESHIRE AND STRAFFORDSHIRE

**Antique Furniture Warehouse**
Unit 3-4 , Royal Oak Buildings, Cooper Street,
Stockport, Cheshire SK1 3QJ
Tel: 0161 429 8590   Fax: 0161 480 5375

**Knutsford Antiques Centre**
113 King Street, Knutsford, WA16 6EH
Tel: 01565 654092

## CORNWALL

**Chapel Street Antiques Market**
61/62 Chapel Street, Penzance TR18 4AE
Tel: 01736 363267
*Dealers: 30-40*

**Waterfront Antiques Complex**
4 Quay Street, Falmouth, Cornwall TR11 3HH
Tel: 01326 311491
*Dealers: 20-25*

## THE COTSWOLDS

**The Antique and Interior Centre**
51A Long Street GL8 8AA
Tel: 01666 505083
*Dealers: 10*

## CUMBRIA AND LANCASHIRE

**Carlisle Antiques Centre**
Cecil Hall, 46A Cecil Street,
Carlisle CA1 1NT
Tel: 0122 8536 910   Fax: 0122 8536 910
carlsle-antiques.co.uk

**Cockermouth Antiques Market**
Courthouse, Main Street,
Cockermouth CA15 5XM
Tel: 01900 826746

## DERBYSHIRE AND NOTTINGHAMSHIRE

**Alfreton Antiques Centre**
11 King Street, Alfreton DE55 7AF
Tel: 01773 520781
alfretonantiques@supanet.com

**Castle Gate Antiques Centre**
55 Castle Gate, Newark NG24 1BE
Tel: 01636 700076   Fax: 01636 700144
*Dealers: 10*

**Chappells and the Antiques Centre Bakewell**
King Street DE45 1DZ
Tel: 01629 812 496   Fax: 01629 814 531
bacc@chappells-antiques.co.uk
*Dealers: 30*

**Memory Lane Antiques Centre**
Nottingham Road, Ripley DE5 3AS
Tel: 01773 570184
*Dealers: 40-50*

**Portland Street Antiques Centre**
Portland Street, Newark NG24 4XF
Tel: 01636 674397   Fax: 01636 674397

**Top Hat Antiques Centre**
70-72 Derby Road, Nottingham NG1 5DF
Tel: 0115 9419 143
sylvia@artdeco-fairs.co.uk

## DEVONSHIRE
**Abingdon House**
136 High Street, Honiton EX14 8JP
Tel: 01404 42108
*Dealers: 20*

**Antique Centre on the Quay, The**
The Quay, Exeter EX2 4AP
Tel: 01392 493501
home free.emailamail.co.uk

**Barbican Antiques Centre**
82-84 Vauxhall Street, Barbican PL4 0EX
Tel: 01752 201752
*Dealers: 40+*

**Honiton Antique Centre McBains Antiques**
Exeter Airport, Industrial Est., Exeter EX5 2BA
Tel: 01392 366261   Fax: 01392 365572
mcbains@netcomuk.co.uk
*Dealers:10*

**Newton Abbot Antiques Centre**
55 East Street, Newton Abbot TQ12 2JP
Tel: 01626 354074
*Dealers:40*

**Sidmouth Antiques and Collectors Centre**
All Saints Road, Sidmouth EX10 8ES
Tel: 01395 512 588

## DORSET
**Bridport Antique Centre**
5 West Allington, Bridport DT6 5BJ
Tel: 01308 425885

**Colliton Antique Centre**
Colliton Street, Dorchester DT1 1XH
Tel: 01305 269398 / 01305 260115

**Emporium Antiques Centre**
908 Christchurch Road, Boscombe,
Bournemouth, Dorset BH7 6DL
Tel: 01202 422380   Fax: 01202 433348
*Dealers: 8*

**Mattar Antique Centre**
Mattar Arcade, 17 Newlands DT9 3JG
Tel: 01935 813464   Fax: 01935 813464

## ESSEX
**Baddow Antique Centre**
The Bringey, Church Street, Great Baddow,
Chelmsford, Essex CM2 7JW
Tel: 01245 476159

**Finchingfield Antiques Centre**
The Green, Finchingfield, Braintree,
Essex CM7 4JX
Tel: 01371 810258   Fax: 01371 810258
*Dealers: 45*

**Harwich Antique Centre**
19 King's Quay Street, Harwich, Essex
Tel: 01255 554719   Fax: 01255 554719
Dealers: 50
harwich@worldwideantiques.co.uk

**Saffron Walden Antiques Centre**
1 Market Row, Saffron Walden,
Essex CB10 1HA
Tel: 01799 524534   Fax: 01799 524703

## HAMPSHIRE AND ISLE OF WIGHT
**Dolphin Quay Antique Centre**
Queen Street, Emsworth,
Hampshire PO10 7BU
Tel: 01243 379994   Fax: 01243 379251
enquiriesnancy@netscapeonline.co.uk

**Eversley Antique Centre Ltd**
Church Lane, Eversley, Hook,
Hampshire RG27 0PX
Tel: 0118 932 8518
*Dealers: 11*

**Lyndhurst Antique Centre**
19-21 High Street, Lyndhurst,
Hampshire SO43 7BB
Tel: 0238 0284 000
*Dealers: 50*

**The Antique Centre**
Britannia Road, Southampton,
Hampshire SO14 0QL
Tel: 0238 0221 022
*Dealers: 46*

**The Antique Quarter**
'Old' Northam Road, Southampton,
Hampshire SO14 0QL
Tel: 0238 0233 393
*Dealers: 15*

## GLOUCESTERSHIRE
**Struwwelpeter**
The Old School House,
175 London Road, Charlton Kings,
Cheltenham Gloucester GL52 6HN
Tel: 01242 230088
*Dealers: 7*

## HEREFORD AND WORCESTERSHIRE

**Antique Centre, The**
5-8 Lion Street, Kidderminster,
Worcestershire DY10 1PT
Tel: 01562 740389  Fax: 01562 740389
*Dealers: 12*

**Hereford Antique Centre**
128 Widemarsh Street, Hereford HR4 9HN
Tel: 01432 266242
*Dealers: 35*

**Leominster Antique Centre**
34 Broad Street, Leominster HR6 8BS
Tel: 01568 615505
*Dealers: 22*

**Leominster Antique Market**
14 Broad Street, Leominster HR6 8BS
Tel: 01568 612 189
*Dealers: 15+*

**Linden House Antiques**
3 Silver Street, Stansted CM24 8HA
Tel: 01279 812 373

**Malvern Link Antique Centre**
154 Worcester Road, Malvern Link,
Worcestershire WR14 1AA
Tel: 01684 575750
*Dealers: 10*

**Ross on Wye Antique Gallery**
Gloucester Road, Ross on Wye,
Herefordshire HR9 5BU
Tel: 01989 762290  Fax: 01989 762291
*Dealers: 91*

**Worcester Antiques Centre**
15 Reindeer Court, Mealcheapen Street,
Worcester WR1 4DF
Tel: 01905 610680/1  Fax: 01905 610681
*Dealers: 45*

## KENT

**Antiques Centre, The**
120 London Road, Tubs Hill TN13 1BA
Tel: 01732 452104

**Coach House Antique Centre**
2a Duck Lane, Northgate, Canterbury,
Kent CT1 2AE
Tel: 01227 463117
*Dealers: 7*

**Copperfield Antique & Craft Centre**
Unit 4, Copperfield's Walkway, Spital Street,
Dartford, Kent DA1 2DE
Tel: 01322 281445
*Dealer: 35*

**Corn Exchange Antiques Centre**
64 The Pantiles, Tunbridge Wells, Kent TN2 5TN
Tel: 01892 539652  Fax: 01892 538454
*Dealers: 11*

**Tenterden Antiques Centre**
66 High Street TN30 6AU
Tel: 01580 765885  Fax: 01580 765655
*Dealers: 20+*

**Tunbridge Wells Antique Centre**
12 Union Square, The Pantiles,
Tunbridge Wells TN4 8HE
Tel: 01892 533708
twantique@aol.com

**Village Antique Centre**
4 High Street, Brasted, Kent TN16 1RF
Tel: 01959 564545
*Dealers: 15*

## LEICESTERSHIRE, RUTLAND AND NORTHAMPTONESHIRE

**Finedon Antique (Centre)**
11-25 Bell Hill, Finedon NN9 5NB
Tel: 01933 681260  Fax: 01933 681779
sales@finedonantiques.com

**The Village Antique Market**
62 High Street, Weedon NN7 4QD
Tel: 01327 342 015
*Dealers: 40*

## LINCOLNSHIRE

**Astra House Antique Centre**
Old RAF Helswell, Nr Caenby Corner,
Gainsborough, Lincolnshire DN21 5TL
Tel: 01427 668312
*Dealers: 50*

**Guardroom Antiques**
RAF Station Henswell,
Gainsborough DN21 5TL
Tel: 01427 667113
*Dealers: 50*

**Henswell Antiques Centre**
Caenby Corner Estate, Henswell Cliff
Gainsborough DN21 5TL
Tel: 01427 668 389  Fax: 01427 668 935
info@Hemswell-antiques.com
*Dealers:270*

**St. Martin's Antique Centre**
23a High Street, St Martin's, Stamford PE9 2LF
Tel: 01780 481158  Fax: 01780 766598

**Stamford Antiques Centre**
The Exchange Hall, Broad Street,
Stamford PE1 9PX
Tel: 01780 762 605  Fax: 01733 244 717
anoc1900@compuserve.com
*Dealers: 40*

## LONDON

**Alfie's Antique Market**
13-25 Church Street NW8 8DT
Tel: 020 7723 6066  Fax: 020 7724 0999
alfies@clara.net

**Antiquarius**
131-41 King's Road SW3 4PW
Tel: 020 7351 5353   Fax: 020 7351 5350
antique@dial.pipex.com

**Bermondsey**
corner of Long Lane & Bermondsey Street
SE1 3UN
Tel: 020 7351 5353

**Camden Passage**
Upper Street, Islington N1
Tel: 020 7359 9969
www.camdenpassage.com

**Grays Mews Antique Markets**
58 Davis Street, and 1-7 Davis Mews WIY 2LP
Tel: 020 7629 7034
*Dearlers: 300*

**Hampstead Antique and Craft Market**
12 Heath Street, London NW3 6TE
Tel: 020 7431 0240   Fax: 020 7794 4620
*Dealers: 20*

**Jubilee Market Hall**
1 Tavistock Court, The Piazza
Covent Garden WC2 E8BD
Tel: 020 7836 2139

**Lillie Road**
237 Lillie Road, SW6
Tel: 020 7381 2500   Fax: 020 7381 8320

**Portobello Road**
In Notting Hill Gate W10 and W11
Tel: 020 7727 7684   Fax: 020 7727 7684
*Dealers: 280*

**Spitalfields,**
65 Brushfield Street E1 6AA
Tel: 020 8983 3779   Fax: 020 7377 1783

## NORFOLK
**Fakenham Antique Centre,**
The Old Congregational Church, 14 Norwich
Road, Fakenham, Norfolk NR21 8AZ
Tel: 01328 862941
*Dealers: 20*

## NORTHUMBERLAND AND DURHAM
**The Village Antique Market**
62 High Street, Weedon NN7 4QD
Tel: 01327 342015
*Dealers: 40*

## OXFORDSHIRE
**Antique on High Ltd**
85 High Street, Oxford OX1 4BG
Tel: 01865 251075   Fax: 0129 665 5580
*Dealers: 38*

**Country Markets Antiques and Collectables**
Country Garden Centre, Newbury Road,
Chilton, nr. Didcot OX11 0QN
Tel: 01235 835125   Fax: 01235 833068
countrymarketsantiquesandcollectables
@breathnet.com
*Dealers: 35*

**Old George Inn Antique Galleries**
104 High Street, Burford, Oxfordshire OX18 4QJ
Tel: 01993 823319
*Dealers: 22*

**Station Mill Antique Centre**
Station Yard Industrial Estate, Chipping Norton,
Oxfordshire OX7 5HX
Tel: 01608 644563   Fax: 01608 644563
*Dealers: 73*

**Swan at Tetsworth**
High Street, Tetsworth, Oxfordshire OX9 7AB,
Tel: 01844 281777   Fax: 01844 281770
*antiques@theswan.co.uk*
*Dealers: 80*

## SHROPSHIRE
**Bridgnorth Antique Centre**
Whitburn Street, Bridgnorth,
Shropshire WV16 4QP
Tel: 01746 768055
*Dealers: 19*

**K. W. Swift**
56 Mill Street, Ludlow SY8 1BB
Tel: 01584 878571   Fax: 01746 714407
*Dealers: 20, book market.*

**Old Mill Antique Centre**
Mill Street, Shropshire WV15 5AG
Tel: 01746 768778   Fax: 01746 768944
*Dealers: 90*

**Princess Antique Centre**
14a The Square, Shrewsbury SY1 1LH
Tel: 01743 343701
*Dealers: 100 stallholders*

**Shrewsbury Antique Centre**
15 Princess House, The Square,
Shrewsbury SY1 1UT
Tel: 01743 247 704

**Shrewsbury Antique Market**
Frankwell Quay Warehouse,
Shrewsbury SY3 8LG
Tel: 01743 350619
*Dealers: 30*

**Stretton Antiques Market**
36 Sandford Avenue, Stretton SY6 6BH
Tel: 01694 723718   Fax: 01694 723718
*Dealers: 60*

## STAFFORDSHIRE
**Lion Antique Centre**
8 Market Place, Uttoxeter, Staffordshire ST14 8HP
Tel: 01889 567717
*Dealers: 28*

## SUFFOLK
**Church Street Centre**
6e Church Street, Woodbridge, Suffolk IP12 1DH
Tel: 01394 388887
*Dealers: 10*

**Long Melford Antiques Centre**
Chapel Maltings, CO10 9HX
Tel: 01787 379287   Fax: 01787 379287
*Dealers: 40*

**Woodbridge Gallery**
23 Market Hill, Woodbridge, Suffolk IP12 4OX
Tel: 01394 386500   Fax: 01394 386500
*Dealers: 35*

## SURREY
**The Antiques Centre**
22 Haydon Place, Corner of Martyr Road,
Guildford GU1 4LL
Tel: 01483 567817
*Dealers: 6*

**The Antiques Warehouse**
Badshot Farm, St George's Road,
Runfold GU9 9HY
Tel: 01252 317590   Fax: 01252 879751
*Dealers: 40*

**Enterprise Collectors Market**
Station Parade, Eastbourne, East Sussex BN21 1BD
Tel: 01323 732690
*Dealers: 15*

**The Hampton Court Emporium**
52-54 Bridge Road, East Molesey,
Surrey KT8 9HA
Tel: 020 8941 8876
*Dealers: 16*

**The Kingston Antiques Market**
29-31 London Road, Kingston-upon-Thames,
Surrey KT2 6ND
Tel: 020 8549 2004   Fax: 020 8549 3839
webmaster@antiquesmarket.co.uk
*Dealers: 90*

**Packhouse Antique Centre**
Hewetts Kilns, Tongham Road, Runfold,
Farnham, Surrey GU10 1PQ
Tel: 01252 781010   Fax: 01252 783876
hewett@cix.co.uk
*Dealers: 80*

**Victoria and Edward Antique Centre**
61 West Street, Dorking, Surrey RH4 1BS
Tel: 01306 889645
*Dealers: 26*

## SUSSEX
**Almshouses Arcade**
19 The Hornet PO19 4JL
Tel: 01243 771994

**Brighton Flea Market**
31A Upper Street, James's Street BN2 1JN
Tel: 01273 624006   Fax: 01273 328665
arwilkinson@aol.com

**Eastbourne Antiques Market**
80 Seaside, Eastbourne BN22 7QP
Tel: 01323 642233
*Dealers: 25*

**Lewes Antique Centre**
20 Cliff High Street, Lewes BN7 2AH
Tel: 01273 476 148 / 01273 472 173
*Dealers: 60*

**The Old Town Antiques Centre**
52 Ocklynge Road, Eastbourne, East Sussex
BN21 1PR
Tel: 01323 416016
*Dealers: 16*

**Olinda House Antiques**
South Street, Rotherfield, Crowborough,
East Sussex TN6 3LL,
Tel: 01892 852609

**Petworth Antiques Market**
East Street, Petworth, GU28 0AB
Tel: 01798 342073   Fax: 01798 344566

## WARWICKSHIRE
**Barn Antique Centre**
Long Marston Ground, Station Road, Long
Marsdon, Stratford-upon-Avon CV37 8RB
Tel: 01789 721399   Fax: 01789 721390
barnantiques@aol.com
*Dealers: 50*

**Bridford Antique Centre**
Warwick House, 94-96 High Street, Bidford on
Avon, Alcester, Warwickshire B50 4AF
Tel: 01789 773680
*Dealers: 7*

**Dunchurch Antique Centre**
16a Daventry Road, Dunchurch, Rugby,
CV22 6NS
Tel: 01788 522450
*Dealers: 10*

**Malthouse Antique Centre**
4 Market Place, Alcester, Warwickshire B49 5AE
Tel: 01789 764032
*Dealers: 20*

**Stables Antique Centre, The**
Hatton Country World, Dark Lane CV35 8XA
Tel: 01926 842405
*Dealers: 25*

**Stratford Antiques and Interiors Centre Ltd**
Dodwell Trading Estate, Evesham Road
CV37 9SY
Tel: 01789 297729   Fax: 01789 297710
info@stratfordantiques.co.uk
*Dealers: 20*

**Vintage Antiques Centre**
36 Market Place, Warwick CV34 4SH
Tel: 01926 491527
vintage@globalnet.co.uk
*Dealers: 20*

**Warwick Antiques Centre**
22 High Street, Warwick CV34 4AP
Tel: 01926 491382 / 01926 495704
*Dealers: 32*

## WILTSHIRE
**Brocante Antiques Centre**
6 London Road, Marlborough SN8 1PH
Tel: 01672 516512   Fax: 01672 516512
brocante@brocanteantiquescentre.co.uk
*Dealers: 20*

**Marlborough Parade Antique Centre, The**
The Parade, Marlborough SN8 1NE
Tel: 01672 515331
*Dealers: 70*

## YORKSHIRE
**Arcadia Antiques Centre**
12-14 The Arcade, Goole,
East Yorkshire DN14 5PY
Tel: 01405 720549
*Dealers: 20*

**Banners Collectables**
Banners Business Centre, Attercliffe Road,
Sheffield, South Yorkshire S9 3QS
Tel: 0114 244 0742
*Dealers: 50*

**Barmouth Road Antique Centre**
**Barmouth Court**
off Abbeydale, Sheffield, South Yorkshire S7 2DH
Tel: 0114 255 2711   Fax: 0114 258 2672
*Dealers: 60*

**Cavendish Antique & Collectors Centre**
44 Stonegate, York YO1 8AS
Tel: 01904 621666   Fax: 01904 644400
*Dealers: 60*

**The Harrogate Antiques Centre**
The Ginnel, off Parliament Street HG1 2RB
Tel: 01423 508857   Fax: 01423 508857
*Dealers: 50*

**Halifax Antique Centre**
Queens Road, Halifax,
West Yorkshire HX1 4OR
Tel: 01422 366 657   Fax: 01422 369 293
antiques@halifaxac.u-net.com
*Dealers: 30*

**Malton Antique Market**
2 Old Maltongate, Malton YO17 0EG
Tel: 01653 692 732

**Pickering Antique Centre**
Southgate, Pickering,
North Yorkshire YO18 8BN
Tel: 01751 477210   Fax: 01751 477210
*Dealers: 35*

**Stonegate Antique Centre**
41 Stonegate, York, North Yorkshire YO1 8AW
Tel: 01904 613888   Fax: 01904 644400
*Dealers: 120*

**York Antiques Centre**
2a Lendal, York YO1 8AA
Tel: 01904 641445 / 641582
*Dealers: 16+*

## SCOTLAND
**Clola Antiques Centre**
Shannas School House,
Clola by Mintlaw AB42 8AE
Tel: 01771 624584   Fax: 01771 624584
*Dealers: 10*

**Scottish Antique & Arts Centre**
Abernyte PH14 9SJ
Tel: 01828 686401   Fax: 01828 686199

## WALES
**Antique Market**
6 Market Street, Hay-on-Wye HR3 5AD
Tel: 01497 820175

**Cardiff Antiques Centre**
10-12 Royal Arcade CF10 2AE
Tel: 01222 398891
*Dealers: 13*

**Chapel Antiques**
Methodist Chapel, Holyhead Road, Froncysyllte,
Denbighshire, Llangollen LL20 7RA
Tel: 01691 777624   Fax: 01691 777624
*Dealers: 20*

**Jacobs Antique Centre**
West Canal Wharf, Cardiff C51 5DB
Tel: 01222 390939
*Dealers: 50*

## A

acrobat 499
Adam, Robert 24
Adams 36
Adams, Dudley 156
Adams, George 450
advertising 160-163
    Gilroy 160
    Horlicks 163
    Guiness 160, 161
    Johnson 160
    Normandie 161
    Disney 160, 162
aerator 489
aeronautica 164-167
    ABC gazettier 164
    cannon shells 165
    certificate 165
    club badge 164
    map 164, 165
    model 164, 165, 166, 167
    propellor 167
    sales leaflet 164
    ticket 165, 166
    timetable 165, 167
aeroplane propellor 459
Afghanistan 62, 105, 107, 108
Africa, map of 55
Agra 61
Akira 200
Akkadian 18
Albanian dagger 38
Alberelli 99, 101
Alberello 95, 96
Alberello, Faenza 94
Aldis 178
Aldridge & Green 447
Alice in Wonderland 161, 479
Allen & Moore 267
Allinono 471
alps 48
Alvar, Aalto 530
amazonite 417
amboyna 304
American Motor Toys 497
amethyst 12, 408, 413, 416
Amlash 12
ammunition pouch 474
amphora 18
amphorae 17
amplifier 429, 434
Amsterdam 49
Anamese 124
Anatolia 59
anchor 424
Anderson, Gerry 495
    and Sylvia 492
Anderson, Hans 49
Andolucia 47
Andrews 132
angel 103
angler's knife 471

animals
    alligator 280, 582
    anteater 476
    bear 87
    beaver 476
    beetle 477, 504
    bird 278, 478, 521, 523
    boar 566
    budgerigar 525
    buffalo 511
    bull 12, 93
    bustard 277
    butterfly 478
    camel 16, 567
    carp 276
    cat 96, 98, 574, 581
    chicken 124
    cockerells 451
    cow 81, 86, 90, 516
    crane 476
    deer 88
    dog 72, 76, 83, 84, 85, 86, 87,
        90, 91, 94, 95, 98, 100, 102,
        114, 122, 137, 270, 278,
        279, 281, 283, 479
    duck 124, 473, 375, 478
    elephant 82, 129, 134, 270,
        271, 390, 512, 525
    falcon 478
    finch 476
    fox 84, 97, 478
    frog 70
    goat 92
    hares 123
    hawk 283
    hedgehog 477
    horse 14, 129, 131, 276, 494,
        496
    horse 554, 565, 567
    insect 477, 479
    jungle cat 479
    lamb 571
    lemur 477
    leopard 83
    lion 19, 21, 26, 79, 83, 84,
        279, 282, 569
    lizard 477
    magpie 479
    mallard drake 478
    mice 281
    monkey 92, 516
    octopus 121
    owl 478, 479
    panda 495
    panther 21
    partridge 478
    peacock 479
    pheasant 478
    pig 64, 80
    polar bear 523, 524
    prawn 557
    rabbit 221, 479, 522

    rhinoceros 491
    rooster 94, 276, 566
    salmon 520
    scorpion 47
    sea horse 95
    sparrow 502
    squirrel 93, 477
    swan 99, 280
    tiger 121
    toad 508
    tortoise 477
    unicorn 21, 279
    wolf 28, 477, 571
    wyvern 21
    zebra 78
Ankor-wat 567
annunciation 576
Anow Games Ltd 497
Antalya 61
Antiques Roadshow 101
antiquities 11-18
Antoinette, Mary 269
anvil 489
Aphrodite 116, 268
Apollo 11, 188
Apostles 17
apothecary jar 101
Arcadia 93
Arcadian 85
Archangel Michael 575, 577
architectural furniture 19-28
Argy-Rousseau 542
Aritaware 114
Armenian 513
armoire 395, 396, 397
armorial 71, 96, 114, 119, 120
    dish 455
    jug 117
    plaques 24
    plates 116
    tablet 23
armour 29-39
arms 29-39
arms of Guildford 34
arms of Lancaster 21
Armstrong, John 54
Arne, Jacobsen 534
Arnhem 524
Arnold Schwin Parckard 168
Art Deco
    armchair 527
    bracelet 411, 415, 417
    brooch 416
    cabinet 533
    candlestick 554, 558
    clock 125
    doors 24
    figure 463
    necklace 413
    piano 430
    silver set 444
    table 389, 392

watch 145, 147
Art Nouveau
  bonheur 288
  chimney 20, 23
  clock 129
  cup 454
  dish 454
  figure 280
  inkwell 543
  jardinière 19
  polyphon 219
  sideboard 528
  table 531
Arte Vetro Murano 540
Ashanti Abzma Owa 509
ashtray 254, 424, 554, 555
Asian works of art 565-567
Assyrian 15, 18
Athena 116
Atkin, H 451
atlases 44-58
ATO 126
aubergine glass 16
Aubrey, Jack 45
Aubusson 62, 63
Audioline 257
Australian 55
Austria 100
Autocourse 41
autometer 221
automobilia 40-43
Averez Secco, Fenazlo 44
Ayyoubid 105
Azari 61, 63
Azores 46

**B**
Babylonian 13
Baccarat 223
Bacchanal 101
backstaff 426
Bactrian 12
Baden-Powell 190
badges 29
Baedeker, Karl 46
bagatelle 504
Bailly, Antony 136
Baird Televisol 237
Baker, C. 152
Baker, Shirley 228, 229
Baku 61
ballot box 458
balsamarium 18
baluster 100, 110
Bambara 510
Bambino 496
Bambocci 309
bamboo 287, 313, 359, 372, 468, 472
Bamiyan 105
Banania 162
Banco de Espana 249
banjo 220

Bank of Scotland 247
Barbarella 232
barbarian helmet 38
Bardot, Brigitte 232
Barnards 438
barograph 425
barometer 125, 137, 448
Barovier 537, 538, 539
barrel 74
barrel tap 563
basalt 15
Bassano 95
Bassett, Captain S.J. 215
Bastar 513
Bateman, Hester 446
Bath 24
Batman 199, 202, 547
Batson, H.A. 441
Battle of Waterloo 187
Baxter, Glen 517, 525
Bayeux 519
bayonet 29, 31
Bazas 140
Bazouch Nimruz 62
Beach Boys, The 241
beads 413
beaker 435
beaker silver 455
Beard, R.A. 56
Beardsley, Audrey 233
Beatles, The 199, 239, 240, 241, 242, 244, 245, 246
Beaufort, Dukes of 21
Beckham, David 198
Bedfordshire 86
beds 284-286
Beecher-Stowe, Harriet 85
beer glass 407
beer stein 30
Belanti 536
Bell & Howell 174, 176
bell, Oriental 121
Bell Telephones 257, 258
Belli, Giovacchino 271
belt buckle 417
belt clasp 31, 33, 34
bench garden 20, 22
Bendorp 161
Benham, Froude 207
Benson, J.W. 150
Benson, Raymond 50
Bentley 42
Berlin 94, 101
Bertius 56
Bertrand, Charlotte 95
Betacom 257
Beurling 136
Biba 480
Bible 49, 58
Bicycles 168-169
bidjar 59
Biedermeier 136, 290, 300, 305, 306, 313, 381
Bigsby 431

Bing 131
bingo 499
binnacle 425
binoculars 460
birdcage 368
bisque 102
Black Sabbath 243
blade ko bizan 34
blade water 36
Blaeu, Johann 44
  Willem and 48, 49
Bland, Cornelius 450
blanket 483
Blockley, Herbert 135
Blomberg, Hugo 261
Blunderbus 35
boat rod 469
bocage 75, 81, 82, 84, 85, 88
Boch & Frères 518
Boehm, J.E. 268
Boer War 75, 189, 248, 267
Bohemian glass 398
Boizit 279
Bojoab bowl 113
Bold, John & William 442
Bolex 177, 178
bollero 482
Bologna, Giam 271
bonbon dish 446
bonheurs du jour 287-288
Bonnet glass 406
bookcarrier 368
Bookcases 289-294
bookends 511, 525, 557
bookmark 467
books 44-58
boot rack 369
boot scraper 488
boot stand 374
border garden 19, 22
border terracotta 19, 22
borer 487
Borneo 512
Botero, Giovanni 48
Bottles 170-173
  drug 99
  glass 399, 401, 405, 406, 407, 410
  Islamic 109
  Kashan 109
  perfume 18
  Roman 15
  scent 399, 401
  tear 15,16
Boucher, Marcel 415
Boucheron 416
Boudriot, Jean 423
Bourjois 170, 171, 172
bouson 380
Bowie, David 240
bowl 78, 82, 84, 90, 99, 427
  Islamic 105, 107, 108, 110, 111
  metalware 276

Oriental 113, 114, 115, 116, 122, 123
box
  Japanese 118
  marine 425, 427
boxes 75, 295-298, 509
boxes, snuff 254-255
boxing items 465
Boydell, John 48
Boydell, Josiah 48
Boydell, Sonia 48
brace 486, 488
bracelet 411
Brandt, Bill 230
brass flask 29
Braun & Hogenberg 51
Braver, Otto 541
Bravo, Manuel Alvarez 229
Brazil, map of 55
breast plate 31, 33
bridle 14
Brigg 262
Brighton & Hove 41
Bristol 88, 89
Britains Ltd 493
Britains' Home Farm 494
Britains' Motor &
  Road Series 493
Britains' Plastic Models 496
Britains' Zoo 495
Britannia 500
British Telecom 256, 261
Broadby, Arthur 516
Broadwood, John 433
bronco 496
bronze antiquities 11, 13, 14, 18
bronze figures 102
bronze
  Persian 18
  reliquary 17
  Roman 16
Bronzien, Ravrio 138
brooch 17, 30, 413, 415, 416, 417, 418, 419, 420, 427
Brooke Bond Tea 500
Brooklands 164, 166
Brownie 176, 178, 180, 181
Browning, John 423
Brussels 48, 98
BSA 169
bucket 373, 374
  champagne 563
Buckley 81, 83
Budge, Ernest 54
buffalo horn 459
buffet 358, 359, 360, 372
Buffy the Vampire Slayer 197
Bulmer, W. & Co. 48
bureaux 299-303
Burmese 512
burner 69, 74, 88, 124
Burnham Smith, David 515, 519, 520
busts 268-269, 570, 571

antiquities 12
  marble 17
  sandstone 28
butler's tray 371, 372
butter tub 119
buttons 420
Butyave 162
Byzantine Roman 15

C
C-type print 226
cabaret set 65, 94
cabinet, Oriental 304
cabinets 304-310
Cadbury's 205
caddy, Oriental 124
Cadillan, B 140
Caeser 137
Caledon 112
calico 379, 380
caligraphy 375
Cambridge 135
Cameo 411
Cameras 174-181
Cameron, James 193
Cameroon 509, 513
campagna 101
campaign chest 335
Canary Islands 46, 48
candelabra 96, 270-275
  silver 444, 445, 447
candleholder 90
candlesticks 270-274, 524, 554, 556, 558
  silver 439, 440, 441, 443, 444, 445, 450
canister 75, 84
canoe 514
Canon 181
Cantagalli 100
canterburies 311-312
Cantonese bowl 123
Cantonese vase 112
cap, officers 35
cap remover 475
caps 460
card case 437
card table 385, 387
Cardin, Pierre 142, 143
Carlsbad 97
Carlton Ware 187
Carpets 59-63
Carrera RS 42
Carroll, Lewis 50
Carrucci, Elinor 226
Carter, John 444
Cartier 141, 142, 143, 144, 147, 296, 417
cartouche 96
Cartwright, Benjamin 447
carved panel 507
carving 510
Cary 155
Casablanca 232

Casarelli, John 156
Castel Durante Crispina 102
castle 73
Catalonia 99
Catalonian 20
Catteau, Charles 518
Caucasus 60, 63
cavalry 36
Ceccherine, Umberto 434
celadon 121
Celadon Koryo 115
Celebes 38
cellaret 370
cencer 124
Cenedese 539, 542, 544, 547
centaur 439
centrepiece 99, 442, 447, 448, 558
ceramics
  English 64-92
  European 93-104
  Oriental 112
  twentieth-century 515-526
Ceres, figure of 81
Cevantes 53
Chad 509, 514
chairs 313-329, 511, 513, 527-536
  deck 22, 25, 26
  folding 23
  garden 19, 20, 27
  harp 313
  high 325
  invalid's 328
  library 317, 318, 323, 324, 325
  piano 316
  rocking 317, 318, 319, 320
  rustic 22
  steamer 25
chaises longues 330-331
Chal, Marc 278
Chalmers, Patrick R 57
chamber pot 404
Chamberlain 71
Chambers, Sir William 24
champagne
  bucket 563
  glass 409
Chanell 72, 415
Chapeau Grendarme 286
charger 101, 455, 456, 555
charger silver 455, 456
Charles V 137, 138
Charlton 194, 202
Chas Hearson & Co Ltd 548
Cheeky 496
Chelsea 68, 70, 84, 92
Chelsea football club 464, 466
Chenghua 115
cherub 93, 96, 97, 98, 102, 125, 138, 213, 271, 272, 276, 416, 507
chess sets 182-186
chests 511, 512, 332-341

bachelor 333
campaign 335
marriage 333
mule 337
of drawers 332-341
serpentine 338
sword 339
Wellington 335, 337
Chesterfield sofa 378
chieftain 509, 511
Chile 44
chimney 20, 23, 24, 27
chimney oak 26
chimney pot 25
chimneypiece 570
Chinese bowl 115
Chinese cabinet 308
Chinese cushion 62
Chinese stool 62
Chinese tankard 114
chinoiserie 304, 375, 391
Chippendale 284, 289, 299, 306, 319, 323, 344, 365, 367, 385, 389
chisel 486
christening cup 449
chronograph 147, 148, 149, 150
chronometer 131, 135, 421
chrysanthemum 96, 115
Churchill, Winston 34, 188
cibachrome 230
cigar cutter 254
cigarette case 437, 451
cigarette lighter 255
cistern 20
clay antiquities 14
clay tablet 18
Cleopatra 451, 572
Clichy 223, 224
clocks 124-140
  armorial 130
  Art Deco 125
  Art Nouveau 129
  balloon 139
  bell strike 125
  boullé 137
  bracket 126, 129, 130, 131, 132, 134, 138
  brass 129, 130
  carriage 126, 130, 132, 134, 135, 137
  cathedral 140
  ceramic 90
  comptoise 140
  electric 132, 133, 134, 137
  empire 140
  French carriage clock 125
  Grandfather clock 136
  longcase clock 127, 128, 132, 133, 135, 138, 140
  mantel clock 126, 127, 128, 129, 131, 132, 133, 134, 135, 136, 137, 138, 139
  musical 126

pendulum 126
set 139
skeleton 136
steamhammer 139
striking 131, 135
swinging 140
table 139
travelling 133
Vitascope 128
wall 131, 134
Coalport 64, 77, 82
coasters 440, 443
coat stand 373
Coca-Cola 231, 555
Cockram, Roger 525
coffee pot 98, 114, 282, 438, 442
coffee set 77
coffer 506
Cogwell & Harrison 473
coil 243
coins 264-267
Coker, Ebenezer 439
Columbia 162, 220
comet 166
commemorative ware 187-192
commodes 332-341
compactum 395
compass 125, 422, 423, 426, 427
compendium 130, 183, 428
compotière 94
computer 491
Concord 167
condiment set 444
confederate states 247
Congo 57, 511
Conil 46
console piano 430
Constable & Co Ltd 45
Conway Maritime Press 426
Conway, William Martin 49
Cook, Captain 46
Copeland 66, 92, 458
Copperfield, David 421
coptic 14
coral 415, 419
corbel terracotta 28
Corgi 246
Corinthian 506
corkscrew 559-564
cornucopia 505
Cornwell, Bernard 46
coro 411
Coronet 175
Cosser 237
cottage 69, 71, 72
country desk 348
Cowardine 549
cowboy 490
Craven 161
creamer 81, 82, 90
creamware 65, 66, 67, 68, 69, 70, 72, 74, 75, 78, 80, 92
credenza 305
creel 468, 471

cribbage 507
Crichton, L.A. 443
cricket bat 459, 463, 464
Crimea 30
Crimean 266
Crispus, C. 50
crocodile skin 215, 298, 470
croquet mallets 460
Crosby, Gordon 43
cross 410, 419
cross-bow 36
crown 574
cruet 449, 450, 454, 568
crystal set 238
Cuban mahogany 351
cuirass 31
Cunard White Star 422, 424, 425
cup 14, 69, 84, 86, 89, 90, 97
cup and saucer 66, 68, 69, 71, 73, 74, 77, 82, 86, 95, 97, 100, 101, 104, 112, 114, 518
cup glass 403
  Islamic 107
  Oriental 117, 118
  silver 441, 452, 454
cupboard 395, 397
cupid 75, 102, 116, 127, 129, 135, 136
currency 509, 511, 513
cushion 59, 483
cutlass 32
Cutler, Thomas 52
Cyanotype 225
cylinder desk 346
cylinder piano 217
cymric dish 451

D
dado plane 489
dagger 29, 32, 34, 35, 36, 37, 38
  Indo-Persian 32
  Indonesian 38
  Japanese 37
  S.A. 35
Daily Telegraph 200, 203
damascus 573
Dan-Khan 513
Darth Vader 259
Daum 537, 539, 540, 544, 545, 546
Davellier 47
davenports 87, 342-343
Davidson, F. 460
Davies, Marcus 227
day beds 330-331, 379
DC Comics 195
decanter 401
deck chair 22, 25, 26
decorative metalware 276-283
decoy duck 473, 475
delft 100
Delftware 76, 77, 82, 84, 89, 90
Delmester, John 449
demi-tasse 86

Dennis Chinaworks 515, 516, 517, 518, 523, 526
Dent 142, 149, 150
Dent, J.M. & Co 44
Derby 91
desks 344-349
 country 348
 cylinder 346
 kneehole 345, 347
 library 347
 partners 344, 345, 347
 pedestal 344, 347
 roll top 346
 tambour 347
 writing 345
dessert service 400, 526
deuddiarw 356
Devon 468
Devonshire 80
diamond 416, 418, 420
Diana, figure of 81
Dickens, Frank 195
DiMaggio, Joe 530
Dinanderie 554
dining chair 318, 320, 322, 324, 327, 328
dining tables 350-351
Dinkie 584
Dinky 500
dinner plates 435
dinner service
 Oriental 119
 silver 450
Dior, Christian 171, 172
diorama 422
dirk 29, 34, 35, 37
Dirty Harry 232
dish 68, 79, 81, 92, 95, 96, 98, 99, 99, 100, 102, 104
 Islamic 108, 109, 111, 282
 Oriental 112, 113, 117, 118, 119, 120, 121, 122, 124
Disney 160, 162, 202, 234
dividers 422, 488
Dogon 514
Dolland 157
dolls 490-504
Dominion 474
Domino 211
doors 352-353
 Art Deco 24
doorway 352, 353
Dore, Gustave 47
Dorrier Dox 166
Doughty, Dorothy 523
Douillon 138
Doulton of Lambeth 23
drain hopper 21
drainer 370
Draper, J.M. 222
Dream Baby 494
Dresden 95
dressers 354-358
drinking set 399

drug bottle 99
 jar 95, 109, 110
drum 37, 94, 431
drumhead 139
drummer 502
Druz 125
dry fly 470, 472
du Maurier, George 45
Dubucand 277
Duffet, Michel 536
dumb waiters 359-360
Duncan, Isadora 47
Dunkirk 425
Durtington 516, 518

E
Eales, Stan 196
earrings 414
 antiquities 13
 Roman 15
earthenware 72, 105, 107, 114, 568
East Azerbaijan 62
East Indiaman 114
Eastern European chair 23
Eastern Iran 63
Eastwood, Clint 232
Eberhard & Co 147
edger 487
Edison 220
Edo 376
Edward VII 248
Eglington, Earl of 443
Egyptian antiquities 11, 14
Egyptian figure 17
Egyptian pot 14
Ekco 236
Eleison 130
Elijah 75
Eliot, George 51
Elkington & Co 446, 453
Elliott 151
Ellis 154
embroidered panel 510
embroideries 480
emerald 416
Emes & Barnard 450, 452
EMI Records 241
Emmanuel, L. 439
Enfield, Cy 186
English ceramics 64-92
entrée dish 438, 449
epaulettes 29, 39
ephemera 193-204
EPNS 556
Erard, S. & P. 431
Ericcson 256, 259, 260
Esquire magazine 195
Essex 90
Esso 493
Estanger 494
Estruscan 417
E.T. 495
etagère 360

Etruscan 101
Eugene, Segay 57
European ceramics 93-104
European works of art 568-571
ewer 106, 107, 111, 115, 403, 406, 525, 572, 573
 silver 443
Exacta Varex 181

F
Faber & Faber 56
Fabergé 420, 448, 452
facemask 12, 30, 38
famille 68
fans 480-483
Fantastic Four 194
Farcot 125
Farlows 471
Farrow & Jackson 563
Fenacci, Rene 234
Ferro 537
fienza 100
figures 67, 75, 79, 81, 83, 85, 93, 95, 97, 101, 102, 268-269, 458, 460, 463, 465, 555, 557, 566, 567, 569, 570, 571, 577
 Art Nouveau 280
 Egyptian 17
 metalware 277, 278, 279, 282
 Oriental 117
Finkelstein, Nat 225, 230
fire engine 490
firearms 29
fireplace marble 21
 Tuscan 21
first world war 192, 247, 266
Fischer 497
fishing 468-472
 creel 471
 lure 472
 priest 472
 reels 468
 rods 468
Fitzgerald, Edward 56
flagon 456, 564
flambé 522
flask 15, 17, 29, 74, 86, 460, 467, 560
flatware 450
fly box 472
fly case 471
fly rod 470
fly wallet 469, 470
flying headgear 463
fob 411
fob watch 142, 143, 145
football 461, 462, 466
 cap 460
 programme 464
 rattle 464
Ford, Charles 68
Ford sedan 493
Ford Zodiac 492
fork 489

Formula 1 42
  car 498
fountain wall 19, 26, 27
Fox, Charles and George 271
franc 250
France, map of 47
Francesconi 551
Frankenstein 233
French Royal Exchange 136
Frères, Nicole 217, 218, 219, 220
Fresson 225
Frisk, Jonas 391
Frodsham, Charles 148
fruit 98
fruit bowl 439
Fruitman, Sheva 225, 227
Fuller, S. & J. 495
funeral jar 566
fusée 136, 140

**G**
gabon 510
Gaddei 511
gaff 470
Gagnier, Olivier 521
Gail, John 154
Gallagher, Noel 430
Gallé 94, 96, 98, 102, 103
Gallé, Emile 406, 409, 410, 538
games 490-504
Ganesh 531
garage 493
garden
  bench 20, 22
  border 19, 22
  chair 19, 20, 23, 27
  fork 489
  furniture 19-28
  gate 28
  pot 20
  recliner 22
  rocking chair 28
  set 25
  sprayer 488
  sprinkler 107, 486
  table 23
  tools 485, 489
Garrards 215
Garter, Order of the 267
Gastaldi, Glaomo 56
gate, garden 28
gates, iron 22
Gaudi 20
gaulin 136
GEC 261
gelatin 225, 227, 228, 229
gem 17
Genin, F.J. 305
geology 49
Georgette 481
Gera 99
German dirk 37
Ghanaian 512
Gillow 309, 314, 396

Gilroy 160
Ginai 101
ginger jar 115
Giusiniani 101
glass 398-410
  amphorae 17
  aubergine 16
  ball 409
  beaker 401, 405, 406, 407, 408
  Bohemian 398, 400, 401, 402, 404, 405, 406, 407, 408, 410
  bottle 399, 401, 405, 406, 407, 410
  carafe 401
  centrepiece 405, 409
  chamber pot 404
  champagne 409
  cup 403
  decanter 401
  ewer 403, 406
  goblet 405, 407
  jar 400
  jug 402, 410
  lamp base 410
  liqueur 408
  panel 568, 571
  port 400, 402
  rummer 408
  shot 410
  tankard 407
  vase 400, 401, 402, 402, 404, 405, 406, 408, 409, 410
  windows 568, 569
  wine 398, 399, 402, 403, 404, 409, 410
globe 52, 428
goblet 405
  silver 446, 453
Godfrey, Bob 201
Godwin, William 49
gold antiquities 13, 15, 16
Gold Key 193
gold wire 29
Goldfinger 231
Goldsmiths Co 137
golf ball 461
golf clubs 459
golf driver 461
golf putter 457, 459
Golly 494
gong 371
Gordon, Dexter 227
gorget 33
gothic arch 28
  windows 27
Gottschalk, Lillian 497
Gouda 516, 517, 518, 519, 522, 524, 525, 526
Gould, John 54
Gôut d'Egypt 140
gramophone 217, 218, 222, 236, 237
Grecian harp 430, 431, 434
Greek antiquities 14

Greek kantharos 16
Green, John 484, 485, 486
Green, T.G. 205, 210
Greenwood, James 46
Grinnard, Thomas 138
Grossmith 173
grotto 313
Grouch, Henry 151
*Guardian, The* 203
Gudea 11
Guere 513
gueridon 372, 386
Guerlain 173
guinea 247, 265, 266
Guinness 160, 161
guitar 12-string 430
  acoustic 433
  amplifier 434
  Broadcaster 432
  Epiphone 431
  Esquire 434
  Fender 429, 432, 434
  Firebird III 433
  Flying Vee 430
  Gibson 430, 431, 433, 434
  Gretsch 429, 431
  Les Paul 431, 434
  Riviera 431
  Stratocaster 432
  Valve Amp 432
  White Falcon 430
gun 473, 474, 475
gun case 473, 475
Gunner 36
Gustavian 378
gut strings 457

**H**
Hadeland 545
Hadius 56
Hague 100
Hague, The 518, 520, 523
hairslides 413
Halifax 65
hall chair 313, 328
Hall, Martin 443
Halstaff & Hannaford 57
Hamilton 421
hand mirror 448
handclapper 506
hanging 483
Hardy 468
Hardy, Bert 225, 229
Hardy creel 469
Hardy Neroda 469
Hardy reel 472
harp 431, 433
harp chair 313
harp lute 429
Harris, Charles Stuart 444
Harrison, George 244
Hartgring, W.P. 100
Hartley's 231
Hartsring, W.P. 519

harvester, model of 99
Harvey, F.B. Darton 55
Haselwood, Arthur 561
hat 29, 481
hat box 215, 296
    case 215
Hauser 51
Hawkins, Jay 241
Hawkman 200
Haxby, Thomas 430
Hazell 461
head-dress 416
heart 93
heater 23
*Heavy Metal* magazine 244
Heinrich 503
Helen of Troy 276
helm 425
helmet 32, 35, 36, 38, 463
    Persian 31
    snipers 30
    Tibetan 29
Hemon 128
Hennel, Robert 454
Henry Williamson Ltd 461
Hepburn, Audrey 226
Hepplewhite 292, 314, 315, 318,
    322
Hera 116
Herbie 195
Hermes 268
hermetique 148
Heywood, H. 439
Hickory 457, 459
Hicks, G.E. 423
Hicks of London 217
hieroglyphic 17
high chair 325
Highland Stoneware 520
Hilliard & Thompson 453
Himalayas 49
Himilayan 511, 512
hinoki 310
Hirado 112, 124
Hispano-moresque 99
Hitchcock, Alfred 234
HMV 218, 222, 235, 237
Hodder & Stoughton 49
Hoffman, Professor 500
Hoffman Suisse1 63
Hogenburg, Braun 46
Holland & Hedgekiss 526
Hollandaise 97
Holmegaard 543, 545
holster pistol 34
Homann, Johann 54
Hondius, Joducas 46
Hopkins, Albert 54
Hopkins, John 226, 227, 228
Hopkins, Thurston 226
Horlicks 163
Hornby 494, 499, 500
Houlston, E.J. 451
house 67, 68, 73

HRH Albert Edward
    of Wales 188
Hry 129
Hubert 495
Hughes, Ted 56
Hulbert, Henry James 65
Humber 168
humidor 255
Hunt, Eileen 516
Hunt, J.&J.F. 448
Hunter, Bugatti 42
hunting items 474
Huntley & Palmers 162
Hurt, Joseph 155
hussars 492

I
Ibex 261
Icutahya 111
Ideal Toy Corporation 493
Ilbery 145, 149
Imari 87, 113, 114
Imari jar 113
Imperial Airways Ltd 165
Incredible Hulk, The 194, 202
Indo-Persian dagger 32
Indonesian dagger 38
inkstand 453
inkwell 107, 525, 543, 579, 580,
    581
International Watch Co 150
invalid's chair 328
Invicta 238
Iran, western 11, 13
iron gates 22
Iron Maiden 242
Iron Man 204
Irven, J.D. 506
Isis 13
Islamic bottle 109
Islamic Ceramics 105-111
Isnik 110
Istrian Rosso d'Verona 20
Italian marble 20

J
Jacinthe De Coty 172
Jackson 162
Jackson, George 442
Jacob 89
Jacobean 138
jade 417
Jaeger-leCaultre 128, 141, 142
Jaguar 41
Jaillot, Herbert 55
Jalland, GH 45
jam pot 92
James, Henry 45
Janssonius, J 55
Japanese
    box 118
    cabinet 305, 307
    dagger 37
    facemask 30, 38

kabuto 33, 36, 37
Kutani 116
jar 94, 95, 100, 101
    Islamic 107, 109
    Oriental 113, 115, 116, 122,
        123
    Persian 108
    Roman 16
Jardin 172
jardinière 368, 371, 372, 440
    Art Nouveau 19
Jasper 223
JAZ 125
jazz bass 434
jelly mould 77, 207, 458
Jennings 53
Jesus 17, 87
jewellery 411-420
jewellery box 298
Jewish 15
jigsaw 497, 503
Jingle House music 243
John's Children 242
Johnson 160
Jolly Baby 163
Jones, Daisy Makeig 84
Jones, George 95
Joseph 86
joss stick holders 122
Judaica 15
jug 67, 68, 70, 71, 72, 73, 76, 78,
    79, 80, 81, 88, 90, 91, 93, 94,
    99, 102, 103, 104, 402, 410
    Islamic 105, 108, 109, 110
    Oriental 116, 117, 120
    silver 435, 436, 437, 438, 441,
        442, 450, 451, 452
Jumeau 491
Junghans 130, 134
Jungle Book 231
Junyao 124
JVC 238

K
kabuto 33, 36, 37
Kajar 572
kakiemon 97
Kalfestewa, H. 414
kantharos, Greek 16
karaja 60
Karrusel1 42
Kashan 106, 108, 109, 573
Kashmiri 443
katani bijin 123
katar dagger 34
katena sword 37
Keith, Walter 451
Keller, G. 452
Kenyon & Craven 233
Keramis 518
keyaki 310
kiaat 511, 513
Kiebel, Albert 187
kilim 59, 63, 513

King Charles II 354
  Cnut 266
  Edward VII 189, 191, 267
  Edward VIII 188, 189
  George I 315, 361, 362
  George II 135, 301, 303, 308, 318, 347, 365, 366, 388, 390, 438
  George III 21, 130, 131, 140, 264, 265, 266, 272, 288, 289, 292, 294, 295, 301, 302, 306, 307, 309, 321, 323, 335, 345, 365, 390, 391, 393, 394, 436, 438, 505
  George IV 293, 351
  George V 187, 188, 189, 191, 192, 250, 265
  George VI 187, 191, 225, 226
  James I 439
  of Larsa 14, 18
  Richard 456
  William 300
  William IV 274, 290, 292, 298, 324, 330, 342, 346, 360, 372, 380
Kinns, Samuel 49
Kirmanshah 435
kitchenalia 205-214
Klemantaski, Louis 43
Klingenthal 31
kneehole desk 345, 347
knife handle 87
knights 495
ko bizan blade 34
Kodak 174, 176, 178, 179, 180
kogo 296
Konga 202
Koni Omega1 77
koran 47, 573
koro 280
Kouros 55
kraak dish 113
Kraakware 117, 119, 121
Kriegsmarine 32
kronen 250
kronor 250
Kufic 105, 107
Kulu 511
Kurdish 63
Kushan 105
kutani 122
Kutchinsky 141
kylin 112, 113

L
L'Alhambra 47
La Poete de la Danse 269
Ladd, W 424
ladle 69, 507, 561, 564
Lagash 11
lamp anchor 423
Lancaster 181
lancet 136

Lancia 498
Lancome 171
landing net 469, 472
Lane, Kenneth J. 413
Lartigue, Jacques-Henri 227
lathe 486
Latin 44
Laugland, John 447
Laurie & Whittle 54
lawn aerator 489
  edger 484, 487
  mower 486
  bowls 463
Layton, Peter 546
Le Maire-Tils 158
Le Mesurier, F.H. 267
Leavitt, Sam 231
Lebas, Chrystel 228
Lecoultre 219
Lee, Christopher 233
Leeds football team 467
Legnano 168
Lehmann 496, 504
Leica 174, 175, 176, 177
Leipzig 46
Lekanis 14, 16
Lench, Ross 83
Lennon 576
Lenon, John 240, 243
Leone, Georg 427
Leroy, L. & Cie 139
Lesieur 126
letter opener 582
Levasseur, V. 47
Lever Brothers 163
Lezzario, Geronimo 99
Lhasa 57
Lhasa Apso 479
Liberty cup 454
library
  chair 317, 318, 323, 324, 325
  desk 347
  steps 368, 369
lifeboat 421
light meter 177, 178, 179
lighting 270-275
Linassier, Claudius 554
Lindner, Doris 516
linen 424
linen press 332, 334, 395, 396, 397
Linstock 36
lion slayer 70
LIP 142
liqueur funnel 564
liqueur glass 408
lithographs 47
Lithyan 409
Liverpool 85
livres 247
lizard skin 460
locket 417
Loetz 537, 538, 540, 546
Lonsdale, Earl of 438

Lorenzl 554
lotto 499
Louis XV 284, 286, 327, 381, 382, 383, 384
Louis XVI 271, 284, 285, 331, 354
Louisiana 249
Low countries 93, 97, 98
Low, Roger 518
lowboys 361
Lowestoft 115
Lowry, Ray 193
Luca, R. de 439
Luce, Arredo 553
Luco Art Metal Co Ltd 422
Luen Wo 446
Luftwaffen Eigentum 178
Luggage 215-216
Lugrunge 135
lure 468
Luristan 11,13,14,18, 60
lute 94
Lysell, Ralph 261

M
Macmillan 58
Madagascar 477
Madeira 46
Madonna 77
magazine case 474
Maggiolina 285
magic 54
magic set 502, 504
Magistratti 551
magnifying glass 437
Magnum 224
mah jong 184
main gauche dagger 38
majolica 95, 98, 99, 101, 102
Majorellel 362
malachite 274
malatya 61
Mali 510, 514
mallacca 466
Malta 45
maltese cross 31
Mambele 512
Mamiya 175
Manchester United 464, 465
Mandarin 114, 120, 481
Mandarin bowl 116
Mandarin pot 112
mandolin 433, 434
Manjbetu 512
manluk 105
Manner, Adam 367
Manners, John Henry 438
Maori 514
Maple & Co 291
Maples 288
Mappin & Webb 444, 448
maprush 60
maps 44-58
Marat, Delores 225

marble 372, 388, 392
  beasts 21
  bust 17
  carrara 23
  chimney 23, 24, 27
  columns 25
  fireplace 21
  Italian 20
  table 18, 25
  urn 21
marbles 498
marcasite 411
marconi 236
Marcuse, Rudolph 277
Marden, Robert 50
Mariana 52
marine items 421-428
mark 250
marquetry 305
marriage coffer 333
Marson, Frederick 437
Martin, Edward 439
Martin, R. Montgomery 57
Martinelli, Flio 547
Marvel 193
mask 16, 510, 511, 512, 513
Maso, Frederick J. 49
masonic 141, 420
masque wall 27
Massarella, N. 521
Master Blaster 496
masur 313, 389
Matabele 509
match strike 254
Matthews, Stanley 247
Mathieson 485
Maurer, Ingo 552
Mauser 473
Maxwell, Robert 16
Mayer, Luigi 48
*Mayfair* magazine 197
Mazarin 124
Mazzega 547
McCartney, Paul 199
McGovern, William M. 57
McLachlan, Ed 203
McQueen, Steve 234
McVitie 63
MDS Ltd 59
meat drainer 83
Meccano Ltd 500
Mechanical Music 217-222
medals 29, 264-267
  sporting 460
Medici, Lorenzo di 269
Mediterranean, chart of 58
Meek, Joe 244
Meglio, Giovanni 433
Mehlem, Frank Anton 524
meissen 93, 95, 96, 97, 101, 102,
  103, 114
mempo 30
menorah 446
Menorca, map of 54

Meopta 180
Mercedes 43
Mereaud 100
Meriton, Samuel 449
Merrythought 504
Mesopotanian 12
Messar, John 165
Messerschmitt M.E. 110 165
metal arch 28
metalware 554-558
  decorative 276-283
Mettlach 30
Mettullus, J 48
MGM 234
Michelangelo 269
Mickey Mouse 258, 492
Middle Eastern works
  of art 572-574
Midsummer Night's Dream, A
  132
Mighty Cutter 484
Mignot, Lucotte 501
Mikkephone 217
militaria 29
military band 497
military chest 302
military cross 265
milk jug 120
Millefiore 224
Miller, Lee 229
MIM 497, 503
Minchin of Monnegall,
  arms of 114
Ming Dynasty 113
miniature 419
Minolta 176
Minton 71, 95
miquelet 39
mirror
  dressing 367
  easel 362
  hand 448
  mantel 362
  neo-classical 367
  Roman 16
  toilet 362, 363, 364, 367
mirrors 362-367
miscellaneous 368-374
Miss Piggy 492
Mizuya 310
model 423, 425, 427, 428, 458,
  519
Model T Ford model 495
Mogg 53
Mojo 242, 243
Mollino, Carlo 531
Monart 545
Monck, George 419
money 247-250
money box 65
Monnington & Western 430
Monte Hale 194
Monteith glass 406
Montelupo 95

Montener, Luif 20
Montgomery of Alamein 31
Moorcroft, Lisa 517
Moorland 517, 518
Morden & Co 171
Morgan 40
Morocco 54
Morphy 183
Morphy Richards 214
Morris, Tony 520
Mortimer, Pierre 54
mosaic 20
Moses 49
mother-of-pearl 297
motorbike 499
Mouhraby 314
mould 77
Mr Popple 45
Mr Punch 262
mug 67, 70, 81, 85, 87, 89, 92,
  421, 445, 447, 525
  silver 445, 447
mughal 59
Mugnes 152
musical instruments 429-434
mule chest 337
Mumluk 110
Munston 56
Muppet Show, The 492
Murday 134
Murphy 235
Murray, John 44
music box 217-221
music stand 311, 312
musical instrument 103
musician 78, 94, 102
Mussolini 490
mustard pot 447
mythological 18

**N**

Nadarman 432
Naga 512
Nailsea 405
Nankin 119
  vase 113
napkin rings 435, 439, 442
Naples 96, 101
Napolean 192, 264
Napoleonic 421, 497
nashiji 34
nautical 85
Navajo 411, 415, 417
naval fiction 45
Nazi 35, 165
necklace 411, 412, 413, 413, 415,
  416, 417, 419, 420
  antiquities 12, 16
  Roman 16
necromancers 49
needlepoint 376
Neff 444
neo-classical
  bookcase 294

mirror 367
Nepalese cushion 61
Neptune 269
Nerzbach & Falk 428
nestorian 108
New England 54
Newman & Co 152
New York 54
Ngombe Doko-Mbudja 510
Ngomee Doko Poto 514
Nicholson pistol 38
Nielsen, Kay 49
Nikkorex 181
Nikon 179
Nina Ricci 173
Nishapur 105, 109, 111
Noah 496
Noch Henry 35
nomadic 60, 61
Normandie 161
Northern Telecom 257
Nuremberg 266
nutcracker 508
Nutting, Henry 454

O

O'Brian, Patrick 45, 51
oak panel 508
*Observer, The* 197
Oddy, Jason 226
Oeil de Perdix 100
oil burner 16
oil lamp 13, 103, 270, 271, 272, 274, 459, 573, 574
Okimono 114, 121
Oldham 163
Omega 99, 141, 147
onyx 416
opium pipe 255
Orange Matamp 434
organette 222
Oriental
    cabinet 304
    ceramics 112
    works of art 565-567
Orissa 511
ormolu 96, 102, 103, 136, 138, 139, 270, 271, 285, 305, 310, 372
ormonial map 49
Orrelius 56
Ortelius, Abraham 44, 52,
Orvieto 99
Osiris antiquities 13
Oswold 137
overdoor 352, 353, 571
Owen, Michael 457
Owens, Owen 135
O*z* magazine 239, 245

P

paintbox 506
Pakefield 421
Palakona 470
Palermo 99

Palestine 48
Palestine, map of 58
Palmyran 17
Pan 388
Pan-Am 165
pantomime 517
paperweights 223-224
papier maché 498, 503, 585
Papua New Guinea 514
paradox gun 475
Paramount Pictures 234
Parker 578, 579, 580, 582, 583, 584
Parlophone 240
parthian 107
partners desk 344, 345, 347
Patek, Philippe 144, 147, 149
Pater 427
Paulin, Pierre 535
Payne, Humphrey 449
pearl 418, 420
pedestal 372
pedestal desk 344, 347
pedigree 502
Peel & Co 216
pelota cradles 460
Pembroke 394
pens 578-585
pen tray 585
pence 248
pencil 585
pendant 411, 413, 418
pengo 248
Pentax 176
pepperette 74
peppermill 437
pepperpot 439
percussion cap and ball 29
percussion pistol 30
perfume bottle 18
Perrier, Francois 46
Persian antiquities 11, 14
    bronze 18
    cushion 60
    helmet 31
    jajim 60
    jar 108
    kilim 60
    Koran 47
    rug 59, 60, 63
    sword 18
    vase 107
Persimmon 459
Pestini, Amati 433
Petermann Fondeur, J. 279
Peters, Ellis 58
Peugeot 490
pew ends 508
pewter 435-456
Phantom II 143
Phil Allan & Co. 57
Philcox, Mary 482
Phillips, Godfrey Ltd 193
Phillips, Richard 49

Phillips, Robert 419
Philpot, Toby 88
phonograph 219, 220, 221
photographs 225-230
piano 430
piano Art Deco 430
    chair 316
    console 430
    grand 431, 432, 433
    square 432
    stool 384
Piastre 248
Picasso 522
piggy bank 80
pigskin 467
pilgrim 11
ping pong bats 466
Pink Floyd 245
pipe tamper 506, 508
pipkins 97
pistol
    Colt 31
    flintlock 35, 38
    holster 34
    percussion 30, 32,33, 36, 39
    pocket 38
    Remington 29
    Rigby 33
    roots 37
    tap action 31
pitcher 107
Pitts, William 264, 444
plane 484, 485, 487, 488, 489
Planet of the Apes 234
planter 19, 27, 91, 487
plaque 91, 94, 576
    sandstone 21
plaques
    armorial 24
plate 64, 69, 70, 71, 72, 73, 74, 75, 77, 80, 86, 89, 96, 98, 101, 103, 104
    militaria 34, 35
    Oriental 112, 116, 117, 118, 119 ,120
platinum 416
*Playboy* magazine 196
Plessey 261
pocket watch 141, 142, 143, 144, 145, 148, 149, 150
Poe, Edgar Allan 54
pokerwork 310
polar 46
Polaroid 181
polyphon 217, 218, 221, 222
Ponte Negro 102
Ponti, Gio 553
Poole 515-526
pop memorabilia 239-246
porsche 42
port glass 400, 402, 403, 404, 406, 407
port hole 422, 428
Portland 88

stone 21
Portugal, map of 44, 55
Posters 231-234
pot 97, 98, 103, 514, 517
  balm 65
  chamber 67, 80
  Egyptian 14
  jam 92
  Oriental 112, 114, 117, 122
  pourri 66, 92
  terracotta 14, 20, 108
Potter, Harry 58
pouffe sculpté 383
Poussin, Nicholas 93
powder
  case 469
  flask 505
Powell, Baden 75
Power, Tyron 234
prattware 75, 76, 86, 88, 90
Preedy, William 444
preserve jar 400
Presley, Elvis 242, 256
Primrose Confectionery Co 193
Prince
  Albert I 191, 266, 267
  Edward 190, 191, 192
  Matchabello 170
  of Wales 76, 188
Princess
  Alexandra 192
  Diana 249
  Elizabeth 189
  Louise 88
  Margaret 189, 226
  of Wales 252
Prins, C.A. 516
Pritchard, Andrew 159
prophet Elijah 577
pruner 484
Prussia 39
Psycho 234
Pullman 499
pulpit 369
punch bowl 116, 454
puppet 494
Purma 175
Putti 526

**Q**
Qantas 164, 166
Quant, Mary 419
Quarne, Daniel 132
Quashqui 63
quatral cup 86
Queen
  Alexandra 191
  Anne 305, 391, 327, 341
  Elizabeth II 187, 188, 189,
    190, 225, 226, 261, 509
  Mary 187, 188, 189, 191, 192,
    265, 300, 380
  Victoria 187, 190, 191, 192,
    247, 262, 267

**R**
R2 D2 257
Rackham, Arthur 44
rad hauer 35
radio 235-238
*Radio Times* 197
Raffaella, Antoine 42
railway
  box 502
  station 501
rajput 59
Raleigh 168
Randle, Alfred 471
rapier 30, 33
Rapin de Thoyzes, P. 58
rattles 453
Reece, W. 138
reel case 468
reflex 174
regimental brooches 264
Reichsbank 247
Reichsmark 250
Reid, W.H. 47
Reims 140
reliquary bronze 17
Rembrandt 526
Remington pistol 29
Renaissance 137
revolver pepperbox 33
Rhein 58
rhinoceros 491
Richard Eckert & Co 95
Riddell, Chris 203
rifle 473, 474, 475
  Turkish 39
Rigby pistol 33
Rijp, A.M. 525
Rinfrescatoio 102
ring 419
River Thames 48
Rivers & Son 126
Robelou, Isaac 157
Robinson, W. Heath 45
robot 490, 496, 498
rock memorabilia 239-246
rocking chair 317, 318, 319, 320
rocking horse 491, 492
Rockwell Publishing 193
rococo 135
rod holder 468
Rolex 142, 144, 146, 147, 148,
  149, 150
roll top desk 346
roller organ 222
Rolling Stones 241
Rolls Royce 41
Roly Poly 498
Roman
  amphorae 17
  antiquities 14
  beaker 13
  bottle 15
  bronze 16
  earrings 15

flask 15, 17
jar 16
mirror 16
necklace 16
soldiers 95
statue 15
vase 22
vessel 16
Romano-British 17
Romano-Egyptian antiquities
  11, 14
Ronalds, Hugh 51
Roobarb 201
roots pistol 37
Rossignol, Charles 490
Rostrato 537
Rothwell Castle 64
rouble 248
Rouillet et Decamps 217
roundel 506
Rowling, J.K. 58
Royal Bonn 524
  Copenhagen 516
  Doulton 421, 522
Rozenburg 96, 100, 518, 520, 523
Rubik's cube 493
ruby 416
rug Indian 59
  Persian 59
rugby jersey 467
rugs 59-63
rule 422
rummer 399, 408
Ruog 58
Rushbrook, G 213
Russell, Thomas 141
Russell, Thos & Son 144, 146
Russian works of art 575-577
rustic chair 22
  stools 21
Rutland, Duke of 438
Ruyihead 116
Ryan, Frederick W. 45
Ryukei 508

**S**
sabre 29, 33
sailor 92
  doll 503
  boy 499
Saint James's Palace 227
Saint Louis 223
Saints
  Fillipo 506
  George 97, 419
  Nicholas 576
  Paul 508
  Theresa 506
sake bottle 112
Salgado, Sebastiao 229
Saljuk 574
salmon fly 469, 471
Salmon & Gluckstein 194
salt shaker 97

Salvers 436
Samarian 14
Sampson Low 57
Sandcore 106
Sands & Hunter 179
sandstone plaque 21
Santa 504
Santa Domingo Pueblo 416
Santareli 101
sapphire 415, 416
Sarawak 509
sardonyx 413
Sartorius, Carl Christian 52
Sassanian 15
satsuma 118
satsuma koro 123
Satsumaware 114
Saunders, Fred 457
Savanarola 382
Saville 170
saw 487
Sawyer, Charles J. 55
scalf clip 418
scent bottle 399, 401
sceptre 514
Schiaparelli 170
school desk 530
Schuco 499
Schweitzer, John Baptiste 433
Sciacca 96, 99
scientific instruments 151-159
    barometer 153
    circumferentor 158
    compass 151, 154
    deviatometer 152
    dial 153, 154, 157, 158
    dip circle 159
    dividers 159
    drawing 156
    equinoctial 152, 155
    hour glass 155
    level 151
    microscope 151, 152, 154, 155,
        157, 159
    monocular 156
    pantograph 154
    protractor 156
    reading glass 158
    rule 153, 159
    scales 158
    sextant 155, 159
    telescope 152, 152, 153, 154,
        155, 156, 157, 159
    theodolite 151, 152
    transit 152
Scofield, James 130
Scotland, Bank of 247
Scots Guards 264
Scott, Digby 443
Scott, Herbert 137
Scottish dirk 34
screens 375-376
scrimshaw 426
scripophily 247-250

sculpture 520
Sculthorp, James 68
seal 18
Searle, Ronald 194
Sears, Deborah 515
seat 381
seaweed 287
second world war 164, 235, 250,
    265, 423, 463
Secret Service, The 495
secretaire 289, 292, 294, 299,
    300, 301, 309, 336
Sefton 94
Seguso, Archimede 537
Selenova 549
Selenus 186
Seljuk 277
Sene, Richard William 58
Sepik 514
serpentine chest 338
settees 377-380
Seuter 58
Seutter, Matthaeus 45
Sèvres 96, 102, 103, 104, 288
sewing
    box 252, 253, 295, 296
    items 251-253
    machine 251, 252, 253
    necessaire 253
    table 251, 252
Sex Pistols 243
sextant 32, 423, 427
Seymour Press 41
Shabti 12
Shadows 497
Shafran, Nigel 226
Shakespeare, William 45, 74
Sharpe, Richard 46
Sharratt 79
Shasavan 60
Shaw & Fische 456
shawl 482, 512
shears 484, 487
Sheraton 292, 350, 364, 374, 392,
    393
Sheraton chair 325, 326
shield 32
Shiller, W. & Son 99
shilling 247, 249, 266
Shimano 168, 169
ship 91
ship's log 426
ship's wheel 426, 428
Shirvan 60, 63
shoe buckles 72
Shona 509
shooting 473-475
shooting stick 466, 473, 474
shoowa 510
shot glass 410
shotgun belt 475
shovel 488
Shropshire 355
shuttle cocks 457

Sicily 99, 100
sideaxe 489
sideboard 357, 358
Sidonia 15
Siemens Brothers 259, 260
sifter 485
silk 481
Silvano, Campeigi 232
silver 435-456
silver brooch 30
Simon & Halbig 497
Singer 253
Sissons, W. & G. 448
Skedoodle 494
ski 459
Skipper 552
Skruf Talaha 542
Slazenger 460
Sleath, Gabriel 438
sled 495
Sleeping Beauty 234
slipware 81, 83, 87, 98, 104
Smith, Benjamin 438, 443
Smith, C. 39
Smith & Sharp 442
Smith, Stephen 447
smoking equipment 254-255
sniper's helmet 30
Snow White 504
snuff boxes 254-255, 445
    Oriental 119
sofas 377-380
Soho International 196
soil sifter 485
soldier 494, 503
Solinger, S.M.F. 37
solitaire 500
Solomonaic Istrian 25
Soumak 61
soup ladle 446
sovereign cas 451
Spawn 195
spearhead 13
Spears 500
Spencer Browning & Reist 153
Spencer of London 31
spice tower 438
Spiderman 194, 198
Spielberg, Stephen 495
spill holder 89
sporting items 457-467
sprayer 488
Springs, John 194
sprinkler 486
squash rackets 462
Staffordshire 65, 66, 67, 68, 70,
    71, 72, 73, 74, 75, 76, 78, 79,
    80, 81, 82, 83, 85, 89, 92
stamp dispenser 440
stand 372, 373, 374
Stanley 152, 485
Stanley, Henry M. 57
Star Trek 193, 260
Star Wars 198, 233, 257

statue 13, 15, 510, 511, 512, 569
 Roman 15
Staunton 185
steamer chair 25
Steiff 491, 501, 502, 503
Steinbeck, John 58
Steinway 431, 432
stele 14
Sterken, Rudolph 518
Stern, Anthony 537
Stilton 160
Stinton 77
stirrup cup 444
Stitchwell 252
Stockert 427
stole 481
stone ball 24
stone fountain 27
Stone, Francis 508
stone lions 26
stonemason 486
stoneware 80, 89, 273
stool 381-384, 509, 511, 512
 rustic 21
storage chest 511
Storr, Pau 438, 449, 454
story board 514
Straight No Chaser 243
straining spoon 439
Strange Tales 196
straw 481
street barrel organ 221
street piano 222
sucrier 96
sugarbowl 70
Sunburst 434
*Sunday Times, The* 200
Sunderland 67, 73, 91, 92
Sundvall 383
Superman 193
Suphide 224
sura 47
Suschitzky, Wolfgang 229
Susanna and the Elders 102
Sutherland 30
swatow dish 118
sweet box 438
Swift, John 453
Swift, Jonathan 44
sword 29, 39, 514
 chest 339
 katena 37
 Persian 18
Sykes, Charles 43
Syria 17, 105, 110

**T**

tables 510, 385-394
 Art Deco 389, 392
 Art Nouveau 531
 breakfast 394
 card 385, 389, 390
 centre 391
 coffee 387, 392

console 389, 391
de chevet 386
dining 386
end 529
folding 23, 393
games 388, 392, 394
gateleg 390
library 388
lustres 404
marble 25, 388
night 391
pub 527
serving 388, 393
sewing 394
shearing 392
side 386, 387, 389, 310, 311, 312, 314
sofa 385, 387
tea 394
tilt 387, 391, 394
tripod 385, 389
urn 385
work 391
tablet antiquities 12
 armorial 23
 clay 18
 marble 18
Tabriz 62
Taisho 375
tallboy 332, 333, 335, 336, 339
tambour desk 347
Tangueld, D.M. 47
tantalus 561, 562
Tanzania 511
tapestry 313, 376
taxidermy 476-479
Taylor 128
Taylor, Baron 47
tea bowl 117
tea caddy 95, 295, 296, 297, 298, 437, 440 445, 505, 507, 508
 Oriental 118
tea service 523, 556
 set 101, 443
tear bottle 15, 16
teddy bear 491
Tekke 61
Telefon Fabrik Automatic 256, 260
telegraph 428
telephones 256-261
telescope 423, 460
telescopic gaff 470
television 235-238
Temple, Shirley 495
tennis racket 458, 461, 462, 466, 467
Tennyson, Lady Louisa 47
terracotta antiquities 12,13,14
 border 19, 22
 bull 93
 corbel 28
 dog 100
 head 566

model 570
pipe 107, 110
pot 14, 20, 108
rooftile 25
teapot 81
tile 69, 73, 74, 76
vase 520
jug 572
textiles 480-483
Thagee 179
Thames, River 48
thermometer 125, 137, 425
Thibouvillelamy 221
Thomas, Emmanuel 53
Thonire 127
Thonissen 133
Thor 193
Thornhill & Co. 425
Thornton 33
Thunderbird bass 433
Thunderbirds doll 492
tiara 414
Tibet 57, 250
Tibetan cushion 59, 61
 helmet 29
Tiffany 443
tile 69, 71, 73, 74, 76, 78, 79, 80, 81, 82, 85, 86, 87, 88, 89, 91, 525
 Flemish 103
 Islamic 107, 109, 110, 111
 Kushan 105
 Turkish 111
Tilson, Joe 557
Timbrell, Robert 454
timepiece 139
Timpo 498
Tindal, Nicholas 58
Tipping Lorden 30
tipstaff 36
Titanic 193, 503
toast rack 449
tobacco box 466
Toleware 535
Tolfino, Vincent 51
toolbox 507
tools 484-489
topaz 415
Tophane 110
Topper, The 200
torchères 368, 369, 370
tortoiseshell 295, 297, 298
Toso 537, 539
toys 490-504
train 491, 494, 498
Trapani 101
tray 93, 371, 372, 374
treen 505-508
tribal art 509-514
Troughton & Simms 151, 154
truck 492
Trumbafit 512
Trumeau 366
Trumpton 512
Tunbridge Ware 251

Tupman 139
tureen 64, 92, 93
   Oriental 119, 121
   silver 450, 454
Turkey 49
Turkish cushion 59
   killij 39
   rifle 39
   stool 61
   tile 111
Turkmen 416
Tuscan fireplace 21
tusk 426
Twell, William 442
twentieth-century
   ceramics 515-526
   furniture 527-536
   glass 537-546
   lighting 547-553
   metalware 554-558
Twinsol 233
two-cornered hat 29

**U**

U.F.O. 497
umbrella stand 527
Uncle Tom's Cabin 85
underworld antiquities 13
uniforms 29
Union Jack 526
Unwin, Fisher 49
Urbino 98
urn 20, 21, 23, 26, 66, 100, 101
   Oriental 115
   stands 369
Ushabti 17

**V**

van 500
Van der Akker, G.P. 518
Van der Elsken, Ed 227, 230
Van der Meer 42
Van Doren, Harold 235
Van Houten, S.G. & Zoon 212
Van Santer 53
Vanity Fair 204
Vannetti, Angelo 268
Vedder, Elihu 56
Velencia 99
venetian rapier 33
Venini 543
Venus de Milo 280
Verge 142, 143, 146
Verlag, TAG 42
Verner Panton 532, 535
Verstraaten, Theodorus 96
Verve, The 242
Vesnal, Q. 277
Vessel Roman 16
Vesta 446
Vialli 463
Vienna 93, 96, 103

View Master 496
Vigo Harbour, map of 55
Viking Press 58
Vincennes 96
violin 433
Virgin Mary 420
Virgin of Kazan 575
Virgin of Vladimir 575
Vistosi 539, 550
vitrine 304, 305, 307, 310
Vizagapatnum 295
Vogue 199, 200
VW Beetle 500

**W**

wagonwheel 369
Wahliss, Ernst 524
Wales, Prince of 76
Walker & Hall 456
Walker, Thos & Son 424
walking sticks 262-263
wall
   fountain 19, 26, 27
   plaque 276
   plate 96
   masque 27
Wallis, J. 47
wardrobes 395-397
Warhol, Andy 231, 239
Warner, Phillip Lee 54
Washington Square 45
washstand 368, 369, 370, 371
watches 141-150
   Art Deco 145
   aviators 143
   chronograph 147, 148, 149
   chronometer 144, 145, 146
   diving 149
   fob 142, 143, 145
   hermetique 148, 149
   holder 70
   Longines 146
   pocket 141, 142, 143, 148,
      149, 150
water jug 90, 94, 102, 105, 109,
   110
watering can 26, 485, 486, 487
Waterman 578, 579
Watkins, William 156
Watson, Helena 95
Watson, W. & Sons 151
Watteau 98
weapon 29, 510, 512
Webb 486
Webb, Thomas & Co 407
Webster, Jimmy 430
Wedgwood 64, 66, 67, 71, 73, 74,
   77, 80, 84, 88, 89, 90, 91, 95
Wellington, Duke of 192
Welsh map 47
Wemyss 64, 80
West, Francis 155

Western Iran 11, 13
whatnots 359-360, 373, 374
wheat sheaf 99
Whisstock, Fred 492
Whitby 415
Whitefriars 538, 541, 543, 544
Whitehead 167
Whiteside, Thos 308
Whittington 135
Who, The 246
Wilding, Dorothy 225
Wilhelmus de Wykeham 267
Wilhelm, Friedrich 266
Wilkinson, H. 443
Willoughby, Bob 226
Willoughby, Howard 55
Wills 161, 162
Wilson, Alex 134
Wilson, T. 289
windmill 66, 137
windows 568, 569
   rests 90
   seat 377
   gothic 27
Windsor Lodge 74
wine coasters 443
   cooler 370, 373, 442, 226
   funnel 559
   glass 398, 399, 402, 403, 404,
      409, 410
   labels 561
wine-related items 559-564
   rinser 398, 405
   taster 561
Wings 241, 242
Wix, J. & Sons 193
Wodehouse, P.G. 51
Worcester 65, 66, 68, 69, 73, 82,
   86, 516, 521, 523, 526
World Cup 248
world, map of 48, 583, 584
writing equipment 578-585
writing set 585
writing slope 579, 581, 583, 584

**X**

X-Files, The 203
X-Men 197, 198

**Y**

Yates & Birch 456
Yeomen of the Guard 501

**Z**

Zaire 510, 512
Zanzibar 215
Zeiss 151
Zimbabwe 511, 513
Zimmerman, A.&J. 467
Zuid-Holland 516, 517, 518, 519,
   522, 524, 525, 526
Zuni 414, 418, 419

# Notes

# Notes

# Notes

# Notes

# <u>Notes</u>

# Notes

# Notes

# Notes

# Notes

# Notes

# Notes

# Notes

# Notes

# <u>Notes</u>

# Notes

# Notes

# Notes

# Notes

# Notes

# <u>Notes</u>

# Notes

# Notes

# Notes

# Notes

# Notes

# Notes

# Notes

## Notes